Workbook
in Spanish Three Years

Revised Edition

ROBERT J. NASSI
Former Teacher of Spanish
Los Angeles Valley Junior College, Los Angeles

BERNARD BERNSTEIN
Former Chairman of the Department of Foreign Languages
Martin Van Buren High School, New York City

THEODORE F. NUZZI
Former Chairman of the Department of Foreign Languages
Francis Lewis High School, New York City

When ordering this book, please specify:
either **13456** or WORKBOOK IN SPANISH THREE YEARS

AMSCO SCHOOL PUBLICATIONS, INC.,
a division of Perfection Learning®

ISBN 978-0-87720-509-8

Please visit our Web sites at:

   www.amscopub.com and *www.perfectionlearning.com*

PREFACE

This *Workbook in Spanish Three Years* has as its principal aims for the student to assist him in his mastery of the elements of the Spanish language, give him a broad understanding of the culture of the Hispanic world, and prepare him for various types of comprehensive examinations, such as the New York State Regents Examination and the College Board Achievement Test. For the teacher, the book aims to organize the basic material taught in the first three years of Spanish, furnish an abundance of varied drills, and provide suitable tests.

The Workbook is so arranged as to make it readily usable. The contents are divided into large units: Verbs, Grammatical Structures, Idioms, Civilization, Composition, Reading Comprehension, and Auditory Comprehension. Within the units, each lesson treats fully one important topic. Mastery Exercises, placed at logical summary points, afford a comprehensive review of several closely-related lessons.

The vocabulary used throughout the book is extensive but carefully selected to fit the needs of the third-year student. An attempt has been made to include each word or idiom several times to promote learning through repetition. Reference vocabularies are found at the end of the book.

Other noteworthy features of the text are: the exclusive use of the foreign language in the unit on Civilization as well as in the cultural vignettes; the testing of reading passages by means of multiple-choice responses; provision for developing the ability to write coherently through suggested composition exercises; a guide for students preparing to take the College Board Achievement Test in Spanish.

In brief, from the points of view both of learning the language and of teaching the language, this *Workbook in Spanish Three Years* should prove of inestimable value.

The authors appreciate the significant contribution of Miss Nunzia Greco, Grover Cleveland High School, New York City, who assisted in the preparation and reading of the manuscript and offered valuable suggestions for improvement.

—The Authors

CONTENTS

Part I—Verbs

v

Part II—Grammatical Structures

Part V

Part VI

Part VII

Part VIII

Appendix

Part I—*Verbs*

Verb Lesson 1—PRESENT TENSE

REGULAR VERBS

entrar:	entr	*-o, -as, -a, -amos, -áis, -an*
comer:	com	*-o, -es, -e, -emos, -éis, -en*
vivir:	viv	*-o, -es, -e, -imos, -ís, -en*

VERBS IRREGULAR IN THE PRESENT TENSE

1. The following verbs are irregular only in the first person singular of the present tense:

caber, to fit, to be room for: *quepo,* cabes, cabe, cabemos, cabéis, caben

caer, to fall: *caigo,* caes, cae, caemos, caéis, caen

conocer, to know, to be acquainted with: *conozco,* conoces, conoce, conocemos, conocéis, conocen
Like conocer:

aborrecer, to hate	**desconocer,** to be unaware of	**ofrecer,** to offer
agradecer, to thank	**establecer,** to establish	**parecer,** to seem
aparecer, to appear	**estremecerse,** to shudder	**permanecer,** to remain
carecer, to lack	**merecer,** to deserve	**pertenecer,** to belong
crecer, to grow	**nacer,** to be born	**reconocer,** to recognize
desaparecer, to disappear	**obedecer,** to obey	

dar, to give: *doy,* das, da, damos, dais, dan

hacer, to make, to do: *hago,* haces, hace, hacemos, hacéis, hacen
Like hacer: **deshacer,** to undo; **satisfacer,** to satisfy

poner, to put, to set: *pongo,* pones, pone, ponemos, ponéis, ponen
Like poner:

componer, to compose	**imponer,** to impose
disponer, to dispose	**oponer(se),** to oppose
exponer, to expose	**proponer,** to propose

saber, to know: *sé,* sabes, sabe, sabemos, sabéis, saben

salir, to go out: *salgo,* sales, sale, salimos, salís, salen

traducir, to translate: *traduzco,* traduces, traduce, traducimos, traducís, traducen
Like traducir: **conducir,** to conduct, to lead; **producir,** to produce; **reducir,** to reduce

traer, to bring: *traigo,* traes, trae, traemos, traéis, traen
Like traer: **atraer,** to attract

valer, to be worth: *valgo,* vales, vale, valemos, valéis, valen

ver, to see: *veo,* ves, ve, vemos, veis, ven

Note

Most verbs that end in **-cer** or **-cir** and that have a vowel directly before the **c**, change the **c** to **zc** in the first person singular. (See **conocer** and **traducir.**)

Exceptions: **decir (digo), hacer (hago), cocer (cuezo).**

Important: Irregular verbs that change **c** to **zc** are identified in the vocabulary lists by **zc** in parentheses after the verb.

2. Other verbs that have irregular forms in the present tense are:

decir, to say, to tell: *digo, dices, dice,* decimos, decís, *dicen*

estar, to be: *estoy, estás, está,* estamos, estáis, *están*

haber, to have: *he, has, ha, hemos,* habéis, *han*

ir, to go: *voy, vas, va, vamos, vais, van*

oír, to hear: *oigo, oyes, oye,* oímos, oís, *oyen*

ser, to be: *soy, eres, es, somos, sois, son*

tener, to have: *tengo, tienes, tiene,* tenemos, tenéis, *tienen*

Like tener:

contener, to contain	**obtener**, to obtain
detener, to detain	**sostener**, to sustain
mantener, to maintain	

venir, to come: *vengo, vienes, viene,* venimos, venís, *vienen*

USES OF THE PRESENT TENSE

1. The present tense may be expressed in three ways in English.

Pablo *sale.*	Paul leaves (is leaving, does leave).
Van a casa.	They go (are going, do go) home.

2. The present tense is often used instead of the future to ask for instructions or to refer to an action that will take place in the immediate future.

¿Lo *pongo* aquí?	Shall I put it here?
¿Qué *hacemos* ahora?	What shall we do now?
Llamo más tarde.	I'll call later.
Después *comemos.*	We'll eat afterwards.

3. The construction **hace** + an expression of time + **que** + the present tense is used to express an action or event that began in the past and continues into the present. In questions, *How long?* is translated by ¿**Cuánto tiempo hace que . . . ?** + the present tense.

Hace un año que vivo aquí. <small>It a year that I am here makes living</small>	I have been living here for a year.
Hace una hora que esperamos. <small>It an hour that we are makes waiting</small>	We have been waiting for an hour.
¿Cuánto tiempo hace que Vd. trabaja? <small>How time does that you are much it working make</small>	How long have you been working?

Note

The present tense + **desde hace** + an expression of time is also used to express a past action or event that continues into the present. In such expressions, the question *How long?* is translated by ¿**Desde cuándo . . . ?** + the present tense.

Vivo aquí desde hace un año. <small>I am here since it a year living makes</small>	I have been living here for a year.
¿Desde cuándo trabaja Vd.? <small>Since when are you working</small>	How long have you been working?

EJERCICIOS

A. En cada grupo, complétense las frases, usando la forma correcta del verbo de la primera frase.

EJEMPLO: Yo *voy* al cine.

Alicia __*va*__ al cine también.

¿Desea Vd. __*ir*__ con nosotros?

1. *Establecen* la fábrica en Chicago.

   Yo _____ mi casa en Los Angeles.

   Mis primos _____ la suya en Nueva York.

2. *Tengo* que regresar a casa.

   ¿_____ Vds. que regresar también?

   Sí, Inés y yo _____ que regresar en seguida.

3. Tú *eres* el hermano de Pepe, ¿verdad?

   Sí, yo _____ su hermano.

   Nosotros _____ de Chile.

4. Concha y Federico *traen* sus discos.

   Yo _____ mis discos también.

   ¿Desea Vd. _____ los suyos?

5. ¿Dónde *ponemos* las maletas?

   Yo siempre las _____ en la alcoba.

   ¿Desea Vd. _____ las mías allí también?

6. ¿Cuándo *vienen* Vds. a visitarme?

   Yo _____ mañana.

   ¿_____ Alicia también?

7. ¿*Da* Vd. una propina al mozo?

   Yo siempre le _____ una propina.

   Casi todos le _____ propinas.

8. ¿Qué *hacen* Vds. esta noche?

   Yo no _____ nada.

   ¿Tiene Vd. algo que _____?

9. Pablo nunca *dice* mentiras.

   Yo no _____ mentiras tampoco.

   Nosotros siempre _____ la verdad.

10. Los actores *aparecen* en las películas.

    Yo no _____ en ninguna película.

    Mi amigo es actor y _____ en buenas películas.

B. Escríbase la forma correcta de cada uno de los verbos (*a, b, c, d*), en lugar del verbo en letra cursiva.

EJEMPLO: No *está* aquí.   (*a*) caber   (*b*) vivir   (*c*) llegar   (*d*) comer

(*a*) _cabe_   (*b*) _vive_   (*c*) _llega_   (*d*) _come_

1. *Escucho* aquel programa.   (*a*) aborrecer   (*b*) cambiar   (*c*) oír   (*d*) desconocer

   (*a*) _____   (*b*) _____   (*c*) _____   (*d*) _____

2. Yo *veo* a mis padres.   (*a*) obedecer   (*b*) necesitar   (*c*) agradecer   (*d*) admirar

   (*a*) _____   (*b*) _____   (*c*) _____   (*d*) _____

3. El campesino *produce* frutas.   (*a*) vender   (*b*) ver   (*c*) tener   (*d*) regalar

   (*a*) _____   (*b*) _____   (*c*) _____   (*d*) _____

4. Tomás *toca* la guitarra.   (*a*) comprar   (*b*) romper   (*c*) mirar   (*d*) esconder

   (*a*) _____   (*b*) _____   (*c*) _____   (*d*) _____

5. Yo *trabajo* en mi cuarto.   (*a*) estar   (*b*) caber   (*c*) permanecer   (*d*) llorar

   (*a*) _____   (*b*) _____   (*c*) _____   (*d*) _____

6. Yo *estudio* mi lección de español.   (*a*) traducir   (*b*) leer   (*c*) saber   (*d*) escribir

   (*a*) _____   (*b*) _____   (*c*) _____   (*d*) _____

7. Yo *compro* el automóvil.   (*a*) ver   (*b*) conducir   (*c*) reconocer   (*d*) detener

   (*a*) _____   (*b*) _____   (*c*) _____   (*d*) _____

8. Se lo *pago* mañana.   (*a*) dar   (*b*) traer   (*c*) ofrecer   (*d*) decir

   (*a*) _____   (*b*) _____   (*c*) _____   (*d*) _____

9. Las flores *brotan* de la tierra.   (*a*) venir   (*b*) nacer   (*c*) salir   (*d*) crecer

   (*a*) _____   (*b*) _____   (*c*) _____   (*d*) _____

10. El esclavo *desea* la libertad.   (*a*) obtener   (*b*) recibir   (*c*) amar   (*d*) desconocer

    (*a*) _____   (*b*) _____   (*c*) _____   (*d*) _____

C. Tradúzcanse las frases al español, de dos maneras, según los ejemplos.

EJEMPLO: How long have you been studying Spanish?
   a. ¿Cuánto tiempo hace que Vd. estudia el español?
   b. ¿Desde cuándo estudia Vd. el español?

1. How long have you been reading?

   a. _____

   b. _____

2. How long have they been living there?

   a. _____

   b. _____

3. How long have you been coming here?

   a. _____

   b. _____

4. How long have you been working?

   a. ---

   b. ---

5. How long has he been waiting?

   a. ---

   b. ---

   EJEMPLO: I have been studying for two hours.
   a. Hace dos horas que estudio.
   b. Estudio desde hace dos horas.

6. I have been working for a week.

   a. ---

   b. ---

7. We have been traveling for a month.

   a. ---

   b. ---

8. They have been attending this school for a year.

   a. ---

   b. ---

9. You have been resting for an hour.

   a. ---

   b. ---

10. She has been here for a long time.

   a. ---

   b. ---

   EJEMPLOS: Shall I bring the refreshments?   ¿Traigo los refrescos?
   I'll bring the refreshments.   Traigo los refrescos.

11. I'll put the package here.   ---

12. Shall I thank him for the gift?   --

13. Shall I prepare the meal?   --

14. We'll go now.   --

15. Shall we wait for Henry?   ---

D. Contéstense en español en frases completas.

1. ¿Saludan Vds. al profesor al entrar en la clase? --------------------------------

   ----

2. ¿Dónde pone Vd. sus libros en la escuela? ------------------------------------

3. ¿Abren Vds. las ventanas cuando hace frío? _____

_____

4. ¿Desaparece Vd. cuando hay trabajo que hacer? _____

_____

5. ¿Debe Vd. estudiar más? _____

6. ¿A qué hora salen Vds. de la escuela? _____

_____

7. ¿Hace Vd. mucho ruido cuando sale? _____

_____

8. ¿Pasa Vd. mucho tiempo charlando con sus amigos? _____

_____

9. ¿Son Vds. buenos alumnos? _____

10. ¿Tiene Vd. que trabajar después de las clases? _____

_____

11. ¿Cuántos regalos le dan sus padres en su cumpleaños? _____

_____

12. ¿Ve Vd. muchos programas de televisión? _____

13. ¿Oye Vd. las noticias del día por radio? _____

14. ¿En qué mes cae su cumpleaños? _____

_____

15. ¿Obedece Vd. siempre a sus padres? _____

16. ¿Cuánto tiempo hace que Vd. es alumno(-a) de esta escuela? _____

_____

17. ¿Cuánto tiempo hace que Vds. asisten a esta clase? _____

_____

18. ¿Cuánto tiempo hace que Vd. desea viajar? _____

_____

19. ¿Desde cuándo tienen Vds. un aparato de televisión? _____

_____

20. ¿Desde cuándo conoce Vd. a su mejor amigo(-a)? _____

_____

E. Tradúzcanse al español.

1. He has been dancing with her for one hour. _____

_____

2. Why does Peter say such things? _____

3. I deserve a good mark in this examination. _____

_____

4. How long have you been in the library? _____

_____

5. What are you going to do this week end? _____

_____

6. Charles and I hope to see them tomorrow. _____

_____

7. This afternoon they are going to write to us. _____

_____

8. I belong to the human race. _____

9. We have to discuss an important matter. _____

_____

10. I do not know the address. _____

11. He gives his sister a pearl necklace. _____

_____

12. These jewels are worth much. _____

13. In the autumn the leaves fall from the trees. _____

_____

14. Every Sunday we hear the church bells. _____

_____

15. I drive the automobile better than my brother. _____

_____

El Escorial es un gran monasterio cerca de Madrid. Fue comisionado por Felipe II y construido por el gran arquitecto español, Juan de Herrera. Durante gran parte de su reinado Felipe II vivió allí, y de allí dirigió el gobierno de España. Contiene un palacio, una biblioteca, un museo, una iglesia, y un Panteón (burial place) de Reyes.

Verb Lesson 2—PRESENT TENSE OF STEM-CHANGING VERBS

STEM-CHANGING VERBS ENDING IN -AR AND -ER

Stem-changing verbs ending in **-ar** or **-er** change the stem vowel in the present tense as follows:

> **e to ie** }
> **o to ue** } in all forms except those for **nosotros** and **vosotros**

pensar, to think: p*ie*nso, p*ie*nsas, p*ie*nsa, pensamos, pensáis, p*ie*nsan

Like pensar:

acertar, to hit the mark, to guess right	**encerrar,** to enclose, to lock up
apretar, to tighten, to squeeze, to be tight	**gobernar,** to govern
atravesar, to cross	**helar,** to freeze
cerrar, to close	**nevar,** to snow
comenzar, to begin, to commence	**quebrar,** to break
confesar, to confess	**remendar,** to patch, to mend
despertar(se), to awaken	**sentarse,** to sit down
empezar, to begin	

descender, to descend: desc*ie*ndo, desc*ie*ndes, desc*ie*nde, descendemos, descendéis, desc*ie*nden

Like descender:

ascender, to ascend	**entender,** to understand
defender, to defend	**perder,** to lose
encender, to light, to ignite	**querer,** to wish, to love, to want

mostrar, to show: m*ue*stro, m*ue*stras, m*ue*stra, mostramos, mostráis, m*ue*stran

Like mostrar:

acordarse (de), to remember	**jugar (u to ue),** to play
acostarse, to go to bed	**recordar,** to remember
almorzar, to eat lunch	**renovar,** to remodel, to renew
contar, to count, to relate	**tronar,** to thunder
costar, to cost	**volar,** to fly
encontrar, to find, to meet	

volver, to return: v*ue*lvo, v*ue*lves, v*ue*lve, volvemos, volvéis, v*ue*lven

Like volver:

conmover, to move (emotionally)	**oler (o to hue),** to smell
devolver, to return, to give back	**poder,** to be able
doler, to pain, to ache	**resolver,** to solve, to resolve
llover, to rain	**soler,** to be in the habit of, to be accustomed to
mover, to move	

STEM-CHANGING VERBS ENDING IN -IR

Stem-changing verbs ending in **-ir** change the stem vowel in the present tense as follows:

> **e to ie**)
> **o to ue** } in all forms except those for **nosotros** and **vosotros**
> **e to i**)

consentir, to consent: *consiento, consientes, consiente, consentimos, consentís, consienten*

    Like consentir:

adquirir (i to ie), to acquire	**mentir,** to lie
advertir, to notify, to warn	**preferir,** to prefer
convertir, to convert	**referir,** to narrate, to refer
divertirse, to enjoy oneself, to have a good time	**sentir,** to regret, to feel sorry
hervir, to boil	**sentirse,** to feel (well, ill)

dormir, to sleep: *duermo, duermes, duerme, dormimos, dormís, duermen*

    Like dormir: **dormirse,** to fall asleep; **morir(se),** to die

pedir, to ask for, to request: *pido, pides, pide, pedimos, pedís, piden*

    Like pedir:

despedirse (de), to take leave (of), to say goodbye (to)	**reñir,** to quarrel, to scold
	repetir, to repeat
gemir, to groan, to moan	**servir,** to serve
impedir, to prevent	**sonreír,** to smile
medir, to measure	**vestir(se),** to dress (oneself)
reír(se), to laugh	

Note

A. The verb **reír** (and **sonreír**) has a written accent mark over the letter **i** in all forms:

        río, ríes, ríe, reímos, reís, ríen

B. In verbs ending in **-uir** (except **-guir**), a **y** is inserted after the **u** in all forms except those for **nosotros** and **vosotros.**

huir, to flee: *huyo, huyes, huye, huimos, huís, huyen*

    Like huir:

concluir, to conclude, to end	**distribuir,** to distribute
construir, to construct	**incluir,** to include
contribuir, to contribute	**influir,** to influence, to have influence
destruir, to destroy	**sustituir,** to substitute

C. Some verbs ending in **-iar** or **-uar** stress the **i** or the **u** (**í, ú**) in all forms except those for **nosotros** and **vosotros.**

enviar, to send: *envío, envías, envía, enviamos, enviáis, envían*

    Like enviar:

confiar (en), to rely (on), to confide (in)	**guiar,** to guide, to drive
espiar, to spy	**resfriarse,** to catch cold
fiarse (de), to trust	**variar,** to vary

continuar, to continue: *continúo, continúas, continúa, continuamos, continuáis, continúan*

    Like continuar: **actuar,** to act; **graduarse,** to be graduated, to graduate

Important: All stem-changing verbs are identified in the vocabulary lists by the type of change **(ie, ue, i, y, í, ú)** after the verb.

EJERCICIOS

A. Cámbiese la forma del verbo en letra cursiva, empleando los sujetos indicados.

1. El señor *vuelve* a casa y *se acuesta*.

    Yo _____ a casa y _____.

    Ellos _____ a casa y _____.

    Nosotros _____ a casa y _____.

2. Yo *quiero* ir a la función, pero no *puedo*.

    Ellos _____ ir a la función, pero no _____.

    Vd. _____ ir a la función, pero no _____.

    Tú _____ ir a la función, pero no _____.

3. Ellos *se sientan* a la mesa y *empiezan* a comer.

    Él _____ a la mesa y _____ a comer.

    Nosotros _____ a la mesa y _____ a comer.

    Yo _____ a la mesa y _____ a comer.

4. En junio *me gradúo* y *me despido* de la escuela.

    En junio nosotros _____ y _____ de la escuela.

    En junio tú _____ y _____ de la escuela.

    En junio ella _____ y _____ de la escuela.

5. Yo *me despierto* y *me visto* pronto.

    Tú _____ y _____ pronto.

    Los niños _____ y _____ pronto.

    Nosotros _____ y _____ pronto.

6. *Concluyen* la discusión y *cierran* la sala.

    Yo _____ la discusión y _____ la sala.

    Vd. _____ la discusión y _____ la sala.

    Nosotros _____ la discusión y _____ la sala.

7. *Nos divertimos* mucho cuando *jugamos* al fútbol.

    Yo _____ mucho cuando _____ al fútbol.

    Ellos _____ mucho cuando _____ al fútbol.

    Tú _____ mucho cuando _____ al fútbol.

8. *Destruye* los papeles y *huye* de la casa.

    Nosotros _____ los papeles y _____ de la casa.

    Yo _____ los papeles y _____ de la casa.

    Vds. _____ los papeles y _____ de la casa.

9. No *me siento* bien cuando *duermo* menos de ocho horas.

Nosotros no _____ bien cuando _____ menos de ocho horas.

Tú no _____ bien cuando _____ menos de ocho horas.

Ella no _____ bien cuando _____ menos de ocho horas.

10. Ellas *actúan* muy bien y *conmueven* al público.

Nosotros _____ muy bien y _____ al público.

Tú _____ muy bien y _____ al público.

Yo _____ muy bien y _____ al público.

11. *Repito* la lección varias veces cuando no la *entiendo*.

Los alumnos _____ la lección varias veces cuando no la _____.

Nosotros _____ la lección varias veces cuando no la _____.

Él _____ la lección varias veces cuando no la _____.

12. *Enciendo* la luz cuando *comienzo* a trabajar.

Nosotros _____ la luz cuando _____ a trabajar.

El maestro _____ la luz cuando _____ a trabajar.

Vosotros _____ la luz cuando _____ a trabajar.

13. *Sonrío* cuando *recuerdo* aquel chiste.

Ellos _____ cuando _____ aquel chiste.

Elena _____ cuando _____ aquel chiste.

Nosotros _____ cuando _____ aquel chiste.

14. Diego *almuerza* y luego *pide* la cuenta.

Yo _____ y luego _____ la cuenta.

Nosotros _____ y luego _____ la cuenta.

Los señores _____ y luego _____ la cuenta.

15. *Confían* en la buena suerte cuando *juegan* al fútbol.

Nosotros _____ en la buena suerte cuando _____ al fútbol.

Yo _____ en la buena suerte cuando _____ al fútbol.

Vosotros _____ en la buena suerte cuando _____ al fútbol.

B. En cada grupo, complétense las frases, usando la forma correcta del verbo de la primera frase.

1. *Atravesamos* varias calles para llegar a la escuela.

¿_____ Vd. muchas calles?

Yo no _____ ninguna calle.

2. *¿Juegan* Vds. al ajedrez?

Nosotros no _____.

Nuestro padre _____ bien.

3. Yo *muevo* la silla.

¿-------------------- Vds. la mesa?

No, nosotros -------------------- el escritorio.

4. Paco *resuelve* el problema.

Nosotros lo ----------------------- también.

Ellos no lo -----------------------.

5. *Volvemos* ahora.

Alicia ----------------- más tarde.

Todos ----------------- lo más pronto posible.

6. Yo *me divierto* mucho en una tertulia.

¿------------------------- Vds.?

Sí, nosotros ------------------------- siempre.

7. *Preferimos* este vestido.

Ella -------------------- el vestido rojo.

¿Qué vestido -------------------- Vd.?

8. Rosa ya *sirve* la ensalada.

Yo -------------------- la carne.

Nosotras -------------------- el té después.

9. Siempre *acertamos* a dar la respuesta correcta.

¿------------------------ Vds. también?

No, pero ella ------------------------ a menudo.

10. No *guío* bien el automóvil.

¿----------------- Vds. bien?

Nosotros ----------------- muy mal.

C. Escríbase la forma correcta de cada uno de los verbos (*a, b, c, d*), en lugar del verbo en letra cursiva.

1. Tomás *piensa* hacerlo.   (*a*) comenzar a   (*b*) consentir en   (*c*) acordarse de   (*d*) preferir

(*a*) ----------------   (*b*) ----------------   (*c*) ----------------   (*d*) ----------------

2. El emperador *abandona* su trono.   (*a*) querer   (*b*) perder   (*c*) preferir   (*d*) defender

(*a*) ----------------   (*b*) ----------------   (*c*) ----------------   (*d*) ----------------

3. *Cuesta* mucho.   (*a*) llover   (*b*) nevar   (*c*) divertirse   (*d*) reírse

(*a*) ----------------   (*b*) ----------------   (*c*) ----------------   (*d*) ----------------

4. El policía *acusa* al ladrón.   (*a*) encontrar   (*b*) encerrar   (*c*) conocer   (*d*) espiar

(*a*) ----------------   (*b*) ----------------   (*c*) ----------------   (*d*) ----------------

5. Todos *resisten*.   (*a*) acertar   (*b*) continuar   (*c*) contribuir   (*d*) servir

(*a*) ----------------   (*b*) ----------------   (*c*) ----------------   (*d*) ----------------

6. No *gano* dinero.   (*a*) adquirir   (*b*) contar   (*c*) distribuir   (*d*) querer

(*a*) _____   (*b*) _____   (*c*) _____   (*d*) _____

7. Los niños *lloran.*   (*a*) gemir   (*b*) mentir   (*c*) reírse   (*d*) reñir

(*a*) _____   (*b*) _____   (*c*) _____   (*d*) _____

8. *Vende* el instrumento.   (*a*) destruir   (*b*) enviar   (*c*) mostrar   (*d*) quebrar

(*a*) _____   (*b*) _____   (*c*) _____   (*d*) _____

9. *Ponen* la casa en el campo.   (*a*) construir   (*b*) destruir   (*c*) renovar   (*d*) recordar

(*a*) _____   (*b*) _____   (*c*) _____   (*d*) _____

10. El presidente *defiende* el país.   (*a*) gobernar   (*b*) guiar   (*c*) pensar en   (*d*) servir

(*a*) _____   (*b*) _____   (*c*) _____   (*d*) _____

D. Contéstense en español en frases completas.

1. ¿Piensa Vd. continuar estudiando el español? _____

2. ¿Suele Vd. pasar mucho tiempo mirando la televisión? _____

_____

3. ¿Recuerda Vd. los años de su infancia? _____

4. ¿Sonríe Vd. cuando se siente feliz? _____

5. ¿Se divierte Vd. durante las vacaciones? _____

6. ¿Repiten Vds. las frases varias veces en la clase de español? _____

_____

7. ¿Cuándo se gradúa Vd.? _____

8. ¿A qué hora empieza Vd. a estudiar sus lecciones? _____

_____

9. ¿Se fía Vd. mucho de sus amigos? _____

10. ¿Cierra Vd. la puerta al salir de casa? _____

11. ¿Envía Vd. regalos a sus amigos para la Navidad? _____

_____

12. ¿A qué hora se acuesta Vd. generalmente? _____

_____

13. ¿Se ríe Vd. de los errores de sus compañeros? _____

_____

14. ¿Duermen Vds. en la clase? _____

15. ¿Pide Vd. permiso a sus padres para salir de noche? _____

_____

16. ¿Se resfría Vd. cuando hace mal tiempo? _____

_____

17. ¿Se despiden Vds. del profesor al salir de la clase? _____

_____

18. ¿A qué hora almuerza Vd.? _____

19. ¿Riñe Vd. a veces con sus padres? ¿Por qué? _____
_____

20. ¿Devuelve Vd. los libros que sus amigos le prestan? _____
_____

E. Tradúzcanse al español.

1. In the winter it snows, and the lakes freeze over. _____
_____

2. I warn you that such punishment is not sufficient. _____
_____

3. The elevator rises and descends smoothly. _____
_____

4. Because of his fall, his right leg hurts him. _____
_____

5. The wind hinders the progress of the boats. _____
_____

6. On the frontier, the travelers convert their dollars to pesos. _____
_____

7. While the soup boils, my mother sets the table. _____
_____

8. This child shows an extraordinary talent for mathematics. _____
_____

9. The price of the meal includes the tax and the tip. _____
_____

10. Customs vary from one country to another. _____
_____

11. He doesn't think of the difficulties of the enterprise. _____
_____

12. The monument measures thirty feet in width and fifty in height. _____
_____

13. A good teacher has much influence on the future. _____
_____

14. He is wearing new shoes, and they are tight. _____
_____

15. Upon entering, he smells the aroma of roast beef. _____
_____

Verb Lesson 3—SPELLING CHANGES IN THE PRESENT TENSE

Verbs with changes in spelling are not really irregular. The spelling change occurs before certain letters in order that the original *sound* may be kept in accordance with the rules for Spanish pronunciation.

1. In verbs ending in **-cer** or **-cir,** the **c** changes to **z** before **o** or **a.**

vencer, to conquer, to overcome: venzo, vences, vence, vencemos, vencéis, vencen
   Like vencer: **convencer,** to convince; **ejercer,** to exert, to exercise, to practice (a profession)

2. In verbs ending in **-ger** or **-gir,** the **g** changes to **j** before **o** or **a.**

dirigir, to direct: dirijo, diriges, dirige, dirigimos, dirigís, dirigen
   Like dirigir:
   afligir, to afflict, to grieve   **fingir,** to pretend
   coger, to seize, to grasp, to catch   **proteger,** to protect
   escoger, to choose, to select   **recoger,** to gather, to pick up
   exigir, to demand, to require

3. In verbs ending in **-guir,** the **gu** changes to **g** before **o** or **a.**

distinguir, to distinguish: distingo, distingues, distingue, distinguimos, distinguís, distinguen
   Like distinguir: **extinguir,** to extinguish

Note

A. Some verbs with spelling changes also have stem changes. (See Verb Lesson 2, page 8.) Some verbs of this type are:

cocer, to cook: *cue*zo, *cue*ces, *cue*ce, cocemos, cocéis, *cue*cen
   Like cocer: **torcer,** to twist, to turn

corregir, to correct: corri*j*o, corri*g*es, corri*g*e, corregimos, corregís, corri*g*en
   Like corregir: **elegir,** to elect, to choose

seguir, to follow, to continue: *sigo,* si*g*ues, si*g*ue, seguimos, seguís, si*g*uen
   Like seguir:
   conseguir, to get, to obtain, to succeed in   **proseguir,** to continue, to proceed
   perseguir, to pursue, to persecute

B. Verbs ending in **-car, -gar,** and **-zar** have no spelling changes in the present tense; changes occur only in the preterite, in commands, and in the present subjunctive. They are discussed in the appropriate chapter.

Important: Verbs with spelling changes are identified in our vocabulary lists by the type of change **(z, j, g)** in parentheses after the verb.

EJERCICIOS

A. Escríbase la forma correcta de cada verbo, empleando los sujetos entre paréntesis.

1. Vd. *corrige* las faltas.

   (yo) _____ (nosotros) _____ (ellos) _____

2. *Siguen* los consejos del sabio.

   (tú) _____ (yo) _____ (vosotros) _____

3. *Convencemos* a los oficiales.

(ellos) ------------------   (Arturo) ----------------------   (yo) --------------------

4. *Proseguimos* el camino.

(yo) ------------------   (ellos) -------------------   (tú) -------------------

5. *Recogemos* las flores.

(él) ------------------   (yo) -------------------------   (ellos) -------------------

6. A las dos millas, *tuerce* a la derecha.

(Vds.) ---------------   (nosotros) -------------------   (yo) --------------------

7. El amo *protege* a los empleados.

(yo) ------------------   (ellos) -------------------   (vosotros) ---------------

8. El dolor le *aflige.*

(tú) ------------------   (la enfermedad) ---------------   (yo) --------------------

9. *Ejerce* la profesión de abogado.

(nosotros) ---------------   (yo) -------------------------   (tú) -------------------

10. *Dirigen* un negocio importante.

(el Sr. Gómez) ------------   (yo) -------------------------   (tú) --------------------

11. Los alumnos *distinguen* entre "tú" y "Vd."

(yo) ------------------   (el maestro) -------------------   (tú) ----------------------

12. *Escogen* la pintura grande.

(tú y yo) -----------------   (yo) -------------------------   (ella) --------------------

13. *Conseguimos* buenas notas.

(yo) ------------------   (ellas) -------------------------   (vosotros) ----------------

14. *Cogen* el autobús de las ocho.

(nosotros) ----------------   (tú) -------------------------   (yo) --------------------

15. El sereno *exige* una propina.

(yo) ------------------   (nosotros) ----------------------   (ellos) -------------------

B. En cada grupo, complétense las frases, usando la forma correcta del verbo de la primera frase.

1. Ella *escoge* una alhaja.

Yo ------------------- un libro.

¿Qué ------------------- Vd.?

2. Ella *protege* a su hermanita.

¿------------------- Vd. a la suya?

Sí, yo ------------------- a la mía.

3. ¿*Recoge* Vd. las frutas?

Sí, yo ------------------- las frutas.

Ellos no ------------------- las frutas; se las comen.

4. *¿Corrige* Vd. sus faltas?

El maestro _ _ _ _ _ _ _ _ _ _ _ _ _ _ _ _ _ _ mis faltas.

Yo no las _ _ _ _ _ _ _ _ _ _ _ _ _ _ _ _ _ _.

5. ¿Qué profesión *ejerce* su hermano?

Mi hermano no _ _ _ _ _ _ _ _ _ _ _ _ _ _ _ _ _ _ ninguna profesión.

Yo _ _ _ _ _ _ _ _ _ _ _ _ _ _ _ _ _ _ la profesión de ingeniero.

6. ¿Quién *dirige* esta escuela?

Yo no la _ _ _ _ _ _ _ _ _ _ _ _ _ _ _ _ _ _.

Creo que los maestros la _ _ _ _ _ _ _ _ _ _ _ _ _ _ _ _ _ _.

7. *¿Distingue* Vd. entre lo bueno y lo malo?

Sí, yo _ _ _ _ _ _ _ _ _ _ _ _ _ _ _ _ _ _ entre los dos.

Todo el mundo _ _ _ _ _ _ _ _ _ _ _ _ _ _ _ _ _ _ entre ellos.

8. ¿Qué *exige* Vd. de sus padres?

Yo no _ _ _ _ _ _ _ _ _ _ _ _ _ _ _ _ _ _ nada de ellos.

Ellos _ _ _ _ _ _ _ _ _ _ _ _ _ _ _ _ _ _ mucho de mí.

9. En todas partes *cuecen* habas.

¿Las _ _ _ _ _ _ _ _ _ _ _ _ _ _ _ _ _ _ Vd. en su casa?

No, yo no las _ _ _ _ _ _ _ _ _ _ _ _ _ _ _ _ _ _.

10. Para evitar trabajo, *¿finge* Vd. estar dormido?

No, yo no _ _ _ _ _ _ _ _ _ _ _ _ _ _ _ _ _ _.

Pero mis hermanos _ _ _ _ _ _ _ _ _ _ _ _ _ _ _ _ _ _ estar enfermos.

   C. Contéstense en español en frases completas.

1. ¿Corrige Vd. las faltas de sus amigos? _
_ _

2. ¿Coge Vd. muchos resfriados en el invierno? _
_ _

3. ¿Finge Vd. una enfermedad para no trabajar? _
_ _

4. ¿Consigue Vd. un empleo para el verano? _
_ _

5. ¿Quién dirige la orquesta de su escuela? _
_ _

6. ¿Sigue Vd. estudiando el español? _
_ _

7. ¿Exige mucho trabajo su profesor de español? _
_ _

8. ¿Escoge Vd. a sus amigos con cuidado? --

----

9. ¿Vence Vd. todas sus dificultades? --

----

10. En la clase, ¿recoge Vd. los papeles del suelo? --------------------------------

----

D. Tradúzcanse al español.

1. I write and address the letter to the company. ----------------------------------

----

2. He knows that I am following his advice. --

----

3. The newspapers are spreading the news rapidly. ---------------------------------

----

4. The heroic policeman chases the criminal. ---------------------------------------

----

5. After the wedding, they gather their gifts. --------------------------------------

----

6. He is kind and protects the animals. ---

----

7. My uncle exerts much influence among the politicians. --------------------------

----

8. After resting, the traveler proceeds on his way (camino). ----------------------

----

9. The memory of her son grieves her. --

----

10. His enthusiasm convinces many people. ---

El cacao se produce en varias partes de la América Latina, sobre todo en el Ecuador, el Brasil, Venezuela, y la República Dominicana. Las bayas (berries) del cacao se encuentran en vainas (pods), que se cortan del tronco del árbol. Después de secarse al sol, las bayas se exportan a todas partes, para ser convertidas en chocolate.

Verb Lesson 4—PRETERITE TENSE

REGULAR VERBS

invitar:	invit	-é, -aste, -ó, -amos, -asteis, -aron
correr:	corr	
admitir:	admit	-í, -iste, -ió, -imos, -isteis, -ieron

VERBS WHICH CHANGE *I* TO *Y* IN THE PRETERITE

caer:	ca	
creer:	cre	
leer:	le	-í, -íste, -yó, -ímos, -ísteis, -yeron
oír:	o	
poseer:	pose	

Note

A. Verbs that end in **-er** or **-ir**, and that contain a vowel immediately before the ending, change in the third person singular and plural from **-ió** to **-yó** and from **-ieron** to **-yeron**. The i has a written accent in all the other forms.

   Exceptions: **traer, atraer,** and all verbs ending in **-guir** (the **u** is not pronounced).

B. Verbs that end in **-uir** (**contribuir, huir,** etc.) also belong in this group, but no accent appears in the endings **-uiste, -uimos,** and **-uisteis**.

VERBS ENDING IN *-CAR, -GAR, AND -ZAR*

Verbs ending in **-car, -gar,** and **-zar** change in the first person singular of the preterite as follows:

c changes to **qu**
g changes to **gu**
z changes to **c**

atacar, to attack: ata**qu**é, atacaste, atacó, atacamos, atacasteis, atacaron
   Like atacar:

acercarse, to approach	**indicar,** to indicate
aplicar, to apply	**marcar,** to designate, to mark
arrancar, to root out, to pull out	**mascar,** to chew
buscar, to look for, to seek	**pescar,** to fish
colocar, to place, to put	**publicar,** to publish
comunicar, to communicate	**replicar,** to reply
dedicar, to dedicate, to devote	**sacar,** to take out
educar, to educate	**sacrificar,** to sacrifice
embarcarse, to embark	**significar,** to mean
equivocarse, to be mistaken	**suplicar,** to beg, to implore
explicar, to explain	**tocar,** to touch, to play (music)
fabricar, to make, to manufacture	

pagar, to pay (for): pa*gu*é, pagaste, pagó, pagamos, pagasteis, pagaron

Like pagar:

agregar, to add	**jugar,** to play
ahogarse, to drown	**llegar,** to arrive
apagar, to put out, to extinguish	**madrugar,** to rise early
cargar, to load	**negar,** to deny
castigar, to punish	**obligar,** to obligate, to compel
colgar, to hang	**pegar,** to stick, to beat
encargar, to put in charge	**rogar,** to ask, to beg
entregar, to deliver, to hand over	

cruzar, to cross: cru*c*é, cruzaste, cruzó, cruzamos, cruzasteis, cruzaron

Like cruzar:

abrazar, to embrace, to hug	**empezar,** to begin
alcanzar, to reach, to overtake	**gozar,** to enjoy
almorzar, to eat lunch	**lanzar,** to throw
amenazar, to threaten	**realizar,** to fulfill, to realize (a profit)
avanzar, to advance	**rezar,** to pray
comenzar, to begin, to commence	**tropezar,** to stumble
deslizarse, to slip, to glide	

STEM-CHANGING VERBS ENDING IN *-IR*

Verbs ending in **-ir** that have a stem change in the present tense also have a stem change in the preterite. In the preterite tense, the stem vowel changes in the third person singular and plural, from **e** to **i** or from **o** to **u**.

convertir, to convert: convertí, convertiste, conv*i*rtió, convertimos, convertisteis, conv*i*rtieron

servir, to serve: serví, serviste, s*i*rvió, servimos, servisteis, s*i*rvieron

dormir, to sleep: dormí, dormiste, d*u*rmió, dormimos, dormisteis, d*u*rmieron

Note

A. The verbs **reír** and **sonreír** are conjugated in the preterite as follows:

reí, reíste, *rió,* reímos, reísteis, *rieron*

sonreí, sonreíste, *sonrió,* sonreímos, sonreísteis, *sonrieron*

B. Verbs ending in **-ir** that have **ñ** directly before the ending (**ceñir, gruñir, reñir**) drop the **i** of the ending in the third person singular and plural of the preterite (**riñó, riñeron**). Note that, because of the **ñ,** the *sound* of the ending is still regular.

Important: All verbs having spelling changes or stem changes in the preterite are identified in our vocabulary lists according to the type of change (**i, u, y, qu, gu, c**).

VERBS IRREGULAR IN THE PRETERITE

1. The following verbs have an irregular stem in the preterite. The endings for these verbs are **-e, -iste, -o, -imos, -isteis, -ieron** (**-eron** if **j** precedes the ending).

andar:	*anduve, anduviste, anduvo, anduvimos, anduvisteis, anduvieron*
caber:	*cupe, cupiste, cupo, cupimos, cupisteis, cupieron*
estar:	*estuve, estuviste, estuvo, estuvimos, estuvisteis, estuvieron*
haber:	*hube, hubiste, hubo, hubimos, hubisteis, hubieron*
hacer:	*hice, hiciste, hizo, hicimos, hicisteis, hicieron*
poder:	*pude, pudiste, pudo, pudimos, pudisteis, pudieron*

poner: *puse, pusiste, puso, pusimos, pusisteis, pusieron*
querer: *quise, quisiste, quiso, quisimos, quisisteis, quisieron*
saber: *supe, supiste, supo, supimos, supisteis, supieron*
tener: *tuve, tuviste, tuvo, tuvimos, tuvisteis, tuvieron*
venir: *vine, viniste, vino, vinimos, vinisteis, vinieron*

decir: *dije, dijiste, dijo, dijimos, dijisteis, dijeron*
producir: *produje, produjiste, produjo, produjimos, produjisteis, produjeron*
traer: *traje, trajiste, trajo, trajimos, trajisteis, trajeron*

2. The verbs **dar**, **ser**, and **ir** are also irregular in the preterite. **Dar** takes the endings of regular -**er**, -**ir** verbs; **ser** and **ir** have the same forms in the preterite.

dar: *di, diste, dio, dimos, disteis, dieron*
ser ⎫
ir ⎭ *fui, fuiste, fue, fuimos, fuisteis, fueron*

Note

A. The third person singular of **hacer** is spelled **hizo**. The **c** changes to **z** to avoid the *k* sound.

B. All verbs ending in -**ducir** are conjugated like **producir**:

conducir, to lead, to drive: **conduje, -iste, -o, -imos, -isteis, -eron**
traducir, to translate: **traduje, -iste, -o, -imos, -isteis, -eron**

C. All compounds of **poner** (**proponer**, etc.), **tener** (**detener**, etc.), **hacer** (**satisfacer**, etc.), **venir** (**convenir**, etc.), and **traer** (**atraer**, etc.) are conjugated in the same manner as the basic verb.

D. Formerly, the preterite forms of **dar**, **ver**, **ser**, and **ir** were written with accent marks: **dí, dió; ví, vió; fuí, fué.** However, the present custom is to omit the accent marks on these forms.

USES OF THE PRETERITE TENSE

1. The preterite tense is used to indicate the beginning or the end of an action or event occurring in the past. It may also narrate a complete event (that is, both beginning and end).

Comenzó a leer el libro.
(beginning)

He began to read the book.

Cesó de llover a las cuatro.
(end)

It stopped raining at 4 o'clock.

Carlos me *visitó* ayer.
(he came and went)

Charles visited me yesterday.

2. Because of the nature of the preterite (beginning or end), the verbs **conocer** (to know), **saber** (to know), **tener** (to have), **querer** (to want), and **poder** (to be able) often have a different meaning in the preterite.

Le *conocí* en México.
(began to know)

I *met* him in Mexico.

¿Cuándo *supieron* la verdad?
(began to know)

When did they *find out* (*learn*) the truth?

Tuve una carta de él esta mañana.
(it came into my possession)

I *received* a letter from him this morning.

No *quiso* hacerlo.
(final decision)

He *refused* to do it.

Pude convencerle.
(finally was able)

I *managed* to convince him.

EJERCICIOS

A. Escríbase la forma correcta del pretérito de cada uno de los verbos (*a, b, c, d*), en lugar del verbo en letra cursiva.

1. Al oír el trueno, *se estremecieron.*   (*a*) huir   (*b*) despedirse   (*c*) agitarse   (*d*) espantarse

    (*a*) _____   (*b*) _____   (*c*) _____   (*d*) _____

2. *Descansé* en San Francisco el martes pasado.   (*a*) quedarse   (*b*) estar   (*c*) embarcarse   (*d*) esperar

    (*a*) _____   (*b*) _____   (*c*) _____   (*d*) _____

3. ¿A qué hora *partieron?*   (*a*) morir   (*b*) salir   (*c*) regresar   (*d*) venir

    (*a*) _____   (*b*) _____   (*c*) _____   (*d*) _____

4. Yo *estudié* demasiado.   (*a*) sufrir   (*b*) sacrificar   (*c*) pagar   (*d*) andar

    (*a*) _____   (*b*) _____   (*c*) _____   (*d*) _____

5. ¿*Terminó* Vd. la novela?   (*a*) conseguir   (*b*) ver   (*c*) concluir   (*d*) comprar

    (*a*) _____   (*b*) _____   (*c*) _____   (*d*) _____

6. Vds. no me *comprendieron.*   (*a*) llamar   (*b*) corregir   (*c*) perdonar   (*d*) detener

    (*a*) _____   (*b*) _____   (*c*) _____   (*d*) _____

7. Al entrar, *vi* a mi mamá.   (*a*) besar   (*b*) hablar   (*c*) buscar   (*d*) abrazar

    (*a*) _____   (*b*) _____   (*c*) _____   (*d*) _____

8. ¿Cuándo *acabó?*   (*a*) llegar   (*b*) irse   (*c*) ocurrir   (*d*) dormirse

    (*a*) _____   (*b*) _____   (*c*) _____   (*d*) _____

9. *Pronunciaron* las palabras difíciles.   (*a*) aprender   (*b*) oír   (*c*) decir   (*d*) repetir

    (*a*) _____   (*b*) _____   (*c*) _____   (*d*) _____

10. ¿*Tomaste* el cheque?   (*a*) dar   (*b*) recibir   (*c*) firmar   (*d*) traer

    (*a*) _____   (*b*) _____   (*c*) _____   (*d*) _____

B. Cámbiese la forma del verbo en letra cursiva, empleando los sujetos indicados (*a, b, c, d*).

1. *Llegamos* a la reunión.   (*a*) Carlos   (*b*) Vds.   (*c*) tú   (*d*) yo

    (*a*) _____   (*b*) _____   (*c*) _____   (*d*) _____

2. Yo *cupe* en el coche.   (*a*) los niños   (*b*) nadie   (*c*) nosotros   (*d*) tú

    (*a*) _____   (*b*) _____   (*c*) _____   (*d*) _____

3. Tú no *pudiste* trabajar.   (*a*) yo   (*b*) el señor   (*c*) ellos   (*d*) Pepe y yo

    (*a*) _____   (*b*) _____   (*c*) _____   (*d*) _____

4. Alguien *tuvo* un accidente.   (*a*) nosotros   (*b*) el artista   (*c*) yo   (*d*) mis amigos

    (*a*) _____   (*b*) _____   (*c*) _____   (*d*) _____

5. ¿Dónde *pusiste* tú los zapatos?   (*a*) Vd.   (*b*) nosotros   (*c*) ellos   (*d*) yo

    (*a*) _____   (*b*) _____   (*c*) _____   (*d*) _____

6. Yo lo *supe* anoche.   (*a*) nosotros   (*b*) Francisca   (*c*) tú   (*d*) Vds.

    (*a*) _____   (*b*) _____   (*c*) _____   (*d*) _____

7. El hombre no *quiso* jugar.   (*a*) tú   (*b*) los niños   (*c*) yo   (*d*) nosotros

(*a*) _____ (*b*) _____ (*c*) _____ (*d*) _____

8. No *hicimos* nada ayer.   (*a*) Vd.   (*b*) yo   (*c*) Carmen y Rosa   (*d*) tú

(*a*) _____ (*b*) _____ (*c*) _____ (*d*) _____

9. Yo *vine* tarde.   (*a*) nosotros   (*b*) el alumno   (*c*) tú   (*d*) Vds.

(*a*) _____ (*b*) _____ (*c*) _____ (*d*) _____

10. Yo no *elegí* eso.   (*a*) Jorge   (*b*) tú   (*c*) ellos   (*d*) nosotros

(*a*) _____ (*b*) _____ (*c*) _____ (*d*) _____

11. Nosotros lo *publicamos* en el periódico.   (*a*) yo   (*b*) Vds.   (*c*) Carlota   (*d*) mis amigos

(*a*) _____ (*b*) _____ (*c*) _____ (*d*) _____

12. *Caí* escalera abajo.   (*a*) ellos   (*b*) vosotros   (*c*) Vd.   (*d*) nosotros

(*a*) _____ (*b*) _____ (*c*) _____ (*d*) _____

13. Le *perseguí* a pie.   (*a*) nosotros   (*b*) Roberto   (*c*) Vd.   (*d*) los soldados

(*a*) _____ (*b*) _____ (*c*) _____ (*d*) _____

14. El profesor *tradujo* la poesía al inglés.   (*a*) yo   (*b*) nosotros   (*c*) los alumnos   (*d*) Vd.

(*a*) _____ (*b*) _____ (*c*) _____ (*d*) _____

15. Yo no *mentí*.   (*a*) nosotros   (*b*) Alfredo y Carlos   (*c*) vosotros   (*d*) ella

(*a*) _____ (*b*) _____ (*c*) _____ (*d*) _____

C. Cámbiese cada verbo al pretérito.

1. *Almuerzo* a las doce. _____
2. Carlos y Felipe *se divierten* juntos. _____
3. *Soy* el primero en llegar. _____
4. *Dice* que sí. _____
5. ¿*Estás* enfermo? _____
6. ¿Dónde *cuelgo* el sombrero? _____
7. No *contribuye* bastante dinero. _____
8. El guía me *conduce* a la carretera principal. _____
9. *Siguen* caminando por las calles. _____
10. Ellos no *sonríen*. _____
11. Nosotros no lo *creemos*. _____
12. ¿Con quién *riñe?* _____
13. La corrida de toros *atrae* a mucha gente. _____
14. ¿Cuánto tiempo *hierve* el agua? _____
15. Esta comida me *satisface*. _____

D. Contéstense en español en frases completas.

1. ¿Aprendieron Vds. mucho en esta clase? -

2. ¿Mascó Vd. chicle en clase hoy? -

3. ¿Recibió Vd. buenas notas el semestre pasado? -

- -

4. ¿Empezó Vd. la lección para mañana? -

5. ¿Se puso Vd. a estudiar para el examen de esta semana? - - - - - - - - - - - - - - -

- -

6. ¿Cuánto tiempo dedicó Vd. a preparar la lección de hoy? - - - - - - - - - - - - - - -

- -

7. ¿Cuándo estuvo Vd. en la biblioteca? -

8. ¿A qué hora apagó Vd. la luz anoche? -

9. ¿Qué película interesante vio Vd. el mes pasado? -

- -

10. ¿Colocó Vd. el sobretodo en el armario? -

- -

11. ¿Vinieron Vds. a la clase a tiempo? -

12. ¿Tocó el maestro discos en la clase? -

13. ¿Qué trajo Vd. a la escuela esta mañana? -

- -

14. ¿Cuántas calles cruzó Vd. para llegar a la escuela? - - - - - - - - - - - - - - - - - - -

- -

15. ¿Adónde fue Vd. ayer? -

16. ¿Entregó Vd. su libro a su compañero? -

- -

17. ¿Avanzó Vd. en sus estudios este año? -

18. ¿Pudo Vd. dormir anoche? -

19. ¿Se vistió Vd. rápidamente hoy? -

20. ¿Qué dio Vd. a sus padres para su aniversario? -

- -

E. Tradúzcanse al español.

1. They brought me many gifts. -

2. He opposed the construction of the monument. -

- -

3. Upon hearing the news, the woman moaned. -

- -

4. I came upon him in the office today. _____

5. Yesterday was August 1. _____

6. When did she acquire the property? _____

7. Finally, I found out what happened. _____

8. He met (conocer) her during the summer vacation. _____

_____

9. They gave me a bouquet of flowers. _____

10. He destroyed it on purpose. _____

11. What produced the explosion? _____

12. They did not smell the smoke. _____

13. His illness hindered his work. _____

14. In a moment, she undid the work of many years. _____

_____

15. The mother distributed candy among the children. _____

_____

El Cristo de los Andes es una estatua construida en 1904 por los gobiernos de Chile y la Argentina en la frontera misma de estos dos países. Conmemora el arreglo de una disputa internacional por medio del arbitraje. Este símbolo de la paz entre los dos países lleva la inscripción siguiente: "Se desplomarán primero estas montañas antes que argentinos y chilenos rompan la paz jurada a los pies del Cristo Redentor." (Sooner shall these mountains crumble before Argentines and Chileans break the peace sworn at the feet of Christ the Redeemer.)

Verb Lesson 5—IMPERFECT TENSE

REGULAR VERBS

tomar:	tom	-aba, -abas, -aba, -ábamos, -abais, -aban
leer:	le	
subir:	sub	-ía, -ías, -ía, -íamos, -íais, -ían

VERBS IRREGULAR IN THE IMPERFECT TENSE

ir:	iba, ibas, iba, íbamos, ibais, iban
ser:	era, eras, era, éramos, erais, eran
ver:	veía, veías, veía, veíamos, veíais, veían

USES OF THE IMPERFECT TENSE

The imperfect tense is used to indicate the continuance of a past action or event, or to describe a situation in past time. Neither the beginning nor the end of the event or situation is indicated. Thus, it is used:

1. To express what was happening, used to happen, or happened repeatedly in the past.

Los pájaros *cantaban.*	The birds were singing.
Vivíamos en esta calle.	We used to live on this street.
Tomás a menudo *llegaba* tarde. **(happened repeatedly)**	Thomas often would arrive (arrived) late.

2. To describe persons or things in the past.

Pedro *era* rubio y *tenía* los ojos azules.	Peter was blond and had blue eyes.
La sala *estaba* llena de gente.	The living room was full of people.

3. To describe a state of mind in the past, with such verbs as **creer, pensar, querer,** and **saber.**

Creían (*Pensaban, Sabían*) que era importante.	They believed (thought, knew) that it was important.
Queríamos comprar un coche nuevo.	We wanted to buy a new car.

4. To express the time of day in the past.

Eran las ocho.	It was eight o'clock.

5. In the construction **hacía** + an expression of time + **que** + the imperfect tense, to describe an action or event that began in the past and continued in the past. In questions, *How long?* is translated by **¿Cuánto tiempo hacía que . . . ?** + the imperfect tense.

Hacía un mes que viajaban. It a month that they were made traveling	They had been traveling for a month.
¿Cuánto tiempo hacía que dormían? How time did it that they were much make sleeping	How long had they been sleeping?

26

Note

The imperfect tense + **desde hacía** + an expression of time is also used to describe an action or event that began in the past and continued in the past. In such expressions, the question *How long?* is translated by **¿Desde cuándo . . . ?** + the imperfect tense.

Viajaban desde hacía un mes.
They were   since   it   a   month
traveling   made

They had been traveling for a month.

¿Desde cuándo dormían?
Since   when   were they
sleeping

How long had they been sleeping?

6. With the preterite to describe a situation that was going on (the *imperfect*) when an action or event occurred, that is, was begun or completed (the *preterite*).

Comíamos cuando nos *llamó.*
(was going on)   (completed action)
(imperfect)   (preterite)

We were eating when he called us.

PRETERITE AND IMPERFECT COMPARED

Preterite	Imperfect
1. Narrates a series of completed actions or events (similar to a moving picture).	1. Describes a situation (similar to a still picture).
2. Indicates a *limit* of the action or event (*either* the beginning *or* the end).	2. Indicates the *continuance* of an action or event (*neither* the beginning *nor* the end).

Note

Was . . . and *were . . .* do not always indicate that the imperfect must be used in Spanish. Compare the following pairs of sentences:

Imperfect	Preterite
Estaban contentos en su casa. (situation)	*Estuvieron* contentos de verlo. (became glad)
They were content in their house.	They were glad to see it.
Era muy alto. (description)	*Fue* herido. (action, event)
He was very tall.	He was wounded.

In describing a situation or a scene, we use the imperfect, even though the English verb is not expressed with *was . . .* or *were . . . .*

El sol **brillaba.**

The sun shone. (The sun was shining.)

EJERCICIOS

A. Cámbiese la forma del verbo en letra cursiva, empleando los sujetos entre paréntesis.

1. Carlos le *llamaba* con frecuencia.

(yo) _____

(nosotros) _____

(ellos) _____

2. Ellos *eran* buenos amigos.

(nosotros) _____

(Vds.) _____

(José y Arturo) _____

3. Su mujer *se oponía* a su plan.

(yo) _____

(las autoridades) _____

(vosotros) _____

4. *Iban* al teatro los sábados.

(yo) _____

(nosotros) _____

(los muchachos) _____

5. *Carecíamos* de pan y agua.

(las víctimas) _____

(yo) _____

(tú) _____

6. Yo *veía* a Felipe todos los días.

(ellos) _____

(tú) _____

(nosotros) _____

7. Los viajeros *eran* de Chile.

(nosotros) _____

(Vd.) _____

(yo) _____

8. Cuando Pedro *iba* a la escuela, no *estudiaba* mucho.

(yo) _____ _____

(ellos) _____ _____

(tú) _____ _____

9. Hacía diez minutos que yo le *esperaba*.

(ellos) _____

(nosotros) _____

(Jorge) _____

10. ¿Cuánto tiempo hacía que Vds. *trabajaban* aquí?

(su padre) _____

(ellos) _____

(tú) _____

B. Contéstense las preguntas según los ejemplos.

EJEMPLO: ¿Está Juan en su cuarto?

Juan estaba en su cuarto cuando entré.

1. ¿Prepara Ana la comida? _____

2. ¿Hace Teresa sus tareas? _____

3. ¿Escribe Manuel una carta? _____

4. ¿Lee Vicente la comedia? _____

5. ¿Fuma Tomás un cigarro? _____

EJEMPLO: ¿Hablan los señores a Julia?

Los señores hablaban a Julia cuando llegamos.

6. ¿Salen los alumnos de la escuela? _____

7. ¿Buscan los niños la pelota? _____

8. ¿Miran los muchachos la televisión? _____

9. ¿Discuten los amigos las noticias? _____

10. ¿Van los jóvenes a la fiesta? _____

C. Cámbiense los verbos al imperfecto y al presente.

	IMPERFECTO	PRESENTE
1. Jaime *llegó* tarde.	_____	_____
2. *Tuvimos* que hacerlo.	_____	_____
3. *Comieron* a las seis.	_____	_____
4. No *pudo* ayudarle.	_____	_____
5. *Estuve* muy enfermo.	_____	_____
6. *Vimos* al director en la cafetería.	_____	_____
7. *Fue* muy importante.	_____	_____
8. Le *dieron* muchos regalos.	_____	_____
9. Alberto *leyó* muchos libros.	_____	_____
10. *Fueron* al centro con nosotros.	_____	_____

D. Cámbiense las frases siguientes al tiempo pasado.

EJEMPLO: Hace mucho tiempo que viven aquí.

Hacía mucho tiempo que vivían aquí.

1. Hace una hora que Inés está en la oficina. _____

2. Hace un año que Enrique es socio de este club. _____

3. Hace una semana que no le veo. _____

4. Hace un mes que trabajan en esa fábrica. _____

5. Hace mucho tiempo que le conocemos. _____

6. ¿Cuánto tiempo hace que Vd. lo sabe? _____

7. ¿Cuánto tiempo hace que ellos viajan? _____

8. ¿Cuánto tiempo hace que tú asistes a esta clase? _____

9. ¿Desde cuándo van a la universidad? _____

10. ¿Desde cuándo tiene Rosa ese perro? _____

E. Subráyese la forma correcta, según el significado de cada frase.

1. La orquesta (tocó, tocaba) el tango pero ellos bailaron el mambo.

2. Sospechaba que el testigo (mintió, mentía) cuando daba su testimonio.

3. Mientras mi hermana ponía la mesa, yo (leí, leía) el periódico.

4. En sus sueños aquella noche, el enfermo (vio, veía) sombras.

5. Juan tenía dos hermanas que (fueron, eran) encantadoras.

6. En la fábrica se (construyeron, construían) televisores cuando yo trabajaba allí.

7. El juez (creyó, creía) al señor que describió el incidente.

8. Hacía diez minutos que (comieron, comían) cuando sonó el teléfono.

9. A menudo me (encontré, encontraba) con Miguel durante mis días de vacaciones.

10. ¿Cuánto tiempo (hizo, hacía) que eran amigos?

F. Tradúzcanse las frases al español.

1. When he had money, he also had many friends. _____

2. She was composing verses while she listened to the music. _____

3. It was one o'clock when she returned. _____

4. We were walking through the park when we met him. _____

5. He would always consult the dictionary. --

----

6. The sun was shining while I strolled along the street. ----------------------

----

7. A stone wall marked the frontier between the two countries. ----------------

----

8. The child had been crying for a long time when they found him. ------------

----

9. The father punished the children when they were bad. --------------------

----

10. How long had she been sleeping? --

----

11. She wore a blue suit and had white gloves. --------------------------------

----

12. We used to travel much when we were rich. --------------------------------

----

13. She was drowning when he saw her. --------------------------------------

----

14. The children couldn't (weren't able to) sleep because of the noise. --------

----

15. He was sure that it was snowing. ---

Rodrigo Díaz de Vivar (1040–1099), llamado el Cid, es famoso en la historia. Se le considera el héroe nacional de España. Fue una de las figuras principales en las guerras de la Reconquista. El título "Cid" significa "señor" en lengua árabe, y fue el título que le dieron los moros que venció.

Verb Lesson 6—MASTERY EXERCISES

(LESSONS 1–5)

A. Escríbanse los verbos en la primera persona singular del presente y del pretérito, y en la tercera persona plural del pretérito.

EJEMPLO: hablar—hablo, hablé, hablaron

	PRESENTE (1ª singular)	PRETÉRITO (1ª singular)	PRETÉRITO (3ª plural)
1. caer			
2. concluir			
3. continuar			
4. divertirse			
5. encargar			
6. hacer			
7. ir			
8. poder			
9. reducir			
10. reírse			
11. reñir			
12. seguir			
13. ser			
14. traer			
15. variar			

B. Cámbiense los verbos al presente.

1. afirmé		13. extinguí	
2. apoyabais		14. helaron	
3. apretó		15. hubo	
4. ascendían		16. impedí	
5. compusieron		17. incluyeron	
6. contuvo		18. influían	
7. convertiste		19. juraron	
8. derramó		20. medían	
9. descendí		21. olió	
10. deshice		22. referí	
11. dominábamos		23. rogaba (él)	
12. me estremecí		24. solía (yo)	

32

25. solicitó _____   28. tronó _____

26. sustituí _____   29. tropezó _____

27. triunfó _____   30. valí _____

C. Cámbiense los verbos al pretérito.

1. me acercaba _____   16. están _____

2. advierten _____   17. llueve _____

3. amenazo _____   18. madrugaba (yo) _____

4. ataco _____   19. nazco _____

5. atraen _____   20. pedían _____

6. caemos _____   21. pongo _____

7. creíais _____   22. me quejaba _____

8. damos _____   23. quepo _____

9. te despiertas _____   24. quiero _____

10. dicen _____   25. rezaba (yo) _____

11. disponían _____   26. sé _____

12. se divertían _____   27. seguís _____

13. duermen _____   28. teníamos _____

14. empiezo _____   29. viene _____

15. os equivocabais _____   30. voy _____

D. Tradúzcanse al español las siguientes expresiones:

1. I seize _____   16. he found out (saber) _____

2. they fled _____   17. I am grateful (agradecer) _____

3. it contains _____   18. the money disappeared _____

4. he was correcting _____   19. I paid _____

5. I heard _____   20. I acquire _____

6. they serve _____   21. we used to read _____

7. she smiled _____   22. you (Vds.) contributed _____

8. I conquer (vencer) _____   23. I used to see _____

9. I explained _____   24. they constructed _____

10. I touched _____   25. I arrived _____

11. they defend _____   26. we were going _____

12. I had lunch _____   27. she was crying _____

13. she was graduated _____   28. he confessed _____

14. I fished _____   29. they remembered _____

15. it belongs _____   30. it was snowing _____

E. Contéstense las siguientes preguntas, empleando el tiempo indicado del verbo.

PRESENTE:

1. ¿Conduce Vd. el coche de la familia? _____

2. ¿Tiene Vd. un estante para libros en su casa? _____

   _____

3. ¿Continúa Vd. con sus estudios en la universidad? _____

   _____

4. ¿Expone Vd. sus ideas claramente? _____

5. ¿Protesta Vd. contra la injusticia? _____

6. ¿Aplica Vd. su inteligencia para resolver un problema? _____

   _____

7. ¿Confía Vd. en su buena suerte? _____

8. ¿Se estremece Vd. al oír el trueno? _____

9. ¿En qué estación se hielan los lagos? _____

10. ¿Muestra Vd. cariño a sus padres? _____

PRETÉRITO:

11. ¿Explicó Vd. la lección de hoy a la clase? _____

12. ¿A qué hora empezó Vd. a estudiar anoche? _____

13. ¿Cruzó Vd. alguna vez la frontera de México? _____

14. ¿Cuándo apagó Vd. la luz en su cuarto anoche? _____

   _____

15. ¿Tradujo Vd. el ejercicio para hoy? _____

16. ¿Gozó Vd. de buena salud el año pasado? _____

17. ¿Pegó Vd. alguna vez a su hermano(-a) menor? _____

18. ¿Dio Vd. un regalo a su mamá el día de su cumpleaños? _____

   _____

19. ¿En qué año comenzó Vd. a estudiar el español? _____

   _____

20. ¿Buscó Vd. un libro en la biblioteca la semana pasada? _____

   _____

IMPERFECTO:

Cuando Vd. era niño(-a) . . .

21. ¿Acostumbraba Vd. cumplir con su promesa? _____

   _____

22. ¿Arrojaba Vd. piedras a los otros chicos? _____

23. ¿Solía Vd. comer pan en la cena? _____

24. ¿Tardaba Vd. mucho en vestirse? _____

25. ¿Se cansaba Vd. del trabajo constante? _____

26. ¿Era su abuelo un hombre generoso? _____

27. ¿Veía Vd. muchas novedades en el teatro? _____

_____

28. ¿Se despertaba Vd. temprano para ver el alba? _____

_____

29. ¿Se interesaba Vd. por la lectura? _____

30. ¿Carecía Vd. de fondos para ir al teatro muchas veces? _____

_____

    F. Tradúzcanse al español. (See Preterite and Imperfect Compared, page 27.)

1. When I left the house, the sun was shining. _____

_____

2. Emil went to bed at 11 o'clock and woke up at 7. _____

_____

3. While he was walking, he suddenly smelled smoke. _____

_____

4. The man finished the novel, closed the book, and stood up. _____

_____

5. I arrived early, while he was still dressing. _____

_____

6. He had been ill for a week when he died. _____

_____

7. The poor man had not eaten for three days when he found five dollars. _____

_____

8. He wrote to us and saw us frequently. _____

_____

9. We were here yesterday at 3 o'clock and then went away. _____

_____

10. While he watched, I began to work. _____

_____

11. They used to contribute much to the club to which they belonged. _____

_____

12. While I was traveling in Mexico, I met Mr. Molina. _____

_____

13. They found out the truth when they read the letter. _____

_____

14. My cousins often visited me when I lived there. _____

_____

15. I received a telegram this morning, and I answered it. _____

_____

16. Lincoln, who was a great president, died in 1865. _____

_____

17. I took the check and ran to the bank. _____

_____

18. How long had you been waiting when she came? _____

_____

19. We got wet when we went out yesterday. _____

_____

20. It stopped raining, and the sun appeared. _____

_____

G. Each of the following passages contains infinitives numbered 1–10. For each infinitive, you will find a choice of two verb forms. Write the letter of the correct form in each pair.

I. Yo (1) *nacer* en Santiago en 1896. En aquel entonces mi padre (2) *tener* unos cuarenta años. En su temprana juventud (3) *ir* a la América Hispana de arquitecto. De la Argentina (4) *pasar* a Chile, donde (5) *conocer* a una chilena. Allí (6) *casarse*, y allí (7) *ver* nacer a sus tres hijos. Al llegar a Nueva York, mi familia (8) *tener* largos años de lucha contra la miseria. Durante esa época, sólo (9) *soñar* con mejorar nuestra fortuna, y (10) *esperar* días mejores.

(1) (a) nacía	(b) nací	_____	(6) (a) se casaba	(b) se casó	_____
(2) (a) tenía	(b) tuvo	_____	(7) (a) veía	(b) vio	_____
(3) (a) iba	(b) fue	_____	(8) (a) tenía	(b) tuvo	_____
(4) (a) pasaba	(b) pasó	_____	(9) (a) soñábamos	(b) soñamos	_____
(5) (a) conocía	(b) conoció	_____	(10) (a) esperábamos	(b) esperamos	_____

II. Esta mañana (1) *abrir* los ojos y (2) *saltar* de la cama. (3) *Vestirse* y (4) *salir*. La mañana (5) *ser* hermosa. En los árboles las aves (6) *cantar* alegremente. Los niños que (7) *jugar* en el patio (8) *parecer* más risueños que nunca. Toda la naturaleza (9) *llevar* un aspecto más joven, más verde, más vivo. Suspirando de placer, Luisita (10) *volver* a pensar en el baile de la noche anterior.

(1) (a) abría	(b) abrió	_____	(6) (a) cantaban	(b) cantaron	_____
(2) (a) saltaba	(b) saltó	_____	(7) (a) jugaban	(b) jugaron	_____
(3) (a) Se vestía	(b) Se vistió	_____	(8) (a) parecían	(b) parecieron	_____
(4) (a) salía	(b) salió	_____	(9) (a) llevaba	(b) llevó	_____
(5) (a) era	(b) fue	_____	(10) (a) volvía	(b) volvió	_____

III. (1) *Ser* ya las cuatro de la tarde. Ramón y Elena (2) *estar* sentados en la sala. De las otras habitaciones (3) *oírse* el lejano rumor de voces, de gente que (4) *hablar* en tono animado. Elena (5) *levantarse* y (6) *acercarse* a la ventana. (7) *Mirar* afuera y (8) *ver* que todavía (9) *caer* la lluvia. (10) *Experimentar* una sensación de tristeza.

(1) (*a*) Eran	(*b*) Fueron	-----	(6) (*a*) se acercaba	(*b*) se acercó	-----
(2) (*a*) estaban	(*b*) estuvieron	-----	(7) (*a*) Miraba	(*b*) Miró.	-----
(3) (*a*) se oía	(*b*) se oyó	-----	(8) (*a*) veía	(*b*) vio	-----
(4) (*a*) hablaba	(*b*) habló	-----	(9) (*a*) caía	(*b*) cayó	-----
(5) (*a*) se levantaba	(*b*) se levantó	-----	(10) (*a*) Experimentaba	(*b*) Experimentó	-----

IV. Alrededor de la mesa la familia (1) *cenar*, chicos y mayores comiendo, riendo, y hablando a la vez. De repente (2) *sonar* la campana del pueblo. ¡Fuego! Todos (3) *dejar* la mesa y (4) *echarse* a correr hacia la plaza. Allí (5) *ver* una escena horrible. (6) *Arder* la casa de un vecino. Por todas partes (7) *encontrarse* gente que (8) *gritar*, y (9) *hacer* esfuerzos inútiles para extinguir el fuego. De pronto (10) *aparecer* en una ventana la figura de una mujer.

(1) (*a*) cenaba	(*b*) cenó	-----	(6) (*a*) Ardía	(*b*) Ardió	-----
(2) (*a*) sonaba	(*b*) sonó	-----	(7) (*a*) se encontraba	(*b*) se encontró	-----
(3) (*a*) dejaban	(*b*) dejaron	-----	(8) (*a*) gritaba	(*b*) gritó	-----
(4) (*a*) se echaban	(*b*) se echaron	-----	(9) (*a*) hacía	(*b*) hizo	-----
(5) (*a*) veían	(*b*) vieron	-----	(10) (*a*) aparecía	(*b*) apareció	-----

V. (1) *Ir* camino de la estación cuando (2) *tropezar* con un amigo que le (3) *detener* para charlar un momento. Al llegar a la estación, (4) *notar* que el tren ya (5) *estar* allí. (6) *Darse* prisa pero (7) *llegar* tarde. (8) *Comenzar* a pasearse por el andén, impaciente, lleno de enojo. (9) *Mirar* el reloj. Las nueve menos veinte. Le (10) *quedar* solamente veinte minutos para llegar a la oficina, y seguramente no llegaría a tiempo.

(1) (*a*) Iba	(*b*) Fue	-----	(6) (*a*) Se daba	(*b*) Se dio	-----
(2) (*a*) tropezaba	(*b*) tropezó	-----	(7) (*a*) llegaba	(*b*) llegó	-----
(3) (*a*) detenía	(*b*) detuvo	-----	(8) (*a*) Comenzaba	(*b*) Comenzó	-----
(4) (*a*) notaba	(*b*) notó	-----	(9) (*a*) Miraba	(*b*) Miró	-----
(5) (*a*) estaba	(*b*) estuvo	-----	(10) (*a*) quedaban	(*b*) quedaron	-----

Hernán Cortés (1485–1547) fue el conquistador de México. Cuando llegaron los españoles, los indios nunca habían visto caballos, y creyeron que hombre y caballo eran una sola persona. También creyeron que Cortés mismo era su antiguo dios, que volvía para gobernarlos. Con solamente 400 soldados, y con la ayuda de Marina, una india que hacía de guía e intérprete, Cortés pudo conquistar la capital azteca, Tenochtitlán (que es hoy la Ciudad de México). Cortés es, tal vez, el más grande de los conquistadores españoles.

Verb Lesson 7—FUTURE AND CONDITIONAL

REGULAR VERBS

FUTURE	ayudar aprender escribir	} -é, -ás, -á, -emos, -éis, -án
CONDITIONAL	ayudar aprender escribir	} -ía, -ías, -ía, -íamos, -íais, -ían

Note

A. The future and the conditional of *all* verbs are formed by adding to the infinitive the *endings* of **haber:** the present endings for the future, and the imperfect endings for the conditional.

> PRESENT: h*e*, h*as*, h*a*, h*emos*, hab*éis*, h*an*

> IMPERFECT: hab*ía*, hab*ías*, hab*ía*, hab*íamos*, hab*íais*, hab*ían*

B. All future endings except **-emos** bear a written accent mark to indicate stress.

C. Verbs that have a written accent in the infinitive (**oír, reír,** etc.) drop that accent in the future and the conditional (**oirían, reiremos,** etc.).

VERBS IRREGULAR IN THE FUTURE AND CONDITIONAL

VERBS THAT DROP THE *e* OF THE INFINITIVE

caber:	*cabr*	
haber:	*habr*	
poder:	*podr*	} -é, -ás, -á, etc.
querer:	*querr*	-ía, -ías, -ía, etc.
saber:	*sabr*	

VERBS THAT CHANGE THE VOWEL (*e* OR *i*) OF THE INFINITIVE TO *d*

poner:	*pondr*	
salir:	*saldr*	
tener:	*tendr*	} -é, -ás, -á, etc.
valer:	*valdr*	-ía, -ías, -ía, etc.
venir:	*vendr*	

VERBS THAT DROP THE *e* AND *c* OF THE INFINITIVE

decir:	*dir*	} -é, -ás, -á, etc.
hacer:	*har*	-ía, -ías, -ía, etc.

Note

Compounds of the irregular verbs are also irregular:

disponer, *dispondré;* **contener,** *contendrán;* **satisfacer,** *satisfaríamos,* etc.

USES OF THE FUTURE TENSE

1. The future tense is used in Spanish, as in English, to express future time.

Vendremos mañana.	We shall come tomorrow.
¿Cuándo *irán* Vds.?	When will you go?

Note

When *will* is used in the sense of *to be willing*, it must be expressed in Spanish by the verb **querer.**

¿Quiere Vd. cerrar la ventana?	Will you (are you willing to) close the window?
No quieren ayudarnos.	They won't (aren't willing to) help us.

2. The future tense is often used together with the present.

Juan *dice* que *irá.*	John says that he will go.

3. The future is used to express *wonderment* or *probability* in the present, and is often translated by such expressions as *I wonder, probably, must, can,* etc.

¿Cuántos años *tendrá?*	I wonder how old he is. (How old can he be?)
¿Qué hora *será?*	I wonder what time it is. (What time can it be?)
Serán las dos.	It is probably (It must be) two o'clock.
Estará cansado.	He must be (He is probably) tired.

USES OF THE CONDITIONAL

1. The conditional is translated into English by *would.*

Ana no lo *pondría* allí.	Anna would not put it there.
Me *gustaría* verlo.	I would like to see it.
¿*Podría* Vd. mostrármelo?	Would you be able to (Could you) show it to me?

Note

A. When *would* is equivalent to *used to,* it is translated by the imperfect tense.

Arturo nos *visitaba* a menudo.	Arthur would (used to) often visit us.

B. When *would* is used in the sense of *to be willing,* it is translated by the preterite tense of **querer.**

No *quiso* pagar la cuenta.	He wouldn't (wasn't willing to, refused to) pay the bill.

2. The conditional is often used together with the past (preterite, imperfect, pluperfect).

Juan $\begin{cases} dijo \\ decía \\ había\ dicho \end{cases}$ que *iría*.

John $\begin{cases} said \\ was\ saying \\ had\ said \end{cases}$ that he would go.

3. The conditional is used to express *wonderment* or *probability* in the past, and is often translated by such expressions as *I wonder, probably, must have, could,* etc.

¿Qué hora *sería* cuando salió?

I wonder what time it was when he went out. (What time could it have been when he went out?)

Serían las dos.

It was probably (It must have been) two o'clock.

Note

The expression **deber de** followed by an infinitive may also be used to express probability, in present or past time.

Deben de estar cansados.

They must be tired.

Ella *debe de tener* veinte años.

She must be twenty years old.

Debían de estar cansados.

They must have been tired.

Ella *debía de tener* veinte años.

She must have been twenty years old.

EJERCICIOS

A. Escríbase la forma correcta del condicional de cada uno de los verbos (*a, b, c, d*), en lugar del verbo en letra cursiva.

1. Ellos no lo *arreglarían*.   (*a*) presenciar   (*b*) admitir   (*c*) castigar   (*d*) consultar

(*a*) _____   (*b*) _____   (*c*) _____   (*d*) _____

2. Lo *veríamos* en una semana.   (*a*) traer   (*b*) hacer   (*c*) tener   (*d*) proponer

(*a*) _____   (*b*) _____   (*c*) _____   (*d*) _____

3. Yo lo *aceptaría* con mucho gusto.   (*a*) hacer   (*b*) vender   (*c*) decir   (*d*) recibir

(*a*) _____   (*b*) _____   (*c*) _____   (*d*) _____

4. El artista *pintaría* el retrato.   (*a*) admirar   (*b*) colgar   (*c*) obtener   (*d*) ver

(*a*) _____   (*b*) _____   (*c*) _____   (*d*) _____

5. Yo sabía que la clase *ayudaría* al maestro.   (*a*) responder   (*b*) convencer   (*c*) obedecer   (*d*) respetar

(*a*) _____   (*b*) _____   (*c*) _____   (*d*) _____

6. *Desearíamos* acompañarle.   (*a*) poder   (*b*) preferir   (*c*) necesitar   (*d*) querer

(*a*) _____   (*b*) _____   (*c*) _____   (*d*) _____

7. Mamá *prepararía* el almuerzo.   (*a*) cocer   (*b*) servir   (*c*) comer   (*d*) quemar

(*a*) _____   (*b*) _____   (*c*) _____   (*d*) _____

8. Creían que Cortés *conquistaría* una nueva colonia.   (*a*) fundar   (*b*) establecer   (*c*) crear   (*d*) conseguir

(*a*) ---------------   (*b*) ---------------   (*c*) ---------------   (*d*) ---------------

9. Dijo que *llegarían* mañana.   (*a*) salir   (*b*) volver   (*c*) venir   (*d*) terminar

(*a*) ---------------   (*b*) ---------------   (*c*) ---------------   (*d*) ---------------

10. *¿Prometerías* hacerlo?   (*a*) saber   (*b*) querer   (*c*) poder   (*d*) preferir

(*a*) ---------------   (*b*) ---------------   (*c*) ---------------   (*d*) ---------------

11. Prometió que él *estaría* allí.   (*a*) quedarse   (*b*) detenerse   (*c*) esperar   (*d*) descansar

(*a*) ---------------   (*b*) ---------------   (*c*) ---------------   (*d*) ---------------

12. ¿Dónde lo *comprarías?*   (*a*) poner   (*b*) hallar   (*c*) colocar   (*d*) buscar

(*a*) ---------------   (*b*) ---------------   (*c*) ---------------   (*d*) ---------------

13. Yo se lo *llevaría* esta noche.   (*a*) dar   (*b*) decir   (*c*) vender   (*d*) entregar

(*a*) ---------------   (*b*) ---------------   (*c*) ---------------   (*d*) ---------------

14. Replicó que *volvería* al día siguiente.   (*a*) venir   (*b*) estudiar   (*c*) salir   (*d*) ir

(*a*) ---------------   (*b*) ---------------   (*c*) ---------------   (*d*) ---------------

15. Vd. *ganaría* bastante dinero.   (*a*) recibir   (*b*) tener   (*c*) perder   (*d*) gastar

(*a*) ---------------   (*b*) ---------------   (*c*) ---------------   (*d*) ---------------

B. Cámbiense los verbos según los ejemplos.

EJEMPLO: León dice que me *escribirá.*

León dijo que me ____*escribiría*____.

1. Creen que la película *será* interesante.

Creían que la película ------------------- interesante.

2. Le aseguro que *valdrá* la pena verlo.

Le aseguré que ------------------- la pena verlo.

3. Mi primo escribe que *vendrá* a visitarme.

Mi primo escribió que ------------------- a visitarme.

4. Le prometo que no lo *haré* otra vez.

Le prometí que no lo ------------------- otra vez.

5. Nos avisan que no *podrán* ayudarnos.

Nos avisaron que no ------------------- ayudarnos.

6. Tomás dice que le *gustará* ir al cine.

Tomás dijo que le ------------------- ir al cine.

7. El general se entera de que la campaña *comenzará.*

El general se enteró de que la campaña -------------------.

8. El maestro nos avisa que el viernes no *tendremos* clase.

El maestro nos avisó que el viernes no ------------------- clase.

9. Estima que *cabrán* trescientas sillas en el aula.

Estimaba que _____ trescientas sillas en el aula.

10. Me dicen que la nueva compañía *fabricará* guantes.

Me dijeron que la nueva compañía _____ guantes.

EJEMPLO: León dijo que me *escribiría*.

León dice que me ___*escribirá*___.

11. Declaró que *buscaría* aventuras en la selva.

Declara que _____ aventuras en la selva.

12. El capitán anunció que el ejército *atacaría* al amanecer.

El capitán anuncia que el ejército _____ al amanecer.

13. Estaba seguro de que tú *sabrías* la respuesta.

Estoy seguro de que tú _____ la respuesta.

14. Ellos creían que *saldríamos* temprano.

Ellos creen que _____ temprano.

15. Le aseguró que no lo *haría*.

Le asegura que no lo _____.

C. Cámbiense las frases según los ejemplos.

EJEMPLOS: Debe de ser muy rico.   Será muy rico.
Deben de estar en casa. Estarán en casa.

1. Deben de ser hermanos. _____

2. Debes de saber la dirección. _____

3. Debe de tener unos quince años. _____

4. Deben de conocer al dueño de la tienda. _____

5. Debe de estar en su cuarto. _____

EJEMPLOS: Debía de ser muy rico.   Sería muy rico.
Debían de estar en casa. Estarían en casa.

6. Debía de ser la una. _____

7. Debía de estar enfermo. _____

8. Debías de recordar la fecha del accidente. _____

9. Debía de haber un camino más corto. _____

10. Debían de tener mucha hambre. _____

D. Cámbiense las frases según los ejemplos.

EJEMPLO: Probablemente están en casa. Estarán en casa.

1. Probablemente es su padre. _____
2. Probablemente tiene unos sesenta años. _____
3. Probablemente está enojado. _____
4. Probablemente hay muchas dificultades. _____
5. Probablemente son las once de la mañana. _____

EJEMPLO: Probablemente estaban en casa. Estarían en casa.

6. Probablemente estaban descansando. _____
7. Probablemente llegaron tarde. _____
8. Probablemente tenían mucho que hacer. _____
9. Probablemente sabían lo que pasó. _____
10. Probablemente lo vieron. _____

E. Tradúzcanse las frases al español según los ejemplos.

EJEMPLO: I wonder what time it is.
            or
        What time can it be?   } ¿Qué hora será?

1. I wonder how much it is worth. _____
2. I wonder who it is. _____
3. Where can they be at this time? _____
4. Who can that man be? _____
5. I wonder what my mother thinks. _____

EJEMPLO: I wonder where they were.
            or
        Where could they be?   } ¿Dónde estarían?

6. I wonder where he went. _____
7. Where could they be hiding the gold? _____
8. I wonder what they thought of her. _____
9. What could that sentence mean? _____
10. I wonder what time it was. _____

F. Contéstense en español en frases completas.

1. ¿Cuándo celebrará Vd. su cumpleaños? _____
2. ¿Habrá una fiesta en su casa? _____

3. ¿Invitará a sus compañeros de escuela? _____

_____

4. ¿Sabrá Vd. saludar a sus amigos en español? _____

_____

5. ¿A qué hora saldrán los invitados? _____

_____

6. ¿Hará Vd. un viaje a Europa algún día? _____

7. ¿Cuándo y con quién irá Vd.? _____

8. ¿Cómo viajarán Vds.? ¿por avión? ¿por barco? _____

9. ¿Cuánto dinero necesitará Vd. para el viaje? _____

10. ¿Tendrán Vds. que obtener un pasaporte? _____

_____

11. ¿Qué países visitarán Vds.? _____

_____

12. ¿Sacará Vd. fotos de los lugares de interés? _____

_____

13. ¿Traerá Vd. recuerdos de su viaje? _____

14. ¿Cuánto tiempo pasará Vd. en Europa? _____

15. ¿Cuándo regresarán Vds.? _____

G. Contéstense en español en frases completas.

1. ¿Diría Vd. una mentira para proteger a su compañero? _____

_____

2. ¿Compraría Vd. algo antes de verlo? _____

_____

3. ¿Qué haría Vd. con un millón de dólares? _____

_____

4. ¿Le gustaría a Vd. vivir en un país extranjero? _____

_____

5. ¿Lucharía Vd. por su patria? _____

_____

6. ¿Prestaría Vd. su cuaderno a su compañero? _____

7. ¿Respetarían Vds. los deseos de sus padres? _____

_____

8. ¿Gastaría Vd. todo su dinero en un día? _____

_____

9. ¿Desearían Vds. formar un club? _____

_____

10. ¿Preferirían Vds. menos exámenes? _____

_____

11. ¿Saldrían Vds. bien en los exámenes sin estudiar? _____

_____

12. ¿Iría Vd. a cualquier universidad? _____

_____

13. ¿Le permitirían sus padres viajar solo(-a)? _____

_____

14. ¿Qué le interesaría hacer este sábado? _____

_____

15. ¿Qué regalo daría Vd. a un niño para su cumpleaños? _____

_____

H. Tradúzcanse al español.

1. She would not like to travel alone. _____

_____

2. I will try to be there at twelve o'clock. _____

_____

3. We shall not arrive on time tomorrow. _____

_____

4. She says that she will be able to go to the dance. _____

_____

5. They assured me that they would pay the next day. _____

_____

6. He told us that it would not happen again. _____

_____

7. I would like to play tennis this afternoon. _____

_____

8. He must have the tickets because I don't have them. _____

_____

9. He wouldn't (did not wish to) lend me the money. _____

_____

10. They would like to take a walk. _____

_____

11. He promised me that he would study. _____

_____

12. Would you like to spend a week in the country? _____

_____

13. It must have been five o'clock when I saw her. _____

_____

14. The owner won't (doesn't wish to) sell the houses. _____

_____

15. The train would always stop there on Sundays. _____

_____

16. She is probably about forty years old. _____

_____

17. It must have been four o'clock when he called me. _____

_____

18. I will invite all my friends to the party. _____

_____

19. We would like to take a trip to Spain. _____

_____

20. There were probably many people at (en) the meeting. _____

_____

El caucho (rubber) se recoge en forma líquida de un árbol que es muy
común en el valle del río Amazonas. Recientemente, la industria cauchera
de Sudamérica ha perdido gran parte de su importancia, debido a la inven-
ción del caucho sintético.

Verb Lesson 8—GERUND (PRESENT PARTICIPLE); PROGRESSIVE TENSES

GERUNDS OF REGULAR VERBS

cantar:	cant	*-ando,* singing
comer:	com	*-iendo,* eating
abrir:	abr	*-iendo,* opening

GERUNDS ENDING IN *-YENDO*

caer:	*cayendo*	oír:	*oyendo*
creer:	*creyendo*	traer:	*trayendo*
leer:	*leyendo*		

VERBS IRREGULAR IN THE GERUND

1. In the gerund, stem-changing **-ir** verbs change the stem vowel from **e** to **i** and from **o** to **u**.

decir:	diciendo	**pedir:**	pidiendo
dormir:	durmiendo	**sentir:**	sintiendo
morir:	muriendo	**venir:**	viniendo

2. Other verbs irregular in the gerund:

ir: *yendo*	poder: *pudiendo*

USES OF THE GERUND (PRESENT PARTICIPLE)

1. The gerund is used with the verbs **estar, seguir, continuar,** and with verbs of motion, to stress the fact that an event is (or was, or will be) in progress or is continuing at the moment indicated. The tenses thus formed are called *progressive tenses.*

Los niños **están jugando.**	The children are playing.
Salió llorando.	He went out crying.
Los tiempos *van cambiando.*	Times are changing.
Siga Vd. *leyendo.*	Keep on reading.
Continuarán estudiando.	They will continue studying. (They will continue to study.)
Venían corriendo.	They came running.

Note

The gerunds of **estar, ir,** and **venir** are not used to form the progressive tenses of these verbs. Instead, the simple tenses are used.

Ella *viene* aquí.	She is coming here.
Rosa *iba* al parque.	Rose was going to the park.

2. The Spanish gerund is often the equivalent of *by* + an English present participle.

Viajando, se aprende mucho.	By traveling, one learns much.
Estudiando, saldrás bien en los exámenes.	By studying, you will pass the examinations.

EJERCICIOS

A. Escríbase el gerundio de cada uno de los verbos (*a, b, c, d*), en lugar del gerundio en letra cursiva.

1. Pasamos el tiempo *jugando*.   (*a*) charlar   (*b*) leer   (*c*) escribir   (*d*) conversar

(*a*) _____   (*b*) _____   (*c*) _____   (*d*) _____

2. Al oír la noticia, salió *gritando*.   (*a*) reírse   (*b*) llorar   (*c*) temblar   (*d*) quejarse

(*a*) _____   (*b*) _____   (*c*) _____   (*d*) _____

3. Estoy *tocando* los discos.   (*a*) oír   (*b*) comprar   (*c*) traer   (*d*) romper

(*a*) _____   (*b*) _____   (*c*) _____   (*d*) _____

4. ¿Qué estaban Vds. *haciendo?*   (*a*) discutir   (*b*) buscar   (*c*) decir   (*d*) contemplar

(*a*) _____   (*b*) _____   (*c*) _____   (*d*) _____

5. La señorita sigue *cantando*.   (*a*) bailar   (*b*) escribir   (*c*) trabajar   (*d*) sonreír

(*a*) _____   (*b*) _____   (*c*) _____   (*d*) _____

6. El señor continúa *hablando*.   (*a*) sufrir   (*b*) esperar   (*c*) fumar   (*d*) dormir

(*a*) _____   (*b*) _____   (*c*) _____   (*d*) _____

7. ¿Por qué estás *llorando?*   (*a*) murmurar   (*b*) saltar   (*c*) gritar   (*d*) interrumpir

(*a*) _____   (*b*) _____   (*c*) _____   (*d*) _____

8. Poco a poco el niño irá *aprendiendo*.   (*a*) comprender   (*b*) acostumbrarse   (*c*) recordar   (*d*) crecer

(*a*) _____   (*b*) _____   (*c*) _____   (*d*) _____

9. *Andando* a la escuela, encontré a mi amigo Jorge.   (*a*) ir   (*b*) caminar   (*c*) acercarse   (*d*) volver

(*a*) _____   (*b*) _____   (*c*) _____   (*d*) _____

10. La cocinera estaba *preparando* la sopa.   (*a*) tomar   (*b*) calentar   (*c*) hervir   (*d*) cocer

(*a*) _____   (*b*) _____   (*c*) _____   (*d*) _____

B. Cámbiense las frases a la forma progresiva con el verbo *estar*.

Ejemplo: El hombre *trabaja*.   *Entraban* en la casa.
            El hombre está trabajando.   Estaban entrando en la casa.

1. Inés y su amiga *dan* un paseo. _____

2. *Leo* el periódico. _____

3. La taza *cae* al suelo. _____

4. *Discuten* los dos sistemas. _____

5. Los niños *nadan* en la piscina. _____

6. *Llovía* mucho. _____

7. Yo *llamaba* a Enrique por teléfono. _____

8. El joven *decía* la verdad. _____

9. *Preparábamos* la comida. _____

10. El sol *brillaba* todo el día. _____

C. Complétense las frases siguientes, empleando en cada frase el gerundio de uno de los siguientes verbos: (Cada verbo debe usarse solamente *una vez*.)

bailar	charlar	escuchar	jugar	poder
cambiar	discutir	estar	leer	ser
caminar	escribir	estudiar	oír	tocar

1. La orquesta está _____ mi canción favorita.

2. ¿Qué estás _____ en esa revista?

3. Los alumnos continúan _____ los verbos.

4. Paso el día _____ con mis compañeros.

5. El profesor sigue _____ el tema.

6. _____ en la clase, se aprende mucho.

7. Las costumbres van _____.

8. Me divierto _____.

9. _____ perezoso, no recibiré buenas notas.

10. Siga Vd. _____ hasta terminar el ejercicio.

11. _____ enfermo, no pudo trabajar.

12. _____ esto, salió en seguida.

13. Estaban _____ cuando entramos.

14. No _____ verlo, se puso los anteojos.

15. _____ por la calle, vi a mi amigo Hugo.

D. Tradúzcanse al español, empleando el gerundio en cada frase.

1. They were traveling by plane. _____

2. By working in the summer, you will earn enough money. _____

_____

3. Keep on taking the same medicine. _____

_____

4. They will keep on working. _____

5. We were listening to an interesting program. _____

_____

6. By traveling, you will see many interesting things. _____

_____

7. She was checking her luggage. _____

8. Jane was reading a novel. _____

9. She continues suffering. _____

10. We are celebrating his birthday. _____

_____

11. She keeps on talking. _____

12. By studying every day, you will receive good grades. _____

_____

13. I am discussing an important matter. _____

_____

14. The children will be playing in the garden. _____

_____

15. They continue living there. _____

El lago Titicaca, entre Bolivia y el Perú, está situado a 12,500 pies sobre el nivel del mar (sea level). Es el lago navegable más alto del mundo. Para navegar en el lago, los indios emplean "balsas," que son botes hechos de una madera muy ligera del mismo nombre.

Verb Lesson 9—PAST PARTICIPLE; COMPOUND TENSES

PAST PARTICIPLES OF REGULAR VERBS

tomar:	tom	*-ado,*	taken
comer:	com	*-ido,*	eaten
sufrir:	sufr	*-ido,*	suffered

PAST PARTICIPLES ENDING IN *-ÍDO*

caer:	*caído*	oír:	*oído*
creer:	*creído*	reír:	*reído*
leer:	*leído*	traer:	*traído*

VERBS IRREGULAR IN THE PAST PARTICIPLE

abrir: *abierto,* opened	morir: *muerto,* died
cubrir: *cubierto,* covered	poner: *puesto,* put
decir: *dicho,* said	resolver: *resuelto,* resolved, solved
escribir: *escrito,* written	romper: *roto,* broken
hacer: *hecho,* done	ver: *visto,* seen
imprimir: *impreso,* printed	volver: *vuelto,* returned

Compounds of the above verbs (**descubrir, deshacer, imponer, devolver,** etc.) are also irregular in the past participle.

COMPOUND TENSES

The past participle is used with the various tenses of the verb **haber** (to have) to form the compound tenses.

PERFECT (PRESENT PERFECT) TENSE

I have entered (eaten, lived), etc.

he		*hemos*	
has	entrado (comido, vivido)	*habéis*	entrado (comido, vivido)
ha		*han*	

PLUPERFECT (PAST PERFECT) TENSE

I had entered (eaten, lived), etc.

había		*habíamos*	
habías	entrado (comido, vivido)	*habíais*	entrado (comido, vivido)
había		*habían*	

PRETERITE PERFECT TENSE

I had entered (eaten, lived), etc.

hube		*hubimos*	
hubiste	entrado (comido, vivido)	*hubisteis*	entrado (comido, vivido)
hubo		*hubieron*	

Note

The preterite perfect tense is used mainly in literary style to indicate that the action or event had just ended. It usually follows such expressions as **cuando** (when); **apenas** (scarcely, hardly); **después que** (after); **luego que, en cuanto, así que, tan pronto como** (as soon as). In conversation and informal writing, the preterite perfect is replaced by the preterite or the pluperfect tense.

Apenas hube llegado cuando me llamó.   I had scarcely arrived when he called me.

En cuanto hubo entrado, todos se levantaron.   As soon as he had entered, everyone got up.

FUTURE PERFECT TENSE

I shall (will) have entered (eaten, lived), etc.

habré ⎫
habrás ⎬ entrado (comido, vivido)
habrá ⎭

habremos ⎫
habréis ⎬ entrado (comido, vivido)
habrán ⎭

CONDITIONAL PERFECT

I would have entered (eaten, lived), etc.

habría ⎫
habrías ⎬ entrado (comido, vivido)
habría ⎭

habríamos ⎫
habríais ⎬ entrado (comido, vivido)
habrían ⎭

PERFECT INFINITIVE

haber entrado (comido, vivido), *to have entered (eaten, lived)*

PERFECT PARTICIPLE

habiendo entrado (comido, vivido), *having entered (eaten, lived)*

Note

The future perfect and conditional perfect are used to express probability in past time.

¿Lo *habrá terminado?*   I wonder if he has finished it.
(Can he have finished it?)

¿Lo *habría terminado?*   I wondered if he had finished it.
(Could he have finished it?)

Habrán perdido las llaves.   They have probably lost the keys.
(They must have lost the keys.)

Habrían perdido las llaves.   They had probably lost the keys.

The expression **deber de** followed by the perfect infinitive may be substituted for the future perfect in expressing probability in past time.

Deben de haber perdido las llaves.   They must have lost the keys.

Debe de haber tomado el libro.   He must have taken the book.

EJERCICIOS

A. Escríbase la forma correcta de cada verbo, empleando los sujetos entre paréntesis.

1. Yo *había ofendido* al jefe.

   (ellos) _____

   (vosotros) _____

   (ella) _____

2. Ellos no *han recibido* una carta de Paco.

   (yo) _____

   (Vd.) _____

   (nosotros) _____

3. *He prometido* traerlo.

   (Vds.) _____

   (tú) _____

   (nosotros) _____

4. *Hemos firmado* el contrato.

   (el señor) _____

   (yo) _____

   (ellos) _____

5. *Se habían expresado* bien.

   (nosotros) _____

   (tú) _____

   (él) _____

6. *¿Ha leído* Vd. este artículo?

   (Vds.) _____

   (tú) _____

   (Elena) _____

7. La criada *ha puesto* las cajas en el suelo.

   (yo) _____

   (nosotros) _____

   (ellos) _____

8. No *habían hecho* nada.

   (Pepe) _____

   (yo) _____

   (nosotros) _____

9. Yo *habría tomado* el tranvía en vez del autobús.

(nosotros) _____

(Ana) _____

(ellos) _____

10. *Habrán vuelto* para las diez.

(yo) _____

(mi amigo) _____

(Vds.) _____

B. Cámbiense los verbos al perfecto (present perfect).

1. *¿Combatirías* la injusticia? _____

2. Arturo *escribe* una carta a su amigo. _____

3. La muchacha *se desmaya.* _____

4. ¿Lo *ves?* _____

5. *Penetró* en la mina. _____

C. Cámbiense los verbos al pluscuamperfecto (pluperfect).

1. *Trajo* el paraguas. _____

2. Muchos *murieron* en el accidente. _____

3. El tirano *se apoderó* del gobierno. _____

4. *Volvió* temprano. _____

5. *Cubrieron* el altar de flores. _____

D. Cámbiense los verbos al futuro perfecto.

1. El barco *se hunde* en el mar. _____

2. *Descubrirán* el secreto. _____

3. *Acabaría* el trabajo. _____

4. *Empezarán* esta mañana. _____

5. *Cayeron* desde la cumbre de la montaña. _____

E. Cámbiense los verbos al condicional perfecto.

1. Yo lo *rompía.* _____

2. *Vi* un ejemplar de aquel libro. _____

3. Rosa no lo *abrirá.* _____

4. Su novia *sonríe* con dulzura. _____

5. *Hicieron* el viaje a pie. _____

F. Cámbiense las frases según los ejemplos.

EJEMPLOS: Deben de haber llegado. Habrán llegado.
Debe de haber entrado. Habrá entrado.

1. Deben de haber vuelto. ---------------------------------

2. Debemos de haberle ofendido. ---------------------------------

3. Deben de haber esperado. ---------------------------------

4. Deben de haber terminado. ---------------------------------

5. Debe de haber muerto. ---------------------------------

G. Contéstense en español en frases completas.

1. ¿Ha visto Vd. muchos partidos de béisbol? ---------------------------------
----

2. ¿Han terminado Vds. ya la lección para mañana? ---------------------------------
----

3. ¿La habrán terminado para la hora de clase mañana? ---------------------------------
----

4. ¿Ha visitado Vd. la capital de nuestro país? ---------------------------------
----

5. ¿Ha decidido Vd. qué carrera va a seguir? ---------------------------------
----

6. ¿Ha estado Vd. ausente este semestre? ---------------------------------
----

7. ¿Ha saludado Vd. hoy a su maestro? ---------------------------------
----

8. ¿Se ha aplicado Vd. a sus estudios este año? ---------------------------------
----

9. ¿Ha sentido Vd. orgullo alguna vez en su vida? ---------------------------------
----

10. ¿Ha cumplido Vd. siempre con su palabra? ---------------------------------
----

11. ¿Ha leído Vd. una novela recientemente? ---------------------------------
----

12. ¿Le ha gustado el estilo del autor? ---------------------------------
----

13. ¿Ha comprendido Vd. el misterio de la gramática? ---------------------------------
----

14. ¿Ha dicho Vd. siempre la verdad? ---------------------------------
----

15. ¿Ha contestado Vd. bien a todas estas preguntas? _____

_____

H. Tradúzcanse al español.

1. Who would have believed it? _____

2. I wonder if he has paid the debt. _____

3. They have solved all their problems. _____

_____

4. I wonder if they had returned the material. _____

_____

5. He will have finished the test by (para) eleven o'clock. _____

_____

6. He is glad to have won the prize. _____

_____

7. Having written the letter, he put it in an envelope. _____

_____

8. Who has broken these cups? _____

9. They must (deber de) have eaten green apples. _____

_____

10. They had printed all his works in five volumes. _____

_____

11. Where can I have put my coat? _____

12. Where have I put my coat? _____

13. His father had died in the Second World War. _____

_____

14. You (tú) must have seen those pictures. _____

15. I am sorry to have arrived late. _____

Pedro Calderón de la Barca (1600–1681) fue el último de los grandes dramaturgos del Siglo de Oro. Escribió sobre temas filosóficos y religiosos, y también de la dignidad humana. Sus dramas más conocidos son *La vida es sueño* y *El alcalde de Zalamea.*

Verb Lesson 10—USES OF *SER* AND *ESTAR*

SER	ESTAR

SER

1. To express a *quality* or *characteristic* of the subject.

   Este vino **es de España.**

   La casa **es de madera.**

   Felipe **es bueno.**

2. To *describe* or *identify* the subject.

   María **es alta** (*joven*).

   El coche **es nuevo** (*blanco*).

   Mi hermano **es médico** (*fuerte*).

   Juana **es rica** (*feliz*).

   ¿Quién es? Soy yo (*es él*).

3. To express *time* and *dates*, and with *impersonal expressions.*

   ¿Qué hora es? Son las dos.

   Hoy **es el tres de marzo.**

   Es necesario estudiar.

4. To express an *action* when used with the past participle. (See #1, page 74.)

   Las ventanas **fueron cerradas** por el profesor.

   La puerta **fue abierta** por el niño.

ESTAR

1. To express *location, position,* or *situation* of the subject.

   Madrid **está en España.**

   ¿Dónde **está la casa?**

   Felipe **está delante de la biblioteca.**

2. To indicate a *state* or *condition* of the subject.

   María **está cansada** (*sentada*).

   El coche **está lleno** (*sucio*).

   Ellos **están alegres** (*tristes*).

   Luis **está enfermo** (*bien*).

   La puerta **está abierta** (*cerrada*).

3. To form the *progressive tenses* (with the gerund).

   Están cantando.

   Estaban jugando.

Note

A. SER: *Quality, characteristic, description,* and *identification* are similar in many respects and may overlap each other in meaning. For instance, in the sentence **La puerta es de madera,** the expression *of wood* may be considered a characteristic or a quality of the door, or a description or an identification of the door.

B. ESTAR: A *condition* may be a *phase:* **Juan está enfermo (triste);** a *temporary state:* **Está cansado (sentado);** or the *result of an action:* **La puerta está cerrada.** Note that a condition does not identify, describe, or express a characteristic.

C. Some adjectives may be used with either **ser** or **estar.** However, the meaning of an adjective used with **ser** will differ from its meaning when used with **estar.**

Es bueno (*malo*).	He is good (bad).	(characteristic)
Está bueno (*malo*).	He is well (ill).	(condition)
Es listo.	He is clever (smart).	(characteristic)
Está listo.	He is ready.	(condition)
Es pálido.	He is pale-complexioned.	(description; identification)
Está pálido.	He is pale.	(condition)

Es seguro.	It is safe (reliable).	(description)
Está seguro.	He is sure.	(condition; state of mind)
El color *es vivo.*	The color is bright.	(description)
Está vivo.	He is alive.	(state; phase)
Es viejo (joven).	He is old (young).	(description)
Está viejo (joven).	He looks old (young).	(condition)
Él *es cansado.*	He is tiresome.	(characteristic)
Él *está cansado.*	He is tired.	(condition; state)

Adjectives used with **ser** and **estar** (like other adjectives) must agree with the subject in gender and number.

Alicia está ocupad**a**.	Alice is busy.
Eran pobre**s**.	They were poor.

EJERCICIOS

A. Escríbanse las formas correctas de *ser* y *estar*, empleando los sujetos indicados y haciendo los otros cambios necesarios.

1. *Felipe es de México y está aquí de visita.*

   a. Yo _____ de México y _____ aquí de visita.

   b. Nosotros _____ de México y _____ aquí de visita.

   c. Ellos _____ de México y _____ aquí de visita.

2. *Yo soy un muchacho bueno, pero ahora estoy malo.*

   a. Ellos _____, pero ahora _____.

   b. Nosotros _____, pero ahora _____.

   c. Tú _____, pero ahora _____.

3. *Ellos son ricos pero no están contentos.*

   a. Tú _____ pero no _____.

   b. Vd. _____ pero no _____.

   c. Nosotros _____ pero no _____.

4. *¿Quién es ese muchacho que está sentado allí?*

   a. ¿Quién _____ esa señorita que _____ allí?

   b. ¿Quiénes _____ esos señores que _____ allí?

   c. ¿Quiénes _____ esas muchachas que _____ allí?

5. *Eran las cinco, y José todavía estaba trabajando.*

   a. _____ la una, y tú todavía _____.

   b. _____ las diez, y ellos todavía _____.

   c. _____ tarde, y nosotros todavía _____.

6. *Era domingo, y la tienda estaba cerrada.*

   a. _____ sábado, y los bancos _____.

   b. _____ el cuatro de julio, y las escuelas _____.

   c. _____ día de fiesta, y el restaurante _____.

7. *El radio es nuevo* pero *está roto.*

   a. La cámara _____ pero _____ .

   b. Los juguetes _____ pero _____ .

   c. El reloj _____ pero _____ .

8. *La puerta fue abierta* por Pedro y todavía *está abierta.*

   a. El cajón _____ por Pedro y todavía _____ .

   b. La ventana _____ por Pedro y todavía _____ .

   c. Las botellas _____ por Pedro y todavía _____ .

9. *El chaleco es negro* pero no *está sucio.*

   a. Mi falda _____ pero no _____ .

   b. Sus calcetines _____ pero no _____ .

   c. El automóvil _____ pero no _____ .

10. *La ventana es grande* y *está llena* de polvo.

   a. Tus zapatos _____ y _____ de polvo.

   b. El escritorio _____ y _____ de polvo.

   c. La catedral _____ y _____ de polvo.

   B. Tradúzcanse al inglés.

1. Mi tía es buena. _____

2. Mi tía no está buena; tiene dolor de estómago. _____

   _____

3. Su hijo es muy malo. _____

4. Su hijo está muy malo; tiene resfriado. _____

   _____

5. El puente es muy seguro. _____

6. Yo estoy seguro de que Pedro lo hará. _____

7. Los muchachos son muy listos. _____

8. Los muchachos están listos para trabajar. _____

9. Los colores eran muy vivos. _____

10. Afortunadamente todos los pasajeros estaban vivos. _____

   _____

11. El señor Cárdenas es viejo; tiene ochenta años. _____

   _____

12. El señor Vives está tan viejo, y tiene solamente cuarenta años. _____

   _____

13. Estando muy cansado, se acostó temprano. _____

   _____

14. ¡Qué cansado es aquel conferenciante! No quiero escuchar más. _____

_____

15. María no es hermosa pero está muy bonita con su vestido nuevo. _____

_____

C. Complétese cada frase con la forma correcta del verbo *ser* o *estar*.

1. Nosotros _____ norteamericanos.

2. El ejército _____ muy lejos.

3. Los chicos _____ jugando en el patio.

4. ¿_____ Vd. listo para salir?

5. Hoy _____ miércoles.

6. Estos productos _____ de Inglaterra.

7. El museo _____ enfrente del parque.

8. _____ importante honrar a sus padres.

9. Las ventanas no _____ limpias.

10. ¡Qué sorpresa tuvo! Todavía _____ pálida.

11. Su camisa _____ limpia.

12. La corbata de Roberto _____ de colores muy vivos.

13. El señor Barja _____ ingeniero.

14. Los muebles _____ llenos de polvo.

15. _____ las once cuando llegaron.

16. Esta novela _____ escrita en el siglo diez y nueve por un autor español.

17. Este coche _____ de Juan.

18. La sopa no _____ caliente.

19. _____ preciso salir en seguida.

20. ¿_____ Vd. satisfecho?

D. Contéstense en español en frases completas.

1. ¿De dónde es Vd.? _____

2. ¿Dónde está Vd. ahora? _____

3. ¿Cómo está Vd. hoy? _____

4. ¿Quién está al lado de Vd.? _____

5. ¿Quién está ausente hoy? ¿Por qué no está aquí? _____

_____

6. ¿Qué está Vd. haciendo ahora? _____

7. ¿De qué color es la pizarra? _____

8. ¿Qué quiere Vd. ser algún día? _____

9. ¿Cómo es Vd.? ¿Es Vd. alto(-a) o bajo(-a)? ¿rubio(-a) o moreno(-a)? ¿gordo(-a) o delgado(-a)? ____

_____

10. ¿Es Vd. un(-a) amigo(-a) fiel? _____

11. ¿Dónde está situada su casa? ¿Es de piedra? ¿de estuco? ¿de madera? ¿de ladrillos? _____

_____

12. ¿Está rodeada de árboles su escuela? _____

_____

13. ¿Está Vd. satisfecho(-a) de sus notas en esta clase? _____

_____

14. ¿Quién es admirado y respetado de todos? _____

_____

15. ¿Está Vd. atento(-a) cuando habla el profesor? _____

_____

16. ¿Quién fue elegido presidente de los Estados Unidos? _____

_____

17. ¿Estaban Vds. ocupados ayer? _____

_____

18. ¿Está Vd. alegre o triste hoy? ¿Por qué? _____

_____

19. ¿Es Vd. un estudiante ejemplar? _____

_____

20. ¿Qué hace Vd. cuando está cansado(-a)? ¿cuando está enojado(-a)? _____

_____

_____

E. Tradúzcanse al español.

1. Who is it? It is I. _____

2. I am Mr. Jones. Is Alice at home? _____

3. Where are they from? They are from Venezuela. _____

_____

4. She is Spanish; he is German. _____

5. The street is short, but it is very wide. _____

_____

6. We were busy today, and I am very tired. _____

_____

7. Why is Jane so sad? Her mother is very ill. _____

_____

8. The house was full of people; some were eating in the patio. _____

_____

9. This chapter is tiresome; it is too long. _____

_____

10. What time is it? It is four o'clock. _____

11. The house is well built; it was built by a famous architect. _____

_____

12. This watch is new; it is (made) of gold. _____

13. Helen is not lazy, but her room is very dirty. _____

_____

14. The young lady who is seated near the window is my cousin. _____

_____

15. Today is Friday; it is the first of June. _____

_____

16. The book is covered because it is new. _____

_____

17. The window is open; it was opened by Henry. _____

_____

18. The meal is good, but the coffee is cold. _____

_____

19. The tables were small and were covered with (de) white tablecloths. _____

_____

20. The essay is long, but it is well written. _____

_____

Colón desembarcó en el Nuevo Mundo el 12 de octubre de 1492, en una isla de las Antillas, a la que dio el nombre de San Salvador. Besó el suelo y, dando gracias a Dios, tomó posesión de la isla en nombre de los Reyes Católicos, Fernando e Isabel. Hoy día la isla lleva el nombre de Watlings Island.

Verb Lesson 11—REFLEXIVE VERBS

lavarse

Present Tense

(yo) *me* lavo	(nosotros, -as) *nos* lavamos
(tú) *te* lavas	(vosotros, -as) *os* laváis
(Vd., él, ella) *se* lava	(Vds., ellos, -as) *se* lavan

Preterite:	*me* lavé, *te* lavaste, etc.
Imperfect:	*me* lavaba, *te* lavabas, etc.
Future:	*me* lavaré, *te* lavarás, etc.
Conditional:	*me* lavaría, *te* lavarías, etc.

Perfect Tense

(yo) *me* he lavado	(nosotros, -as) *nos* hemos lavado
(tú) *te* has lavado	(vosotros, -as) *os* habéis lavado
(Vd., él, ella) *se* ha lavado	(Vds., ellos, -as) *se* han lavado

Pluperfect:	*me* había lavado, *te* habías lavado, etc.
Future Perfect:	*me* habré lavado, *te* habrás lavado, etc.
Conditional Perfect:	*me* habría lavado, *te* habrías lavado, etc.

Gerund (Present Participle)

lavándo*me*, lavándo*te*, lavándo*se*, lavándo*nos*, lavándo*os,* etc.

Commands

láve*se* Vd.	láven*se* Vds.
láva*te* tú	lava*os* vosotros
no *se* lave Vd.	no *se* laven Vds.
no *te* laves tú	no *os* lavéis vosotros

POSITION OF REFLEXIVE PRONOUNS

The reflexive pronoun, like the other object pronouns, generally precedes the verb. However, when used with an infinitive, a present participle (gerund), or an affirmative command, the reflexive pronoun follows the verb and is attached to it.

Normal Position

Se lava.	He washes himself.
Nos hemos lavado.	We have washed ourselves.

63

EXCEPTIONS

INFINITIVE	Quiero lavar*me*. *or* *Me* quiero lavar.	I want to wash myself.
GERUND (PRESENT PARTICIPLE)	Estamos lavándo*nos*. *or* *Nos* estamos lavando.	We are washing ourselves.
AFFIRMATIVE COMMAND	<u>Láven*se*</u> Vds. (affirmative) *but* No <u>*se* laven</u> Vds. (negative)	Wash yourselves. Don't wash yourselves.

Note

A. The reflexive pronoun may either follow and be attached to the infinitive or the gerund, or precede the "conjugated" form of the verb.

B. When the reflexive pronoun is attached to the gerund or the affirmative command, a written accent mark is required on the stressed vowel of the verb in order to keep the original stress.

If not required for stress, the accent mark is omitted: **diles, ponte,** etc.

USES OF THE REFLEXIVE PRONOUNS

1. The reflexive pronoun is another form of object pronoun, either direct or indirect. It indicates that the subject and the object of the sentence are the same person or thing.

Nosotros levantamos el baúl.	We lift the trunk.
Nosotros *nos* levantamos.	We stand up. (We lift ourselves.)
Pongo el sombrero en la mesa.	I put the hat on the table.
Me pongo el sombrero.	I put on my hat. (I put the hat on myself.)

Note

A. Other verbs with special reflexive meanings are:

BASIC MEANING	REFLEXIVE MEANING
aburrir, to bore	**aburrirse,** to bore oneself (to become bored)
acostar, to put to bed	**acostarse,** to put oneself to bed (to go to bed)
bañar, to bathe (someone)	**bañarse,** to bathe oneself (to take a bath)
cansar, to tire	**cansarse,** to tire oneself (to become tired)
colocar, to place (something)	**colocarse,** to place oneself
engañar, to deceive	**engañarse,** to deceive oneself (to be mistaken)
esconder, to hide (something)	**esconderse,** to hide (oneself)
parar, to stop (something)	**pararse,** to stop oneself (to stop)
sentar, to seat	**sentarse,** to seat oneself (to sit down)

B. Some verbs are used reflexively, even though the reflexive meaning is not evident.

acordarse (de), to remember	**escaparse (de),** to escape (from)
apoderarse (de), to take possession (of)	**figurarse,** to imagine
apresurarse (a), to hurry	**irse,** to go away
aprovecharse (de), to avail oneself (of), to profit (by)	**morirse,** to pass away, to die
atreverse (a), to dare (to)	**negarse (a),** to refuse (to)
desayunarse, to have breakfast	**olvidarse (de),** to forget
desmayarse, to faint	**pasearse,** to stroll
empeñarse (en), to insist (on)	**quejarse (de),** to complain (of)
	tratarse (de), to concern, to be a question (of)

2. Reflexive verbs may be used to express a reciprocal action, which corresponds to the English *each other, one another.*

Nos escribimos.	We write to each other.
Pepe y Elena *se* aman.	Joe and Helen love one another.

Note

Uno a otro (Una a otra) or **el uno al otro (la una a la otra)** may be added to clarify the meaning of the sentence.

Las muchachas *se* miran.	The girls look at each other (*or* look at themselves).
Las muchachas *se* miran *una a otra* (*la una a la otra*).	The girls look at each other.
Pepe y Elena *se* aman *uno a otro* (*el uno al otro*).	Joe and Helen love each other.

3. Reflexive verbs are often used to express the passive voice. This occurs when the subject is a thing (not a person), and when the agent (doer) is not indicated. (See Note 2, page 74.)

Aquí *se habla* español. (singular) (singular)	Spanish is spoken here.
Estos libros *se venderán* a un precio barato. (plural) (plural)	These books will be sold at a low (cheap) price.

EJERCICIOS

A. Escríbase la forma correcta de cada uno de los verbos (*a, b, c, d*), en lugar del verbo en letra cursiva.

1. El marinero *se alejó* de la bella isla.   (*a*) acordarse   (*b*) olvidarse   (*c*) despedirse   (*d*) apoderarse

(*a*) _____   (*b*) _____   (*c*) _____   (*d*) _____

2. No *se encierre* Vd. en su habitación.   (*a*) acostarse   (*b*) dormirse   (*c*) esconderse   (*d*) quedarse

(*a*) _____   (*b*) _____   (*c*) _____   (*d*) _____

3. ¿De qué *te enojas?*   (*a*) preocuparse   (*b*) quejarse   (*c*) enfadarse   (*d*) alegrarse

(*a*) _____   (*b*) _____   (*c*) _____   (*d*) _____

4. Creo que ellos *se han marchado.*   (*a*) equivocarse   (*b*) irse   (*c*) quedarse   (*d*) despertarse

(*a*) _____   (*b*) _____   (*c*) _____   (*d*) _____

5. Llovió ayer, y yo *me mojé*.   (*a*) resfriarse   (*b*) afligirse   (*c*) enfadarse   (*d*) turbarse

(*a*) _____   (*b*) _____   (*c*) _____   (*d*) _____

6. *Cállense* Vds. en seguida.   (*a*) irse   (*b*) pararse   (*c*) lavarse   (*d*) rendirse

(*a*) _____   (*b*) _____   (*c*) _____   (*d*) _____

7. Vamos a *desayunarnos* pronto.   (*a*) levantarse   (*b*) pasearse   (*c*) casarse   (*d*) acostarse

(*a*) _____   (*b*) _____   (*c*) _____   (*d*) _____

8. No *se enfade* Vd.   (*a*) apresurarse   (*b*) asustarse   (*c*) preocuparse   (*d*) fiarse

(*a*) _____   (*b*) _____   (*c*) _____   (*d*) _____

9. *Estoy lavándome*.   (*a*) peinarse   (*b*) bañarse   (*c*) desayunarse   (*d*) vestirse

(*a*) _____   (*b*) _____   (*c*) _____   (*d*) _____

10. Juana y Rosa *se escriben*.   (*a*) ayudarse   (*b*) saludarse   (*c*) abrazarse   (*d*) besarse

(*a*) _____   (*b*) _____   (*c*) _____   (*d*) _____

B. En cada grupo, complétense las frases, usando la forma correcta del verbo de la primera frase.

1. *Me confundo* con tantos verbos.

¿_____ tú también?

Nosotros no _____ si estudiamos.

2. María *se interesa* por el arte.

Nosotros _____ por la música.

¿_____ vosotros por algo?

3. Ella *se ha sacrificado* por sus hijos.

Los hijos no _____ por nadie.

Es noble _____ por alguien.

4. *Se fijó* en el retrato.

¿_____ Vds. en el mismo retrato?

Nosotros _____ en la otra pintura.

5. Algunos muchachos no *se portan* bien.

¿_____ Vds. bien?

Debemos _____ bien.

6. No *se quite* Vd. la chaqueta ahora.

_____ Vd. la chaqueta más tarde.

No quiero _____ la chaqueta.

7. ¿Cómo *se llaman* Vds.?

Yo _____ Pedro.

Mi hermano _____ Luis.

8. Voy a *ponerme* el traje azul.

¿Qué traje vas a _____?

Estoy _____ el traje gris.

9. *¿Se comunican* Vd. y su amigo?

Sí, ----------------------------- cada semana.

Los buenos amigos deben ----------------------------- a menudo.

10. Yo *me quedaré* en el campo por un mes.

Federico ----------------------- por dos semanas.

¿Cuánto tiempo piensan Vds. ----------------------?

C. Contéstense en español en frases completas.

1. ¿Por qué se enfada el profesor a veces con Vd.? ---------------------------

----

2. ¿Con qué se cubre Vd. cuando llueve? ----------------------------------

----

3. ¿Se quejan Vds. cuando el profesor les da muchas tareas? ----------------

----

4. ¿Se entrega Vd. a su trabajo con entusiasmo? --------------------------

----

5. ¿A qué hora quiere Vd. desayunarse? ----------------------------------

----

6. ¿Cuándo se celebra nuestra fiesta nacional? ---------------------------

----

7. ¿Se asusta Vd. de la oscuridad? ---------------------------------------

----

8. ¿Deben los hombres quitarse el sombrero al entrar en un ascensor? -------

----

9. ¿Se ponen Vds. tristes cuando terminan las vacaciones? -----------------

----

10. ¿Se cansa Vd. dando largos paseos? ------------------------------------

----

11. ¿Se baña Vd. antes de desayunarse? ------------------------------------

----

12. ¿Se callan Vds. mientras está hablando el profesor? --------------------

----

13. ¿Se preocupan los padres demasiado por sus hijos? ---------------------

----

14. ¿Admite Vd. su error cuando se equivoca? -----------------------------

----

15. ¿Se apresura Vd. a regresar a casa después de las clases? ---------------

----

D. Tradúzcanse al español.

1. He takes a bath every morning. _____

2. Have you brushed your teeth this morning? _____

_____

3. I became frightened and began to (echarse a) run. _____

_____

4. Do not get angry; they will go away. _____

_____

5. She fainted when she saw the accident. _____

6. She has washed her (la) face and (las) hands. _____

_____

7. He is shaving and washing. _____

8. The barber shaved the man. _____

_____

9. She used to appear at the window every evening. _____

_____

10. I have put on my white shoes. _____

11. The pupil raised his (la) hand. _____

12. He approached the fire to warm himself. _____

13. I thought that stamps were sold in that store, but I was mistaken. _____

_____

14. He insisted on leaving at once, but we refused to accompany him. _____

_____

15. Do not take off your coat; we are not going to stay here more than a few minutes. _____

_____

_____

Verb Lesson 12—MASTERY EXERCISES

(LESSONS 7–11)

A. Escríbase la forma correcta del futuro y del condicional.

	FUTURO	CONDICIONAL
1. El pasajero *tuvo* que facturar su maleta.	------------------	------------------
2. Yo *defiendo* mis derechos.	------------------	------------------
3. *Salió* sin afeitarse.	------------------	------------------
4. *Querían* tomar parte en la acción.	------------------	------------------
5. En el comedor *caben* una mesa y siete sillas.	------------------	------------------
6. *Limité* mis gastos.	------------------	------------------
7. Hoy no *vamos* a pescar.	------------------	------------------
8. El escultor *hizo* una imagen de mármol.	------------------	------------------
9. Sin duda *dijeron* algo ridículo.	------------------	------------------
10. *Sé* portarme como caballero honrado.	------------------	------------------
11. El diamante *vale* mucho.	------------------	------------------
12. El sol *se puso* detrás de la montaña.	------------------	------------------
13. Esto nos *agradó*.	------------------	------------------
14. El ciudadano *reclamó* sus derechos.	------------------	------------------
15. *Te sentaste* en un sillón cómodo.	------------------	------------------
16. *Vendimos* las demás cosas a un precio barato.	------------------	------------------
17. Al fin, *llegaron* a la aldea desierta.	------------------	------------------
18. El pícaro *mentía* con cara inocente.	------------------	------------------
19. Al pasar el pueblo, *torcimos* a la izquierda.	------------------	------------------
20. *Alcé* el saco pesado.	------------------	------------------

B. Tradúzcanse al español las expresiones en inglés, empleando las formas compuestas (perfectas o progresivas).

1. Ella *continues crying* _____ a causa de su muñeca rota.

2. Dispense Vd.; yo *have broken* _____ la lámpara.

3. Tú *have omitted* _____ la mitad del cuento.

4. No pude entender lo que ellos *were saying* _____.

5. Yo *am getting dressed* _____ para salir.

6. La nieve *had fallen* _____ durante la noche.

7. Ellos *are getting bored* _____ con esta película.

8. Nosotros lo *would have done* _____ mejor.

9. Isabel *has described* _____ el suceso con muchos detalles.

10. El avaro *had acquired* _____ muchas propiedades.

11. El dependiente *has wrapped* _____ el paquete.

12. *It has stopped* _____ ya de llover.

13. Para mañana el sastre *will have finished* _____ el traje.

14. Para el invierno la nieve *will have covered* _____ el valle.

15. El poeta *had written* _____ unos versos para su novia.

16. *He was mixing* _____ agua con la leche cuando entró el inspector.

17. Para las ocho *they will have opened* _____ la zapatería.

18. ¿Qué *had she said* _____ a su madre?

19. ¿*Have you decorated* _____ vosotros el salón para la fiesta?

20. Antes de regresar, *we will have seen* _____ el Gran Cañón.

C. Tradúzcanse al español las expresiones en inglés, empleando las formas reflexivas.

1. *Stand up* _____ Vd. y *don't lean* _____ en la pared.

2. Yo estaba *enjoying myself* _____ en el circo, y *I refused* _____ a volver a casa.

3. Los novios *will get married* _____ en abril; la boda *will take place* _____ _____ en la iglesia.

4. *Take care of yourselves* _____; Vds. deben *to take advantage* _____ de las horas de sol.

5. *He feels* _____ enfermo, y *he complains* _____ de dolor de cabeza.

6. *They did not laugh* _____ de sus chistes y *took leave* _____ de él en seguida.

7. Quería *to become* _____ médico, pero sus padres *opposed* _____ a sus planes.

8. Juan y María prometieron *to love each other* _____ siempre y *to write to each other* _____ todos los días.

9. Un hombre que *was called* _____ Gómez *was drowned* _____ ayer en la piscina.

10. En aquella tienda *are sold* _____ zapatos y calcetines; las puertas *open* (are opened) _____ a las ocho.

11. *I fell asleep* _____ a las once, *waking up* _____ a las siete de la mañana siguiente.

12. Las dos niñas *looked at each other* _____ y luego *greeted each other* _____ _____.

13. El muchacho *fell down* _____ y *hurt himself* _____.

14. *Don't make fun* _____ Vd. de los desgraciados; mejor es *to keep silent* _____.

15. *Don't be astonished* _____; yo *have taken charge* _____ de este negocio.

D. Contéstense en español en frases completas.

1. ¿De qué color son sus zapatos? _____

_____

2. ¿Se ha desmayado Vd. alguna vez en su vida? _____

_____

3. ¿Sabe Vd. expresarse bien en español? _____

_____

4. ¿Qué dirán sus padres si Vd. recibe malas notas? _____

_____

5. ¿A qué hora se juntará Vd. con sus amigos hoy? _____

_____

6. ¿Le gustaría tomar un helado ahora? _____

_____

7. ¿A qué hora se sentó Vd. anoche para estudiar? _____

_____

8. ¿Está Vd. aburriéndose en esta clase? _____

_____

9. ¿A qué hora estará Vd. en casa esta tarde? _____

_____

10. ¿Qué hace Vd. cuando el maestro dice "Levántese Vd."? _____

_____

11. ¿Se lleva Vd. bien con sus amigos? _____

_____

12. ¿Estaba brillando el sol cuando Vd. se despertó hoy? _____

_____

13. ¿Están Vds. listos para escribir al dictado? _____

_____

14. ¿En qué país está Vd.? _____

_____

15. ¿A qué hora se desayunó Vd. hoy? _____

_____

E. Tradúzcanse al español.

1. The knife is very sharp; don't cut yourself. _____

_____

2. This bottle is empty; this morning it was full of water. _____

_____

3. They will be in Germany in October and November.

4. He threw himself into the water to rescue the child.

5. The drink is bitter; don't drink it.

6. He hopes to cure himself by exposing himself to the sun's rays.

7. My two best friends are from France; they are French.

8. You are wrong; today is not March 10.

9. Not being able to imagine such cruelty, he refused to believe what he had heard.

10. Don't move from that place; remain there for an hour.

11. It was December 24; the next day would be Christmas.

12. He was referring to a battle of the Second World War.

13. A religious procession will start (iniciar) the ceremony.

14. Her new blouse is of silk; it is beautiful.

15. Mr. Rodríguez keeps adding paintings to his collection.

F. Each of the following passages contains forms of the verb *to be* numbered 1–10. For each English form, you will find a choice of two Spanish verb forms. Write the letter of the correct verb form in each pair.

I. (1) *It was* las tres de la tarde. (2) *It was* un día hermoso de agosto. Los árboles (3) *were* cargados de frutas que más tarde (4) *would be* recogidas por niños y mayores. El aire (5) *was* lleno del rumor de pájaros e insectos que se aprovechaban de la luz del sol. En los campos de trigo y de maíz, los agricultores (6) *were* trabajando entre gritos y risas. El cielo (7) *was* completamente libre de nubes. (8) *It was* una escena de belleza ideal. —Esto (9) *is* vivir—pensaba el turista, respirando fuerte. La tristeza que había sentido antes iba cambiando. Ahora (10) *he was* alegre.

(1) (*a*) Estaban	(*b*) Eran	_____	(6) (*a*) estaban	(*b*) eran	_____
(2) (*a*) Estaba	(*b*) Era	_____	(7) (*a*) estaba	(*b*) era	_____
(3) (*a*) estaban	(*b*) eran	_____	(8) (*a*) Estaba	(*b*) Era	_____
(4) (*a*) estarían	(*b*) serían	_____	(9) (*a*) está	(*b*) es	_____
(5) (*a*) estaba	(*b*) era	_____	(10) (*a*) estaba	(*b*) era	_____

II. Luisito (1) *is* un muchacho de trece años. (2) *He is* alto y rubio, y tiene una sonrisa de ángel. (3) *He is* bueno, listo, y simpático, pero bastante pícaro y atrevido. Ayer se subió a un manzano, y comió un par de manzanas verdes. Ahora (4) *he is* enfermo, con fiebre, y tiene que (5) *to be* en cama todo el día. Le visité esta mañana, y (6) *he was* pálido. Le pregunté:—¿Cómo (7) *are you?*

Me contestó con voz muy débil:—(8) *I am* muy malo hoy.

El médico dice que la enfermedad no (9) *is* grave, y que dentro de dos o tres días Luisito (10) *will be* tan bueno como antes.

(1) (a) está	(b) es	_____	(6) (a) estaba	(b) era	_____
(2) (a) Está	(b) Es	_____	(7) (a) estás	(b) eres	_____
(3) (a) Está	(b) Es	_____	(8) (a) Estoy	(b) Soy	
(4) (a) está	(b) es	_____	(9) (a) está	(b) es	_____
(5) (a) estar	(b) ser	_____	(10) (a) estará	(b) será	_____

III. Los aztecas (1) *were* dueños del Valle de México. Su capital (2) *was* Tenochtitlán [que hoy día (3) *is* la Ciudad de México]. (4) *It was* situada en un lago, y (5) *it was* totalmente rodeada de agua. Para llegar allí, (6) *it was* necesario cruzar por medio de uno de los numerosos puentes. En el centro de la ciudad (7) *was* el palacio del emperador. (8) *They were* una raza bárbara y militar, y se habían hecho propietarios de mucho terreno ajeno. Cuando llegó Cortés, muchas naciones (9) *were* sujetas al poder de los aztecas. Su gobierno (10) *was* severo y cruel, y practicaban el culto del sacrificio humano en los altares de sus templos.

(1) (a) estaban	(b) eran	_____	(6) (a) estaba	(b) era	_____
(2) (a) estaba	(b) era	_____	(7) (a) estaba	(b) era	_____
(3) (a) está	(b) es	_____	(8) (a) Estaban	(b) Eran	_____
(4) (a) Estaba	(b) Era	_____	(9) (a) estaban	(b) eran	_____
(5) (a) estaba	(b) era	_____	(10) (a) estaba	(b) era	_____

IV. El director de la expedición (1) *was* el Sr. Suárez. (2) *He was* un hombre de mucha experiencia, de origen gallego, que había (3) *been* navegante y que había (4) *been* en muchas luchas contra el océano. (5) *It was* martes, el treinta de enero, cuando salimos, y nos dirigimos al continente de África, donde, según él, (6) *was* el tesoro. El mar (7) *was* tranquilo. Una noche (8) *we were* sentados en el salón, cuando uno de los compañeros de la empresa le preguntó si (9) *he was* seguro de que el mapa (10) *was* genuino. Lleno de ira, se levantó de su asiento.

(1) (a) estuvo	(b) fue	_____	(6) (a) estaba	(b) era	_____
(2) (a) Estaba	(b) Era	_____	(7) (a) estaba	(b) era	_____
(3) (a) estado	(b) sido	_____	(8) (a) estábamos	(b) éramos	_____
(4) (a) estado	(b) sido	_____	(9) (a) estaba	(b) era	_____
(5) (a) Estaba	(b) Era	_____	(10) (a) estaba	(b) era	_____

V. El Sr. Torres (1) *was* de España. (2) *He was* español de nacimiento. Había venido a Buenos Aires para (3) *to be* administrador del negocio de su padre, en la industria de lana. (4) *He was* viudo, y vivía con sus hijas y sus nietos. Su trabajo (5) *was* fácil, y tenía muchas horas libres. Su casa (6) *was* situada en la avenida principal de la ciudad y (7) *was* de buena construcción, de ladrillos. Tenía una biblioteca que también (8) *was* despacho, con gran número de libros, cuadros, y curiosidades. (9) *He was* muy aficionado a la lectura, y prefería obras de historia. La puerta siempre (10) *was* abierta para los amigos y conocidos.

(1) (a) estaba	(b) era	_____	(6) (a) estaba	(b) era	_____
(2) (a) Estaba	(b) Era	_____	(7) (a) estaba	(b) era	_____
(3) (a) estar	(b) ser	_____	(8) (a) estaba	(b) era	_____
(4) (a) Estaba	(b) Era	_____	(9) (a) Estaba	(b) Era	_____
(5) (a) estaba	(b) era	_____	(10) (a) estaba	(b) era	_____

Verb Lesson 13—PASSIVE VOICE

In the active voice, the subject generally performs some action. In the passive voice, the subject is acted upon.

ACTIVE: *El hombre compró el libro.* | The man bought the book.

PASSIVE: *El libro fue comprado por el hombre.* | The book was bought by the man.

1. If the agent (doer) is mentioned or implied, the passive voice is formed by a word-for-word translation: subject + **ser** + past participle + **por** + doer.

Esas carreteras *fueron construidas por* el gobierno.
_{doer} | Those highways were built by the government.

Todos mis amigos **han sido invitados por** Carlos.
_{doer} | All my friends have been invited by Charles.

La fiesta **será celebrada por** los habitantes.
_{doer} | The festival will be celebrated by the inhabitants.

Colón salió de España el 3 de agosto; el 12 de octubre América *fue descubierta.* (doer, Columbus, implied) | Columbus left Spain on August 3; on October 12 America was discovered.

Note

A. In forming the passive voice, the past participle is used as an adjective and must agree with the subject in gender and number.

B. *By* is usually translated by **por.** If the past participle expresses feeling or emotion, rather than action, *by* is translated by **de.**

Es **amado (respetado, admirado)** *de* todos. | He is loved (respected, admired) by all.

Era **temido (odiado, envidiado)** *de* la gente. | He was feared (hated, envied) by the people.

2. If the agent (doer) is not mentioned or implied, and the subject is a *thing*, the reflexive construction is used. In such instances, the subject usually follows the verb.

Aquí *se habla* español. Aquí *se hablan* español y francés.
(singular) (singular) (plural) (plural) | Spanish is spoken here. Spanish and French are spoken here.

¿A qué hora *se cierran* las tiendas?
(plural) (plural) | At what time are the stores closed?

Se publicó el libro.
(singular) (singular) | The book was published.

Se perdieron los documentos.
(plural) (plural) | The documents were lost.

Desde aquí *se pueden ver* los monumentos.
(plural) (plural) | From here the monuments can be seen.

74

3. *a.* The pronoun **se** is also used as an indefinite subject. In such instances, it is not reflexive and is used only with the third person singular of the verb.

> **se dice:** it is said, one says, people say, they say, you say
> **se cree:** it is believed, one believes, people believe, they believe, you believe
> **se sabe:** it is known, one knows, people know, they know, you know

Instead of the above, **dicen** (they say), **creen** (they believe), and **saben** (they know) are often used with indefinite subjects.

Se dice⎫
Dicen ⎭ que es muy rico.

It is said⎫
They say⎭ that he is very rich.

b. The indefinite **se** is used to express the passive when (1) the doer is indefinite (not mentioned or implied), and (2) a *person* is acted upon.

Se mató al hombre.	The man was killed. [Someone (indefinite) killed the man.]
Se *le* mató.	He was killed. [Someone (indefinite) killed him.]
Se mató a los hombres.	The men were killed. [Someone (indefinite) killed the men.]
Se *les* mató.	They were killed. [Someone (indefinite) killed them.]
Se castigará a la niña.	The child will be punished. [Someone (indefinite) will punish the child.]
Se *la* castigará.	She will be punished. [Someone (indefinite) will punish her.]
Se castigará a las niñas.	The children will be punished. [Someone (indefinite) will punish the children.]
Se *las* castigará.	They will be punished. [Someone (indefinite) will punish them.

Note

Although the person acted upon is a direct object, the form **les** is used (instead of **los**) for the masculine plural.

c. Instead of the indefinite **se** construction, the active voice third person plural is often used.

Mataron al hombre (a los hombres).	They killed the man (the men). (indefinite)
Le (Los) *mataron.*	They killed him (them). (indefinite)
Castigarán a la niña (a las niñas).	They will punish the child (the children). (indefinite)
La (Las) *castigarán.*	They will punish her (them). (indefinite)

SUMMARY

	DOER (AGENT) EXPRESSED	DOER (AGENT) NOT EXPRESSED	
THING	I. *Word-for-Word Translation* Las camisas **serán vendidas por** el dependiente.	II. *Reflexive* **Se venderán** camisas.	THING
PERSON	El alcalde **fue elegido por** el pueblo.	III. *Indefinite* **Se eligió** al alcalde. (Se le eligió.) **Eligieron** al alcalde. (Le eligieron.)	PERSON

EJERCICIOS

A. En cada frase, escríbase la forma pasiva, empleando cada uno de los sujetos indicados.

1. Las casas *fueron destruidas* por el fuego.

Ambos edificios _____

La fábrica _____

El hotel _____

Los muebles _____

2. La ciudad *sería atacada* por el enemigo.

Nuestro ejército _____

Las fortalezas _____

Los soldados _____

El castillo _____

3. El café *será servido* por el camarero.

Los refrescos _____

La comida _____

Las bebidas _____

Los postres _____

4. Los escritores *fueron alabados* por los críticos.

La nueva revista _____

El dramaturgo _____

Las poetisas _____

El ensayo _____

5. Los vasos *fueron rotos* por los niños.

La bicicleta _____

El palo _____

Las plumas _____

Los papeles _____

6. El contrato *ha sido firmado* por el señor Torres.

Los documentos _____

La carta _____

Las tarjetas _____

El cheque _____

7. El accidente *había sido anunciado* por las autoridades.

Las elecciones _____

Los juegos _____

La noticia _____

El descubrimiento _____

8. Los proyectos *serán discutidos* por los socios.

El asunto _____

Las reglas _____

La constitución _____

Los impuestos _____

9. La señora *era respetada* de todos.

El director _____

Los profesores _____

Las jóvenes _____

La emperatriz _____

10. Los dictadores *son temidos* de la gente.

Las tropas _____

El tirano _____

La policía _____

Su influencia _____

B. Cámbiese cada frase a la forma pasiva según el ejemplo.

EJEMPLO: Este artista pintó el cuadro.

El cuadro fue pintado por este artista.

1. La criada limpió la casa. _____

2. La gente elige al presidente. _____

3. La cocinera preparará el pollo. --------------------------------

----

4. El perro mordió al cartero. --------------------------------

----

5. Los oficiales observaron el vuelo del avión. --------------------------------

----

6. Esta compañía emplea a muchas personas. --------------------------------

----

7. El juez condenó a los criminales. --------------------------------

----

8. Teresa ha engañado a los muchachos. --------------------------------

----

9. Todos admiraban a Pepe. --------------------------------

10. Los novios anunciarán el día de la boda. --------------------------------

----

11. Un arquitecto famoso construyó esta casa. --------------------------------

----

12. Los españoles habían fundado muchas misiones. --------------------------------

----

13. Los vecinos aman a los chicos. --------------------------------

14. El autor publicará sus obras. --------------------------------

15. El policía persiguió al ladrón. --------------------------------

C. Cámbiese cada frase del singular al plural o viceversa según el ejemplo.

EJEMPLO: Se abre la tienda a las nueve.

Se abren las tiendas a las nueve.

1. Se cierra el restaurante a las ocho. --------------------------------

2. Aquí se sacan los pasaportes. --------------------------------

3. Se vendió la casa. --------------------------------

4. Se celebraron las fiestas. --------------------------------

5. Se han publicado sus novelas. --------------------------------

6. ¿Dónde se encuentra su cuarto? --------------------------------

7. Se perdieron las llaves. --------------------------------

8. ¿A qué hora se servirá la comida? --------------------------------

9. Se podía ver la montaña a lo lejos. --------------------------------

10. Se deben discutir los problemas. --------------------------------

D. Tradúzcanse de dos maneras las expresiones en inglés.

EJEMPLO: *It is known* ___*Se sabe, Saben*___ que el mundo es redondo.

1. En este tranvía, *you pay* _____ al entrar.

2. *It is not believed* _____ que la luna sea de queso verde.

3. *They say* _____ que el ruso es una lengua muy difícil de aprender.

4. *One can see* _____ que esta moneda es falsa.

5. *People cross* _____ el río por medio del puente.

6. Aquí *they eat* _____ a las nueve.

7. *One learns* _____ estudiando.

8. En este mercado *people buy* _____ y *sell* _____
_____.

9. *One enters* _____ por la puerta, no por la ventana.

10. *You go up* _____ por la escalera.

E. Cámbiense los verbos según los ejemplos.

EJEMPLOS: *Nombraron* ministro al Sr. Gómez.

    ___*Se nombró*___ ministro al Sr. Gómez.

    Le eligieron alcalde.

    ___*Se le eligió*___ alcalde.

1. *Aconsejaron* bien a los discípulos aplicados.

    _____ bien a los discípulos aplicados.

2. *Aplaudieron* al cantante y al compositor célebres.

    _____ al cantante y al compositor célebres.

3. *Nos ayudarán.*

    _____.

4. *Cogieron* al hombre que robó la plata.

    _____ al hombre que robó la plata.

5. *Escuchan* al abuelo con atención.

    _____ al abuelo con atención.

6. Durante la batalla *hirieron* al conde.

    Durante la batalla _____ al conde.

7. *Invitaron* al filósofo a dar una conferencia.

    _____ al filósofo a dar una conferencia.

8. *Le acusaron* del crimen.

    _____ del crimen.

9. *Mataron* al tirano.

    _____ al tirano.

10. *Pegarán* a los niños malos.

   ---------------------- a los niños malos.

11. En ese país *querían* al príncipe bondadoso.

   En ese país ------------------ al príncipe bondadoso.

12. *Encerraron* al escudero en la torre del castillo.

   ---------------------- al escudero en la torre del castillo.

13. *Estiman* mucho a las enfermeras hábiles.

   ---------------------- mucho a las enfermeras hábiles.

14. *Quitarán* al carretero su caballo.

   ---------------------- al carretero su caballo.

15. En el pueblo *respetaban* mucho al sacerdote amable.

   En el pueblo ---------------------- mucho al sacerdote amable.

   F. Contéstense en español en frases completas.

1. ¿Cómo se dice "railroad" en español? ------------------------

2. ¿A qué hora se cena en su casa? ------------------------

3. ¿Se venden guantes en una panadería? ------------------------

   ----

4. ¿Qué se lee en un periódico? ------------------------

5. ¿Por quiénes fue construido el acueducto de Segovia? (romanos) ------------------------

   ----

6. ¿En dónde se compran medicinas? ------------------------

7. ¿Se cree hoy día que el mundo sea llano? ------------------------

   ----

8. ¿Se debe respetar a los padres? ------------------------

9. ¿A quiénes se cura en un hospital? ------------------------

10. ¿A dónde se va para comprar zapatos? ------------------------

   ----

11. ¿Se debe castigar a los niños de vez en cuando? ------------------------

   ----

12. ¿En dónde se encierra a los criminales? ------------------------

   ----

13. ¿Se organizarán bailes en la escuela este semestre? ------------------------

   ----

14. ¿En qué país se habla griego? ------------------------

15. ¿Por quién fue descubierto el Nuevo Mundo? ------------------------

   ----

G. Tradúzcanse al español.

1. The country was conquered by our forces. _____
_____

2. He is respected by all. _____

3. The examination has been corrected by the teacher. _____
_____

4. The book will be read by many people. _____

5. Spanish is spoken here. _____

6. People say that he is very generous. _____

7. It has been said that he is very rich. _____

8. The American continent was explored by the Spaniards. _____
_____

9. She is admired by everyone. _____

10. The lessons have been explained by the teacher. _____
_____

11. People believe that war can be avoided. _____
_____

12. The nation was governed by a dictator. _____
_____

13. He was hated by the public. _____

14. Smoking is prohibited in the school. _____

15. An accident was avoided. _____

16. They say that nothing is impossible. _____

17. The judges were appointed by the President. _____
_____

18. They were imitated by other nations. _____

19. Many articles have been written by the class. _____
_____

20. She will be greeted by her friends. _____

21. Flowers are sold in this store. _____

22. It is not known if he will return. _____

23. The error had been discovered by a student. _____
_____

24. Many interesting monuments can be seen in Mexico. _____
_____

25. It was believed that he was very ill. _____
_____

Verb Lesson 14—FORMATION OF THE SUBJUNCTIVE

FORMATION OF THE PRESENT SUBJUNCTIVE

REGULAR VERBS

1. The present subjunctive of most verbs is formed by dropping the ending **-o** of the first person singular (**yo** form) of the present indicative and adding the following endings:

-**ar** verbs: *-e, -es, -e, -emos, -éis, -en*

-**er** ⎫
-**ir** ⎭ verbs: *-a, -as, -a, -amos, -áis, -an*

INFINITIVE	PRESENT INDICATIVE *Yo* FORM	PRESENT SUBJUNCTIVE
tomar	tomo	tom*e*, tom*es*, tom*e*, tom*emos*, tom*éis*, tom*en*
comer	como	com*a*, com*as*, com*a*, com*amos*, com*áis*, com*an*
escribir	escribo	escrib*a*, escrib*as*, escrib*a*, escrib*amos*, escrib*áis*, escrib*an*

caber	quepo	quep*a*, *-as*, *-a*, etc.
coger	cojo	coj*a*, *-as*, *-a*, etc.
conocer	conozco	conozc*a*, *-as*, *-a*, etc.
destruir	destruyo	destruy*a*, *-as*, *-a*, etc.
distinguir	distingo	disting*a*, *-as*, *-a*, etc.
salir	salgo	salg*a*, *-as*, *-a*, etc.

SPELLING CHANGES IN THE PRESENT SUBJUNCTIVE

2. In the present subjunctive of verbs ending in **-car, -gar,** and **-zar, c** changes to **qu, g** to **gu,** and **z** to **c.** These spelling changes are the same as those that occur in the **yo** form of the preterite. (See pages 19—20.)

INFINITIVE	PRETERITE *Yo* FORM	PRESENT SUBJUNCTIVE
buscar	busqué	*busque, -es, -e,* etc.
pagar	pagué	*pague, -es, -e,* etc.
alzar	alcé	*alce, -es, -e,* etc.

Note

In the verb **averiguar,** the **u** changes to **ü** before an **e: averigüé**—preterite; **averigüe**—present subjunctive. This is done to keep the sound of the **u,** which otherwise would be silent.

Stem-Changing Verbs in the Present Subjunctive

3. *a.* Stem-changing **-ar** and **-er** verbs have the same stem changes in the present subjunctive as in the present indicative (**e** to **ie**, **o** to **ue**).

> **cerrar:** c*ie*rre, c*ie*rres, c*ie*rre, cerremos, cerréis, c*ie*rren
> **volver:** v*ue*lva, v*ue*lvas, v*ue*lva, volvamos, volváis, v*ue*lvan

b. Stem-changing **-ir** verbs have the same stem changes in the present subjunctive as in the present indicative (**e** to **ie**, **o** to **ue**, **e** to **i**). In the **nosotros** and **vosotros** forms, the stem vowel **e** changes to **i** and the stem vowel **o** changes to **u**.

> **sentir:** s*ie*nta, s*ie*ntas, s*ie*nta, s*i*ntamos, s*i*ntáis, s*ie*ntan
> **dormir:** d*ue*rma, d*ue*rmas, d*ue*rma, d*u*rmamos, d*u*rmáis, d*ue*rman
> **pedir:** p*i*da, p*i*das, p*i*da, p*i*damos, p*i*dáis, p*i*dan

c. Some verbs ending in **-iar** or **-uar** stress the **i** or the **u** (**í**, **ú**) in all forms except those for **nosotros** and **vosotros**.

> **enviar:** env*í*e, env*í*es, env*í*e, enviemos, enviéis, env*í*en
> **continuar:** contin*ú*e, contin*ú*es, contin*ú*e, continuemos, continuéis, contin*ú*en

(See Note C, page 9, for additional verbs like **enviar** and **continuar**.)

Present Subjunctive of Irregular Verbs

4. The following verbs have irregular forms in the present subjunctive:

> **dar:** *dé,* des, *dé,* demos, deis, den
> **estar:** *esté, estés, esté,* estemos, estéis, *estén*
> **haber:** *haya, hayas, haya, hayamos, hayáis, hayan*
> **ir:**   *vaya, vayas, vaya, vayamos, vayáis, vayan*
> **saber:** *sepa, sepas, sepa, sepamos, sepáis, sepan*
> **ser:**   *sea, seas, sea, seamos, seáis, sean*

Miguel de Unamuno (1864–1936), de la "Generación del '98," fue filósofo, ensayista, poeta, y novelista. Su obra más característica es *Del sentimiento trágico de la vida*.

FORMATION OF THE IMPERFECT SUBJUNCTIVE

The imperfect subjunctive of *all* verbs is formed by dropping the **-ron** ending of the third person plural of the preterite tense and adding either the **-ra** or **-se** endings.

-ra, -ras, -ra, '-ramos, -rais, -ran

or

-se, -ses, -se, '-semos, -seis, -sen

Infinitive	Preterite Third Plural	Imperfect Subjunctive
llegar	llega*ron*	llega*ra*, llega*ras*, llega*ra*, llegá*ramos*, llega*rais*, llega*ran* *or* llega*se*, llega*ses*, llega*se*, llegá*semos*, llega*seis*, llega*sen*
vender	vendie*ron*	vendie*ra*, vendie*ras*, vendie*ra*, vendié*ramos*, vendie*rais*, vendie*ran* *or* vendie*se*, vendie*ses*, vendie*se*, vendié*semos*, vendie*seis*, vendie*sen*
dormir	durmie*ron*	durmie*ra*, durmie*ras*, etc., *or* durmie*se*, durmie*ses*, etc.
pedir	pidie*ron*	pidie*ra*, etc., *or* pidie*se*, etc.
decir	dije*ron*	dije*ra*, etc., *or* dije*se*, etc.
ir, ser	fue*ron*	fue*ra*, etc., *or* fue*se*, etc.
creer	creye*ron*	creye*ra*, etc., *or* creye*se*, etc.

Note

The **nosotros** form of the imperfect subjunctive is the only form that has an accent mark (on the vowel immediately *before* the ending).

FORMATION OF THE PERFECT AND PLUPERFECT SUBJUNCTIVE

The perfect subjunctive is formed by the present subjunctive of **haber** followed by a past participle.

haya
hayas } entrado
haya

hayamos
hayáis } entrado
hayan

The pluperfect subjunctive is formed by the imperfect subjunctive of **haber** followed by a past participle.

hubiera (hubiese)
hubieras (hubieses) } dicho
hubiera (hubiese)

hubiéramos (hubiésemos)
hubierais (hubieseis) } dicho
hubieran (hubiesen)

EJERCICIOS

A. Escríbanse los verbos en el presente de subjuntivo empleando los sujetos *yo, nosotros, ellos.*

Ejemplo: hablar—yo hable, nosotros hablemos, ellos hablen

	Yo	Nosotros	Ellos
1. buscar			
2. trabajar			
3. odiar			
4. llegar			
5. traer			
6. conocer			
7. ser			
8. hacer			
9. dar			
10. escoger			
11. oír			
12. distinguir			
13. averiguar			
14. leer			
15. emplear			
16. ir			
17. poner			
18. estar			
19. alcanzar			
20. salir			
21. caber			
22. construir			
23. acercarse			
24. saber			
25. venir			

B. Escríbanse los verbos en el presente de subjuntivo empleando los sujetos *yo, nosotros, ellos.*

Ejemplo: contar—yo cuente, nosotros contemos, ellos cuenten

	Yo	Nosotros	Ellos
1. encontrar			
2. pensar			
3. volver			
4. continuar			
5. perder			
6. sonreír			
7. preferir			
8. dormir			
9. conseguir			
10. sentir			
11. sentarse			
12. vestirse			
13. soler			
14. enviar			
15. negar			
16. huir			
17. acostarse			
18. despedirse			
19. atravesar			
20. actuar			
21. seguir			
22. divertirse			
23. jugar			
24. empezar			
25. repetir			

C. Escríbanse los verbos en la tercera persona plural del pretérito y en la primera persona singular del imperfecto de subjuntivo (2 formas).

EJEMPLO: entrar—entraron, entrara, entrase

	PRETÉRITO, 3ª PLURAL	IMPERFECTO DE SUBJUNTIVO, 1ª SINGULAR	
		-ra	*-se*
1. visitar			
2. andar			
3. querer			
4. abrir			
5. caer			
6. morir			
7. decir			
8. sentir			
9. estar			
10. tener			
11. hacer			
12. traer			
13. dormir			
14. ir			
15. sentarse			
16. lucir			
17. extender			
18. venir			
19. haber			
20. conducir			
21. averiguar			
22. dar			
23. envolver			
24. saber			
25. sorprender			
26. ser			
27. destruir			
28. poder			
29. satisfacer			
30. recoger			

D. Cámbiese cada verbo del presente de subjuntivo a la forma correspondiente del imperfecto de subjuntivo (2 formas).

EJEMPLO: viva—viviera, viviese

1. escriba _____
2. se deslicen _____
3. luzcan _____
4. digas _____
5. averigüen _____
6. quiera _____
7. demostremos _____
8. duerman _____
9. agreguéis _____
10. pongamos _____
11. vaya _____
12. sean _____
13. rodeemos _____
14. parezca _____
15. signifiquen _____
16. continúe _____
17. protejamos _____
18. ruegue _____
19. almuerces _____
20. envíen _____

E. Cámbiese cada verbo del imperfecto de subjuntivo a la forma correspondiente del presente de subjuntivo.

1. deseásemos _____
2. trajesen _____
3. dieran _____
4. prefiriese _____
5. estudiasen _____
6. destruyerais _____
7. pensasen _____
8. murieseis _____
9. hubiese _____
10. condujésemos _____
11. hiciera _____
12. estuvieras _____
13. amenazase _____
14. adquirieras _____
15. perdiera _____
16. creyésemos _____
17. sintieran _____
18. riera _____
19. volviesen _____
20. detuviera _____

F. Cámbiese cada verbo a la forma indicada del perfecto y del pluscuamperfecto de subjuntivo. (In 1–10, use the **-ra** form of the pluperfect subjunctive; in 11–20 use the **-se** form.)

	PERFECTO DE SUBJUNTIVO	PLUSCUAMPERFECTO DE SUBJUNTIVO
1. (yo) vender		
2. (él y yo) escribir		
3. (tú) leer		
4. (Vd.) ver		
5. (tú) abrir		
6. (nosotros) hacer		
7. (yo) poner		
8. (él) volver		
9. (yo) añadir		
10. (vosotros) arrojar		
11. (nosotros) cubrir		
12. (ellas) romper		
13. (nosotros) creer		
14. (yo) mostrar		
15. (tú) bajar		
16. (ella) decir		
17. (tú) oír		
18. (yo) descubrir		
19. (nosotros) describir		
20. (Rosa) morir		

G. Cámbiese cada forma del indicativo a la forma correspondiente del subjuntivo.

	INDICATIVO	FORMA CORRESPONDIENTE DEL SUBJUNTIVO
EJEMPLOS: PRESENTE:	hablan	*hablen*
IMPERFECTO:	comíamos	*comiéramos (comiésemos)*
PERFECTO:	he mostrado	*haya mostrado*
PLUSCUAMPERFECTO:	habías vendido	*hubieras (hubieses) vendido*

1. oyen _____
2. queríamos _____
3. he cerrado _____
4. sigo _____
5. había hecho _____
6. conoce _____
7. escribo _____
8. sacan _____
9. tomaba _____
10. han creído _____
11. vemos _____
12. iba _____
13. tenemos _____
14. dais _____
15. habíamos dicho _____
16. poníamos _____
17. pagan _____
18. está _____
19. servís _____
20. hemos comido _____
21. nos divertimos _____
22. vengo _____
23. éramos _____
24. producía _____
25. sé _____

El Castillo del Morro, en el puerto de La Habana, es una fortaleza construida por los españoles en tiempos coloniales, para proteger la ciudad contra los ataques de los piratas. Todavía se conserva hoy día.

Verb Lesson 15—USES OF THE SUBJUNCTIVE (PART I)

I. NOUN CLAUSE: Dependent clause used as the object of the sentence.

1. The subjunctive is used in noun clauses when the verb of the main clause expresses a *wish*, real or implied, such as advice, command, desire, hope, permission, preference, request.

---

aconsejar, to advise
decir, to tell (to order)
dejar, to let, to allow
desear, to wish, to want
esperar, to hope
exigir, to require, to demand
hacer, to make, to cause

insistir (en), to insist (on)
mandar, to command, to order
¡Ojalá que . . . ! May God grant that . . . ! Would to God that . . . ! If only . . . !
pedir, to request, to ask

permitir, to permit, to allow
preferir, to prefer
prohibir, to forbid, to prohibit
querer, to wish, to want
rogar, to beg, to request
suplicar, to beg, to plead

Le **aconsejaron** que *saliera* en seguida.
(advice)   (subjunctive)

They advised him to leave (that he leave) at once.

Les **digo** que *entren.*
(command)   (subjunctive)

I tell them to enter (that they should enter).

Quieren que *lleguemos* temprano.
(desire)   (subjunctive)

They want us to arrive (wish that we arrive) early.

¡**Ojalá** que Vds. no se *enfermen!*
(desire)   (subjunctive)

God grant (Would to God) that you don't become ill!

Espero que *se queden* aquí.
(hope)   (subjunctive)

I hope that they remain here.

El profesor no **permite** que los alumnos
(permission)
hablen en la clase.
(subjunctive)

The teacher does not permit the pupils to speak (that the pupils speak) in class.

Mis padres **prefieren** que yo no *mire* ese
(preference)   (subjunctive)
programa de televisión.

My parents prefer that I do not watch that television program.

Te **ruego** que *vengas.*
(request)   (subjunctive)

I beg you to come (that you come).

2. The subjunctive is used in noun clauses when the verb of the main clause expresses an *emotion*, such as fear, joy, sorrow, regret, surprise.

---

alegrarse (de), to be glad (of)
sentir, to be sorry, to regret
sorprenderse (de), to be surprised

temer, to fear
tener miedo (de), to fear, to be afraid of

Temían que no *volviera.*
(fear)   (subjunctive)

They were afraid that he would not return.

Me alegro de que Vds. lo *hayan visto.*
(joy)   (subjunctive)

I am glad that you have seen it.

Sentimos que ellos no *puedan* hacer el viaje
(regret, sorrow)   (subjunctive)
con nosotros.

We regret (We are sorry) that they cannot make the trip with us.

¿Se sorprenden Vds. de que *haya* examen
(surprise)   (subjunctive)
hoy?

Are you surprised that there is an examination today?

3. The subjunctive is used in noun clauses when the verb in the main clause expresses *doubt, disbelief, denial.*

dudar, to doubt	no creer, not to believe	negar, to deny

Dudamos que lo *sepan.*
(doubt)   (subjunctive)

We doubt that they know it.

No creo que Pedro lo *halle.*
(disbelief)   (subjunctive)

I don't believe that Peter will find it.

Niegan que esto *sea* importante.
(denial)   (subjunctive)

They deny that this is important.

but

Creo (No dudo) que Pedro lo **hallará.**
(belief)   (indicative)

I believe (I *don't* doubt) that Peter will find it.

Note

Because of the uncertainty indicated, the verbs **dudar** and **creer,** when used interrogatively, are usually followed by the subjunctive.

¿Cree Vd. que *vengan?*
(uncertainty)   (subjunctive)

Do you believe that they will come?

4. The subjunctive is used in noun clauses when the main clause contains an impersonal expression, unless the impersonal expression indicates certainty.

es dudoso, it is doubtful	**es menester** ⎫
es importante, it is important	**es necesario** ⎬ it is necessary
es imposible, it is impossible	**es preciso** ⎭
es lástima, it is a pity	**es posible,** it is possible
es mejor ⎫ it is better	**es probable,** it is probable
más vale ⎭	**importa,** it is important

Es preciso que yo lo *compre.*

It is necessary that I buy (for me to buy) it.

Era importante que lo *viéramos.*

It was important that we should see (for us to see) it.

Es probable que *vayan.*

It is probable that they will go.

but

Es cierto que **irán.**
(certainty)   (indicative)

It is certain that they will go.

Es evidente que él no lo **sabe.**
(certainty)   (indicative)

It is evident that he does not know it.

Es verdad que Juan **está** enfermo.
(certainty)   (indicative)

It is true that John is sick.

Note

A. In all of the previous examples, the verb in the main clause and the verb in the dependent clause have *different* subjects. If in English the subjects are the same, **que** is omitted in Spanish, and the *infinitive* is used instead of the subjunctive.

Ellos quieren *ir* a la fiesta.
(They)   (they)

They wish to go (that *they* may go) to the party.

Me alegro de *estar* aquí.
(I)   (I)

I am glad that *I* am here (to be here).

B. The verbs **dejar, hacer, mandar, permitir,** and **prohibir** may be followed by either the subjunctive or the infinitive.

Me manda que *salga.*⎫
Me manda **salir.** ⎭   He orders me to leave.

Déjele que *hable.*⎫
Déjele **hablar.** ⎭   Let him speak.

SEQUENCE OF TENSES

The tense of the subjunctive depends on the form of the main verb.

VERB IN MAIN CLAUSE	VERB IN DEPENDENT CLAUSE
Present Indicative Present Perfect Future Command	Present Subjunctive *or* Perfect Subjunctive
Preterite Pluperfect Imperfect Conditional	Imperfect Subjunctive *or* Pluperfect Subjunctive

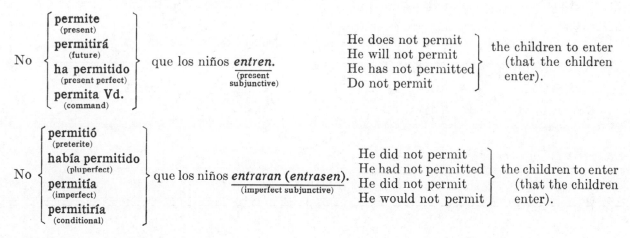

No ⎧ **permite** (present)
   ⎪ **permitirá** (future)
   ⎨ **ha permitido** (present perfect)
   ⎩ **permita Vd.** (command) ⎭ que los niños *entren.* (present subjunctive)

He does not permit ⎫
He will not permit ⎪
He has not permitted ⎬ the children to enter (that the children enter).
Do not permit ⎭

No ⎧ **permitió** (preterite)
   ⎪ **había permitido** (pluperfect)
   ⎨ **permitía** (imperfect)
   ⎩ **permitiría** (conditional) ⎭ que los niños *entraran (entrasen).* (imperfect subjunctive)

He did not permit ⎫
He had not permitted ⎪
He did not permit ⎬ the children to enter (that the children enter).
He would not permit ⎭

Dudo que lo *hayan visto.*
(present)   (perfect subjunctive)   I doubt that they have seen it.

Dudaba que lo *hubieran (hubiesen) visto.*
(imperfect)   (pluperfect subjunctive)   I doubted that they had seen it.

EJERCICIOS

A. En cada frase subráyese la forma correcta del verbo entre paréntesis.

1. No permitió que yo (vaya, fuera) en busca del doctor.

2. Yo creo que él (consiga, conseguirá) hacerse médico.

3. Siento que Vds. lo (hayan, hubiesen) cortado.

4. ¡Ojalá que el niño no se (caiga, cayera) del árbol!

5. Sabemos que algo maravilloso (ha, haya) ocurrido.

6. No es cierto que él (está, esté) enfermo.

7. Dígale que se (levanta, levante).

8. El maestro prohibe que nosotros (escribamos, escribimos) con lápiz.

9. Es probable que ella lo (tiene, tenga).

10. El gobierno exige que nosotros (pagamos, paguemos) los impuestos.

11. Me pidió que le (ayudaría, ayudase).

12. Espero que vosotros (podéis, podáis) quedaros aquí.

13. Permitió que yo le (acompañara, acompañaba).

14. Te suplicamos que (obedecer, obedezcas) la ley.

15. Es verdad que mañana no (sea, es) día de fiesta.

16. Nos alegramos de que él (ha, haya) vuelto.

17. Es imposible que Vd. lo (hiciera, haga).

18. Nos han pedido que (vamos, vayamos) a la botica.

19. Sentían que él (hubiera, había) salido.

20. ¡Ojalá que el enemigo no (atacará, ataque) mañana.

    B. Cámbiese el infinitivo al subjuntivo, empleando el sujeto entre paréntesis.

    Ejemplo: Es posible *encontrar* un buen empleo.   (Vd.)
               Es posible que Vd. encuentre un buen empleo.

1. Es importante *salir* bien en los exámenes.   (Vds.)

----

2. Desean *poner* la mesa.   (ella)

----

3. Sería mejor *apartarse* de los combates.   (Vds.)

----

4. Querían *quedarse* en casa.   (yo)

----

5. Se alegran de *haber visto* a sus abuelos.   (Juan)

----

6. Insistió en *guardar* cama todo el día.   (el niño)

----

7. Espero *volver* pronto.   (mi tío)

----

8. Prefieren *pasar* las vacaciones en el campo.   (nosotros)

----

9. Es preciso *referirse* a las autoridades.   (Vds.)

----

10. Tenían miedo de *venir*.   (tú)

----

11. Sería imposible *asistir* a la conferencia.   (él)

----

12. Es importante *nombrar* un presidente.   (el club)

----

13. Temían *viajar* por avión.   (su hijo)

----

14. Sentía *haber molestado* a los vecinos.   (Vd.)

----

15. Más vale *adornar* el salón hoy.   (los miembros)

C. Complétense las frases usando la forma correcta del subjuntivo.

EJEMPLO: Es probable que él lo tenga.

Era probable que él lo ___*tuviera*___.

1. Exige que Vds. se lo concedan.

Exigió que Vds. se lo _____.

2. Temían que su hijo no aspirase a hacerse abogado.

Temen que su hijo no _____ a hacerse abogado.

3. Es lástima que la acera no sea más ancha.

Era lástima que la acera no _____ más ancha.

4. Dígales que lo corten.

Les dijo que lo _____.

5. No había querido que el policía pusiese en libertad al ladrón.

No ha querido que el policía _____ en libertad al ladrón.

6. Desean que yo llegue temprano.

Deseaban que yo _____ temprano.

7. Sentí que Vds. no conviniesen en ello.

Siento que Vds. no _____ en ello.

8. Se alegran de que Vd. haya ganado el premio.

Se alegraban de que Vd. _____ el premio.

9. Pidieron que nosotros fuéramos a la botica.

Pedirán que nosotros _____ a la botica.

10. Fue necesario que el carpintero lo construyera.

Será necesario que el carpintero lo _____.

11. Te aconsejaría que no perdieras el alfiler.

Te aconsejo que no _____ el alfiler.

12. Le rogué que me lo enseñase.

Le ruego que me lo _____.

13. Niego que Carlos haya usado la máquina.

Negaba que Carlos _____ la máquina.

14. No es posible que ocurra tal desastre.

No fue posible que _____ tal desastre.

15. No creía que ellos hubieran declarado su intención.

No cree que ellos _____ su intención.

D. Escríbase la forma correcta del verbo en letra cursiva.

1. Será preciso que ellos *elegir* un alcalde.   _____

2. No creemos que esto *ser* de algodón.   _____

3. El pordiosero esperaba que yo le *dar* una limosna.   _____

4. Estoy seguro de que el burro *comer* el trigo.   _____

5. Era necesario *estudiar* para el examen.   _____

6. Temíamos que ellos *aumentar* el precio de los billetes.   _____

7. Es cierto que la bandera *tener* cincuenta estrellas.   _____

8. Se alegró de *encontrar* su bolsa.   _____

9. Pidió que nosotros *llenar* el baúl.   _____

10. Es lástima que ella no *haber* mantenido su entusiasmo.   _____

11. ¿Es posible que la botella *estar* vacía?   _____

12. Me prohiben *iniciar* mis proyectos.   _____

13. Dudo que *haber* mucho peligro.   _____

14. Colón negó que el mundo *ser* llano.   _____

15. Deseo que tú *principiar* a estudiar la geografía.   _____

16. Es probable que *cesar* de llover pronto.   _____

17. Es imposible que yo lo *completar* este mes.   _____

18. Insisten en que Tomás *venir* en seguida.   _____

19. Mi papá exigió que yo le *imitar*.   _____

20. No creían que Vd. *omitir* aquel párrafo.   _____

21. Me dicen que yo *quedarse* con ellos.   _____

22. ¡Ojalá que no *ocurrir* una catástrofe!   _____

23. Mandé que ellos *traer* la cuenta.   _____

24. Tenemos miedo de que él no *proceder* con cuidado.   _____

25. Dígales que no *matar* el insecto.   _____

E. Tradúzcanse al español los verbos en letra cursiva.

1. Dudábamos que ellos *would know* la respuesta. ------------------------

2. Fue lástima que nosotros no *could* estar allí. ------------------------

3. Te suplico que *you do not leave* con tanta prisa. ------------------------

4. ¿Duda Vd. que él se *has broken* la pierna? ------------------------

5. Siento que Vds. lo *have cut*. ------------------------

6. Importa que vosotros no *become tired* con el trabajo. ------------------------

7. Más vale que ellos *buy* el coche gris. ------------------------

8. ¿Creen Vds. que el casamiento *will take place* el lunes? ------------------------

9. Nos rogó que *we put* sellos en los sobres. ------------------------

10. Su padre se empeña en que Juan *draw apart* de tales compañeros. ------------------------

11. ¿Es posible que aquella señora *has* un marido tan feo? ------------------------

12. Me aconsejó que *I use* el subjuntivo en ese caso. ------------------------

13. Yo no dudo que él *is* valiente. ------------------------

14. Es evidente que esto *will last* mucho tiempo. ------------------------

15. Quería *them to visit* el monumento. ------------------------

16. Le pidieron al sabio que *he should give* su opinión. ------------------------

17. Desearía que Vd. *would write* a menudo. ------------------------

18. Desean *to eat* las peras. ------------------------

19. Querían *to divide* la cantidad en tres partes iguales. ------------------------

20. Prefirieron *to keep* el secreto. ------------------------

F. Contéstense en español en frases completas.

1. ¿Desea Vd. salir bien en los exámenes? _____

_____

2. ¿Es necesario que Vd. se acueste temprano? _____

_____

3. ¿Cree Vd. que esta lección sea fácil? _____

_____

4. ¿Permite el maestro que Vds. conversen en la clase? _____

_____

5. ¿Le prohiben sus padres que fume? _____

_____

6. ¿Es preciso que Vd. cuide a su hermanito(-a) de vez en cuando? _____

_____

7. ¿Exige el maestro que Vds. estudien mucho? _____

_____

8. ¿Es cierto que Vd. ha cumplido diez y seis años? _____

_____

9. ¿Duda Vd. que llueva hoy? _____

10. ¿Es importante que una persona descanse después de trabajar? _____

_____

11. ¿Prefiere Vd. que se cierre la escuela mañana? _____

_____

12. ¿Desea Vd. que se forme un club español en la escuela? _____

_____

13. ¿Le mandan sus padres que haga cosas difíciles? _____

_____

14. ¿Niega Vd. que el mundo sea redondo? _____

_____

15. ¿Es verdad que Vd. tiene un hermano menor? _____

_____

G. Tradúzcanse al español.

1. He wants me to attend the university. _____

_____

2. I hope to see that region some day. _____

3. It is a pity that you (tú) are not here every day. _____

_____

4. I doubt that they have found it. _____

5. I do not doubt that Peter will find it. _____

6. He ordered me to serve the soup. _____

7. It is evident that you have not seen it. _____

8. It is important to choose good friends. _____

_____

9. The teacher forbids us to write in (con) pencil. _____

_____

10. We wanted them to read the article. _____

_____

11. I am glad to see you. _____

12. It is doubtful that they will convince him. _____

13. He advised us to forbid it. _____

14. I am sure that the bottle is full. _____

15. He did not believe that she had done it. _____

Verb Lesson 16—USES OF THE SUBJUNCTIVE (PART II)

II. ADVERB CLAUSE: Dependent clause used as an adverb. An adverb clause answers the questions *when? where? how? why?* etc.

1. The subjunctive is used in adverb clauses if *uncertainty, doubt, anticipation,* or *indefiniteness* is expressed. Adverb clauses are usually introduced by the following conjunctions:

a fin de que⎫ **para que** ⎬ in order that, so that **a menos que,** unless **antes (de) que,** before	**con tal que,** provided that **en caso de que,** in case (that) **sin que,** without

Terminaré el trabajo **antes de que** ellos *vuelvan.*	I shall finish the work before they return. (whenever that may be)
Leyó el artículo despacio **para que** *pudiéramos* entenderlo.	He read the article slowly so that we could understand it. (We may or may not have understood it.)
Salió **sin que** yo lo *supiera.*	He left without my knowing it. (in such a way that I would not know it)

2. The following conjunctions require the subjunctive if uncertainty, doubt, anticipation, or indefiniteness is implied. Otherwise, the indicative is used.

aunque, although, even though, even if **cuando,** when **de manera que**⎫ with the result that, so that, **de modo que** ⎬ in such a way that **después (de) que,** after	**en cuanto**⎫ **luego que** ⎬ as soon as **tan pronto como**⎬ **así que** ⎭ **hasta que,** until **mientras,** while

SUBJUNCTIVE	INDICATIVE
Aunque *cueste* mucho dinero, lo compraré.	**Aunque** costó mucho dinero, lo compré.
Although it may cost a lot of money, I'll buy it. (I don't know how much it costs.)	Although it cost a lot of money, I bought it. (It did cost a lot of money.)
Espere Vd. **hasta que** ellos *vengan.*	Esperó **hasta que** ellos *vinieron.*
Wait until they come. (whenever that may be)	He waited until they came. (They did arrive.)
Te llamaré **cuando** *llegue* a casa.	Siempre me llama **cuando llega** a casa.
I will call you when I arrive home. (whenever that may be)	He always calls me when he arrives home. (his normal custom)
Leyó despacio, **de modo que** ellos *pudieran* entender.	Leyó despacio, **de modo que** ellos **pudieron** entender.
He read slowly, so that they would be able to understand. (not known if they understood)	He read slowly, so that they were able to understand. (They understood.)

Dijo que lo haría **así que** le *pagáramos.*

He said he would do it as soon as we paid him.

Lo hizo **así que** le **pagamos.**

He did it as soon as we paid him.

Note

If in English the subjects of the main and the dependent clauses are the *same*, **que** is usually omitted in Spanish, and the *infinitive* is used.

Terminaré el trabajo *antes de volver.*
(I)   (I)

I shall finish the work before I return (before returning).

Espere Vd. *hasta volver* a casa.
(you)   (you)

Wait until you return home (until returning home).

Leyó el artículo despacio *para entender*lo.
(he)   (he)

He read the article slowly to understand it.

Salió *sin decir* adiós.
(he)   (he)

He left without saying good-bye.

3. The subjunctive is used after compounds of **-quiera** and similar indefinite expressions.

dondequiera, wherever	**cuandoquiera,** whenever
cualquier(a) (*pl.* **cualesquiera**), whatever, any	**por** + adj. or adv. + **que,**
quienquiera (*pl.* **quienesquiera**), whoever	however, no matter how

No se lo daré, **quienquiera** que *sea.*

I will not give it to him, whoever he may be.

Aceptaré **cualquier** puesto que Vd. me *ofrezca.*

I shall accept any job you offer me.

Por difícil que *sea*, lo haré.

However (No matter how) difficult it may be, I shall do it.

III. ADJECTIVE CLAUSE: Dependent clause used as an adjective (modifying a noun or pronoun).

The subjunctive is used in adjective clauses if the antecedent (the noun or pronoun in the main clause) is *indefinite* or *negative*.

SUBJUNCTIVE	INDICATIVE
Busca **un esposo** que *sea* alto y guapo.	Tiene un esposo que **es** alto y guapo.
She is looking for a husband who is tall and handsome. (She may never find one.)	She has a husband who is tall and handsome. (She has one.)
¿Conoce Vd. a **alguien** que *quiera* trabajar?	Conoce a alguien que **quiere** trabajar.
Do you know anyone who wants to work? (indefinite)	He knows someone who wants to work. (definite person meant)
No puedo encontrar a **nadie** que *pueda* ayudarme.	Encontré a un hombre que **puede** ayudarme.
I can't find anyone who can help me. (negative)	I found a man who can help me. (There is such a person.)

Note

In adverb and adjective clauses, the tense of the subjunctive depends on the tense of the main verb, as in noun clauses.

IV. CONTRARY-TO-FACT CONDITIONS

1. The imperfect and pluperfect subjunctives are used in contrary-to-fact conditions, as follows:

	"IF" CLAUSE	"RESULT" CLAUSE
PRESENT TIME	Imperfect Subjunctive, **-se** or **-ra** form	Conditional *or* Imperfect Subjunctive, **-ra** form only
PAST TIME	Pluperfect Subjunctive, **-se** or **-ra** form	Conditional Perfect *or* Pluperfect Subjunctive, **-ra** form only

Si yo *estudiase (estudiara)* más, *recibiría (recibiera)* buenas notas.

If I studied more, I would receive good grades. (I don't receive good grades.)

Si yo *hubiese (hubiera) estudiado* más, *habría (hubiera) recibido* buenas notas.

If I had studied more, I would have received good grades. (I didn't receive good grades.)

but

Si **estudio** más, **recibiré** buenas notas.

If I study more, I will receive good grades. (I may receive good grades.)

2. The imperfect and pluperfect subjunctives are also used after **como si** (as if).

Vd. le trata **como si** *fuera* un niño.

You treat him as if he were a child. (but he isn't)

Me miró **como si** yo *hubiera cometido* un crimen.

He looked at me as if I had committed a crime. (but I hadn't)

Note

The present subjunctive is never used in "if" clauses.

3. The **-ra** forms of the imperfect subjunctive of **querer, poder,** and **deber** are often used instead of the conditional of these verbs to express a polite request or statement.

Quisiera comprarlo.

I would like to buy it.

¿Pudiera Vd. hacerlo hoy?

Could you do it today?

Debiéramos verlo.

We should (ought to) see it.

EJERCICIOS

A. Contéstense las preguntas según los ejemplos. (See #1, page 99.)

EJEMPLO: ¿Va Vd. a comer?
　　　　No comeré a menos que Vd. coma también.

1. ¿Va Vd. a esperar? --

2. ¿Va Vd. a trabajar? --

3. ¿Va Vd. a regresar? --

4. ¿Va Vd. a almorzar? --

5. ¿Va Vd. a entrar? --

EJEMPLO: ¿Desea Vd. ir a la fiesta?

   Iré a la fiesta con tal que Vd. vaya también.

6. ¿Desea Vd. jugar al tenis?

----

7. ¿Desea Vd. volver a casa?

----

8. ¿Desea Vd. asistir a la reunión?

----

9. ¿Desea Vd. cantar una canción?

----

10. ¿Desea Vd. desayunarse ahora?

EJEMPLO: ¿Vio Vd. a Tomás?

   No, él se fue sin que yo le viera.

11. ¿Habló Vd. a Carlos? --

12. ¿Dio Vd. el dinero a Jaime? ---------------------------------

13. ¿Mostró Vd. la foto a Pedro? --------------------------------

14. ¿Leyó Vd. la carta a Alfonso? -------------------------------

15. ¿Informó Vd. al guardia? ------------------------------------

EJEMPLO: ¿Llegan mañana?

   Te llamaré antes (de) que lleguen.

16. ¿Vienen mañana? ---

17. ¿Vuelven hoy? ---

18. ¿Se van esta tarde? ---

19. ¿Se marchan esta mañana? -----------------------------------

20. ¿Se verificará hoy? ---

EJEMPLO: ¿Va a nevar?

   ¿Qué haremos en caso de que nieve?

21. ¿Va a llover? ---

22. ¿Va a hacer frío? ---

23. ¿Va a costar mucho? ---

24. ¿Va a ser difícil? --

25. ¿Va a llegar tarde? ---

EJEMPLO: ¿Tomó el tren?

       Su padre le dio dinero para que tomara el tren.

26. ¿Fue al cine?

----

27. ¿Asistió a la función?

----

28. ¿Viajó por barco?

----

29. ¿Vio el partido de fútbol?

----

30. ¿Compró una bicicleta?

B. Cámbiense las frases según los ejemplos.

EJEMPLOS: Descansará antes de volver.

      Descansará antes de que ellos ___*vuelvan*___.

      Descansó antes de volver.

      Descansó antes de que ellos ___*volviesen*___.

1. Llamaré antes de salir.

   Llamaré antes de que Vd. _____.

2. Va al parque para ver a sus amigos.

   Va al parque para que sus amigos le _____.

3. Lo hizo sin saberlo.

   Lo hizo sin que nosotros lo _____.

4. Compró tres entradas para ver el partido de fútbol.

   Compró tres entradas para que él y sus amigos _____ el partido de fútbol.

5. Cenaremos antes de marcharnos.

   Cenaremos antes de que Vds. _____.

6. Tomó las cerezas sin hablar al dueño.

   Tomó las cerezas sin que el dueño le _____.

7. Compró un aparato de televisión a fin de mirar los programas.

   Compró un aparato de televisión a fin de que sus hijos _____ los programas.

8. Devolvió el diario sin leerlo.

   Devolvió el diario sin que yo lo _____.

9. Compró papel para escribir una carta.

   Compró papel para que su hermana _____ una carta.

10. Voy a descansar antes de comer.

   Voy a descansar antes de que nosotros _____.

C. Cámbiense los verbos al subjuntivo según el ejemplo. (See #2, pages 99–100.)

EJEMPLO: Esperó hasta que yo vine.

Esperará hasta que yo ___venga___.

or

Prometieron esperar hasta que yo ___viniese___.

1. No se lo entregué hasta que me pagó.

   No se lo entregaré hasta que me _____.

2. Me avisaron cuando estaban listos.

   Prometieron avisarme cuando _____ listos.

3. Siempre le envío el cheque tan pronto como recibo las mercancías.

   Le enviaré el cheque tan pronto como _____ las mercancías.

4. No escribí el ensayo aunque tenía el tiempo.

   No voy a escribir el ensayo aunque _____ el tiempo.

5. Les gustó el apartamiento luego que lo vieron.

   Sabían que les gustaría el apartamiento luego que lo _____.

6. Fueron a visitarle después que llegó.

   Iremos a visitarle después que _____.

7. Arregló los asientos de modo que todo el público podía ver la función.

   Arreglará los asientos de modo que todo el público _____ ver la función.

8. Todos se callaban mientras discurría el político.

   Todos se callarán mientras _____ el político.

9. Me quité el sombrero así que entré en la casa.

   Me quitaré el sombrero así que _____ en la casa.

10. Vivió en aquella ciudad hasta que murió.

    Vivirá en aquella ciudad hasta que _____.

11. Cuando vamos a España, siempre visitamos la Alhambra.

    Cuando _____ a España, visitaremos la Alhambra.

12. Separaron a los prisioneros de manera que cada uno se quedaba solo.

    Van a separar a los prisioneros de manera que cada uno _____ solo.

13. En cuanto Juan se unió al grupo, todos se pusieron en marcha.

    En cuanto Juan _____ al grupo, todos se pondrán en marcha.

14. Compré la alhaja, aunque subieron el precio.

    Voy a comprar la alhaja, aunque _____ el precio.

15. Tan pronto como el cartero nos vio, nos dio unas cartas.

    Tan pronto como el cartero nos _____, nos dará unas cartas.

D. Contéstense las preguntas según los ejemplos. (See #3, page 100.)

EJEMPLOS: ¿Cuándo irá?

Cuandoquiera que ___*vaya*___, no importa.

¿Quién será?

Quienquiera que ___*sea*___, podrá entrar.

¿Es interesante?

Por interesante que ___*sea*___, no lo leeré.

1. ¿Quién lo hará? Quienquiera que lo _____, lo hará bien.

2. ¿Dónde está? Dondequiera que _____, tendrá que moverse.

3. ¿Es bravo el toro? Por bravo que _____, no tengo miedo.

4. ¿Cuándo vendrá? Cuandoquiera que _____, no nos quejaremos.

5. ¿Qué libro escogerá? Cualquier libro que _____, le interesará.

6. ¿Adónde viajará? Adondequiera que él _____, encontrará cosas nuevas.

7. ¿Es difícil la lección? Por difícil que _____, la aprenderemos.

8. ¿Quién lo verá? Quienquiera que lo _____, se asombrará.

9. ¿Cuándo llegaremos? Cuandoquiera que _____, nos darán de comer.

10. ¿Pronuncia bien el alumno? Por bien que _____, siempre podrá mejorarse.

E. Cámbiense los verbos al subjuntivo según el ejemplo. (See III, Adjective Clause, page 100.)

EJEMPLO: Tengo una revista que es interesante.

Busco una revista que ___*sea*___ interesante.

1. Yo poseo una gramática que tiene muchos ejercicios.

Busco una gramática que _____ muchos ejercicios.

2. Compraron una casa que tenía un patio grande.

Querían comprar una casa que _____ un patio grande.

3. Conozco a un hombre que puede ayudarme.

¡Ojalá que encuentre un hombre que _____ ayudarme!

4. Tenía un coche que funcionaba bien.

Necesitaba un coche que _____ bien.

5. Conozco a una mujer que pesa doscientas libras.

No hay ninguna mujer aquí que _____ doscientas libras.

6. Veo a una persona que sabe la dirección.

¿Hay alguien que _____ la dirección?

7. Ve un traje que le gusta.

Busca un traje que le _____.

8. Yo he hablado con alguien que ha visto una corrida de toros.

No he hablado con nadie que _____ visto una corrida de toros.

9. Vive en un apartamiento que está cerca del parque.

Quiere vivir en un apartamiento que _ _ _ _ _ _ _ _ _ _ _ _ cerca del parque.

10. Juan siempre me dice algo que me interesa.

Juan nunca me dice nada que me _ _ _ _ _ _ _ _ _ _ _ _ _ _ _ _ .

11. Encontró a un cochero que sabía conducir bien.

No pudo encontrar ningún cochero que _ _ _ _ _ _ _ _ _ _ _ _ _ _ conducir bien.

12. Todos los soldados del rey eran valientes.

El rey buscaba soldados que _ _ _ _ _ _ _ _ _ _ _ valientes.

13. Juanito es un alumno que estudia mucho.

No hay nadie que _ _ _ _ _ _ _ _ _ _ _ _ _ _ _ _ mucho.

14. Encontramos un restaurante donde sirven buenas comidas.

Deseamos encontrar un restaurante donde _ _ _ _ _ _ _ _ _ _ _ _ _ _ buenas comidas.

15. El Sr. Mendoza es un guía que conoce bien la ciudad.

Busco un guía que _ _ _ _ _ _ _ _ _ _ _ _ _ _ bien la ciudad.

F. Cámbiense las frases, de dos maneras, según los ejemplos. (See IV, Contrary-to-Fact Conditions, page 101.)

EJEMPLO: Si tengo el tiempo, los visitaré.
      a. Si tuviese (tuviera) el tiempo, los visitaría (visitara).
      b. Si hubiese (hubiera) tenido el tiempo, los habría (hubiera) visitado.

1. Si necesita dinero, se lo pedirá a su padre.

   a. _ *a.*

   b. _ *b.*

2. Si nos levantamos tarde, no llegaremos a tiempo.

   a. _ *a.*

   b. _ *b.*

3. Si aprendo el español, haré un viaje a España.

   a. _ *a.*

   b. _ *b.*

4. Si me ofrece un puesto, lo aceptaré.

   a. _ *a.*

   b. _ *b.*

5. Si trabajas allí, ganarás mucho dinero.

   a. _ *a.*

   b. _ *b.*

6. Si recibo el dinero, lo compraré.

   a. _ *a.*

   b. _ *b.*

7. Si van a la playa, se divertirán.

_a._ _____

_b._ _____

8. Si vienes tarde, no te esperaré.

_a._ _____

_b._ _____

9. Si hace mal tiempo, nos quedaremos en casa.

_a._ _____

_b._ _____

10. Si veo a Tomás, se lo contaré.

_a._ _____

_b._ _____

EJEMPLOS: Le tratan como a un niño; no es un niño.

Le tratan _como si fuera un niño_ .

No sabemos si vendrá.

No sabíamos _si vendría_ .

11. Lo dice en broma; no es una broma.

Lo dice _____ .

12. El maestro no sabe si los alumnos estudiarán.

El maestro no sabía _____ .

13. Baila como un bailarín profesional; no es un bailarín profesional.

Baila _____ .

14. No dice si vendrá el lunes.

No dijo _____ .

15. Habla como cubano; no es cubano.

Habla _____ .

G. Cámbiense los verbos según los ejemplos. (See #3, page 101.)

EJEMPLOS: _¿Puede Vd._ venir a mi casa?   _¿Pudiera Vd._ venir a mi casa?

Debes hacerlo.   _Debieras_ hacerlo.

Queremos ver esta película.   _Quisiéramos_ ver esta película.

1. _¿Puedes_ prestarme diez dólares? ¿_____ prestarme diez dólares?

2. _¿Pueden Vds._ acompañarnos? ¿_____ acompañarnos?

3. _¿Puede Vd._ decirme dónde está la casa? ¿_____ decirme dónde está la casa?

4. _Debes_ ser más cortés. _____ ser más cortés.

5. _Debemos_ visitar a nuestros primos. _____ visitar a nuestros primos.

6. _Debo_ estudiar más. _____ estudiar más.

7. *Quiero* invitarle a una fiesta. _____ invitarle a una fiesta.

8. *Quieren* hacer un viaje a México. _____ hacer un viaje a México.

9. *¿Quieren Vds.* tomar una taza de café? ¿_____ tomar una taza de café?

10. *Queremos* ir a la playa. _____ ir a la playa.

H. Subráyese la forma correcta del verbo entre paréntesis.

1. Yo pienso volver antes que el niño (despertarse, se despierta, se despierte, se despertase).

2. Cayó al río sin que nadie le (empujar, empujaba, empuje, empujara).

3. Prometieron volver a casa en cuanto (poder, podían, puedan, pudiesen).

4. Busco una taquígrafa que (tener, tiene, tenga, tuviera) una máquina de escribir.

5. Tuvo que correr para (alcanzarnos, nos alcanzó, nos alcance, nos alcanzase).

6. Vamos a hacer un viaje tan pronto como (recibir, recibimos, recibamos, recibiéramos) dinero.

7. En caso de que (hacer, hace, haga, hiciera) calor, quítese Vd. la americana.

8. Cuando (tener, tendré, tenga, tuviera) el tiempo, iré a visitarle.

9. Se tiró al agua a fin de (salvar, salvó, salve, salvara) a la hermosa princesa.

10. El profesor trabaja mucho a fin de que los alumnos (adelantar, adelantan, adelanten, adelantasen) en sus estudios.

11. No hay nada que (ser, es, sea, fuera) difícil para él.

12. Cuandoquiera que nosotros le (visitar, visitamos, visitemos, visitásemos), no estará en casa.

13. Si él (saber, sabría, sepa, supiera) eso, vendría en seguida.

14. Habla como si (tener, tiene, tenga, tuviese) mucha confianza.

15. La carta no cabe en el sobre, a menos que Vd. la (doblar, dobla, doble, doblara).

16. No alumbrarán las calles hasta que (anochecer, anochecerá, anochezca, anocheciera).

17. Se graduó cuando (tener, tenía, tenga, tuviera) diez y siete años.

18. Iré a la fiesta con tal que Vd. (ir, irá, vaya, fuese) también.

19. Cualquier libro que Vd. (leer, leerá, lea, leyese), aprenderá algo.

20. El detective salió sin (registrar, registró, registre, registrara) la casa.

21. El presidente dio un breve discurso antes de (leer, leyó, lea, leyera) la noticia.

22. No le creerán aunque (decir, dirá, diga, dijera) la verdad.

23. No le creyeron aunque (decir, dijo, diga, dijese) la verdad.

24. Intentó mudar de casa de manera que nadie le (hallar, halló, halle, hallase).

25. Por rico que (ser, será, sea, fuese), no querrá prestarnos dinero.

I. Tradúzcanse al español las palabras en inglés.

1. Ella no lo haría a menos que *it were* _____ necesario.

2. Te prestaré el dinero con tal que *you promise* _____ devolvérmelo.

3. Llevó el libro a casa para que su esposa lo *might read* _____.

4. No había nadie que lo *saw* _____.

5. Dondequiera que él *goes* _____, le podrán hallar.

6. Por difícil que *it seems* _____, yo lo haré.

7. Si nosotros *were able* _____, iríamos al baile.

8. Si nosotros *had been able* _____, habríamos ido al baile.

9. El director nos habla como si *we were* _____ tontos.

10. Nunca podréis leer a menos que *you learn* _____ el alfabeto.

11. Antes que los conquistadores *arrived* _____, los indios ya habían desarrollado una civilización.

12. Escribí la traducción tan pronto como *I arrived* _____ a casa.

13. Entré en el salón sin que *his seeing me* _____.

14. En caso de que ella *needs* _____ una pluma, préstele la mía.

15. Quienquiera que *calls* _____, no abras la puerta.

J. Tradúzcanse al español.

1. We will make the trip with you, provided that it does not snow. _____ _____

2. I will buy you whatever gift you want. _____ _____

3. If I did that, I would not deny it. _____

4. His father gave him money in order that he could travel by boat. _____ _____

5. We tried to explain the problem so that no doubt would remain. _____ _____

6. There is no one who knows the answer. _____

7. If he had known that, he would have come the next day. _____ _____

8. Call me before they leave. _____

9. You will not learn much unless you study. _____ _____

10. He spoke for an hour without my interrupting him. _____ _____

11. Every morning when I see him I greet him. _____ _____

12. Wait for me until I return. _____

13. They waited for me until I returned. _____

14. Although he did not know how to swim, he enjoyed himself in the water. _____ _____

15. That man gives me advice as though he were my father. _____ _____

Verb Lesson 17—FORMAL AND FAMILIAR COMMANDS

FORMAL COMMANDS

Formal commands with **Vd.** and **Vds.** are always expressed by the present subjunctive. (See Verb Lesson 14, page 82.)

tomar:	tom*e* Vd.	tom*en* Vds., take
volver:	vuelv*a* Vd.	vuelv*an* Vds., return
venir:	*venga* Vd.	*vengan* Vds., come
ir:	*vaya* Vd.	*vayan* Vds., go
dar:	*dé* Vd.	*den* Vds., give

INDIRECT COMMANDS

Indirect commands introduced in English by *let, may,* or *have* are also expressed by the present subjunctive.

Que *hable* él (ella).	Let him (her) speak.
Que *oigan* la verdad.	Let them hear the truth.
Que *sean* felices.	May they be happy.
Que lo *haga* Juana.	Let (Have) Jane do it.

Note

Indirect commands are usually introduced by **que.**

LET US (LET'S)

1. *Let us* is expressed by the first person plural of the present subjunctive.

Esperemos un momento.	Let us wait a moment.
Salgamos ahora.	Let us leave now.

2. *Let us go* is expressed by the special form **vamos,** unless the sentence is negative. Negatively, the regular subjunctive form **vayamos** is used.

Vamos al teatro hoy.	Let us go to the theater today.
No vayamos al teatro hoy.	Let us not go to the theater today.

3. **Vamos a** + infinitive may also be used to express *let us.*

Vamos a cantar. (*or Cantemos.*)	Let us sing.
Vamos a aprender (*or Aprendamos*) la lección para mañana.	Let us learn the lesson for tomorrow.

FAMILIAR COMMANDS

REGULAR VERBS

1. The singular (**tú**) form of the familiar affirmative command is the same as the third person singular of the present indicative.

2. The plural (**vosotros**) form of the familiar affirmative command is formed by changing the **-r** ending of the infinitive to **-d.**

3. The negative forms are all expressed by the present subjunctive.

		AFFIRMATIVE	NEGATIVE
mirar:		mira tú	no mires tú
		mirad vosotros	no miréis vosotros
correr:		corre tú	no corras tú
		corred vosotros	no corráis vosotros
dormir:		duerme tú	no duermas tú
		dormid vosotros	no durmáis vosotros

Note

The familiar plural forms (**vosotros, -as**) are rarely used in Latin America. The polite form (**ustedes**) is used for the familiar plural as well as for the polite plural.

IRREGULAR VERBS

The only irregular commands occur in the affirmative singular. All other familiar commands are regular.

decir:	*di* tú	decid vosotros	no digas tú	no digáis vosotros
hacer:	*haz* tú	haced vosotros	no hagas tú	no hagáis vosotros
ir:	*ve* tú	id vosotros	no vayas tú	no vayáis vosotros
poner:	*pon* tú	poned vosotros	no pongas tú	no pongáis vosotros
salir:	*sal* tú	salid vosotros	no salgas tú	no salgáis vosotros
ser:	*sé* tú	sed vosotros	no seas tú	no seáis vosotros
tener:	*ten* tú	tened vosotros	no tengas tú	no tengáis vosotros
valer:	*val* tú	valed vosotros	no valgas tú	no valgáis vosotros
venir:	*ven* tú	venid vosotros	no vengas tú	no vengáis vosotros

OBJECT PRONOUNS WITH COMMANDS

1. Object pronouns (including reflexive pronouns) are attached to affirmative commands. In negative commands, object pronouns precede the verb.

a. Ayúde*le* Vd.   No *le* ayude Vd.
b. Tráigan*lo* Vds.   No *lo* traigan Vds.
c. Hagámos*lo*.   No *lo* hagamos.
d. Levánta*te* tú.   No *te* levantes tú.
e. Aprended*lo* vosotros. No *lo* aprendáis vosotros.
f. Di*les* el secreto.   No *les* digas el secreto.

Note

When an object pronoun is attached to an affirmative command, a written accent mark is usually required in order to keep the original stress. (See sentences *a, b, c, d* above.) If not required for stress, the accent mark is omitted. (See sentences *e* and *f* above.)

2. With indirect commands introduced by **que**, the object pronoun always precedes the verb.

Que *lo* haga Juana.   Que no *lo* haga Juana.
Que *se* vayan en seguida. Que no *se* vayan en seguida.

3. In expressing the affirmative *let us* with reflexive verbs, the final **-s** of the verb ending is dropped before adding the reflexive pronoun **nos**.

Sentémonos (= *Sentemos* + *nos*).	Let's sit down.
Vámonos (= *Vamos* + *nos*).	Let's go (away).

4. In the **vosotros** form affirmative of reflexive verbs, the final **-d** is dropped before adding the reflexive pronoun **os**.

Sentaos (= *Sentad* + *os*).	Sit down.
Divertíos (= *Divertid* + *os*).	Enjoy yourselves.

Exception: **Idos** (= **Id** + **os**), *leave, go away.*

EJERCICIOS

A. Cámbiense las frases según los ejemplos.

EJEMPLO: No deseo repetir el cuento.   Repítalo Vd. No lo repita Vd.

1. No deseo abandonar este sitio.   _____
2. No deseo castigar a mi sobrino.   _____
3. No deseo empujar el coche.   _____
4. No deseo ofender a Rosa.   _____

EJEMPLO: No voy a hacer el trabajo. Que __*lo haga*__ Conchita.

5. No voy a comprar el tabaco. Que _____ su amigo.
6. No voy a poner la mesa.   Que _____ Teresa.
7. No voy a conducir el coche. Que _____ Enrique.
8. No voy a pagar al vendedor. Que _____ él.

EJEMPLO: No queremos volver. Que __*vuelvan*__ ellos.

9. No queremos trabajar. Que _____ ellos.
10. No queremos ir.   Que _____ ellas.
11. No queremos salir.   Que _____ los hombres.
12. No queremos almorzar. Que _____ los niños.

EJEMPLO: Ellos toman café. __*Tomemos*__ café también.

13. Ellos viajan en avión.   _____ en avión también.
14. Ellos rezan a Dios.   _____ a Dios también.
15. Ellos vuelven a la catedral. _____ a la catedral también.
16. Ellos dan un paseo.   _____ un paseo también.

EJEMPLO: Juan se lava cada día. __*Lavémonos*__ cada día también. __*No nos lavemos*__.

17. Ellos se acuestan a las diez. _____ a las diez también. _____
18. Mi tío se va mañana.   _____ mañana también. _____
19. María se sienta allí.   _____ allí también. _____
20. Ellas se visten rápidamente. _____ rápidamente también. _____

B. Escríbase el imperativo formal de cada uno de los verbos (*a, b, c, d*), en lugar del verbo en letra cursiva.

1. *Entre* Vd. en seguida.   (*a*) volver   (*b*) salir   (*c*) empezar   (*d*) sentarse

   (*a*) ---------------- (*b*) ---------------- (*c*) ---------------- (*d*) ----------------

2. *Compremos* el maíz.   (*a*) repartir   (*b*) exportar   (*c*) vender   (*d*) buscar

   (*a*) ---------------- (*b*) ---------------- (*c*) ---------------- (*d*) ----------------

3. *Hagan* Vds. el contrato.   (*a*) acabar   (*b*) concluir   (*c*) entregar   (*d*) escribir

   (*a*) ---------------- (*b*) ---------------- (*c*) ---------------- (*d*) ----------------

4. No *lleguen* Vds. tarde.   (*a*) ir   (*b*) trabajar   (*c*) venir   (*d*) salir

   (*a*) ---------------- (*b*) ---------------- (*c*) ---------------- (*d*) ----------------

5. No *escriba* Vd. las frases.   (*a*) leer   (*b*) repetir   (*c*) traducir   (*d*) pronunciar

   (*a*) ---------------- (*b*) ---------------- (*c*) ---------------- (*d*) ----------------

6. Que *compilen* ellos la lista.   (*a*) aprender   (*b*) enviar   (*c*) mostrar   (*d*) repetir

   (*a*) ---------------- (*b*) ---------------- (*c*) ---------------- (*d*) ----------------

7. *Tome* Vd. el libro.   (*a*) abrir   (*b*) devolver   (*c*) buscar   (*d*) estudiar

   (*a*) ---------------- (*b*) ---------------- (*c*) ---------------- (*d*) ----------------

8. *Vea* Vd. las flores.   (*a*) comprar   (*b*) oler   (*c*) recoger   (*d*) mirar

   (*a*) ---------------- (*b*) ---------------- (*c*) ---------------- (*d*) ----------------

9. *Cortemos* la mala hierba.   (*a*) arrancar   (*b*) destruir   (*c*) quemar   (*d*) cubrir

   (*a*) ---------------- (*b*) ---------------- (*c*) ---------------- (*d*) ----------------

10. *Escúchele* Vd.   (*a*) oír   (*b*) invitar   (*c*) creer   (*d*) saludar

    (*a*) ---------------- (*b*) ---------------- (*c*) ---------------- (*d*) ----------------

11. Que *se ocupen* ellos de mover los muebles.   (*a*) asustarse   (*b*) cansarse   (*c*) encargarse   (*d*) quejarse

    (*a*) ---------------- (*b*) ---------------- (*c*) ---------------- (*d*) ----------------

12. No le *visite* Vd.   (*a*) responder   (*b*) esperar   (*c*) seguir   (*d*) amenazar

    (*a*) ---------------- (*b*) ---------------- (*c*) ---------------- (*d*) ----------------

13. *Levántense* Vds.   (*a*) despertarse   (*b*) perderse   (*c*) vestirse   (*d*) figurarse

    (*a*) ---------------- (*b*) ---------------- (*c*) ---------------- (*d*) ----------------

14. *Celebremos* el doce de octubre.   (*a*) salir   (*b*) madrugar   (*c*) observar   (*d*) esperar

    (*a*) ---------------- (*b*) ---------------- (*c*) ---------------- (*d*) ----------------

15. No *se asuste* Vd.   (*a*) enojarse   (*b*) acostarse   (*c*) irse   (*d*) aburrirse

    (*a*) ---------------- (*b*) ---------------- (*c*) ---------------- (*d*) ----------------

C. Cámbiese cada frase según los ejemplos.

EJEMPLO: José no lee su libro.

José, _____*lee*_____ tu libro; no _____*leas*_____ la revista.

1. Rosa no obedece a su madre.

   Rosa, _____ a tu madre; no _____ a tu amiga.

2. Pedro no cierra la boca.

   Pedro, _____ la boca; no _____ el libro.

3. Alfredo no busca su gato.

   Alfredo, _____ tu gato; no _____ el perro.

4. Carolina no vuelve a su asiento.

   Carolina, _____ a tu asiento; no _____ a la pizarra.

5. Alberto no trae su cámara.

   Alberto, _____ tu cámara; no _____ tu tocadiscos.

   EJEMPLO: Carlos no se sienta a la mesa.

   Carlos, _____*siéntate*_____ a la mesa; no _____*te sientes*_____ al escritorio.

6. Inés no se lava la cara.

   Inés, _____ la cara; no _____ el pelo.

7. Jorge no se despierta temprano.

   Jorge, _____ temprano; no _____ al mediodía.

8. Juan no se acerca a los claveles.

   Juan, _____ a los claveles; no _____ a las rosas.

9. Pablo no se viste en seguida.

   Pablo, _____ en seguida; no _____ tan despacio.

10. Alicia no se pasea cuando hace sol.

    Alicia, _____ cuando hace sol; no _____ cuando llueve.

    EJEMPLO: Rosa no viene a la cocina ahora.

    Rosa, _____*ven*_____ a la cocina ahora; no _____*vengas*_____ más tarde.

11. León no tiene paciencia.

    León, _____ paciencia; no _____ inquietud.

12. Miguel no sale del rincón.

    Miguel, _____ del rincón; pero no _____ de casa.

13. Mercedes no hace el viaje por avión.

    Mercedes, _____ el viaje por avión; no lo _____ por buque.

14. Ramón no dice la verdad.

    Ramón, _____ la verdad; no _____ mentiras.

15. Bárbara no va a la sastrería.

    Bárbara, _____ a la sastrería; no _____ a la carnicería.

EJEMPLO: Los niños no hablan español en la clase.

Niños, _____*hablad*_____ español en la clase; no _____*habléis*_____ inglés.

16. Las chicas no dan un beso a su padre.

Chicas, _____ un beso a vuestro padre; no _____ a vuestro primo.

17. Los niños no terminan las legumbres.

Niños, _____ las legumbres; no _____ el jamón.

18. Los alumnos no continúan la lectura.

Alumnos, _____ la lectura; no _____ la conversación.

19. María y José no beben chocolate.

María y José, _____ chocolate; no _____ café.

20. Los camareros no sirven el pescado.

Camareros, _____ el pescado; no _____ el pavo.

EJEMPLO: Juanito y Pedro no se acuestan temprano.

Juanito y Pedro, _____*acostaos*_____ temprano; no _____*os acostéis*_____ tarde.

21. Los jóvenes no se dedican a la caridad.

Jóvenes, _____ a la caridad; no _____ a los placeres.

22. Mis amigos no se van a la madrugada.

Amigos, _____ a la madrugada; no _____ al anochecer.

23. Las muchachas no se reúnen en el salón.

Muchachas, _____ en el salón; no _____ en el jardín.

24. Sus hijos no se ríen de tonterías.

Hijos, _____ de tonterías; no _____ de la verdad.

25. Diego y Berta nunca se ponen serios.

Diego y Berta, _____ serios, pero no _____ tristes.

EJEMPLO: El vestíbulo está sin iluminar (no está iluminado).

_____*Iluminadlo*_____ de noche; no _____*lo iluminéis*_____ de día.

26. Los libros están sin arreglar.

_____ en este estante; no _____ en aquél.

27. Estas manzanas son para comer.

_____ más tarde; no _____ ahora.

28. Esta casa está sin pintar.

_____ si os gusta; no _____ si no os gusta.

29. Este drama todavía está sin representar.

_____ en el Teatro Español; no _____ en el Teatro Alba.

30. El camino no está bien marcado en el mapa.

_____ claramente; no _____ mal.

D. Tradúzcanse al español las expresiones en inglés.

1. *Do not hand* _____ Vd. la copa al huésped.

2. Lucía, si tienes hambre, *make yourself* _____ una tortilla.

3. Chicos, Arturo está arriba; *go up* _____ al quinto piso.

4. Perdió la joya; *have her look for it* _____ en la arena.

5. *Let's spend* _____ la primavera en las Provincias Vascongadas. (two ways)

6. *Don't lose* _____ tú el collar de perlas.

7. *Believe me* _____, muchachos; la vida militar es diferente de la vida civil.

8. *Let's not wait for* _____ los resultados de las pruebas.

9. María, *tell me* _____ la verdad.

10. La alfombra es nueva; *step on it* _____ Vds. con cuidado.

11. Juanito, *don't eat* _____ los dulces; *put them* _____ en el plato.

12. *Let's not go away* _____ en marzo; hace mucho fresco entonces.

13. Hijos, *cover yourselves* _____ con la frazada; hace frío.

14. Berta, *don't look at yourself* _____ en el espejo todo el día.

15. *Wash* _____ tú el cuello y las orejas; aquí tienes jabón.

E. Tradúzcanse al español.

1. Rosita, tell me what happened. _____

2. Let's sleep till 9 A.M. (two ways) _____

3. Don't have her serve the coffee now. _____

4. James, bring me a pencil. _____

5. Have them enter the house. _____

6. Help each other (Vds.) always. _____

7. Fred, enjoy yourself at (en) the theater. _____

8. Don't become angry, young lady. _____

9. Peter and Vincent, behave well at (en) the party. _____

10. Children, play with the neighbors' son. --

----

11. Don't have them go to the park. --

----

12. Let's go to bed late tonight. --

----

13. Richard, come here at 8 o'clock tonight. --

----

14. Paul, don't sit in that chair; it is dirty. --

----

15. Children, don't say such things. --

----

16. Don't be deceived, sir; this one is better. --

----

17. Madam, count the money before leaving. --

----

18. Have him explain the lesson. --

----

19. I know that it's difficult, but do it (Vds.) now. ------------------------------------

----

20. Let's not get up early tomorrow. --

El henequén (hemp) es una planta que se produce en Yucatán. Las fibras (fibers) se secan al sol, y después se usan para hacer cuerdas (rope).

Verb Lesson 18—MASTERY EXERCISES

(LESSONS 13–17)

A. Tradúzcanse al español las expresiones en inglés. (See Verb Lesson 13, page 74.)

1. Los traidores *were condemned* _____ a muerte por el rey.

2. *They say* _____ que la Alhambra es una maravilla.

3. La propiedad *was sold* _____ por el dueño.

4. Por falta de armas, *was lost* _____ la guerra.

5. En un banquete *the hero was honored* _____.

6. Las deudas *will be paid* _____ por el comerciante.

7. Aquí *are spoken* _____ español y francés.

8. En la Segunda Guerra Mundial *the Germans were defeated* _____.

9. Su hermosura *is admired* _____ de todo el mundo.

10. En aquella tienda *are sold* _____ comestibles.

11. *He was invited* _____ a tomar café.

12. El libertador *was respected* _____ de toda la republica.

13. En este autobús *you pay* _____ al entrar.

14. La condesa *has been invited* _____ al palacio por la reina.

15. *It was believed* _____ que nuestro equipo era excelente.

16. Finalmente *have been published* _____ las obras del poeta.

17. El segundo capítulo *was written* _____ por un periodista inteligente.

18. Mirando el calendario, *one can see* _____ que marzo es el tercer mes.

19. La batalla fue violenta, y *was shed* _____ mucha sangre.

20. *It is said* _____ que la experiencia es el mejor maestro.

B. Escríbanse los verbos en el presente de subjuntivo empleando los sujetos *yo, nosotros, ellos.*
(See Verb Lesson 14, page 82.)

	Yo	Nosotros	Ellos
1. acercarse			
2. alzar			
3. averiguar			
4. caber			
5. cerrar			
6. coger			
7. conocer			
8. continuar			
9. dar			
10. destruir			

	Yo	Nosotros	Ellos
11. distinguir			
12. divertirse			
13. dormir			
14. enviar			
15. escribir			
16. estar			
17. haber			
18. hacer			
19. ir			
20. mostrar			
21. oír			
22. pagar			
23. pedir			
24. querer			
25. rodear			
26. saber			
27. ser			
28. traducir			
29. traer			
30. venir			

C. Escríbanse los verbos en el imperfecto de subjuntivo empleando los sujetos *yo, nosotros, ellos.* (In 1–10, use the *-ra* form; in 11–20, the *-se* form.) (See Formation of the Imperfect Subjunctive, page 84.)

Ejemplos: aprender—aprendiera, aprendiéramos, aprendieran
aprendiese, aprendiésemos, aprendiesen

	Yo	Nosotros	Ellos
1. andar			
2. caber			
3. caer			
4. conducir			
5. dar			
6. decir			
7. destruir			
8. estar			
9. haber			

	Yo	Nosotros	Ellos
10. hacer			
11. ir			
12. morir			
13. poder			
14. poner			
15. querer			
16. saber			
17. sentir			
18. tener			
19. traer			
20. volver			

D. Escríbase en español la forma correcta de las expresiones en inglés. (See Verb Lesson 15, page 91.)

1. Prohibieron que el prisionero *protest* _____ contra el castigo.

2. Dudamos que la espada *is* _____ de acero fino.

3. No es probable que el contador *has made* _____ un error.

4. Esperaban que la nieve *would cover* _____ los montes con una manta blanca.

5. Juana no desea *to put* _____ servilletas sucias en la mesa.

6. Colón temía que sus naves *would be lost* _____ entre las olas.

7. Será preciso *for her to buy* _____ mantequilla de primera calidad.

8. Me aconsejaron que *I study* _____ lenguas extranjeras.

9. Su padre le ruega *to spend* _____ quince días con la familia en la costa.

10. No creían que la peluquería *would be* _____ abierta aquel día.

11. Más vale que Vds. *make* _____ el viaje en mayo que en junio.

12. Es importante *to study* _____ las ciencias exactas.

13. Mi padre quería *me to take part* _____ en los deportes.

14. Se empeña en *returning* _____ al país hispanoamericano donde nació.

15. El alumno tiene miedo de *receiving* _____ un cero.

16. Es mejor que los peluqueros *do not work* _____ los domingos.

17. Fue necesario *to find* _____ en seguida un remedio para el veneno.

18. Mi madre insistía en que yo *hang up* _____ el sobretodo y el sombrero.

19. Era cierto que *he would acquire* _____ mucha riqueza en el comercio.

20. ¡Ojalá que tú *show* _____ interés por la aritmética!

21. Me sorprendo de que las gallinas *lay* (poner) _____ tantos huevos.

22. Es dudoso que el lechero *will bring* _____ la leche hoy.

23. No nos permiten *to show* _____ nuestras habilidades.

24. Se sorprendió de *hearing* _____ el acento curioso del oficial.

25. ¿Es posible que el pescador *will return* _____ sin pescado?

26. Mi madre me pide *to get dressed* _____ inmediatamente.

27. Siento que *there is* _____ lodo en la calle.

28. Nos dicen *not to delay in* _____ poner un telegrama a nuestros amigos mexicanos.

29. Nos alegramos de que el curso *is* _____ tan interesante.

30. Importaba mucho que la contestación *be* _____ clara y completa.

31. Me mandan *to comb* _____ el cabello.

32. No creo que la caída *has caused him* _____ daño.

33. Insisto en que tú *hand over* _____ las nueces que tienes en el bolsillo.

34. Todo el pueblo se alegró de que el campesino *had found* _____ su burro.

35. Es verdad que la fe *is* _____ un gran consuelo.

36. El profesor exige que *they compile* _____ una lista de nombres españoles.

37. Dudaban que esa región *had* _____ un clima seco.

38. Es lástima que la cosecha *has not been* _____ abundante este año.

39. Prefiero que mis hijos *preserve* _____ sus ilusiones agradables.

40. Los padres no quieren *to see* _____ lágrimas en los ojos de la niña.

E. Escríbase en español la forma correcta de las expresiones en inglés. (See Verb Lesson 16, page 99.)

1. El muchacho hizo los cambios necesarios antes que el maestro *arrived* _____.

2. Aunque la puesta del sol *may be* _____ hermosa en la montaña, no quiero ir allá.

3. Cuandoquiera que *we receive* _____ su carta, saldremos de aquí.

4. *I would like* _____ comprar una docena de huevos.

5. Cuando *I am thirsty* _____, beberé agua.

6. Si yo tuviera mil dólares, *I would take* _____ un viaje al oeste.

7. Gasta mucho dinero a fin de que sus hijas *may receive* _____ buena instrucción.

8. No hagamos nada hasta que ellos *solve* _____ el problema.

9. Antes de *entering* _____ en la casa, echó una mirada al reloj.

10. Si viajan por el desierto, *they won't find* _____ plantas.

11. En caso de que las medias *are* _____ demasiado largas, devuélvalas.

12. Después que todos *arrived* _____, se cerró la puerta.

13. No hay mal que *lasts* _____ cien años.

14. ¿*Could you* _____ pasarme la sal?

15. Caminó hasta *reaching* _____ la orilla del río.

16. En casa tengo un libro que *costs* _____ cinco dólares.

17. El trabajador tomará la sopa con tal que *he has* _____ apetito.

18. Tan pronto como Juan *earns* _____ la cantidad necesaria, comprará un anillo para su novia.

19. Buscamos una máquina que *doesn't have* _____ defectos.

20. Si *we go* _____ a Barcelona, visitaremos el monasterio de Montserrat.

21. Mientras *there is* _____ paz, todos viviremos felices.

22. Adondequiera que *you go* _____, aquí esperaré tu vuelta.

23. *They should* _____ arreglar los números en columnas para evitar confusión.

24. Luego que *I read* _____ esta página, la discutiremos.

25. Mientras *he walked* _____, el sudor le corría por el rostro.

26. Si no hiciese mal tiempo, *I would wear* _____ ropa ligera.

27. Envolvió el paquete de manera que el carretero *would be able* _____ llevarlo fácilmente.

28. Deseaba encontrar un empleado que *wrote* _____ correctamente.

29. Su llanto era amargo, sin que las lágrimas le *ran down* _____ por las mejillas.

30. Ayer vi un manzano que ya *had* _____ mucha fruta.

31. Así que *I see him* _____, le daré la noticia.

32. No lleve Vd. capa a menos que *it is cold* _____.

33. Por rápidamente que el tren *runs* _____, llegará tarde.

34. En cuanto *he received* _____ el golpe, se cayó.

35. Cuando *I heard* _____ el canto de los pájaros, me sentí dichoso.

36. Yo puedo llenar el tintero sin *spilling* _____ la tinta.

37. Trataron de animar a la pobre viuda para que ella *might not lose* _____ la esperanza.

38. Si las fresas hubieran sido maduras, las *I would have eaten* _____.

39. No conozco a nadie que *needs* _____ ayuda.

40. Si *you have* _____ buena memoria, podrás aprender el proverbio.

F. Escríbase en español la forma correcta de las expresiones en inglés. (See Verb Lesson 17, page 110.)

1. *Let them hear* _____ la explicación del maestro.

2. *Leave* _____ tú de la casa por la puerta de atrás.

3. *Come* _____ conmigo la víspera de Año Nuevo; os divertiréis mucho.

4. Aquí tiene Vd. el recibo; *don't destroy it* _____; es importante.

5. *Don't be* _____ soberbio, hijo; es mejor que seas modesto.

6. *Learn* _____ Vds. algo de la importancia histórica de España.

7. *Let's sit down* _____ a la orilla del lago para descansar un rato. (two ways)

8. Sr. Gómez, *speak to us* _____ acerca de la vida europea.

9. *Let's serve* _____ el arroz con pollo ahora, mientras está caliente. (two ways)

10. *Don't go* _____ hacia el norte, Juan; hace frío allí.

11. Aquí tienes los platos; *put them* _____ en la mesa.

12. Si deseas ver trajes bonitos y pintorescos, *come* _____ a México conmigo.

13. Si compraste un vestido de última moda, *show it to me* _____.

14. *Let us trust* _____ de la justicia y de Dios. (two ways)

15. *Join* _____ a los buenos, amiguito, no a los malos.

16. *Take out* _____ Vd. el azúcar del saco y *mix it* _____ con el agua.

17. Chico, *don't play* _____ música popular; no me gusta.

18. *Let's not invite* _____ a esa pareja a la fiesta.

19. *Let him tell me* _____ en qué renglón debo firmar.

20. Todavía le debes quinientos dólares; *pay them to him* _____.

21. *Have* _____ la seguridad de que el resultado será favorable para ti.

22. *Prepare yourselves* _____ para la defensa de vuestra patria.

23. *Don't tell* _____ tu pensamiento a todo el mundo.

24. *Give me* _____ Vds. una cuchara para comer la sopa.

25. *Be* _____ bueno, hijo, y te daré un peso.

  G. Tradúzcanse al español.

1. As soon as we reach the inn, we'll be able to rest. _____

_____

2. Cover yourselves well, my children; it is cool. _____

_____

3. The ladies will be protected. _____

_____

4. The pupil is glad to enter the classroom. _____

_____

5. After my father finishes breakfast, the family will take a ride in the automobile. _____

_____

6. I would like to learn Portuguese and Spanish. _____

_____

7. Don't approach the bear's cage; it is dangerous. _____

_____

8. It is evident that in the desert there are neither plants nor water. _____

_____

9. However modest he may be, he can be proud of his many merits. _____

_____

10. Let's not take a walk this afternoon; it's going to rain. _____

_____

11. It is known that John is in love with Helen. _____

12. It was impossible for don Quijote to remain in the inn. _____

13. Whoever does it will do it well. _____

14. Honor (tú) your father and your mother, says the Bible. _____

15. I will give you the receipt in order that you may sign it. _____

16. If the pupil had had imagination, he would have understood the lesson. _____

17. The city of Lima was founded by Pizarro. _____

18. The army was glad that the conquest had been easy. _____

19. There is no place where we can find rest. _____

20. The lazy pupil will be punished by the teacher. _____

21. We will have to wait an hour before the train arrives. _____

22. Have the pupils correct their mistakes. _____

23. God grant that the boy will not imitate bad models! _____

24. If I had a sweetheart, I would present her (with) a gold chain. _____

25. The criminal will be punished. _____

26. As soon as the teacher entered the room, everyone became quiet. _____

27. Foreign languages are not learned easily. _____

28. We went up to the top of the pyramid to admire the view. _____

29. I order you to leave immediately. _____

30. May they live a hundred years! _____

31. The barber shops will open at 9 o'clock. _____

32. Let's leave instantly. _____

33. Enjoy yourself (Vd.) wherever you go. _____

34. He waited at the inn until his friends arrived. _____

35. Don't construct (Vds.) the house of bricks, but of stucco. _____

36. If you (tú) know the truth, tell it to her. _____

37. He denied that the sunset was pretty. _____

38. Don't step on (tú) the rug with your dirty shoes. _____

39. He dreams of great deeds, provided that there is no danger. _____

40. It will be necessary for him to learn German. _____

H. Each of the following passages contains infinitives numbered 1–10. For each infinitive, you will find a choice of two verb forms. Write the letter of the correct verb form in each pair.

I. Quería (1) *encontrar* un regalo especial que le (2) *gustar* a su esposa. Pasó días buscándolo en las tiendas. Por fin vio un alfiler precioso con cadena de oro. Era muy caro.

—Por mucho que (3) *costar*, lo compraré —dijo. Ahora es necesario que lo (4) *esconder*, para que ella no lo (5) *ver*, porque no quiero que (6) *saber* nada de esto antes de la Navidad.

Entró en casa con cara risueña, y buscó un lugar aparte que (7) *ser* seguro, pero sin éxito. Su esposa le miraba con expresión extraña.

—¿Por qué me miras como si (8) *ser* un criminal?—gritó él, con enojo.

(9)—*Querer* que no me (10) *gritar*—contestó ella.

(1) (a) encontrar (b) encontrase ____   (6) (a) sabe (b) sepa ____
(2) (a) gustaba (b) gustara ____   (7) (a) era (b) fuese ____
(3) (a) cueste (b) cuesta ____   (8) (a) fuera (b) soy ____
(4) (a) escondo (b) esconda ____   (9) (a) Quería (b) Quisiera ____
(5) (a) vea (b) verá ____   (10) (a) gritas (b) gritaras ____

II. El médico le aconsejó que (1) *guardar* cama porque tenía un catarro. No quería (2) *pasar* todo el día en casa; no obstante, su madre insistió en que lo (3) *hacer*. Pasó un día desagradable. Sintió no (4) *poder* ver a sus amigos. A la mañana siguiente, apenas se despertó, le dijo a su madre que (5) *estar* bien y que tenía el propósito fijo de salir. Pero ella le prohibió que (6) *salir* hasta que (7) *llegar* el médico.

—¡Ojalá que (8) *venir* pronto! Porque si no (9) *venir*, saldré aún sin su permiso—dijo.

—No creo que (10) *hacer* eso—le contestó su madre con calma, pero en tono firme.

(1) (a) guardaba (b) guardara ____   (4) (a) poder (b) pudiera ____
(2) (a) pasar (b) pasase ____   (5) (a) estaba (b) estuviese ____
(3) (a) hacía (b) hiciera ____   (6) (a) salía (b) saliera ____

(7) (a) llegaba   (b) llegara   _ _ _ _ _   (9) (a) viene   (b) viniese   _ _ _ _ _

(8) (a) vendrá   (b) venga   _ _ _ _ _   (10) (a) harás   (b) hagas   _ _ _ _ _

III. Colón negaba que el mundo (1) *ser* llano, y pidió a su majestad la reina Isabel que le (2) *ayudar* a probar lo contrario.

—Si yo (3) *tener* unas naves, (4) *poder* encontrar una nueva ruta occidental que me (5) *conducir* a las Indias.

Además de las naves, buscó unos navegantes que no (6) *tener* miedo de (7) *salir* al mar infinito. Pero no había nadie que (8) *atreverse* a confiarse a la furia y violencia de los elementos. Sin embargo, Colón no se resignó al fracaso total de su proyecto. Tenía el espíritu firme.

—Aunque (9) *tener* que buscarlos en las cárceles, los encontraré—se dijo;—y cuando los (10) *encontrar*, podremos embarcarnos.

(1) (a) fuese   (b) era   _ _ _ _ _   (6) (a) tenían   (b) tuviesen   _ _ _ _ _

(2) (a) ayude   (b) ayudara   _ _ _ _ _   (7) (a) salir   (b) saliese   _ _ _ _ _

(3) (a) tendría   (b) tuviera   _ _ _ _ _   (8) (a) se atrevía   (b) se atreviera   _ _ _ _ _

(4) (a) pudiera   (b) podré   _ _ _ _ _   (9) (a) tenga   (b) tendré   _ _ _ _ _

(5) (a) conducirá   (b) condujera   _ _ _ _ _   (10) (a) encuentre   (b) encuentro   _ _ _ _ _

IV. Si (1) *aprender* el español, iré a España. Quienquiera que (2) *haber* hecho tal viaje me dice que es un país encantador. No dudo que (3) *tener* razón. Es probable que (4) *ir* en la primavera. Espero (5) *hacer* un viaje directo, en avión, con tal que (6) *tener* bastante dinero. Así que (7) *llegar* allí, trataré de ver todas las diversas cosas que tiene la España actual. Después de unos días en Madrid, recorreré el país de un extremo a otro sin descanso. Adondequiera que (8) *ir*, estoy seguro de (9) *poder* sacar muchas fotos para mostrárselas más tarde a mis amigos íntimos. Es lástima que ellos no (10) *poder* acompañarme.

(1) (a) aprendo   (b) aprendiera   _ _ _ _ _   (6) (a) tendré   (b) tenga   _ _ _ _ _

(2) (a) ha   (b) haya   _ _ _ _ _   (7) (a) llegaré   (b) llegue   _ _ _ _ _

(3) (a) tienen   (b) tengan   _ _ _ _ _   (8) (a) iré   (b) vaya   _ _ _ _ _

(4) (a) iré   (b) vaya   _ _ _ _ _   (9) (a) poder   (b) pueda   _ _ _ _ _

(5) (a) hacer   (b) haga   _ _ _ _ _   (10) (a) podrán   (b) puedan   _ _ _ _ _

V. Antes que (1) *salir* el sol, ya corrían a través de los campos. Importaba que (2) *llegar* a su destino, un pueblo cercano, a una distancia de diez millas de allí, de modo que (3) *poder* reunirse con los otros.

—Luego que (4) *llegar*, podremos descansar—pensaba el jefe.

—Por rápidamente que (5) *correr* nuestros caballos—dijo un soldado con amargura—es imposible que (6) *estar* allí a tiempo.

—En todo caso—dijo el jefe con ira—es necesario (7) *creer* en un milagro, hacer esfuerzos como si (8) *ser* posible. Hay que andar sin tardanza, sin que el enemigo (9) *darse* cuenta.

Cuando (10) *llegar*, vieron con emoción a sus compañeros esperando debajo de los árboles.

(1) (a) salir   (b) saliera   _ _ _ _ _   (6) (a) estaremos   (b) estemos   _ _ _ _ _

(2) (a) llegarían   (b) llegasen   _ _ _ _ _   (7) (a) creer   (b) creamos   _ _ _ _ _

(3) (a) pudieran   (b) podrían   _ _ _ _ _   (8) (a) fuera   (b) era   _ _ _ _ _

(4) (a) llegamos   (b) lleguemos   _ _ _ _ _   (9) (a) se da   (b) se dé   _ _ _ _ _

(5) (a) corran   (b) corren   _ _ _ _ _   (10) (a) llegaron   (b) llegasen   _ _ _ _ _

MASTERY VERB DRILL CHART

This chart is designed to test your mastery of the forms and uses of verbs. Write Spanish sentences like those below, using other verbs in place of *cantar*.

to sing	*cantar*
1. He wants *to sing*.	Desea *cantar*.
2. I *am singing*.	Yo *canto*.
3. *Do* they *sing?*	¿*Cantan* ellos?
4. John and Mary *used to sing*.	Juan y María *cantaban*.
5. We *were singing*.	Nosotros *cantábamos*.
6. She *didn't sing* yesterday.	Ella *no cantó* ayer.
7. We *will sing*.	Nosotros *cantaremos*.
8. *Would* they *sing?*	¿*Cantarían* ellas?
9. We *have not sung*.	*No hemos cantado*.
10. He *had sung*.	Él *había cantado*.
11. They *are singing*.	*Están cantando*.
12. I *would have sung*.	Yo *habría cantado*.
13. They *will have sung*.	Ellos *habrán cantado*.
14. Hardly *had* they *sung*, . . .	Apenas *hubieron cantado*, . . .
15. *Sing!* (polite)	¡*Cante* Vd.! (¡*Canten* Vds.!)
16. *Sing!* (fam. sing.)	¡*Canta* tú!
17. *Sing!* (fam. pl.)	¡*Cantad* vosotros!
18. *Do not sing!* (fam. sing.)	¡*No cantes* tú!
19. *Do not sing!* (fam. pl.)	¡*No cantéis* vosotros!
20. *Let's sing!*	¡*Cantemos* nosotros! (¡Vamos a *cantar!*)
21. *Let's not sing!*	¡*No cantemos* nosotros!
22. *Let* them *sing!*	¡Que *canten* ellos!
23. We *have been singing* for a long time.	Hace mucho tiempo que nosotros *cantamos*.
24. I *had been singing* for a long time.	Hacía mucho tiempo que yo *cantaba*.
25. I *sang* it two days ago.	Lo *canté* hace dos días.
26. How long *have* you *been singing?*	¿Desde cuándo *canta* Vd.?
27. Before *singing*, . . .	Antes de *cantar*, . . .
28. They want me *to sing*.	Desean que yo *cante*.
29. They wanted me *to sing*.	Deseaban que yo *cantara* (*cantase*).
30. They ask us *to sing*.	Nos piden que *cantemos*.
31. They asked us *to sing*.	Nos pidieron que *cantáramos* (*cantásemos*).
32. I am glad that they *sing*.	Me alegro de que ellos *canten*.

33. I am glad *to sing.*	Me alegro de *cantar.*
34. I doubt that they *will sing.*	Dudo que ellos *canten.*
35. She didn't believe that I *would sing.*	Ella no creía que yo *cantara (cantase).*
36. He denied that his brother *was singing.*	Negó que su hermano *cantara (cantase).*
37. We are sorry that he *is singing.*	Sentimos que él *cante.*
38. They were sorry that we *were singing.*	Sentían que nosotros *cantáramos (cantásemos).*
39. I am afraid that they *will not sing.*	Temo que ellos *no canten.*
40. It is necessary that she *sing.*	Es necesario que ella *cante.*
41. It was doubtful that I *would sing.*	Era dudoso que yo *cantara (cantase).*
42. It is certain that he *is singing.*	Es cierto que él *canta.*
43. I hope to find a man who *sings.*	Espero encontrar un hombre que *cante.*
44. There is no one who *sings.*	No hay nadie que *cante.*
45. Whoever *sings* it, will do it well.	Quienquiera que lo *cante,* lo hará bien.
46. We will do it when you *sing.*	Lo haremos cuando Vd. *cante.*
47. They will go out before he *sings.*	Ellos saldrán antes que él *cante.*
48. If they *sing,* I'll be there this afternoon.	Si ellos *cantan,* estaré allí esta tarde.
49. If I *sang* it, it would please you.	Si yo lo *cantase (cantara),* le gustaría a Vd.
50. If she *had sung,* I would have known it.	Si ella *hubiese (hubiera) cantado,* yo lo habría sabido.

La **América Latina produce casi todo el café que se usa en los Estados Unidos. El café viene de un arbusto (bush) llamado el cafeto. Las bayas (berries) se recogen a mano, y se ponen al sol para secarse. Después se envían a una fábrica, de donde se exportan a todas partes.**

Part II—*Grammatical Structures*

Grammar Lesson 1—NOUNS AND ARTICLES

GENDER OF NOUNS

All nouns in Spanish are either masculine or feminine.

1. *a*. Nouns that refer to male beings or that end in **-o** are usually masculine. Nouns that refer to female beings or that end in **-a** are usually feminine.

MASCULINE	FEMININE
el tipo, the type	**la distancia,** the distance
el hombre, the man	**la mujer,** the woman, the wife
el hijo, the son	**la hija,** the daughter

b. Some nouns that end in **-a** are masculine.

el clima, the climate	**el poeta,** the poet
el día, the day	**el problema,** the problem
el drama, the drama	**el programa,** the program
el idioma, the language	**el telegrama,** the telegram
el mapa, the map	**el tranvía,** the trolley car

c. A few nouns ending in **-o** are feminine.

la mano, the hand   **la radio,** the radio

2. Nouns ending in **-dad, -tad, -tud, -ión, -umbre,** or **-ie** are generally feminine.

la ciudad, the city	**la unión,** the union
la dificultad, the difficulty	*Exception:* **el avión,** the airplane
la juventud, youth	**la certidumbre,** the certainty
	la especie, the species, the kind

3. Masculine nouns that refer to people and end in **-or, -és,** or **-n** add **a** to form the feminine.

MASCULINE	FEMININE
el escultor, the sculptor	**la escultora,** the sculptress
el francés, the Frenchman	**la francesa,** the Frenchwoman
el alemán, the German	**la alemana,** the German
Exceptions:	
el emperador, the emperor	**la emperatriz,** the empress
el actor, the actor	**la actriz,** the actress

Note

If a masculine noun of this type bears a written accent on the last syllable, the accent is dropped when **a** is added to form the feminine:

francés—francesa   alemán—alemana

4. *a.* Some nouns are either masculine or feminine, depending on their meaning.

MASCULINE	FEMININE
el capital, the capital (money)	**la capital,** the capital (city)
el cura, the priest	**la cura,** the cure
el guía, the guide (male)	**la guía,** the guidebook, the guide (female)
el policía, the policeman	**la policía,** the police

b. Some nouns referring to people do not change their form but distinguish their gender only by the article.

el (la) artista, the artist   **el (la) joven,** the youth
el (la) azteca, the Aztec   **el (la) testigo,** the witness

5. Days of the week, months of the year, and names of rivers are masculine.

el lunes, Monday   **(el) septiembre,** September   **el Amazonas,** the Amazon (river)

6. The gender of other nouns must be learned individually.

7. Some masculine-feminine contrasts are:

varón y hembra, male and female   **poeta y poetisa,** poet and poetess
marido y mujer, man and wife   **príncipe y princesa,** prince and princess

PLURAL OF NOUNS

1. Nouns ending in a vowel form the plural by adding **s.**

el líquido, the liquid	**los líquidos,** the liquids
la conquista, the conquest	**las conquistas,** the conquests
el hombre, the man	**los hombres,** the men

2. Nouns ending in a consonant (including **-y**) form the plural by adding **es.**

el papel, the paper	**los papeles,** the papers
el rey, the king	**los reyes,** the kings, the rulers

Note

A. Nouns ending in **-z** change the **-z** to **-c** before adding **es: lápiz, lápices.**

B. Sometimes it is necessary to add or drop a written accent in order to keep the original stress:

joven—jóvenes   examen—exámenes   francés—franceses   reunión—reuniones

C. Except for nouns ending in **-és,** nouns ending in **-s** do not change in the plural:

el (los) lunes   el (los) paréntesis

3. When a mixed group (masculine and feminine) is meant, the masculine plural form of the noun is used.

los hijos = el hijo y la hija (los hijos y las hijas)
los amigos = el amigo y la amiga (los amigos y las amigas)
los abuelos = el abuelo y la abuela
los señores Gómez = Mr. & Mrs. Gómez

FORMS OF THE ARTICLES

1. There are four definite articles in Spanish that represent the English article *the*.

	SINGULAR	PLURAL
MASCULINE	el	los
FEMININE	la	las

Note

A. Feminine nouns that begin with the *stressed* sound of **a** (**a-** or **ha-**) take the article **el** in the singular. In the plural, the article is **las.**

el *a*lma, the soul   **las** almas, the souls

el *ha*cha, the ax   **las** hachas, the axes

but

la amiga ⎫
la alumna ⎭ initial **a-** is not stressed

B. The masculine article **el** combines with the prepositions **de** and **a** to form **del** and **al.**

C. There is also a neuter article **lo,** used with adjectives, which does not vary in form.

lo bueno, the good (that which is good)

2. There are two indefinite articles in Spanish that represent the English article *a (an)*.

MASCULINE: **un**   FEMININE: **una**

Note

The forms **unos** and **unas** mean *some, several, a few*, etc.

SPECIAL USES OF THE ARTICLES

The definite article is used in Spanish, but omitted in English, as follows:

1. Before the names of languages, except after **hablar, en,** or **de.**

El **español** es importante hoy día.   Spanish is important nowadays.
   but

Mi amigo **habla francés.**   My friend speaks French.

Todo el libro está escrito **en alemán.**   The whole book is written in German.

La clase **de español** es interesante.   The Spanish class is interesting.

Note

If an adverb occurs between **hablar** and a name of a language, the article is used with the language.

Habla **bien** *el* español.   He speaks Spanish well.

2. Before titles, except when addressing the person.

El señor Gómez salió ayer.	Mr. Gómez left yesterday.
but	
¿Cómo está Vd., **señora** Álvarez?	How are you, Mrs. Álvarez?

Note

The article is omitted before **don (doña), Santo (San, Santa).**

3. Instead of the possessive adjective, with parts of the body or personal possessions (clothing, etc.).

Ella tiene *el pelo* rubio.	She has blond hair. (Her hair is blond.)
Se puso *el sombrero.*	He put on his hat.

4. With the time of day (**la, las** = hour, hours).

Es *la una.*	It is one o'clock.
Me acuesto a *las diez.*	I go to bed at ten o'clock.

5. Before nouns used in a general or abstract sense.

El hombre es mortal.	Man is mortal.
La libertad es preciosa.	Liberty is precious.
Los diamantes son caros.	Diamonds are expensive.

6. Before infinitives used as nouns. Such nouns are always masculine.

El mentir es un vicio.	Lying is a vice.

7. With the names of seasons.

Me gusta *la primavera (el verano, el otoño, el invierno).*	I like spring (summer, autumn, winter).

8. With the days of the week, except after the verb **ser.**

Iré al teatro *el sábado.*	I will go to the theater (on) Saturday.
Los viernes hay pruebas.	(On) Fridays there are tests.
but	
Hoy **es jueves.**	Today is Thursday.

9. Before certain geographic names.

los Andes, the Andes		**la Florida,** Florida	
la Argentina, Argentina		**la Habana,** Havana	
el Brasil, Brazil		**el Orinoco,** the Orinoco (river)	
el Canadá, Canada		**el Paraguay,** Paraguay	
el Ecuador, Ecuador		**el Perú,** Peru	
ìos Estados Unidos, the United States		**el Uruguay,** Uruguay	

Note

Even with geographic names that ordinarily are not used with the article, the article is used if the name is modified.

América tiene muchas riquezas.	**España** está en Europa.
La América del Sur tiene muchas riquezas.	*La España del siglo XVI* me interesa.

10. To express *a* (*an*) with weights or measures.

un dólar *la libra* | a dollar a pound
diez centavos *la docena* | ten cents a dozen

NEUTER ARTICLE *LO*

1. The neuter article **lo** precedes an adjective used as a noun to express a quality or an abstract idea.

Lo pintoresco me atrae. | The picturesque (That which is picturesque) attracts me.

Pienso *lo mismo* que Vd. | I think the same as you.

2. **Lo** + adjective (or adverb) + **que** = *how*.

Ya veo *lo bueno (buena) que* es. | I see how good he (she) is.

Me sorprende *lo rápidamente que* corre. | I am surprised at how quickly he runs.

Note

Since the article **lo** is neuter, it has no plural form. Therefore, **lo** is used whether the adjective is masculine or feminine, singular or plural.

OMISSION OF THE ARTICLES

1. The articles are omitted:

a. Before nouns in apposition.

Madrid, capital de España, está en el centro del país. | Madrid, the capital of Spain, is in the center of the country.

Lope de Vega, dramaturgo español, escribió muchas comedias. | Lope de Vega, a Spanish dramatist, wrote many plays.

b. Before numerals expressing the numerical order of rulers.

Carlos Quinto | Charles the Fifth
Isabel Segunda | Isabel the Second

2. The indefinite article is omitted:

a. Before predicate nouns denoting a class or group (social class, occupation, nationality, religion, etc.).

Es peluquero. | He is a barber.
Soy americano. | I am (an) American.
Quiero hacerme médico. | I want to become a doctor.

Note

If the predicate noun is modified, the indefinite article is expressed.

Era *un peluquero hábil.* | He was a skillful barber.
Quiero ser *un médico bueno.* | I want to be a good doctor.

b. Before or after certain words that in English ordinarily have the article: **otro** (another), **cierto** (a certain), **ciento** (a hundred), **mil** (a thousand), **tal** . . . (such a . . .), **¡qué** . . . ! (what a . . . !).

otra carta	another letter
cierto día	a certain day
cien dólares	one (a) hundred dollars
mil soldados	one (a) thousand soldiers
tal hombre	such a man
¡Qué memoria!	What a memory!

EJERCICIOS

A. Para cada uno de los sustantivos (nouns) siguientes, escríbanse (1) su artículo definido, (2) la forma plural del artículo definido, y (3) la forma plural del sustantivo:

EJEMPLO: pluma—la pluma; las plumas

1. mujer _____
2. aula _____
3. muchedumbre _____
4. idioma _____
5. papel _____
6. rey _____
7. aguja _____
8. drama _____
9. viernes _____
10. hacha _____
11. telegrama _____
12. tranvía _____
13. alma _____
14. ciudad _____
15. especie _____
16. almohada _____
17. hazaña _____
18. base _____
19. nariz _____
20. deber _____
21. ala _____
22. ley _____
23. mano _____
24. amistad _____
25. ave _____
26. clima _____
27. luz _____
28. problema _____
29. serie _____
30. domingo _____

B. Escríbase la forma plural de los sustantivos que siguen:

1. avión _____
2. unión _____
3. lápiz _____
4. ademán _____
5. joven _____
6. paréntesis _____
7. águila _____
8. posesión _____
9. colchón _____
10. sábado _____
11. catalán _____
12. corazón _____
13. líquido _____
14. francés _____
15. fósforo _____
16. género _____
17. kilómetro _____
18. límite _____
19. línea _____
20. maldición _____
21. mérito _____
22. volcán _____
23. varón _____
24. obligación _____
25. taxímetro _____
26. sábana _____
27. portugués _____
28. pirámide _____
29. plátano _____
30. razón _____

C. Escríbase la forma femenina que corresponde a cada uno de los sustantivos que siguen.

EJEMPLO: el caballero—la dama

1. el hombre _____
2. el gallo _____
3. don _____
4. el alemán _____
5. el actor _____
6. el marido _____
7. el artista _____
8. el emperador _____
9. el varón _____

10. el bailarín _____
11. el poeta _____
12. el escultor _____
13. el príncipe _____
14. el rey _____
15. el ruso _____
16. el padre _____
17. el abuelo _____

18. el ladrón _____
19. el policía _____
20. el francés _____
21. el toro _____
22. el hijo _____
23. el conde _____
24. el esposo _____
25. el joven _____

D. Tradúzcanse al español las expresiones en inglés.

1. A Vd. le gusta *the picturesque* _____, y a mí *the same* _____.

2. *Sadness* _____ y *melancholy* _____ son sensaciones semejantes.

3. *On Saturdays* _____ y *on Sundays* _____ me desayuno tarde.

4. *The Andes* _____ marcan la frontera entre *Chile and Argentina* _____
_____.

5. *The beautiful* _____ y *the sad* _____ atraen a los poetas.

6. Carlos *the Third* _____ siguió a Felipe *the Fifth* _____ en el trono de España.

7. Es imposible trabajar en *such a* _____ fábrica; voy a buscar *another* _____ empleo.

8. En gran parte de *South America* _____ se habla *Spanish* _____.

9. *Brazil* _____ y *Colombia* _____ exportan mucho café a *the United States* _____.

10. *The possible* _____ se ejecuta en seguida; *the impossible* _____ exige más tiempo.

11. La niña es muy guapa; tiene *blond hair* _____ y *blue eyes* _____
_____.

12. En *winter* _____, se hielan los lagos; en *spring* _____, *nature* _____ parece renovarse.

13. Es *a good plumber* _____, pero desea ser *a carpenter* _____.

14. La señora se puso *her hat* _____ y *her gloves* _____, y se marchó.

15. ¡*What an* _____ idea! ¿Cómo se puede realizar *such a* _____ proyecto?

16. ¡Mire Vd. *how easily* _____ escribe Juanito!

17. *Mr. & Mrs.* _____ Rivera construyen una casa magnífica en Los Ángeles.

18. *Buying* _____ y *selling* _____ son la base *of commerce* _____.

19. *The Amazon* _____ es el río más grande de *South America* _____ _____.

20. *The civil* _____ debe ser superior a *the military* _____.

21. *General* _____ Álvarez y *Captain* _____ Guzmán quieren a la linda hija de *Mrs.* _____ Hernández.

22. El cartero viene a *nine o'clock* _____ y a *one o'clock* _____.

23. *Eggs* _____ se venden a setenta centavos *a* _____ docena.

24. Vds. no pueden figurarse *how easy* _____ es aprender a nadar.

25. *Spanish* _____ y *French* _____ son idiomas que deben estudiarse.

26. *Gold* _____ y *silver* _____ son preciosos para *men* _____.

27. *Spain* _____ es pintoresca hoy, pero me interesa más *Spain* _____ del Siglo de Oro.

28. Según el calendario, *summer* _____ principia en junio, y *autumn* _____ en septiembre.

29. Hoy es *Tuesday* _____, y mañana será *Wednesday* _____.

30. Me encanta oírlos; saben conversar en *Portuguese* _____ e *Italian* _____.

E. Contéstense en español en frases completas.

1. ¿Cuál es el río más grande de la América del Sur? _____ _____

2. ¿A qué hora se levanta Vd. los jueves? _____ _____

3. Al entrar en la clase, ¿cómo saluda Vd. al maestro? _____ _____

4. ¿Qué día de la semana asiste Vd. al cine? _____ _____

5. ¿Qué se lleva en los pies? ¿en las manos? ¿en la cabeza? _____ _____

6. ¿Qué quiere Vd. ser? _____ _____

7. ¿Qué país hispanoamericano quiere Vd. visitar? _____ _____

8. ¿En qué estación tiene Vd. sus vacaciones? _____ _____

9. ¿En qué estación caen las hojas de los árboles? _____

_____

10. ¿Qué idioma se habla en el Uruguay? _____

    F. Tradúzcanse al español.

1. Upon going out, he was surprised at how dark the night was. _____

_____

2. Saint Theresa was a religious writer of the sixteenth century. _____

_____

3. What a memory he has! He remembers all the historical dates. _____

_____

4. We ought to struggle for liberty and independence. _____

_____

5. Lima, the capital of Peru, has a long history. _____

_____

6. The witness said that she had seen the accident. _____

_____

7. At eleven o'clock I am going to the Spanish class. _____

_____

8. He sold the apples at twenty cents a pound. _____

_____

9. Saint Isidro, the patron (saint) of Madrid, was a peasant. _____

_____

10. My friend Joseph married a pretty German girl. _____

_____

11. I am accustomed to brush my teeth twice a day. _____

_____

12. Mr. Zorrilla is a Spaniard; his wife is a Russian. _____

_____

13. Fishing and swimming are prohibited in this lake. _____

_____

14. Isabel the Second was the daughter of Ferdinand the Seventh. _____

_____

15. Dr. Suárez accompanied Miss Alonso to the dance. _____

_____

16. Peru and Bolivia are neighboring countries. _____

_____

17. The bank closes at three o'clock on Fridays. _____

_____

18. Instead of getting lost in the capital, I prefer to buy a guidebook. _____

_____

_____

19. Love, friendship, and beauty are the soul of poetry. _____

_____

20. Because of the vacation, I like summer more than the other seasons. _____

_____

_____

21. The good (part) of the matter is that the police know the criminal. _____

_____

22. The human race is divided into male and female. _____

_____

23. On Thursdays I take my piano lesson. _____

_____

24. Why don't you consult Dr. Menéndez? He is a good doctor. _____

_____

_____

25. The king's son is called a prince; and his daughter, a princess. _____

_____

_____

La Piedra del Sol es un famoso ejemplo de la escultura azteca. Las figuras representan los días, los elementos, etc. Los aztecas la usaban como calendario, y con ella podían marcar con gran exactitud los días y los años.

Grammar Lesson 2—POSSESSION

1. Possession is expressed in Spanish by **de** + the possessor. This corresponds to *'s* or *s'* in English.

la cabra *del árabe*	the Arab's goat
la fama *de don Quijote*	Don Quixote's fame
la pluma *de Luis*	Louis' pen

2. To avoid repetition in a sentence, the noun representing the thing possessed is replaced by its definite article plus **de.**

Mi libro y *el* (= el libro) *de Jorge* son nuevos.	My book and George's (= that of George) are new.
Su impresión es diferente de *la* (= la impresión) *de su tío.*	His impression is different from his uncle's (= that of his uncle).

POSSESSIVE ADJECTIVES

	Short Form	Long Form
my	mi, mis	mío, -a, -os, -as
your (*fam. sing.*)	tu, tus	tuyo, -a, -os, -as
your, his, her, its, their	su, sus	suyo, -a, -os, -as
our	nuestro, -a, -os, -as	
your (*fam. pl.*)	vuestro, -a, -os, -as	

1. The short form always precedes the noun; the long form always follows the noun. Both forms agree in gender and number with the person or thing possessed, *not* with the possessor.

nuestro país	our country
sus alhajas	his (your, her, its, their) jewels
¡Dios mío!	My God!
una prima tuya	a cousin of yours

Note

The specific meanings of **su (sus)** and **suyo (-a, -os, -as)** may be made clear by replacing these forms with the article and adding **de Vd. (Vds.), de él (ella),** or **de ellos (ellas)** after the noun.

las alhajas *de él*	his jewels
una prima *de ellos*	a cousin of theirs

2. The definite article usually replaces the possessive adjective when referring to parts of the body or personal possessions (clothing, etc.).

Juan se quitó *los zapatos.*	John took off his shoes.
El alumno levantó *la mano.*	The pupil raised his hand.
Pablo abrió *el paraguas.*	Paul opened his umbrella.

POSSESSIVE PRONOUNS

mine	el mío, la mía, los míos, las mías
yours (*fam. sing.*)	el tuyo, la tuya, los tuyos, las tuyas
yours, his, hers, its, theirs	el suyo, la suya, los suyos, las suyas
ours	el nuestro, la nuestra, los nuestros, las nuestras
yours (*fam. pl.*)	el vuestro, la vuestra, los vuestros, las vuestras

1. Possessive pronouns are formed by the definite article + the long form of the possessive adjective.

2. The possessive pronoun agrees in number and gender with the noun it replaces, *not* with the possessor.

Mi automóvil es más hermoso que *el* (= el automóvil) *suyo.*	My automobile is more beautiful than yours.
Esos libros y *los* (= los libros) *míos* son novelas.	Those books and mine are novels.

Note

A. The specific meanings of **el suyo (la suya, los suyos, las suyas)** may be made clear by dropping **suyo (-a, -os, -as)** and adding **de Vd. (Vds.), de él (ella),** or **de ellos (ellas)** after the article.

sus plumas y *las de Vd.*	his pens and yours

B. After the verb **ser,** the article preceding the possessive pronoun is generally omitted.

Estas corbatas *son mías.*	These neckties are mine.
Aquella corbata *es suya.*	That necktie is his.

WHOSE

1. *Whose?* (interrogative pronoun) is expressed in Spanish by **¿De quién es (son) . . . ?** or **¿De quiénes es (son) . . . ?**

¿De quién es el cuaderno? Es del maestro.	Whose notebook is it? (Whose is the notebook?) It is the teacher's.
¿De quiénes es el coche? ¿De los Sres. Molina?	Whose auto is it? (Whose is the auto?) Mr. and Mrs. Molina's?
¿De quién son estos libros? Son de Jorge.	Whose books are these? (Whose are these books?) They are George's.

Note

If the English *whose?* is not followed by the verb *to be,* the English sentence must be reworded to fit the Spanish pattern.

¿De quién es el cumpleaños que cae el tres de abril?	Whose birthday falls on April 3?

2. *Whose* (relative adjective) is expressed in Spanish by **cuyo (-a, -os, -as).** It agrees in gender and number with the person or thing possessed and not with the possessor.

El hombre *cuya casa* compré vive ahora en Toledo.	The man whose house I bought now lives in Toledo.

EJERCICIOS

A. Escríbase la forma correcta del adjetivo y del pronombre posesivos según el ejemplo.

EJEMPLO: (my) __mi__ libro; (mine) __el mío__

1. (his) _____ alegría; (his) _____
2. (our) _____ amor; (ours) _____
3. (your, *fam. sing.*) _____ dedos; (yours) _____
4. (their) _____ cortesía; (theirs) _____
5. (his) _____ criadas; (his) _____
6. (your, *fam. pl.*) _____ hermana; (yours) _____
7. (her) _____ ovejas; (hers) _____
8. (their) _____ cariño; (theirs) _____
9. (your, *fam. sing.*) _____ vicios; (yours) _____
10. (our) _____ sobrinas; (ours) _____

B. Escríbanse (1) el pronombre posesivo (**el suyo, la suya, los suyos, las suyas**), y (2) la forma posesiva que haga más claro el significado. (See Note A, page 140.)

EJEMPLOS: pluma (his) __la suya__ or __la de él__

libro (yours, *pl.*) __el suyo__ or __el de Vds.__

1. comercio   (theirs)   _____ or _____
2. compañía   (his)   _____ or _____
3. consejos   (hers)   _____ or _____
4. impresiones (theirs)   _____ or _____
5. deudas   (his)   _____ or _____
6. ideas   (yours, *sing.*)   _____ or _____
7. jefe   (his)   _____ or _____
8. edad   (yours, *sing.*)   _____ or _____
9. interés   (hers)   _____ or _____
10. hombros   (yours, *pl.*)   _____ or _____

C. Complétense las frases según los ejemplos. (See *Whose*, page 140.)

EJEMPLOS: Whose book are you reading? __¿De quién es__ el libro que Vd. lee?

Whose (*pl.*) book did they take? __¿De quiénes es__ el libro que tomaron?

1. Whose jacket are you wearing? ¿_____ la chaqueta que Vd. lleva?
2. Whose paintings did you see? ¿_____ las pinturas que Vd. vio?
3. Whose magazine are you reading? ¿_____ la revista que Vd. lee?
4. Whose money did they spend? ¿_____ el dinero que gastaron?

5. Whose monument is that? ¿_____ ese monumento?

6. Whose (*pl.*) automobile did they wash? ¿_____ el automóvil que lavaron?

7. Whose poetry do you like? ¿_____ la poesía que le gusta a Vd.?

8. Whose property will you buy? ¿_____ la propiedad que Vds. comprarán?

9. Whose (*sing.*) letters did he mail? ¿_____ las cartas que echó al correo?

10. Whose secretary is absent today? ¿_____ la secretaria que está ausente hoy?

   D. Tradúzcanse al español las expresiones en inglés.

1. *My* abrigo está en el baúl. ¿Dónde están *yours? Ours* están en el armario.

   _____

2. *Her* alhajas cuestan mucho. *Barbara's* son más caras. *Ours* no valen nada.

   _____

3. ¿*Whose* es aquel monumento? Es *Columbus'*. Es famoso por *his* descubrimientos.

   _____

4. *His* cumpleaños cae en abril. ¿Cuándo cae *Alice's? Hers* cae en julio.

   _____

5. El ladrón ha robado *my* dinero. ¿Os robó *yours* también? No, nosotros tenemos *ours* en el cajón.

   _____

6. Vi a Juana fuera de *my* casa. ¿Le devolviste *her* juguetes? No, pero le presté *mine*.

   _____

7. Estas joyas no son *mine*. ¿Son *Lucy's?* No, son *Joseph's sister's*.

   _____

8. Anteayer perdí *my* paraguas. ¿Era azul *yours?* No, *mine* era negro.

   _____

9. La pluma verde es *his*. ¿*Whose* es la pluma amarilla? Es *Anna's*.

   _____

10. He gastado todo *my* capital. ¿Qué has hecho con *yours? Mine* está en el banco.

    _____

11. El empleado acaba de cobrar *his* sueldo. ¿Habéis recibido *yours?* Sí, pero es menos que *the boss'*.

    _____

12. La muchacha *whose* nombre es Luisa es hermosa. No es tan bella como *my* novia. Pero es más

    hermosa que *yours*. _____

13. Pablo se puso *his* sombrero. Alicia se quitó *hers*. La señora se quitó *her* guantes.

    _____

14. ¿*Whose* es esta pelota? No sé *whose* es. Solamente sé que no es *mine*.

    _____

15. *Our* bandera es roja, blanca, y azul. *England's* también. ¿De qué colores es *Mexico's?*

    _____

E. Contéstense en español en frases completas.

1. ¿Acompaña Vd. a sus padres cuando van al cine? _____

2. ¿Cuándo cae su cumpleaños? ¿Cuándo cae el de su primo? _____

3. ¿Se quita o se pone Vd. los zapatos al salir de casa? _____

4. ¿Escribe Vd. cartas a sus condiscípulos? _____

5. ¿Cuál es su clase favorita? _____

6. ¿De quién es la linda corbata que Vd. lleva hoy? _____

7. ¿Le gusta a Vd. sacar fotos de sus amigos? _____

8. ¿De quién es la bandera que está en la clase? _____

9. ¿Oyen y comprenden Vds. bien mis palabras? _____

10. ¿De quién son los libros que están en su cuarto? _____

11. ¿Hasta qué hora de la noche estudia Vd. sus lecciones? _____

12. ¿Son mejores las notas de los otros estudiantes que las de Vd.? _____

13. ¿Contestan Vds. pronto cuando les habla su profesor? _____

14. ¿Conserva Vd. recuerdos de sus vacaciones? _____

15. ¿Prefiere Vd. cenar en su propia casa o en la de su amigo? _____

16. ¿Cómo saluda Vd. a su maestro? _____

17. ¿De quiénes es la costumbre de asistir a la corrida de toros? _____

18. ¿Es Vd. más gordo(-a) que sus hermanos? _____

19. ¿Se lava Vd. las manos antes de comer? _____

_____

20. ¿De quién es el dinero que Vd. lleva en el bolsillo? _____

_____

F. Tradúzcanse al español.

1. The dictator declared that his army would defeat that of the enemy. _____

_____

2. Your (*fam. sing.*) plans and mine are good. _____

_____

3. The woman whose son was married yesterday is my aunt. _____

_____

4. The ship's captain observed the city's strange customs. _____

_____

5. Her family and her uncle's live near the city's limits. _____

_____

6. Whose dictionary did you consult? My father's. _____

_____

7. None of the employees knows the boss' address. _____

_____

8. Today's newspaper relates the news of their misfortune. _____

_____

9. It is a lake whose waters are clear and cool. _____

_____

10. His daughter and that of his friend danced almost all night. _____

_____

11. In whose chair are you seated? In Mr. Zuleta's? _____

_____

12. The boy had to carry his father's suitcase and his brother's. _____

_____

13. Whose is the blue hat? It is Elizabeth's. _____

_____

14. Whose garden is this? It is more beautiful than mine. _____

_____

15. Our president has more problems than England's king has. _____

_____

16. Spain's literature has a longer history than Brazil's. _____

_____

17. I like the poet whose verses I read last night. _____

_____

18. Henry's vacation will take place in the same month as his sister's. _____

_____

19. Her beauty shines more than the sun's rays. _____

_____

20. Whose class is this? It is Miss Rivera's Spanish class. _____

_____

En el mundo hispánico celebran no sólo el cumpleaños de una persona sino también el día de su santo. Hay un santo por cada día del año. Es muy común darle a un niño el nombre del santo en cuyo día nació. Si las dos fechas no coinciden, el día del santo se celebra muchas veces con otra fiesta—como si fuera un segundo cumpleaños.

DEMONSTRATIVE ADJECTIVES

	MASCULINE	FEMININE
this these	este estos	esta estas
that those	ese esos	esa esas
that those	aquel aquellos	aquella aquellas

Demonstrative adjectives precede the nouns they modify and agree with them in number and gender.

este libro	this book
esas plumas	those pens

Note

Este (**estos,** etc.), *this* (*these*), refers to what is near or directly concerns *me, the speaker*. **Ese** (**esos,** etc.), *that* (*those*), refers to what is near or directly concerns *you, the person addressed*. **Aquel** (**aquellos,** etc.), *that* (*those*), refers to what is remote from both the speaker and the person addressed, or does not directly concern either of us. Thus, **este, ese,** and **aquel** correspond to the 1st, 2nd, and 3rd persons.

Este lápiz que tengo es rojo.	*This* pencil that *I* have is red.
Juan, déme Vd. *ese* libro que tiene en la mano.	John, give me *that* book *you* have in your hand.
Juan, déme Vd. *aquel* libro que tiene María.	John, give me *that* book that *Mary* has.

DEMONSTRATIVE PRONOUNS

	MASCULINE	FEMININE	NEUTER
this (one) these	éste éstos	ésta éstas	esto
that (one) those	ése ésos	ésa ésas	eso
that (one) those	aquél aquéllos	aquélla aquéllas	aquello

1. Demonstrative pronouns agree in number and gender with the nouns they replace.

este libro y *aquél* (= aquel libro)	this book and that (one)

2. The neuter forms (esto, eso, aquello) do not refer to specific nouns but to statements, ideas, understood nouns, etc. Therefore, they do not vary in number and gender. In questions such as ¿Qué es esto?, the neuter form is used because the noun is not known. After the noun has been mentioned (in the response), its gender and number must be indicated by using the corresponding form of the adjective or pronoun (estas, éstas; aquel, aquél).

Pablo siempre llegaba tarde, y *eso* no le gustaba al maestro.	Paul always came late, and the teacher did not like that.
Su padre está enfermo, y *esto* le hace triste.	His father is ill, and this makes him sad.
¿Qué es *esto*? Es una flor. ¿Es bonita *esta* flor? Sí.	What is this? It is a flower. Is this flower pretty? Yes.

Note

A. The demonstrative pronouns are distinguished from the demonstrative adjectives by a written accent mark. The neuter forms of the pronouns have no such accent mark, since there is no corresponding neuter adjective.

B. The English translations of the singular forms of the demonstrative pronouns often add the word *one: this (one), that (one)*.

este muchacho y *aquél*	this boy and that (one)

3. The pronoun éste (-a, -os, -as) is used to translate *the latter* (the latest, the most recently mentioned); and aquél (-la, -los, -las) translates *the former* (the most remotely mentioned).

Juan es mayor que Pablo; *éste* tiene seis años, the latter *aquél* tiene nueve. the former	John is older than Paul; *the former* is nine years old, *the latter* is six.

Note

In English, we usually say "the former and the latter." In Spanish, the order is reversed; éste (the latter) is expressed first.

4. The definite article (el, la, los, las) followed by de or que is often translated as a pronoun.

el (*la*) *de* María, that of (the one of) Mary
los (*las*) *de* María, those of (the ones of) Mary

el (*la*) *que* está aquí, the one that is here
los (*las*) *que* están aquí, the ones that are here

mi corbata y *la* (= la corbata) *de* mi hermano	my necktie and that of my brother (my brother's)
El vestido de María es distinto *del de* Juana; es muy parecido *al que* lleva Isabel.	Mary's dress is different from Joan's; it is very similar to the one Elizabeth is wearing.

EJERCICIOS

A. Cámbiense las formas demostrativas al plural o al singular, y háganse todos los otros cambios necesarios.

1. Esa librería está abierta todo el día.

   -- todo el día.

2. Creo que aquellos abogados son inteligentes.

   Creo que --.

3. Tengo confianza absoluta en este médico.

Tengo confianza absoluta en _____.

4. Esta almohada es demasiado dura.

_____ demasiado _____.

5. Esas miradas tuyas me encantan.

_____ me _____.

6. Aquel actor no sabe actuar.

_____ no _____ actuar.

7. ¿Son de oro estos anillos?

¿_____ de oro _____?

8. Ese oso es muy feroz.

_____ muy _____.

9. Aquel pajarito es muy bonito, ¿verdad?

_____ muy _____, ¿verdad?

10. Aquellos sucesos ocurrieron en noviembre.

_____ en noviembre.

11. Es imposible atravesar este río.

Es imposible atravesar _____.

12. Aquel aparato no es muy sencillo.

_____ no _____ muy _____.

13. Esa panadería se cierra los domingos.

_____ los domingos.

14. Aquel viejo tendrá unos ochenta años.

_____ unos ochenta años.

15. Esos autobuses van hacia el centro.

_____ hacia el centro.

B. En cada una de las frases que siguen, subráyese la forma demostrativa correcta.

1. Esta mujer es linda; *that one* es fea.   (*a*) esa   (*b*) aquélla   (*c*) eso

2. No se permite entrar por esa puerta, sino por *this one*.   (*a*) esto   (*b*) éste   (*c*) ésta

3. *This* país es mi patria.   (*a*) Esto   (*b*) Este   (*c*) Esta

4. Alfredo y Carlota son hermanos; *the latter* es menor que aquél.   (*a*) ésta   (*b*) éste   (*c*) aquélla

5. Este calendario marca las fiestas; *that one*, no.   (*a*) ese   (*b*) ése   (*c*) aquello

6. Esta cosecha es más abundante que *those* de los años pasados.   (*a*) las   (*b*) el   (*c*) esos

7. ¿Cuál de las dos escoge Vd., *this one* o aquélla?   (*a*) éste   (*b*) ésta   (*c*) esa

8. ¿Qué es *this*?   (*a*) esto   (*b*) éste   (*c*) ésta

9. Coloque Vd. la malèta en *this* armario, no en aquél.   (*a*) esto   (*b*) ésta   (*c*) este

10. No me gusta *that*.   (*a*) esto   (*b*) eso   (*c*) aquél

11. En esta cafetería cobran menos que en *that one*.   (*a*) eso   (*b*) aquella   (*c*) aquélla

12. Esa capa es más barata que *that* de Isabel.   (*a*) ésa   (*b*) aquélla   (*c*) la

13. En la lucha entre moros y cristianos, éstos vencieron a *the former*.   (*a*) ésos   (*b*) aquél (*c*) aquéllos

14. *Those* ejercicios son más difíciles que éstos.   (*a*) Aquello   (*b*) Ése   (*c*) Esos

15. Este paquete es más pesado que *that one*.   (*a*) éste   (*b*) ése   (*c*) ese

C. Escríbase el pronombre demostrativo, empleando la forma correcta del artículo (el, la, los, las).

1. La vida de Luis XIV fue más alegre que *that* _____ de Felipe II.

2. Pude resolver mi propio problema, pero no *Richard's* _____.

3. La gente de México y *that* _____ de la Argentina hablan español.

4. Nuestro ejército y *that* _____ del enemigo lucharon en el campo de batalla.

5. ¿Será posible llevar a cabo mis planes y *those* _____ que Vd. ha propuesto?

6. El nuevo empleado es tan perezoso como *the one* _____ que se marchó.

7. Los impuestos de este año son más que *those* _____ del año anterior.

8. El clima andaluz no es semejante *to that* _____ de otras partes de Europa.

9. Hizo una declaración en nombre de su propia hija y *that* _____ de su vecino.

10. Los montes del norte son enormes; *those* _____ del sur son más pequeños.

D. Escríbase la forma correcta de *that* o *those*. (See Note, page 146.)

1. *That* _____ vista a lo lejos es magnífica.

2. ¿Hallaste *those* _____ cinco centavos que tienes?

3. Soy feliz a causa de *that* _____ favor que me hiciste.

4. Vamos a *that* _____ restaurante que tú recomendaste; el dueño es muy simpático.

5. En *that* _____ ciudad donde vives hace frío casi todo el año.

6. En junio voy a visitar *that* _____ parque.

7. *That* _____ tarde charlaron treinta minutos.

8. Venga Vd. conmigo; voy a comprar *those* _____ juguetes que los huérfanos desean.

9. Alicia, pareces encantadora en *that* _____ vestido.

10. Tienes la cara muy linda con *those* _____ anteojos.

E. Tradúzcanse las frases según el ejemplo. (See #3, page 147.)

EJEMPLO: Juan y María; *the former is fat, the latter is slim*.

Juan y María; __ésta__ es delgada, __aquél__ es gordo.

1. El general y el capitán; *the former is old, the latter is young*.

El general y el capitán; _____ es joven, _____ es viejo.

2. Mis guantes y los tuyos; *the former are white, the latter are black*.

Mis guantes y los tuyos; _____ son negros, _____ son blancos.

3. Elena y Pablo; *the former is diligent, the latter is lazy.*

Elena y Pablo; _____ es perezoso, _____ es aplicada.

4. Don Quijote y Sancho; *the former was an idealist, the latter was a realist.*

Don Quijote y Sancho; _____ fue realista, _____ fue idealista.

5. El almuerzo y la cena; *the former is eaten by day, the latter is eaten at night.*

El almuerzo y la cena; _____ se come de noche, _____ se come de día.

F. Contéstense en español, en frases completas, empleando en las respuestas un pronombre demostrativo, si es posible.

1. ¿Sacó Vd. ese libro de la biblioteca? _____

2. ¿Qué es esto que tengo en la mano? _____

3. La plata es más preciosa que el cobre; ¿cuál prefiere Vd., éste o aquélla? _____

_____

4. ¿Va Vd. a dar un paseo hoy? _____

5. Durante el año hace calor y frío; ¿le gusta más éste o aquél? _____

_____

6. ¿Cuándo compró Vd. esa corbata? _____

7. ¿Cambiaría Vd. esa pluma por la de Ana? _____

_____

8. ¿Exige mucho trabajo este maestro? _____

9. ¿Quiere Vd. borrar la pizarra con este borrador? _____

_____

10. ¿Sabe Vd. contestar bien a estas preguntas? _____

_____

G. Tradúzcanse al español.

1. This is impossible; I cannot accept this gift. _____

_____

2. This medicine is bitter; I prefer that one. _____

_____

3. That book is more interesting than this one. _____

_____

4. This dress is green; that one is blue. _____

_____

5. This is my problem: that girl does not love me. _____

_____

6. Helen and Richard are pupils; the former is studious, the latter is lazy. (Reverse the order.) _____

_____

7. Johnny, take off that shirt and put on this one. _____

_____

8. What is that? This is a leaf. --

----

9. These pictures don't interest me; I like those. --------------------------------------

----

10. Follow that man; he stole this woman's purse. -------------------------------------

----

11. Blasco Ibáñez and Campoamor were writers; the former was a novelist, the latter was a poet. (Reverse the order.) ---

----

12. This lesson is easier than last week's. --

----

13. Lima and Quito are cities; the former is in Peru, the latter is in Ecuador. (Reverse the order.) --

14. Those flowers are not as pretty as those you brought last week. ---------------------

----

15. I do not know those girls, but these are my cousins. ----------------------------------

----

16. Don't lose this money; that would be a pity. --

----

17. These gloves are (of) the same color as those you bought last month. ----------------

----

18. Bring us other plates; these are dirty. ---

----

19. Do you prefer these apples to those? --

----

20. That tall man is captain of this ship. ---

----

21. This book describes the capitals of all those countries. -------------------------------

----

22. These Mexican songs are similar to those of Spain. ------------------------------------

----

23. This chain is of gold; that one is of copper. ---

----

24. Michael and Louis are brothers; the former is tall, the latter is short. (Reverse the order.) ------

----

25. This farmer raises chickens and cows; the former are small, the latter are large. (Reverse the order.) --

----

Grammar Lesson 4—ADJECTIVES AND ADVERBS

ADJECTIVES

I. FORMS OF ADJECTIVES

1. *a.* Adjectives that end in -o in the masculine, and most adjectives expressing nationality, form the feminine by changing o to a or by adding **a.**

> **seco, seca,** dry
> **español, española,** Spanish

b. Other adjectives have the same form for both the masculine and feminine.

> **popular, popular,** popular
> **agradable, agradable,** pleasant
> **agrícola, agrícola,** agricultural

c. The following adjectives, which end in a consonant, add **a** for the feminine even though they do not indicate nationality.

> **encantador, encantadora,** charming
> **hablador, habladora,** talkative
> **trabajador, trabajadora,** hard-working
> **traidor, traidora,** treacherous

2. The plural is formed by:

a. adding **s** to adjectives whose singular form ends in a vowel: **secos, españolas, agradables.**

b. adding **es** to adjectives whose singular form ends in a consonant: **españoles, populares.**

Note

A. Adjectives whose singular form ends in -z change z to c in the plural: **feliz, felices.**

B. Sometimes it is necessary to add or to drop a written accent mark in order to keep the original stress, or because the accent is no longer needed to indicate stress.

> **joven, jóvenes,** young
> **francés, francesa, franceses, francesas,** French
> **inglés, inglesa, ingleses, inglesas,** English
> **alemán, alemana, alemanes, alemanas,** German
> **cortés, corteses,** courteous, polite

II. POSITION OF ADJECTIVES

1. *a.* Descriptive adjectives usually follow the nouns they modify.

> un **libro** *interesante*   an interesting book
> la **casa** *blanca*   the white house

b. Descriptive adjectives are sometimes placed before the noun. In such cases,

(1) they lose their literal meaning.

Wáshington fue un **_gran_ hombre.**
(figurative meaning)

> *but*

Mi tío es un **hombre _grande,_** casi un gigante.
(literal meaning)

Washington was a great man.

My uncle is a big man, almost a giant.

(2) they describe a quality of the noun that we generally take for granted.

Admiré los árboles, con sus *verdes* hojas.

> *but*

En el otoño, hay pocas **hojas** *verdes* en los árboles.

I admired the trees, with their green leaves. (We generally think of leaves as being green.)

In the autumn, there are few green leaves on the trees. (We distinguish green leaves, the normal color, from yellow, red, or brown leaves in autumn.)

Common adjectives that change in meaning with a change in position are:

	WHEN USED AFTER THE NOUN	WHEN USED BEFORE THE NOUN
antiguo, -a	old (ancient)	old (former), old-time
cierto, -a	sure, reliable	a certain
grande	large, big	great
mismo, -a	him (her, it)-self	same
nuevo, -a	new	another, different
pobre	poor	unfortunate
simple	silly, simpleminded	simple, mere

c. Some adjectives are used either before or after the noun, without any significant difference in meaning.

> un **día** *bueno (malo)*
> un ***buen (mal)* día** } a good (bad) day

2. Limiting adjectives (numbers, articles, possessive and demonstrative adjectives, adjectives of quantity) usually precede the noun.

> *dos* plumas, two pens
> *los* héroes, the heroes
> *mis* primos, my cousins
>
> *aquel* hombre, that man
> *tal* cosa, such a thing
> *menos* dinero, less money

Common adjectives of quantity are:

algunos (-as), some
cada, each, every
cuanto (-a, -os, -as), as much
más, more
menos, less
mucho (-a, -os, -as), much, many
ningunos (-as), no, not any

numerosos (-as), numerous
poco (-a, -os, -as), little, few
tanto (-a, -os, -as), so much, so many
todo (-a, -os, -as), all, every
unos (-as), some, a few
varios (-as), several

III. AGREEMENT OF ADJECTIVES

    1. Adjectives agree in gender and number with the nouns they modify.

Juana es aplica*da*.	Jane is studious.
Mis **hijos** son perezos*os*.	My children are lazy.

    2. An adjective that modifies two or more nouns of different gender is in the masculine plural.

La pluma y **el lápiz** son roj*os*.	The pen and the pencil are red.

IV. SHORTENING OF ADJECTIVES

    1. The following adjectives drop the final **-o** when used before a masculine singular noun:

uno, one, a, an	*un* libro, one (a) book
bueno, good	un *buen* caballo, a good horse
malo, bad	un *mal* año, a bad year
primero, first	el *primer* día, the first day
tercero, third	el *tercer* piso, the third floor
alguno, some	*algún* día, some day
ninguno, no, not any	*ningún* dinero, no money

Note

If a preposition comes between these adjectives and the noun, the full form of the adjective is used.

uno **de** los tres	one of the three
el *tercero* **del** grupo	the third (one) of the group

    2. **Santo** becomes **San** before the masculine name of a saint, except with names beginning with **To-** or **Do-**.

San Juan	Saint John
San Francisco	Saint Francis
but	
Santo Tomás	Saint Thomas
Santo Domingo	Saint Dominic
Santa Teresa	Saint Theresa

    3. **Grande** becomes **gran** when used before a singular noun of either gender.

un *gran* hombre	a great man
una *gran* poetisa	a great poetess
but	
un edificio **grande**	a large building
una casa **grande**	a large house

    4. **Ciento** becomes **cien** before a noun of either gender, and before the numbers **mil** and **millones**. This does not occur with multiples of **ciento** (**doscientos, trescientos,** etc.), or in combination with any other number (**ciento diez**).

cien libros (muchachas)	one (a) hundred books (girls)
cien mil años	one (a) hundred thousand years
cien millones de dólares	one (a) hundred million dollars

but

cuatrocientos coches (**cuatrocientas** personas)	four hundred cars (four hundred people)
ciento veinte y siete sillas	one (a) hundred twenty-seven chairs

ADVERBS

1. Adverbs are regularly formed from adjectives by adding **-mente** to the feminine singular form of the adjective.

un hombre **rico**	a rich man
un hombre *ricamente* vestido	a richly dressed man
Es un trabajador **hábil**.	He is a skillful worker.
Lo fabricó *hábilmente*.	He made it skillfully.

Note

In a series of two or more "**-mente**" type adverbs, -mente is used only with the last.

Paco escribió *clara, rápida,* y *fácilmente*.	Frank wrote clearly, rapidly, and easily.
(Note the feminine forms.)	

2. Adverbial phrases may be formed by the use of **con** plus a noun.

La joven cantaba *con alegría* (alegremente).	The young girl sang with happiness (happily).
Saludó a la dama *con cortesía* (cortésmente).	He greeted the lady with courtesy (courteously).

3. The words **más, menos, poco, mucho, mejor, peor,** and **demasiado** may be used either as adjectives or adverbs.

Pablo es *más* pobre que yo; tiene *menos* dinero. 　(adverb)　　　　　　(adjective)	Paul is poorer than I; he has less money.
La Sra. Álvarez es *demasiado* rica; tiene *demasiadas* joyas. 　　　　　(adverb)　　(adjective)	Mrs. Álvarez is too rich; she has too many jewels.
María canta *peor* que su hermana; ésta tiene *mejor* voz. 　　　(adverb)　　(adjective)	Mary sings worse than her sister; the latter has a better voice.

Note

As adjectives, **mucho, poco,** and **demasiado** vary in gender and number; as adverbs, they do not change.

4. Some adverbs have forms distinct from the adjective forms.

bueno, good	**bien,** well
malo, bad	**mal,** badly, ill

Arturo es un *buen* músico y toca *bien* el piano. 　　　　　(adjective)　　　(adverb)	Arthur is a good musician and plays the piano well.
Juanito es un muchacho *malo;* trata *mal* a su hermana. 　　　　　　　(adjective)　(adverb)	Johnny is a bad boy; he treats his sister badly.

EJERCICIOS

A. Escríbanse las formas femenina singular y masculina plural de los siguientes adjetivos:

	FEMININE SINGULAR	MASCULINE PLURAL
1. brillante		
2. joven		
3. militar		
4. castellano		
5. horrible		
6. feliz		
7. fácil		
8. encantador		
9. peor		
10. capaz		
11. moral		
12. ardiente		
13. común		
14. árabe		
15. oriental		
16. agrícola		
17. conforme		
18. americano		
19. célebre		
20. mundial		
21. feroz		
22. hábil		
23. central		
24. madrileño		
25. doble		
26. útil		
27. general		
28. hablador		
29. corriente		
30. cortés		

B. Tradúzcanse al español las palabras en inglés.

1. No puedo ofrecerte *any* (negative) _____ consejos.

2. *No* _____ castigo es suficiente para ese criminal.

3. *Saint* _____ Jorge es el santo patrón de Inglaterra.

4. El *third* _____ libro desapareció del estante.

5. El *first* _____ viaje de Colón se verificó en 1492.

6. Lea Vd. la *first* _____ página.

7. *Saint* _____ Bárbara vivió hace muchos siglos.

8. Siempre consultaba *a* _____ diccionario.

9. Hay más de *one hundred* _____ clases de insectos.

10. El grupo se reúne el *first* _____ martes del mes.

11. *Some* _____ día seré rico.

12. Ese muchacho tiene *bad* _____ costumbres.

13. Velázquez fue un *great* _____ pintor.

14. Éste no es un *good* _____ piano.

15. Cervantes y Lope de Vega fueron *great* _____ escritores.

16. El ejército consistía en menos de *one hundred* _____ mil tropas.

17. Colón descubrió la isla de *Saint* _____ Domingo.

18. Anunció la *good* _____ noticia.

19. Es necesario que me compres *some* _____ corbatas.

20. *That* _____ poeta compone *bad* _____ versos.

21. Le afligía *an* _____ enfermedad.

22. Ayer fue un *bad* _____ día.

23. Ésta es la *third* _____ vez que te aconsejo.

24. *Some* _____ ciudadanos no saben sus derechos.

25. *One hundred seventy-six* _____ alumnos sufrieron la prueba.

    C. Tradúzcanse al español las expresiones en inglés.

1. *That actor* _____ muestra *little talent* _____.

2. *Poor man!* _____ Se cayó y se hizo daño.

3. No quiso poner su capital en una *dangerous enterprise* _____.

4. *No song* _____ suena tan dulce como ésa.

5. El labrador fue un *poor man* _____.

6. En el armario había *six hats* _____.

7. En los rincones se veían *several images* _____.

8. El *boss himself* _____ puso el sello en el sobre.

9. *Each nation* _____ tiene su *own government* _____.

10. Tengo un *new job* _____.

11. *Our liberty* _____ es preciosa.

12. Quiero presentarle a mi *old friend* _____.

13. *The white snow* _____ cubrió *all the land* _____.

14. A lo lejos se elevaban las *high mountains* _____.

15. El diario de hoy llevará *reliable news* _____.

16. *Some members* _____ llegaron a la reunión a las siete.

17. Los *two cats* _____ comieron del *same plate* _____.

18. *The whole town* _____ contribuyó dinero para el hospital.

19. No se mezcle Vd. en *such matters* _____.

20. Al amanecer, vieron una *desert island* _____.

21. Falta un *mere detail* _____.

22. *A certain inventor* _____ carecía de fondos.

23. No bebas *so much coffee* _____; no podrás dormir.

24. Los *brilliant rays* _____ del sol alumbraron el día.

25. *This* _____ viejo es un *simpleminded man* _____.

26. El empleado envolvió *each package* _____ en papel.

27. ¿*How many pencils* _____ hay en el escritorio?

28. *That newspaper* _____ publica *interesting articles* _____.

29. El peluquero tenía una *pretty granddaughter* _____.

30. La *new magazine* _____ acaba de publicarse.

D. Fórmense adverbios de los adjetivos, y tradúzcase al inglés cada adverbio.

EJEMPLO: ricos—ricamente, richly

1. felices _____   _____

2. valiente _____   _____

3. constantes _____   _____

4. popular _____   _____

5. afortunadas _____   _____

6. actuales _____   _____

7. ciertos _____   _____

8. impaciente _____   _____

9. curioso _____   _____

10. excelentes _____   _____

E. Escríbase una expresión adverbial (con + sustantivo) que corresponda a los adverbios.

EJEMPLO: cortésmente—con cortesía

1. claramente _____   6. frecuentemente _____

2. seguramente _____   7. alegremente _____

3. dulcemente _____   8. orgullosamente _____

4. amargamente _____   9. curiosamente _____

5. violentamente _____   10. tristemente _____

F. Contéstense en español en frases completas.

1. ¿Es grande o pequeño el automóvil de su familia? _____

_____

2. ¿Es España un país agrícola o comercial? _____

_____

3. ¿Pertenece Vd. al club español de la escuela? _____

_____

4. ¿Fue fácil la conquista de México? _____

_____

5. ¿Son más cariñosos sus padres o sus tías? _____

_____

6. ¿Quién es la muchacha rubia (morena) de la tercera fila? _____

_____

7. ¿Tiene Vd. pocos o muchos amigos? _____

_____

8. ¿Le gusta a Vd. una toronja fresca por la mañana? _____

_____

9. ¿Tiene Vd. admiración para alguna persona de esta clase? _____

_____

10. ¿Confiaría Vd. sus secretos íntimos a personas discretas? _____

_____

11. ¿Toma Vd. baños fríos o calientes? _____

_____

12. ¿Saluda Vd. cortésmente (con cortesía) a sus conocidos? _____

_____

13. ¿Es demasiado difícil el español? _____

_____

14. ¿Es Vd. más o menos perezoso(-a) que sus condiscípulos? _____

_____

15. ¿Le gusta a Vd. la compañía de gente culta? _____

_____

16. ¿Hace Vd. ejercicios físicos todos los días? _____

_____

17. ¿Cuál es el baile típico de México? _____

_____

18. ¿Tiene nuestro presidente fama mundial? _____

_____

19. ¿Prefiere Vd. una almohada blanda o dura? _____

_____

20. ¿Viajó Colón hacia el este o el oeste para descubrir el Nuevo Mundo? _____

_____

21. ¿Está Vd. orgulloso(-a) de sus notas en esta clase? _____

_____

22. ¿Es más profundo un lago o el mar? _____

_____

23. ¿Es seguro el techo de su casa? _____

_____

24. ¿Son simpáticos sus condiscípulos? _____

_____

25. ¿Escucha Vd. atentamente (con atención) en esta clase? _____

_____

G. Tradúzcanse al español.

1. The electrical apparatus does not work (funcionar) in this dry climate. _____

_____

2. Upon entering the dark house, he felt a vague terror. _____

_____

3. All his neighbors made useless efforts to extinguish the fire. _____

_____

4. Some treat their enemies severely and cruelly. _____

_____

5. The old grandmother will send a post-card to her beloved grandson. _____

_____

6. The pen is more powerful than the sword. _____

_____

7. Gabriela Mistral and Rubén Darío were famous poets of Spanish America. _____

_____

8. My mother cooks well, but my aunt cooks badly. _____

_____

9. The supreme authority in this village is the new mayor. _____

_____

10. In our modern civilization, such a war should not occur. _____

_____

11. For political reasons the governor lowered the taxes. _____

12. In the large hall there were more than 200 chairs. _____

13. The wounded soldier felt a sharp pain. _____

14. On the opposite side of the street, he saw a great cathedral. _____

15. Mr. Hernández has a large library; it contains approximately a thousand books. _____

16. Poor man! In spite of his hundred million dollars, he is unfortunate. _____

17. The French lady spoke with a foreign accent. _____

18. The poor slave would not complain of his bad treatment. _____

19. They found themselves in a square room with gray walls. _____

20. Each bus is capable of carrying many passengers. _____

La llama es un animal de los Andes del Perú, algo semejante al camello, aunque mucho más pequeño que éste. Sirve a los indios de varios modos. Se usa como bestia de carga, y su lana se emplea en la fabricación de ropa.

Grammar Lesson 5—COMPARISONS

COMPARISONS OF INEQUALITY

1. Adjectives are compared as follows:

POSITIVE	bello(-a, -os, -as)	beautiful
COMPARATIVE	más(menos) bello(-a, -os, -as)	more (less) beautiful
SUPERLATIVE	el (la, los, las) . . . más (menos) bello(-a, -os, -as)	the most (least) beautiful

Este monumento es *bello.*	This monument is beautiful.
Ése es *más (menos) bello que éste.*	That one is more (less) beautiful than this one.
Aquél es *el* monumento *más (menos) bello del país.*	That one is the most (least) beautiful monument in the country.
Aquella flor es *la más (menos) bella del jardín.*	That flower is the most (least) beautiful (one) in the garden.
Es *la mejor (peor)* actriz *del mundo.*	She is the best (worst) actress in the world.

Note

A. In the superlative, if a noun is expressed, it is placed between the article (**el, la, los, las**) and the adjective.

B. After the superlative, *in* is expressed by **de.**

2. The comparative forms of **bueno, malo, grande,** and **pequeño** are irregular.

POSITIVE	COMPARATIVE	SUPERLATIVE
bueno(-a, -os, -as), good	**mejor(-es),** better	el (la) mejor / los (las) mejores } the best
malo(-a, -os, -as), bad	**peor(-es),** worse	el (la) peor / los (las) peores } the worst
grande(-s), great, big	**mayor(-es),** greater, older	el (la) mayor / los (las) mayores } the greatest, the oldest
	más grande(-s), larger	el (la) más grande / los (las) más grandes } the largest
	menos grande(-s), less large	el (la) menos grande / los (las) menos grandes } the least large
pequeño(-a, -os, -as), small	**menor(-es),** minor, lesser, younger	el (la) menor / los (las) menores } the least, the youngest
	más pequeño(-a, -os, -as), smaller	el (la) más pequeño(-a) / los (las) más pequeños(-as) } the smallest
	menos pequeño(-a, -os, -as), less small	el (la) menos pequeño(-a) / los (las) menos pequeños(-as) } the least small

162

Note

A. **Mejor** and **peor** generally precede the noun. **Mayor** and **menor** generally follow the noun.

mi *mejor* amigo	my best friend
la **hermana** *mayor*	the older (oldest) sister

B. The regular and irregular comparative forms of **grande** and **pequeño** have different meanings. **Más grande** and **más pequeño** compare differences in size or height (physical meaning); **mayor** and **menor** compare differences in age or status (figurative meaning).

mi hermano *más pequeño*	my smaller (smallest) brother
mi hermano *menor*	my younger (youngest) brother

3. Adverbs are compared as follows:

rápidamente, quickly	más (menos) rápidamente, more (less) quickly	lo más (menos) rápidamente, the most (least) rapidly

Este tren corre *rápidamente*.	This train runs rapidly.
Ése corre *menos rápidamente*.	That one runs less rapidly.
Aquél corre *lo menos rápidamente de todos*.	That one runs the least rapidly of all.

Note

A. Since adverbs do not modify nouns, the article used with the superlative form is **lo** (neuter).

B. As with adjectives, the superlative form of the adverb is followed by **de.**

4. The English word *than* is most often translated by **que.**

Es más alta *que* yo.	She is taller than I.
Tienen menos dinero *que* yo.	They have less money than I.

Before a number, *than* is translated by **de** if the sentence is affirmative. If the sentence is negative, **que** is used.

Ganó más (menos) *de* ocho dólares.	He earned more (less) than eight dollars.
but	
No ganó más **que** ocho dólares.	He earned only eight dollars. (He didn't earn more than eight dollars.)

If the second part of the comparison has a different verb, **de** is used, together with some form of **el (la, los, las, lo) que.**

Gasta más dinero *del que* gana su padre.	He spends more money than his father earns.
Leyó menos libros *de los que* le recomendó el maestro.	He read fewer books than the teacher recommended.

Note

In each of the above sentences, the nouns **dinero** and **libros** are the objects of both verbs: **gasta—dinero, gana—dinero** (understood); **leyó—libros, recomendó—libros** (understood). If the noun is not the object of both verbs, or if the thing compared is an adjective or adverb, **de lo que** is used.

Gasta más dinero *de lo que* crees.	He spends more money than you think.
Habla más rápidamente *de lo que* escribe.	He speaks more rapidly than he writes.

In the first sentence above, the word **dinero** is not the object of both verbs (**gasta—dinero,** but **crees—que gasta dinero**). In the second sentence, the point of comparison is **rápidamente,** an adverb.

COMPARISONS OF EQUALITY

tan + adjective or adverb + **como,** as . . . as

Ella no es *tan pobre como* él.	She is not as poor as he.
Mi coche corre *tan rápidamente como* el suyo.	My car runs as fast as hers.

tanto(-a, -os, -as) + noun + **como,** as much (as many) . . . as

Esta vaca da *tanta leche como* aquélla.	This cow gives as much milk as that one.
Recibió *tantos juguetes como* pidió.	He received as many toys as he asked for.

tanto(-a, -os, -as) (pronoun) + **como,** as much (as many) . . . as

Leímos *tanto como* ellos.	We read as much as they.

Some expressions of comparison are:

lo más pronto posible
tan pronto como posible } as soon as possible

Venga a verme *lo más pronto posible.* .Come to see me as soon as possible.

cuanto(-a, -os, -as) más (menos) . . . , **tanto(-a, -os, -as) más (menos)** . . . } the more (less) . . . ,
cuanto(-a, -os, -as) más (menos) . . . , **más (menos)** . . . } the more (less) . . .

Cuanto más habla, *(tanto) menos* escucho.   The more he talks, the less I listen.

Note

Tanto may be omitted in the above expression.

ABSOLUTE SUPERLATIVE (NO COMPARISON)

1. To express a very high degree of an adjective, when no comparison is involved, **-ísimo(-a, -os, -as)** is often added to the adjective. The meaning is the same as **muy** plus the adjective.

muy barato
baratísimo } very cheap

Note

A. *Very much* is expressed by **muchísimo,** never by "muy mucho."

B. Adjectives ending in a vowel drop the final vowel before adding **-ísimo.**

C. Adjectives ending in **-co, -go,** or **-z** change **c** to **qu, g** to **gu,** and **z** to **c** before adding **-ísimo.**

fresco—fres**qu**ísimo   largo—lar**gu**ísimo   feroz—fero**c**ísimo

2. To form adverbs from adjectives that end in **-ísimo,** add **-mente** to the feminine form of the adjective: **riquísimamente, lentísimamente.**

EJERCICIOS

A. Escríbanse las formas superlativas de los adjetivos según el ejemplo.

EJEMPLO: bonito—las estrellas; más bonitas—bonitísimas

1. atento   los dependientes   _____   _____
2. difícil   la cura   _____   _____
3. feliz   el carnicero   _____   _____

4. generoso   el amo   ---------------------------   ---------------------------

5. breve   las ceremonias   ---------------------------   ---------------------------

6. profundo   la herida   ---------------------------   ---------------------------

7. popular   los juegos   ---------------------------   ---------------------------

8. cansado   el cochero   ---------------------------   ---------------------------

9. rápido   las corrientes   ---------------------------   ---------------------------

10. amargo   el destino   ---------------------------   ---------------------------

11. rico   las señoras   ---------------------------   ---------------------------

12. tonto   el sastre   ---------------------------   ---------------------------

13. dulce   los besos   ---------------------------   ---------------------------

14. barato   el arroz   ---------------------------   ---------------------------

15. triste   las consecuencias   ---------------------------   ---------------------------

B. Subráyese la forma correcta entre paréntesis.

1. En la tertulia hubo más (que, de los que, de) treinta invitados.

2. Mi tía es mayor (de, de la que, que) mi mamá.

3. Hay más gitanos en Francia (que, de, de los que) en Inglaterra.

4. Este queso no pesa más (que, de, del que) un kilogramo.

5. Aquel chico es menos inocente (de lo que, que, del que) sus padres creen.

6. El pueblo tenía menos (que, de los que, de) mil habitantes.

7. En esta aldea hay más guardias (que, de los que, de) necesitan.

8. Puso en el plato más carne (de lo que, que, de la que) podría comer.

9. No voy a comprar más tarjetas (que, de lo que, de las que) puedo usar.

10. Se graduará más pronto (del que, que, de lo que) Vds. pueden imaginarse.

11. Aquel joven es más loco (que, de lo que, del que) Vds. pueden figurarse.

12. En la orquesta había más (que, de lo que, de) cien músicos.

13. ¡Ojalá tuviera más dinero (que, del que, de) encuentro en el bolsillo!

14. En el invierno hay más nieve (de la que, que, de lo que) en el otoño.

15. Luisa parece menos linda hoy (de lo que, de la que, que) ayer.

C. Tradúzcanse al español las expresiones en inglés.

1. Mi fortuna no es *smaller than* ---------------------------- la de mi socio.

2. Los españoles no eran *as numerous as* ---------------------------- los indios.

3. En su habitación hacía casi *as much heat as* ---------------------------- en la mía.

4. La princesa es *smaller than* ---------------------------- el príncipe.

5. La princesa es *younger than* ---------------------------- el príncipe.

6. Esta secretaria es *worse than* ---------------------------- la anterior.

7. Pablo estaba *very busy* ---------------------------- (one word)

8. Septiembre es *better than* _____ enero.

9. Probablemente hay *as many roses as* _____ claveles en el jardín.

10. Paco es mi hermano *youngest* _____.

11. Su esposo no le permite hacer *as many purchases as* _____ desea.

12. La zapatería es *larger than* _____ la peluquería.

13. Cervantes no escribió *as many dramas as* _____ Lope de Vega.

14. Mi sacrificio puede considerarse *greater than* _____ el tuyo.

15. El cielo es *as blue as* _____ el mar.

16. La sábana es *less large than* _____ la cama.

17. Los sobres deben ser *larger than* _____ las cartas.

18. Trabaja *as diligently as* _____ cualquiera por el bien de la humanidad.

19. Ese comerciante es *very miserly* _____. (one word)

20. La avenida en que yo vivo es *very wide* _____. (one word)

   D. Contéstense en español en frases completas.

1. ¿Fue ayer un día más claro que hoy? _____

   _____

2. ¿Trabaja Vd. menos de lo que aconseja el maestro? _____

   _____

3. ¿Abandonaría Vd. a su mejor amigo? _____

   _____

4. ¿Es Vd. tan fuerte como su hermano(-a)? _____

   _____

5. ¿Le dan sus padres más dinero del que Vd. puede gastar? _____

   _____

6. ¿Es Vd. el (la) estudiante más aplicado(-a) de esta clase? _____

   _____

7. ¿Es mejor la radio que la televisión? _____

   _____

8. ¿Escucha Vd. atentísimamente en la clase? _____

   _____

9. ¿Está Vd. acostumbrado(-a) a comer más de lo que necesita? _____

   _____

10. ¿Está Vd. más cómodo(-a) en casa que en un hotel? _____

   _____

11. ¿Es larguísima la distancia desde su casa a la escuela? _____

   _____

12. ¿Hay tanta lluvia en agosto como en abril? _____

_____

13. ¿Hace tanto calor en la primavera como en el verano? _____

_____

14. ¿Es tan feroz el león como el oso? _____

_____

15. ¿Hay tantos insectos en diciembre como en julio? _____

_____

16. ¿Estudió Vd. muchísimo anoche? _____

_____

17. ¿Lleva Vd. a la escuela menos libros de los que necesita? _____

_____

18. ¿Está Vd. cansadísimo(-a) después de un día de trabajo? _____

_____

19. ¿Es más bella la primavera que el invierno? _____

_____

20. ¿Hay más páginas en el libro de gramática de las que Vd. puede estudiar? _____

_____

E. Tradúzcanse al español.

1. There are more museums in Germany than I can visit. _____

_____

2. The Amazon is longer than the Orinoco. _____

_____

3. The more he eats, the more he wants. _____

_____

4. The banker was the most respected man in the group. _____

_____

5. That soldier fought the least heroically of the whole army. _____

_____

6. "Cerebro" has as many letters as "céntimo." _____

_____

7. Grandmothers are more indulgent than mothers. _____

_____

8. The Romans were not as barbarous as the Aztecs. _____

_____

9. The baker makes more bread than he can sell. _____

_____

10. This magazine describes the capitals of more than forty states. -------------------------

----

11. The cook threw as much salt into the soup as into the salad. -------------------------

----

12. There was more fruit (*pl.*) in the orchard than they could eat. -------------------------

----

13. The bull was fiercer than the bullfighter had imagined. -------------------------

----

14. This author speaks as wittily as he writes. -------------------------

----

15. It was the most glorious victory of the campaign. -------------------------

----

16. Has that scientist much genius? He has as much as any other. -------------------------

----

17. The more it rains, the less it snows. -------------------------

----

18. Cortés' conquest was more glorious than that of Pizarro. -------------------------

----

19. The small knife is not as sharp as the big one. -------------------------

----

20. The donkey walks more slowly than the horse. -------------------------

----

Los sacerdotes que acompañaron a los conquistadores al Nuevo Mundo se dedicaron a civilizar al indio y convertirle a la fe católica. Hasta hoy día se ven, en Tejas, Nuevo México, Arizona, y California, los restos de las misiones que establecieron. Una misión generalmente consistía en una iglesia, una escuela, y varios otros edificios. Muchos de estos centros llegaron a ser ciudades importantes.

Grammar Lesson 6—MASTERY EXERCISES

(LESSONS 1–5)

A. Escríbase la forma del género (gender) opuesto de las palabras que siguen: (See Grammar Lesson 1, page 129.)

EJEMPLOS: la alemana—el alemán
el amigo—la amiga

1. la enemiga _____ 11. el varón _____

2. la princesa _____ 12. el joven _____

3. el marido _____ 13. la portuguesa _____

4. la gallina _____ 14. la mamá _____

5. el emperador _____ 15. el rey _____

6. el esposo _____ 16. la artista _____

7. la poetisa _____ 17. la condesa _____

8. el italiano _____ 18. el francés _____

9. doña _____ 19. la azteca _____

10. la escultora _____ 20. el testigo _____

B. Escríbase el artículo definido delante de cada uno de los sustantivos. (See Grammar Lesson 1, page 129.)

1. _____ naciones

2. _____ ciudad

3. _____ almas

4. _____ alumnos

5. _____ especie

6. _____ unión

7. _____ mapa

8. _____ avión

9. _____ idioma

10. _____ muchedumbre

11. _____ hacha

12. _____ clima

13. _____ mano

14. _____ tranvía

15. _____ drama

C. Escríbanse las formas posesivas que correspondan a los sustantivos. (See Grammar Lesson 2, page 139.)

EJEMPLO: (their) __su__ hermano; (theirs) __el suyo__

1. (their) _____ víctima; (theirs) _____

2. (our) _____ victorias; (ours) _____

3. (your, *fam. sing.*) _____ sacrificio; (yours) _____

4. (her) _____ reloj; (hers) _____

5. (his) _____ amor; (his) _____

6. (my) _____ salud; (mine) _____

7. (your, *pol. pl.*) _____ obra; (yours) _____

8. (your, *fam. pl.*) _____ proyectos; (yours) _____

9. (its) _____ aspecto; (its) _____

10. (his) _____ virtudes; (his) _____

11. (our) _____ tierra; (ours) _____

12. (my) _____ sistema; (mine) _____

13. (his) _____ propiedades; (his) _____

14. (her) _____ voto; (hers) _____

15. (my) _____ sentimientos; (mine) _____

D. Escríbanse las formas demostrativas que correspondan a los sustantivos. (See Grammar Lesson 3, page 146.)

EJEMPLO: (this) ___*este*___ hermano; (this one) ___*éste*___

1. (these) _____ orquestas; (these) _____

2. (that, *near*) _____ castillo; (that one) _____

3. (this) _____ flor; (this one) _____

4. (those, *remote*) _____ botellas; (those) _____

5. (those, *remote*) _____ pasajeros; (those) _____

6. (this) _____ respuesta; (this one) _____

7. (these) _____ uvas; (these) _____

8. (those, *near*) _____ salidas; (those) _____

9. (that, *remote*) _____ pico; (that one) _____

10. (these) _____ peligros; (these) _____

E. Escríbase la forma correcta del adjetivo, poniéndolo en la posición correcta. (See Grammar Lesson 4, page 152.)

EJEMPLOS: absoluto _____ autoridad ___*absoluta*___

un ___*una*___ pluma _____

1. ideal _____ belleza _____

2. varios _____ docenas _____

3. abundante _____ cosecha _____

4. hablador _____ abuela _____

5. soberbio _____ emperatrices _____

6. agrícola _____ país _____

7. extranjero _____ acento _____

8. cada _____ actor _____

9. amargo _____ medicina _____

10. cariñoso _____ abuelos _____

11. alguno _____ hotel _____

12. duro _____ colchón _____

13. ajeno _____ posesión _____

14. ciento _____ automóviles _____

15. capaz _____ administradores _____

F. Tradúzcanse al español las expresiones en inglés.

1. El general notó *how heroically* _____ que peleaban sus fuerzas.

2. Las vacas y las cabras comían *the green grass* _____.

3. Experimentó *the deepest love in* _____ su vida.

4. Carlota es *younger than* _____ su novio.

5. ¡Ay, *Captain* _____ Alvarez! Las tropas enemigas avanzan.

6. *Those* _____ libros son *Raymond's* _____; *ours* _____ están por ahí.

7. *Poor beast!* _____ Se ha roto *its* _____ pierna izquierda.

8. Con gesto impaciente, firmó *the important checks and letters* _____.

9. *The prettiest girl in* _____ la clase consintió en salir conmigo.

10. *Spanish* _____ es la lengua oficial de *Argentina* _____.

11. Desde el balcón *a friend of mine* _____ observó el vuelo de los pájaros.

12. *Commerce* _____ es la base de *our wealth* _____.

13. ¡*What a* _____ memoria tiene Vd., señor maestro!

14. Roberto ganó *one hundred seventeen* _____ dólares el mes pasado.

15. En toda la ciudad no había *more than a hundred* _____ guardias.

16. *The more* _____ se posee, *the more* _____ se desea.

17. Fabrican calcetines y los venden a veinte centavos *a pair* _____.

18. La isla de *Saint* _____ Domingo fue descubierta por Colón.

19. Los aviones vuelan *very rapidly* _____. (one word)

20. Alfonso *XIII* _____ fue el último rey de España.

21. *His* _____ pensamientos eran semejantes a *those* _____ de Sócrates.

22. Sólo tengo dudas; ¡ojalá tuviera *reliable news* _____!

23. Imitó a su héroe *more faithfully than* _____ yo hubiera creído.

24. *Mr.* _____ Gómez se asustó al encontrarse solo en el bosque.

25. Con el dedo, indicó *the third* _____ estante.

26. La vida civil es *less dangerous than* _____ la vida militar.

27. *The picturesque* _____ me hace una *deep impression* _____ _____.

28. Yo cuidaré *my* _____ propiedad, y tú cuidarás *yours* _____.

29. En la capilla se encontraban *as many images as* _____ en la catedral.

30. El caballero bajó *his head* _____ con ademán triste.

31. *This* _____ planta es del Perú; *that one* _____ de Chile.

32. El banquero era *very rich* _____ (one word)

33. ¿*Whose* _____ es el tocadiscos que está en el escritorio?

34. Hoy es *Monday* _____; *on Tuesday* _____ me marcho de aquí.

35. Alberto y Bárbara son hermanos; *the former is twelve years old* _____ _____, *the latter fourteen* _____.

G. Tradúzcanse las frases al español.

1. Peace is better than war. _____

2. To take leave of someone, in Spanish one says "adiós". _____
_____

3. Giving is a virtue; stealing is a vice. _____
_____

4. This apparatus is not cheap, but it is the worst in the factory. _____
_____

5. Several Arabs appeared, mounted on horseback. _____
_____

6. "What is this?" asked the teacher, lifting an object. _____
_____

7. The farmer and the merchant work hard; the former in the country, the latter in an office. _____
_____
_____

8. The lawyer knows how to speak Portuguese and English. _____
_____

9. The hen lays fewer eggs than I need. _____
_____

10. No father has as much patience as ours. _____
_____

11. He doesn't write as well as Louise. _____
_____

12. Six hundred ladies attended the function. _____
_____

13. He contributed more money than my uncle for the orphans. _____
_____

14. France is smaller than the United States. _____
_____

15. The teacher doesn't want to correct my essay, but he corrected Mary's. _____
_____
_____

16. Upon hearing the bells of the church, the boy put on his hat and left the house. _ _ _ _ _ _ _ _ _ _ _

_ _

_ _

17. My uncle has four daughters; the youngest is called Martha. _ _ _ _ _ _ _ _ _ _ _ _ _ _ _ _ _ _ _

_ _

18. Saint Theresa wrote religious essays. _

_ _

19. The next day they undertook their great adventure. _

_ _

20. That day seemed very long. (one word) _

21. Her eyes are blue and her hair is black. _

_ _

22. Charles V was the father of Philip II. _

_ _

23. Columbus himself wouldn't be able to navigate in such darkness. _ _ _ _ _ _ _ _ _ _ _ _ _ _ _ _ _

_ _

24. At breakfast, he had fresh bread and milk. _

_ _

25. Whose serape is in the closet? It isn't mine. _

_ _

26. You have been absent more times than any other pupil. _

_ _

27. He is a skillful shoemaker, but he wants to be a barber. _

_ _

28. She composed the verses easily and quickly. _

_ _

29. In the garden there were a hundred species of plants. _

_ _

30. He did the work very easily. (one word) _

_ _

31. His project resulted (in) a failure because he had forgotten a mere detail. _ _ _ _ _ _ _ _ _ _ _ _

_ _

_ _

32. Get up immediately; you have an appointment at nine o'clock. _ _ _ _ _ _ _ _ _ _ _ _ _ _ _ _ _ _

_ _

33. The inspector had little intelligence and much authority. _

_ _

34. Cervantes wrote in the Golden Age, the glorious era of Castilian literature. _ _ _ _ _ _ _ _ _ _ _ _ _ _

_ _

_ _

35. December marks the beginning of winter; March, the beginning of spring. _ _ _ _ _ _ _ _ _ _ _ _ _ _

_ _

_ _

En Hispanoamérica "la fiesta de los quince" es una ocasión especial para las muchachas porque generalmente a esa edad empiezan a salir con muchachos. La "quinceañera" se viste de blanco para esta fiesta y va acompañada de sus padres y 14 muchachas. Al llegar a la fiesta, ella se quita los zapatos de tacón bajo y se pone zapatos de tacón alto para mostrar que ya es mujer y no niña. Según la costumbre, la quinceañera baila primero con su padre y luego con el joven que es su pareja ("date") en esa ocasión.

Grammar Lesson 7—PERSONAL PRONOUNS

SUBJECT PRONOUNS

SINGULAR	PLURAL
yo, I **tú,** you (*fam.*) **usted (Vd.),** you **él,** he **ella,** she	**nosotros, -as,** we **vosotros, -as,** you (*fam.*) **ustedes (Vds.),** you **ellos,** they (*masc.*) **ellas,** they (*fem.*)

Subject pronouns are not used in Spanish as often as in English. In most cases, the verb ending indicates the subject. Spanish subject pronouns are used for clarity, emphasis, and politeness.

Él leía mientras *yo* cantaba.	He was reading while I was singing.
No hagas eso; *yo* debo hacerlo.	Don't do that; *I* must do it.
Pase *Vd.;* tome *Vd.* asiento.	Enter; take a seat.

Note

The English word *it* is not expressed as a subject in Spanish.

¿Dónde está? Está en el cajón.	Where is it? It is in the drawer.

PREPOSITIONAL PRONOUNS

SINGULAR	PLURAL
mí, me **ti,** you (*fam.*) **usted (Vd.),** you **él,** him, it **ella,** her, it **sí,** yourself, himself, herself, itself	**nosotros, -as,** us **vosotros, -as,** you (*fam.*) **ustedes (Vds.),** you **ellos,** them (*masc.*) **ellas,** them (*fem.*) **sí,** yourselves, themselves

1. The prepositional pronoun is used as the object of a preposition and always follows the preposition.

No es **para** *mí;* es **para** *ellos.*	It's not for me; it's for them.

2. The pronouns **mí, ti,** and **sí** combine with the preposition **con** as follows:

    conmigo, with me

    contigo, with you (*fam.*)

    consigo, with you (yourself), with him (self), with her (self), with them (selves)

Note

A. The prepositional pronouns are identical with the subject pronouns, except for the forms **mí, ti,** and **sí.**

B. The forms **conmigo, contigo,** and **consigo** do not change in gender and number.

C. The familiar plural form **vosotros, -as** is used in Spain, but is rarely used in Spanish America, where the form **ustedes** is preferred.

SOME COMMON PREPOSITIONS

a, to, at
acerca de, about
además de, besides
alrededor de, around
ante, before, in the presence of
antes de, before
cerca de, near
con, with
contra, against
de, of, from
debajo de, beneath, under

delante de, in front of
dentro de, within
desde, from, since
después de, after
detrás de, behind
durante, during
en, in, on
encima de, above, on top of
enfrente de, in front of, opposite
entre, between, among
frente a, in front of

fuera de, outside of
hacia, toward
hasta, until
lejos de, far from
para, for, in order to
por, for, by, through
según, according to
sin, without
sobre, over, above
tras, after

OBJECT PRONOUNS

INDIRECT	DIRECT
SINGULAR	SINGULAR
me, (to) me **te,** (to) you (*fam.*) **le,** (to) you, (to) him, (to) her, (to) it	**me,** me **te,** you (*fam.*) **le,** you (*masc.*), him **lo,** him, it (*masc.*) **la,** you (*fem.*), her, it (*fem.*)
PLURAL	PLURAL
nos, (to) us **os,** (to) you (*fam.*) **les,** (to) you, (to) them	**nos,** us **os,** you (*fam.*) **los,** you, them (*masc.*) **las,** you, them (*fem.*)

Note

A. The forms **me, te, nos,** and **os** are both direct and indirect object pronouns. They are also reflexive pronouns. (See #1, page 64.)

B. Before an indirect object pronoun, the prepositions *to, for,* or *from* are understood, never stated.

Me dio el dinero.
(to) me

He gave me the money.

Me compró el libro.
(for) me

He bought me the book.

Me cobró el dinero.
(from) me

He collected the money from me.

POSITION OF OBJECT PRONOUNS

The object pronouns, direct or indirect, normally precede the verb. However, when used with an infinitive, a gerund (present participle), or an affirmative command, they are attached to the verb.

NORMAL POSITION

Juan *me* ve.   John sees me.

El maestro *les* ha hablado.   The teacher has spoken to them.

EXCEPTIONS

INFINITIVE	Deseo enviar*lo.* *or* *Lo* deseo enviar.	I want to send it.
GERUND (PRESENT PARTICIPLE)	Estoy enviándo*lo.* *or* *Lo* estoy enviando.	I am sending it.
AFFIRMATIVE COMMAND	Enví*elo* Vd. <u>(affirmative)</u> *but* No *lo* envíe Vd. <u>(negative)</u>	Send it. Don't send it.

Note

A. The object pronouns may either be attached to the infinitive or the gerund, or precede the "conjugated" form of the verb.

B. When the object pronoun is attached to the gerund or the affirmative command, a written accent mark is required on the stressed vowel of the verb in order to keep the original stress.

DOUBLE OBJECT PRONOUNS

1. When a verb has two object pronouns, the indirect object pronoun (usually a person) precedes the direct object pronoun (usually a thing).

Juan *me* lo da.   John gives it to me.

Juan *te* la da.   John gives it to you (*fam.*).

Juan *se* los da.   John gives them to you (him, her, them).

Juan *nos* las da.   John gives them to us.

Note

A. **Le** and **les** change to **se** before **lo, la, los, las.**

Juan **le** da el libro.   John gives the book to you (him, her).

Juan *se* lo da.   John gives it to you (him, her).

B. The various meanings of **se** may be clarified by adding **a Vd. (Vds.), a él (ella), a ellos (ellas).**

Su madre *se* lo da *a ella (a ellos).*   Her mother gives it to her (to them).

2. With regard to the verb, the position of double object pronouns is the same as outlined for single object pronouns.

NORMAL POSITION

Me lo da.   He gives it to me.

EXCEPTIONS

INFINITIVE	Desea dár*melo*. *or* *Me lo* desea dar.	He wants to give it to me.
GERUND (PRESENT PARTICIPLE)	Está dándo*melo*. *or* *Me lo* está dando.	He is giving it to me.
AFFIRMATIVE COMMAND	Dé*melo* Vd. (affirmative) *but* No *me lo* dé Vd. (negative)	Give it to me. Don't give it to me.

Note

A. Double object pronouns are kept together, never separated.

B. When both object pronouns are attached to the verb, a written accent mark must be used in order to keep the original stress.

EJERCICIOS

A. Cámbiense a pronombres las palabras en letra cursiva.

1. En la batalla de Lepanto, los cristianos los vencieron a _____ (*los turcos*).

2. Hay que tener paciencia con _____ (*los ciegos y los sordos*).

3. La zapatería está cerca de _____ (*la sastrería*).

4. Durante _____ (*la conferencia*) el público se mostraba impaciente.

5. Enfrente de _____ (*la reja*) el amante declaró su amor.

6. Entre _____ (*las expresiones de satisfacción general*) se oían unas quejas.

7. El testigo hizo su declaración ante _____ (*el juez*).

8. Quien no la ha visto a _____ (*Sevilla*), no ha visto maravilla.

9. Desde aquí hasta _____ (*el museo*) hay tres millas.

10. Contra _____ (*su voluntad*) tuvo que presenciar la escena.

11. Todos los viajeros deben bajar en _____ (*la próxima estación*).

12. España goza de _____ (*buen clima*), principalmente en el sur.

13. Después de _____ (*la función*) iremos a tomar un refresco.

14. Fuera de _____ (*su sueldo*), no tiene recursos.

15. Encima de _____ (*la montaña*), los exploradores pusieron la bandera de su patria.

B. Tradúzcanse al español las palabras en inglés.

1. Según _____ (*her*), vieron un baúl, y dentro de _____ (*it*) había ropa vieja.

2. Las cuatro entradas que has comprado no bastan. Para _____ (*you*) y para _____ (*me*), necesitamos dos; y para _____ (*them*), tres más.

3. El artista se asomó al balcón, y desde _____ (*it*) miraba la muchedumbre que pasaba delante de _____ (*him*).

4. No muy lejos de _____ (*us*), se veía una casa, y detrás de _____ (*it*), algunos montes.

5. Escuchadme bien: cerca de _____ (*you*) hay un árbol, y debajo de _____ (*it*), encontraréis un tesoro.

6. Esta muñeca es.para _____ (*you*); diviértete con _____ (*it*).

7. Me acuerdo de _____ (*them*), pero _____ (*they*) nunca se acuerdan de _____ (*me*).

8. Con su bicicleta recorrió toda la ciudad, montada en _____ (*it*) y llevando con _____ [*her(self)*] una guía.

9. Entraron en la casa; dentro de _____ (*it*) estaba la familia: los padres, y además de _____ (*them*), los tres hijos.

10. _____ (*With you*) es imposible ir de compras; siempre encuentras a un conocido, y con _____ (*him*) te pones a charlar.

11. Recibió la cuenta del camarero, se levantó de la mesa, y dejó sobre _____ (*it*) una propina para _____ (*him*).

12. Él quiere ir _____ (*with me*), pero yo prefiero ir sin _____ (*him*).

13. Con un "adiós" triste, se alejó de _____ (*us*) y fue hacia _____ (*her*).

14. La avenida era ancha; caminando por _____ (*it*), vieron que estaba llena de chicas, y con _____ (*them*), sus novios.

15. Compró un cuaderno para _____ (*himself*), y se puso a escribir en _____ (*it*).

C. Cámbiense las frases según los ejemplos.

EJEMPLOS: Va a colgar *el vestido.*   *a.* Va a _*colgarlo*_.

                                      b. _*Lo va a*_ colgar.

         Está colgando *el vestido.* *a.* Está _*colgándolo*_.

                                      b. _*Lo está*_ colgando.

1. Continúa cosiendo *la manga.*   *a.* Continúa _____.

                                   b. _____ cosiendo.

2. Desea abrir *la caja.*   *a.* Desea _____.

                                   b. _____ abrir.

3. El cura comienza a leer *a los niños*.

    a. El cura comienza a _____ .

    b. El cura _____ leer.

4. Siguió guardando *silencio*.

    a. Siguió _____ .

    b. _____ guardando.

5. Intenta interrumpir *al patrón*.

    a. Intenta _____ .

    b. _____ interrumpir.

6. Desean hablar *al maestro*.

    a. Desean _____ .

    b. _____ hablar.

7. ¿Quiere Vd. examinar *mis documentos?*

    a. ¿Quiere Vd. _____ ?

    b. ¿_____ Vd. examinar?

8. ¿Qué piensas decir *a la actriz?*

    a. ¿Qué piensas _____ ?

    b. ¿Qué _____ decir?

9. Debe cruzar *el puente*.

    a. Debe _____ .

    b. _____ cruzar.

10. Trataron de averiguar *la verdad*.

    a. Trataron de _____ .

    b. _____ averiguar.

11. Estaba pintando *retratos*.

    a. Estaba _____ .

    b. _____ pintando.

12. Está escribiendo *a Antonio y Catalina*.

    a. Está _____ .

    b. _____ escribiendo.

13. Van a cargar *el burro*.

    a. Van a _____ .

    b. _____ cargar.

14. Necesita ganar *novecientos dólares*.

    a. Necesita _____ .

    b. _____ ganar.

15. ¿Quiere Vd. dar algo *a los huerfanitos?*

    a. ¿Quiere Vd. _____ algo?

    b. ¿_____ Vd. dar algo?

D. Cámbiense las frases según los ejemplos.

EJEMPLOS: Hable Vd. *al profesor*.   Háblele Vd.

          No hable Vd. *al profesor*. No le hable Vd.

1. Haga Vd. *los arreglos*. _____

2. No atraviesen Vds. *el río*. _____

3. Hablen Vds. *al autor*. _____

4. No cantes tú *esa canción*. _____

5. Compila tú *la lista*. _____

6. No esconda Vd. *el diamante*. _____

7. Arregle Vd. *las camas*. _____

8. Consideren Vds. *el caso*. _____

9. Confiese Vd. *su crimen*. ------------------------------------

10. Convence tú *a tu adversario*. ------------------------------------

11. Enseñe Vd. bien *a la clase*. ------------------------------------

12. Noten Vds. *los detalles*. ------------------------------------

13. No escribáis *a Diego y Carlota*. ------------------------------------

14. Prosiga Vd. *su camino*. ------------------------------------

15. Suelte Vd. *ese gato*. ------------------------------------

E. Cámbiense las palabras en letra cursiva, empleando pronombres según los ejemplos.

EJEMPLOS: El mozo *sirvió el almuerzo a las señoras*.   Se lo sirvió.

Los alumnos *van a entregar sus informes al profesor*. Van a entregárselos.

1. El presidente *va a declarar su intención a los periodistas*. ------------------------------

2. *Envíen Vds. el paquete a dóña Francisca*. ------------------------------

3. El alcalde *distribuirá regalos a los enfermos* en el hospital. ------------------------------

4. *No digas mentiras a tus padres*. ------------------------------

5. *Viene a pedir ayuda a la policía*. ------------------------------

6. *Prepare Vd. la cena para su marido*. ------------------------------

7. La pobre mujer *echó la culpa a su esposo*. ------------------------------

8. *Robó la plata a Alfredo*. ------------------------------

9. La tribu vencida *cedió mucho terreno al conquistador*. ------------------------------

10. En el mapa *nos indicó las fronteras*. ------------------------------

11. *Piensa anunciar el resultado a su hermana Marta*. ------------------------------

12. Otra vez *está repitiendo el cuento a sus sobrinos*. ------------------------------

13. *No entregue Vd. la llave al administrador*. ------------------------------

14. Colón *ofreció a la reina el Nuevo Mundo*. ------------------------------

15. *Intentaron robar las alhajas a la dama*. ------------------------------

F. Escríbanse en español las frases siguientes, cambiando a pronombres las palabras en letra cursiva:

1. El criado aplicó *el oído*, y de dentro oyó *voces*.

    El criado ------------------------, y de dentro ----------------.

2. El ensayista siguió leyendo *el artículo* en *la revista*.

    El ensayista siguió ---------------- en --------------.

3. El emperador dirigió *palabras severas al avaro*.

    El emperador ------------------------------.

4. El explorador no va a recomendar *al marinero* para *otro empleo*.

    El explorador no va a ---------------- para ----------.

5. No expliques tú *cosas inútiles a tu nieta*.

    No -------------------------- tú.

6. Fijándose en *el cielo*, vieron *las nubes grises*.

Fijándose en _____, _____.

7. Cortés distribuyó *regalos* entre *los aztecas*.

Cortés _____ entre _____.

8. El trabajador metió *las naranjas* en *la cesta*.

El trabajador _____ en _____.

9. La actriz no quiere demostrar *su talento a los huéspedes*.

La actriz no quiere _____.

10. Juró *venganza* ante *la imagen*.

_____ ante _____.

11. La emperatriz regaló *una pulsera a la condesa*.

La emperatriz _____.

12. El abuelo espera encargar *el negocio a su nieto*.

El abuelo espera _____.

13. El prisionero se huyó de *la cárcel* y se dirigió hacia *el bosque*.

El prisionero se huyó de _____ y se dirigió hacia _____.

14. Los griegos enseñaron *su civilización a los romanos*.

Los griegos _____.

15. Proteja Vd. *a sus hijos* contra *los peligros*.

_____ Vd. contra _____.

G. Contéstense en español, empleando pronombres en lugar de las expresiones en letra cursiva.

EJEMPLO: ¿Tiene Vd. *admiración* por *su padre?*

Sí, la tengo por él.

1. ¿Le gusta a Vd. comer *pan?* _____

2. ¿Llevaría Vd. *un sombrero de paja* en *un día de frío?* _____

3. ¿Tiene un coche *cuatro ruedas?* _____

4. ¿Riñe Vd. a menudo con *sus hermanos(-as)?* _____

5. ¿Sabe Vd. coser con *aguja e hilo?* _____

6. ¿Pone Vd. *un punto* al fin de *cada frase?* _____

7. Al salir, ¿lleva Vd. consigo *un pañuelo?* _____

8. ¿Mueve Vd. *los labios* para hacer *sonidos?* _____

9. ¿Grita Vd. *a una persona* para despertarla? _____

10. ¿Ha mascado Vd. *chicle* alguna vez? _____

11. ¿Pisaría Vd. *una alfombra nueva* con *zapatos sucios?* _____

_____

12. ¿Siente Vd. *dolor* en *el brazo izquierdo?* _____

13. Cuando hace frío, ¿lleva Vd. *ropa de lana?* _____

14. ¿Comprende Vd. *el uso del subjuntivo?* _____

15. ¿Da Vd. *saludos a sus conocidos?* _____

16. ¿Condenaría Vd. *a alguien* por *una leve falta?* _____

17. ¿Mira Vd. *la televisión* después *del trabajo?* _____

18. ¿Tiene su coche *llantas de caucho* en *las ruedas?* _____

19. ¿Lleva Vd. *zapatos* en *la cabeza?* _____

20. ¿Solicitaría Vd. *fondos* para *los pobres?* _____

_____

21. ¿Hay *una luz eléctrica* en *la esquina de su calle?* _____

22. ¿Está Vd. dispuesto(-a) a correr *riesgos* para ganar *dinero?* _____

_____

23. ¿Ha visto Vd. *elefantes* en *el circo?* _____

24. ¿Escoge Vd. *el paño* para *sus vestidos?* _____

25. ¿Prestaría Vd. *dinero a sus amigos,* si pudiera? _____

_____

H. Tradúzcanse al español.

1. Return (vosotros) it to them. (the money to John and Joseph) _____

_____

2. I will continue selling them to them. (newspapers to the passengers) _____

_____

3. Does she prefer to come with me or with him? _____

_____

4. We cannot tell it to you now. (the truth to you, *fam. plur.*) _____

_____

5. He will tell it to him. (the case to the judge) _____

_____

6. Send (tú) it to her immediately. (the package to Louise) _____

_____

7. He promised it to her. (eternal love to Juliet) _____

_____

8. We are going to write it to him. (a letter to the teacher) _____

_____

9. This check is for you (*fam.*), and the other one is for her. _____

_____

10. They were proposing it to them. (a new plan to their friends) _____

_____

11. The employees have not given it to him. (a gift to the boss) ------------------

----

12. Will he explain them to us today? (Spanish verbs) ------------------

----

13. Good morning, my dear Mr. Gómez. Enter; take off your coat. ------------------

----

14. I hope to show it to them tomorrow. (the necklace to the ladies) ------------------

----

15. He had devoted it to her. (much time to his mother) ------------------

----

16. She took a trip, and took her daughter with her. ------------------

----

17. Bring me coffee; I can't begin the day without it. ------------------

----

18. He paid it to him. (the debt to the baker) ------------------

----

19. Distribute (Vd.) them to them. (candies to the children) ------------------

----

20. He doesn't want to indicate it to them. (the road to the travelers) ------------------

----

A la vuelta de Colón a España, después de su primer viaje, los reyes Fernando e Isabel le recibieron con honores, nombrándole Almirante. Colón no sólo describió lo que había visto en el Nuevo Mundo, sino que pudo mostrar ejemplos de las aves, las plantas, y el oro que había encontrado allí. También había llevado unos indios, que los reyes miraron con gran curiosidad.

INTERROGATIVES

The most common interrogative expressions are:

Pronouns	Adverbs
¿quién(-es)?, who? ¿prep. + quién(-es)?, . . . whom? ¿qué?, what? ¿cuál(-es)?, what? which? ¿cuánto(-a)?, how much? ¿cuántos(-as)?, how many?	¿cómo?, how? ¿para qué?, why? (for what purpose?) ¿por qué?, why? (because of what?) ¿dónde?, where? ¿cuándo?, when?

Adjectives
¿qué?, what? which?   ¿cuánto(-a)?, how much?   ¿cuántos(-as)?, how many?

A. ¿Qué?—¿Cuál?

As pronouns, **¿qué?** is used when asking for a *description, definition,* or *explanation;* and **¿cuál(-es)?** is used when asking for a *choice* or *selection.*

¿Qué es esto?	What is this?
¿Cuál de los dos desea Vd.?	Which of the two do you want?
¿Cuáles son los meses del año?	What are the months of the year?

As an adjective, **¿qué?** is generally used instead of **¿cuál(-es)?**

¿Qué libro desea Vd.?	Which book do you want?

B. ¿Por qué?—¿Para qué?

Both expressions may be translated in English as *Why?* **¿Por qué?** is used when asking *because of what?* **¿Para qué?** is used when asking *for what purpose?*

¿Por qué no viene Vd. con nosotros? Porque no quiero.	Why don't you come with us? Because I don't want to.
¿Para qué desea Vd. consultar ese libro? Para ver las fotos.	Why do you want to consult that book? To see the photos.

Note

A. **¿Por qué?** is logically used in a question if the reply begins with **porque** (because); **¿para qué?** is used if the reply begins with **para.**

B. Interrogative words, whether in direct or indirect questions, have written accent marks. Indirect questions, however, do not have question marks.

¿Quién es? No sé quién es.	Who is he? I don't know who he is.

EXCLAMATIONS

Exclamatory words, like interrogative words, have written accent marks. The most common exclamatory words are:

> ¡Qué . . . !, What . . . ! What a . . . ! How . . . !
> ¡Cuánto(-a) . . . !, How much . . . !
> ¡Cuántos(-as) . . . !, How many . . . !
> ¡Cuán . . . !, How . . . !

¡Qué día!	What a day!
¡Qué grande es!	How large it is!
¡Cuánto dinero tiene!	How much money he has!

Note

A. Exclamatory sentences have an inverted exclamation mark (¡) at the beginning and a normal one (!) at the end.

B. If the noun is modified, the exclamation is made more intense by placing **tan** or **más** before the adjective.

¡Qué día *tan* (*más*) hermoso!	What a beautiful day!

C. Before an adjective or adverb, ¡**qué** . . . ! (how . . . !) may be replaced by ¡**cuán** . . . ! **Cuán** occurs mainly in literary style.

¡Qué fácilmente lo hace! ⎫ *¡Cuán* fácilmente lo hace! ⎭	How easily he does it!

RELATIVE PRONOUNS

> **que,** that, which, who
> **quien(-es),** who
> **el (la, los, las) cual(-es),** which, who
> **lo cual,** which
> **el (la) que,** (the one) which, (the one) who, he (she) who
> **los (las) que,** (the ones) which, (the ones) who, those who
> **lo que,** what, which
> **cuyo(-a, -os, -as),** whose (relative adjective)

1. The most frequently used relative pronoun is **que**; it refers to both persons and things. After a preposition, however, **que** refers only to things; **quien(-es)** refers to persons.

	No Preposition	Preposition
Persons	el hombre *que* habló	la mujer *con quien* hablé
Things	el libro *que* leo	la pluma *con que* escribo

2. **Quien(-es)** is also used as subject to express *he (she, those, the one, the ones) who.* An alternate form is **el (la, los, las) que.**

Quien estudia siempre aprenderá.	He (She) who studies will always learn.
Los que estudian siempre aprenderán.	Those who study will always learn.

3. If there are two possible antecedents, **quien(-es)** or **que** is used to indicate the nearer of the two. The more distant antecedent is indicated by a form of **el (la, los, las) cual(-es)** or **el (la, los, las) que.** This use helps (through gender and number) to clarify the antecedent.

La madre de Felipe, *quien (que)* está <u> </u> (antecedent) enfermo, le cuida con cariño. (*Philip* is ill.)	The mother of Philip, who is ill, cares for him lovingly.
La madre de Felipe, *la cual (la que)* está en- <u> </u> (antecedent) ferma, no saldrá hoy. (*The mother* is ill.)	Philip's mother, who is ill, will not go out today.

4. The relative pronouns **el (la, los, las) cual(-es)** and **el (la, los, las) que** are also used after prepositions other than **a, con, de, en,** regardless of the location of the antecedent.

Subió a la cumbre, *desde la cual* <u> </u> (antecedent) (*desde la que*) vio el valle.	He climbed to the mountain top, from which he saw the valley.
La casa *delante de la cual (delante de la que)* (antecedent) estamos es la antigua residencia del gobernador.	The house in front of which we are standing is the old residence of the governor.

5. *a.* **Lo que** (= that which) is always used to express *what* as a relative pronoun (not interrogative).

Le di *lo que* me pidió.	I gave him what he asked me for.

b. The neuter forms **lo que** and **lo cual** are used to express *which* if the antecedent is a clause or an idea.

Pepe llegó tarde, *lo que (lo cual)* no le gustó al maestro.	Joe arrived late, which did not please the teacher.

6. **Cuyo(-a, -os, -as),** meaning *whose,* refers to both persons and things. It is a relative adjective and agrees with the thing (or person) possessed, not with the possessor.

El muchacho *cuya corbata* llevo es mi primo.	The boy whose tie I am wearing is my cousin.

EJERCICIOS

A. Fórmense preguntas según los ejemplos. (See Interrogatives, page 185.)

EJEMPLO: _¿Qué es la vida?_ La vida es un misterio.

1. _____ El acero es un metal.

2. _____ El béisbol es un deporte.

3. _____ La cabra es un animal.

4. _____ Un discípulo es un alumno.

5. _____ Un ensayista es un escritor.

EJEMPLO: *¿Qué libro desea Vd.?* Deseo este libro.

6. --- Me gusta más el mes de agosto.

7. --- Prefiero la blusa roja.

8. --- El quinto capítulo es el más interesante.

9. --- Asistiremos a la función de esta noche.

10. --- Nuestro equipo ganará.

EJEMPLO: *¿Cuál es la fecha de hoy?* Hoy es el veinte de marzo.

11. --- La comida de mediodía es el almuerzo.

12. --- Este señor es el habitante más viejo.

13. --- Carlota es la alumna más aplicada.

14. --- Buenos Aires es la capital de la Argentina.

15. --- Mi intención es salir.

EJEMPLO: *¿Cuál es el maestro más caro?* La experiencia es el maestro más caro.

16. --- Nuestra estación es la próxima.

17. --- Aquéllos son los turistas americanos.

18. --- Esta lámpara es la más brillante.

19. --- El centavo es la moneda de menos valor.

20. --- Andar a pie es la manera más barata de viajar.

B. Subráyese el pronombre interrogativo correcto. (See Interrogatives, page 185.)

1. ¿(Por qué, Para qué) le afligen tanto sus recuerdos? Porque ha sido un mal hombre.

2. No sé (dónde, donde) está el Escorial.

3. Me indicó (cuántos, cómo) podría penetrar en el vestíbulo.

4. ¿(Cuál, Dónde) es el pueblo más cercano?

5. ¿(Por qué, Para qué) han construido el acueducto? Para llevar agua.

6. ¿(Qué, Quién) es más inteligente, León o Manuel?

7. ¿(Cuándo, Quién) se abre la zapatería?

8. ¿(Cuánto, Cómo) adquirió sus riquezas?

9. ¿De (quién, cuál) es esta moneda de cobre?

10. ¿(Por qué, Para qué) compró el brazalete? Para regalárselo a su esposa.

11. Acaso me digas (porque, cuándo) llegarás.

12. Le pregunté en (qué, lo que) mes había más hielo.

13. Le pregunté (por qué, para qué) no tenía apetito. Confesó que ya había comido.

14. Quiero averiguar (cuáles, qué) son los puntos de interés.

15. ¿(Cuántos, Dónde) están las Provincias Vascongadas?

16. ¿(Cuántos, Qué) pies tiene el gato?

17. Dígame (cómo, cuántos) días hay en septiembre.

18. ¿(Cuál, Qué) es la oscuridad? La falta de claridad.

19. ¿A (cuál, qué) hora comienza la corrida?

20. ¿(Qué, Cuál) de esos países conquistó Pizarro?

C. Subráyese la forma exclamativa correcta. (See Exclamations, page 186.)

1. ¡(Qué, Cuánta) desgracia! Salí mal en la prueba de ayer.

2. ¡(Cuál, Qué) idioma tan difícil!

3. ¡(Cuán, Qué) memoria! Sabe todas las fechas históricas.

4. ¡(Qué, Cómo) lentamente anda el burro!

5. ¡(Qué, Lo que) entusiasmo muestra por la música!

6. ¡(Cuántas, Cómo) alhajas le compró su esposo!

7. ¡(Qué, Lo que) historia más larga!

8. ¡(Cuán, Qué) mujer tan habladora!

9. ¡(Cómo, Cuán) hábilmente maneja el auto!

10. ¡(Cuáles, Qué) hechos tan heroicos!

11. ¡(Cuánto, Cuán) agudo es el cuchillo!

12. ¡(Qué, Cómo) cruelmente trata a sus parientes!

13. ¡(Cuán, Qué) gracia tiene la niña!

14. ¡(Cuántos, Cuán) aficionados asistieron al partido de fútbol!

15. ¡(Cómo, Qué) aplicado se muestra tu nieto!

D. Subráyese la expresión correcta. (See Relative Pronouns, pages 186–187.)

1. El bosque era oscuro, (lo cual, quien) les inspiró terror.

2. La enfermera de (quien, la cual) hablo trabaja en ese hospital.

3. A pesar de todo, hay que pagar los impuestos del gobierno, (el cual, los cuales) son muy altos.

4. Las leyendas de los moros, (quienes, cuyas) reinaron muchos siglos en España, son interesantes.

5. En la sala vio una cortina, detrás de (que, la cual) se escondió.

6. (Lo cual, Lo que) él dice no importa.

7. (Lo que, El que) imita buenos modelos será bueno.

8. Debemos mucho al sol, (de quienes, cuyos) rayos nos calientan.

9. Mencionó las razones en (que, los que) se apoyaba.

10. Conozco a varios madrileños, para (que, los cuales) siento verdadero afecto.

11. (Lo que, Quien) reconoce sus faltas, las debe corregir.

12. El inspector sacó un cuaderno en (que, lo que) escribió el nombre del testigo.

13. (Los cuales, Las que) aborrecen el mal vivirán felices.

14. Se acercaron a la catedral, delante de (que, la cual) quedaron asombrados.

15. No pudo realizar los sueños (quienes, que) tenía.

16. No puede figurarse (cual, lo que) piensa su amante.

17. La admiración (que, la cual) tengo por él es inmensa.

18. Aquel señor, (cuyo, cuya) nieta es mi amiga, es ingeniero.

19. Marta, a (que, quien) di las violetas, me sonrió con dulzura.

20. La actriz (que, la cual) fue aplaudida por el público no lo merecía.

E. Tradúzcanse al español las palabras inglesas.

1. ¿*Why* _____ salió Vd. de compras tan tarde? No quería salir temprano.

2. El guía *who* _____ nos acompañó era griego.

3. El galán reparó en la señorita, *which* _____ le molestó a ella.

4. Fue un día glorioso en *which* _____ nuestras fuerzas triunfaron.

5. ¿*Why* _____ busca Vd. un contador? Para arreglar las cuentas.

6. La bicicleta de Miguel, *which* _____ es nueva, funciona bien.

7. ¡*How* _____ rápidamente vuelan los aviones!

8. Con aire misterioso abrió la maleta, dentro de *which* _____ guardaba los documentos importantes.

9. ¿*What* _____ es un comedor?

10. Los pescadores, entre *whom* _____ se encontraban varios policías, gritaban y luchaban.

11. Recomendó de nuevo *what* _____ había recomendado antes.

12. ¡*How many* _____ fortunas se perdieron aquel día!

13. ¿*Whose* _____ es este anillo de platino?

14. *He who* _____ limita sus gastos siempre tendrá dinero.

15. ¡*How much* _____ me alegro de estar con Vds.!

16. ¿*What* _____ cambios harán en la casa?

17. ¿*Who* _____ se acordó de traer el tocadiscos?

18. El papá de Berta, *who* _____ es marinero, ha salido al mar.

19. El comerciante *whose* _____ suerte era mala perdió mucho.

20. ¿*Which* _____ de estas camisas prefiere Vd., las amarillas o las pardas?

21. ¿*By whom* _____ fueron comprados los billetes?

22. El ilustre compositor con *whom* _____ estudié me enseñó mucho.

23. ¡*What a* _____ desastre! Cinco personas murieron en el accidente.

24. Las fondas *which* _____ están en el camino son buenas.

25. *Those who* _____ conocen las joyas estiman los diamantes.

F. Contéstense en español en frases completas.

1. ¿Cómo se informa Vd. de los sucesos del día? _____

2. ¿Ha estado Vd. alguna vez en un pico desde el cual se podía contemplar mucho terreno? _____

3. ¿Por qué le gusta a Vd. el otoño? _____

4. ¿Sabe Vd. lo que es un desierto? _____

5. ¿Dónde guarda Vd. la navaja con que se afeita? _____

6. ¿Cuáles son las flores que le gustan más? _____

7. ¿Dónde vivían los aztecas a quienes venció Cortés? _____

8. ¿Con quién estudia Vd. generalmente? _____

9. ¿Qué significa el proverbio "Quien más tiene, más quiere"? _____

10. ¿Quién fue el escudero con quien viajó don Quijote? _____

11. ¿Qué país hispanoamericano produce mucho azúcar? _____

12. ¿Cuál es el insecto que más le molesta a Vd.? _____

13. ¿Por quién fue hecha la primera bandera americana? _____

14. ¿Cuántos condiscípulos tiene Vd. en esta clase? _____

15. ¿Para qué se usa un vaso? _____

G. Tradúzcanse al español.

1. The explorer did not know where or when he would come upon ferocious animals. _____

2. He wanted to see the palace, near which was a museum. _____

3. The beach, whose sand was gray, was very popular. _____

_____

4. How many continents are there, and what are they? _____

_____

5. The Indians with whom he lived treated him with kindness. _____

_____

6. What a day! How much rain has fallen! _____

_____

7. The child's doll, which is very large, says "Mama". _____

_____

8. He hung the suit in the closet, which was (estar) very dark. _____

_____

9. What a ship! How slowly it goes! _____

_____

10. Who is that man? He is Mr. Gómez. What is he? He is a banker. _____

_____

11. For whom did you buy that machine, and how much did you pay? _____

_____

12. The artist understands what is picturesque. _____

_____

13. Those who make fun of the unfortunate are very cruel. _____

_____

14. Why did the carpenter buy so much wood? In order to build a house. _____

_____

15. Which are the eyeglasses that you use for reading? _____

_____

16. Why didn't you wash your hands with soap? _____

_____

17. He who has much can spend much. _____

_____

18. The harvest was abundant, which pleased the farmers. _____

_____

19. The piano that is in the living room is the one I play. _____

_____

20. The current of the river, which was very swift, carried her downstream. _____

_____

Grammar Lesson 9—NEGATIVES; *PERO—SINO*

NEGATIVES

The principal negative words and their affirmative opposites are:

NEGATIVE	AFFIRMATIVE
no, no, not	**sí,** yes
nadie, no one, nobody, not anyone	**alguien,** someone, somebody
nada, nothing, not anything	**algo,** something
nunca ⎫ never, not ever **jamás** ⎭	**siempre,** always
tampoco, neither, not either	**también,** also
ninguno(-a), no, none, not any	**alguno(-a),** some, any
ni . . . ni, neither . . . nor; not . . . nor	**o . . . o,** either . . . or
sin, without	**con,** with

The most common negative word is **no.** It always precedes the verb.

Vd. *no sabe* la lección.	You don't know the lesson.
¿No sabe Vd. la lección?	Don't you know the lesson?

If an object pronoun precedes the verb, the negative word precedes the object pronoun.

Vd. *no* la *sabe.*	You don't know it.

Spanish sentences may have two or more negative words. If one of the negative words is **no,** it must precede the verb. If **no** is omitted, the other negative must precede the verb.

No veo *a nadie.* ⎫ *A nadie* veo. ⎭	I see no one. (I don't see anyone.)
No lo leyó *tampoco.* ⎫ *Tampoco* lo leyó. ⎭	He didn't read it either. (Neither did he read it.)
No usó *ni* papel *ni* lápiz. ⎫ *Ni* papel *ni* lápiz usó. ⎭	He used neither paper nor pencil. (He didn't use either paper or pencil.)

Note

If the negative word is preceded by a preposition, it retains that preposition when placed before the verb: **A nadie veo.**

Any, anyone, anything, and *ever* are translated by **ninguno, nadie, nada,** and **nunca (jamás)** (*a*) to express a comparison, and (*b*) when a negative thought is implied.

Sabe la historia mejor que *nadie.*	She knows history better than anyone.
La niña desea una muñeca más que *nada.*	The child wants a doll more than anything.
Ahora lo cree más que *nunca.*	Now he believes it more than ever.
¿Ha estado Vd. *jamás* en Venezuela?	Have you ever been in Venezuela?
¿Tiene Vd. dinero? No tengo *ninguno.*	Have you any money? I don't have any.
Salió sin decir *nada.*	He left without saying anything.

Ninguno, used as an adjective, may be replaced by **alguno.** When so used, **alguno** follows the noun, and the negative is more emphatic.

No tengo *ninguna* amiga.⎤
No tengo amiga *alguna.*⎦   I have no friend. (I don't have any friend.)

NEGATIVE EXPRESSIONS

Él no lo ve. *Ni* yo *tampoco.*	He doesn't see it. Neither do I. (Nor I either.)
Ya no tengo mis millones.	I no longer have my millions.
No me quedan *más que* diez centavos.⎤ *No* me quedan *sino* diez centavos.⎦	I have no more than ten cents left. (I have only ten cents left.)
¿Estás listo? *Todavía no.*	Are you ready? Not yet.
¿Puede Vd. pagarme? *Ahora no.*	Can you pay me? Not now.
Ni siquiera visita a su madre.	He does not even visit his mother.
¿Cómo van las cosas? *Sin novedad.*	How are things going? Nothing new. (The same as usual.)

PERO—SINO

Both **pero** and **sino** are translated *but.* However, their use differs. **Sino** is used only if the first clause of the sentence is negative and the second clause is in direct contrast to the first.

No habla portugués, *sino* español.	He doesn't speak Portuguese, but Spanish.
No llevaba camisa blanca, *sino* azul.	He wasn't wearing a white shirt, but a blue one.
No me gusta estudiar, *sino* ir al cine.	I don't like to study, but to go to the movies.

Note

A. In the above examples, the second part of the sentence is in direct contrast to the first: Portuguese is not Spanish, blue is not white, etc.

B. The comparison is always between two equivalent parts of speech (noun—noun, adjective—adjective, infinitive—infinitive).

If the two contrasting verbs are not infinitives, **sino que** is used instead of **sino.**

No cerró la puerta, *sino que* la dejó abierta.	He didn't close the door, but left it open.

In all other cases, **pero** is used.

No llueve, **pero** va a llover más tarde.	It's not raining, but it's going to rain later.
Tiene dinero, **pero** no es feliz.	He has money, but he is not happy.

Note

Pero means *but nevertheless;* **sino** means *but on the contrary.*

EJERCICIOS

A. Escríbanse las frases siguientes, empleando solamente *una* expresión negativa:

EJEMPLO: No leyó ningún libro.

    Ningún   libro leyó.

1. No se preocupó de nada.

   _____ se preocupó.

2. Hoy día no afirma nadie que el mundo es llano.

   Hoy día _____ afirma que el mundo es llano.

3. El valor de una obra maestra no se mide ni en dólares ni en pesetas.

   El valor de una obra maestra _____ se mide.

4. No dudaba jamás de la calidad de las mercancías.

   _____ dudaba de la calidad de las mercancías.

5. No le faltaba nada a la emperatriz.

   _____ le faltaba a la emperatriz.

6. No se atrevió nadie a dar un grito.

   _____ se atrevió a dar un grito.

7. No vio nada alrededor de sí.

   _____ vio alrededor de sí.

8. Yo no me he desayunado tampoco.

   Yo _____ me he desayunado.

9. No encerraron a nadie en la cárcel.

   _____ encerraron en la cárcel.

10. Fernando no comió ni carne ni pan.

    Fernando _____ comió.

11. Ese empleo no me conviene tampoco.

    Ese empleo _____ me conviene.

12. Ese hombre no paga jamás sus deudas.

    Ese hombre _____ paga sus deudas.

13. No hay ningún alimento tan bueno como la leche.

    _____ hay tan bueno como la leche.

14. No tiene habilidad para nada.

    _____ tiene habilidad.

15. No como nunca en esa cafetería.

    _____ como en esa cafetería.

B. Escríbanse las frases siguientes, empleando *dos* expresiones negativas:

Ejemplo: Nada tiene. ____No____ tiene ____nada____.

1. Nunca sacrificaba su dignidad.

   _____ sacrificaba _____ su dignidad.

2. El pobre agricultor ni burro ni caballo tenía.

   El pobre agricultor _____ tenía _____.

3. Ningunos discos hay en el cajón.

   _____ hay _____ en el cajón.

4. El dictador ni alma ni corazón tenía.

   El dictador _____ tenía _____.

5. El cartero nunca me trae el correo.

   El cartero _____ me trae _____ el correo.

6. Nada quieren meter en la bolsa.

   _____ quieren meter _____ en la bolsa.

7. A mí tampoco me gustan los impuestos.

   A mí _____ me gustan _____ los impuestos.

8. Ninguna estación me gusta tanto como el verano.

   _____ me gusta _____ tanto como el verano.

9. Nada sabe de la aritmética.

   _____ sabe _____ de la aritmética.

10. A ninguna conozco tan guapa como ella.

    _____ conozco _____ tan guapa como ella.

11. Nadie se equivocó.

    _____ se equivocó _____.

12. A nadie se le ocurrió asistir a la feria.

    _____ se le ocurrió _____ asistir a la feria.

13. Ningunos dientes le quedan en la boca.

    _____ le quedan _____ en la boca.

14. Tampoco me gustan las cerezas.

    _____ me gustan _____ las cerezas.

15. Actualmente, nadie tiene el espíritu generoso.

    Actualmente, _____ tiene _____ el espíritu generoso.

C. Cámbiense las frases a la forma negativa según los ejemplos.

EJEMPLO: Alguien rompió la estatua.

_____*Nadie*_____ rompió la estatua.

1. Yo también voy a Europa.

    Yo _____ voy a Europa.

2. Siempre perdía la esperanza.

    _____ perdía la esperanza.

3. Alguien salió a coger la gallina.

    _____ salió a coger la gallina.

4. O al teatro o al circo voy el lunes.

    _____ al teatro _____ al circo voy el lunes.

5. Deseaba aprender algún idioma extranjero.

    _____ idioma extranjero deseaba aprender.

EJEMPLO: En el combate alguien fue herido.

En el combate ___*no*___ fue herido ___*nadie*___.

6. Sus palabras significan algo.

    Sus palabras _____ significan _____.

7. Siempre me echan la culpa.

    _____ me echan _____ la culpa.

8. De noche algunos gatos solían maullar detrás de la casa.

    De noche _____ solían maullar _____ gatos detrás de la casa.

9. Siempre cuento con mis amigos.

    _____ cuento _____ con mis amigos.

10. Vio algo en la arena.

    _____ vio _____ en la arena.

Contéstense en sentido negativo según el ejemplo.

EJEMPLO: ¿Han hecho todos los arreglos?

___*No*___ han hecho arreglo ___*alguno*___.

11. ¿Tiene ella un novio?

    Ella _____ tiene novio _____.

12. ¿Hay muchas fondas en el pueblo?

    _____ hay fonda _____ en el pueblo.

13. ¿Tiene influencia con los políticos?

    _____ tiene influencia _____ con los políticos.

14. ¿Quedan muchas hojas en los árboles?

_____ queda hoja _____ en los árboles.

15. ¿Derramó ella muchas lágrimas?

Ella _____ derramó lágrima _____.

Contéstense en sentido negativo, cambiando los sustantivos a pronombres según los ejemplos.

EJEMPLOS: ¿Siempre limita Vd. sus gastos? _____*Nunca los*_____ limito.

¿Comió Vd. las naranjas? _____*No las*_____ comí.

16. ¿Toma Vd. el autobús para ir al centro?

_____ tomo para ir al centro.

17. ¿Sacaron muchas fotografías?

_____ sacaron.

18. ¿Matarán muchos insectos?

_____ matarán.

19. ¿Visitó Vd. a su primo?

_____ visité.

20. ¿Siempre dan limosna a los pordioseros?

_____ dan a los pordioseros.

D. Úsese la forma correcta escogiendo *pero, sino,* o *sino que.*

1. No quería quedarse allí, _____ marcharse.

2. Le invitaron a la fiesta, _____ no fue.

3. El clima de allí no es húmedo, _____ seco.

4. No le gusta jugar al tenis, _____ al fútbol.

5. Mi hermanito no desea ser abogado, _____ médico.

6. No puso el dinero en el bolsillo, _____ lo gastó.

7. España no es un país industrial, _____ agrícola.

8. Tiene fiebre, _____ estará bien mañana.

9. No se huyó, _____ luchó heroicamente.

10. La ley es severa, _____ debemos obedecerla.

E. Contéstense, expresando en sentido negativo todas las palabras posibles.

1. ¿Le ha dado el maestro mucho trabajo? _____

2. ¿Sabe Vd. hablar diversas lenguas? _____

3. ¿Duerme Vd. la siesta algunas tardes? _____

4. ¿Siempre se moja Vd. cuando hay lluvia? _____

5. ¿Cuál prefiere Vd. beber, vino o vinagre? _____

6. ¿Tiene Vd. necesidad de algo? _____

7. ¿Compró Vd. algo en la botica anteayer? _____

8. ¿Cuál prefiere Vd., abril o enero? _____

9. ¿Ha ido Vd. jamás adonde no le han invitado? _____
_____

10. ¿Prestó Vd. a alguien su cámara? _____

11. ¿Hay algo que le moleste a Vd.? _____

12. ¿Ha experimentado Vd. algo desagradable en su vida? _____
_____

13. ¿Conoce Vd. a alguien que odie la libertad? _____
_____

14. ¿Siempre trata Vd. a sus amigos igualmente? _____
_____

15. ¿Siempre obliga Vd. a sus conocidos a hacerle favores? _____
_____

F. Tradúzcanse al español las expresiones en inglés.

1. *There is no* _____ música tan animada como la música española.

2. Desgraciadamente, no demostró talento *either* _____ para las ciencias *or* _____ las artes.

3. ¿Han mudado de casa ya, con todos los muebles? *Not yet* _____.

4. ¿Cómo van las cosas? *Nothing new* _____.

5. Yo no soy capaz de subir ese monte; ni Vd. *either* _____.

6. Nuestro maestro explica la lección más claramente que *anyone* _____.

7. No he visto *ever* _____ un monasterio tan magnífico como el Escorial.

8. ¿Le quedan muchos huevos? *Not even* _____ una docena.

9. No encontró *anything* _____ con qué decorar su nueva falda.

10. El rey no tenía confianza en *any* _____ de los ciudadanos.

11. Papá, cómprame una muñeca. *Not now* _____.

12. ¿Ha visto Vd. *ever* _____ una espada de acero tan fino?

13. No llevaba *not even* _____ la americana.

14. Comenzó a agitar el pañuelo con más fuerza que *ever* _____.

15. Siendo viejo y débil, él *no longer* _____ puede subir a las alturas.

16. A *no one* _____ dijimos que hoy es la víspera de la fiesta.

17. ¿Cómo está Vd. de salud? *Same as usual* _____.

18. Ella no posee *any* _____ diamantes. *Neither does her mother* _____
_____.

19. *No* _____ acción tuya puede influir en mi juicio.

20. La moral no permite *either* _____ el vicio *or* _____ la mentira.

G. Tradúzcanse al español.

1. Is the water boiling? Not yet. ---

2. She raised her eyes and looked toward the west, but saw nothing. ----------------------

3. The traveler didn't carry either passport or documents. ---------------------------------

4. The sciences no longer attract me. ---

5. Nowadays, experience is more important than ever. ---

6. He doesn't want to stay in bed, but to get dressed and go out. ----------------------------

7. Last Wednesday no one approached the governor's palace. ------------------------------

8. Do you want a cup of tea? Not now. ---

9. I don't like butter, nor cheese either. --

10. The pupil didn't have to translate the paragraph, but to read it. ---------------------

11. He spent a month in the south without buying anything. -----------------------------------

12. She is a good person and never speaks about her neighbors. -------------------------------

13. There was no illness like that of (the) Princess Jane. -------------------------------------

14. The unfortunate man doesn't even have a blanket with which to cover himself. ----------

15. How are you? Same as usual. ---

16. The ground wasn't flat, but mountainous. ---

17. Have you ever strolled on (por) the avenue at nightfall? ----------------------------------

18. He didn't want to sacrifice himself for anyone. --

19. This automobile is small, but it is very comfortable. _____

_____

20. The pies were very expensive, so (conque) he didn't buy any. _____

_____

21. There were only fifty people on the beach. _____

_____

22. No one fought against the Moors as heroically as El Cid. _____

_____

23. I no longer go to the bullfights. _____

_____

24. I never eat pears, nor grapefruit either. _____

_____

25. They won't get married in April, but in June. _____

_____

Los gitanos de España son célebres por su habilidad en la música y en el baile. La mayor parte de los gitanos son de Andalucía, y saben interpretar los bailes de aquella región, tales como el fandango, la seguidilla, y el flamenco.

Grammar Lesson 10—NUMBERS; TIME; DATES

CARDINAL NUMBERS

0	cero	31	treinta y uno,-a, un
1	uno,-a, un	40	cuarenta
2	dos	41	cuarenta y uno,-a, un
3	tres	50	cincuenta
4	cuatro	51	cincuenta y uno,-a, un
5	cinco	60	sesenta
6	seis	61	sesenta y uno,-a, un
7	siete	70	setenta
8	ocho	71	setenta y uno,-a, un
9	nueve	80	ochenta
10	diez	81	ochenta y uno,-a, un
11	once	90	noventa
12	doce	91	noventa y uno,-a, un
13	trece	99	noventa y nueve
14	catorce	100	ciento (cien)
15	quince	101	ciento uno,-a, un
16	diez y seis (dieciséis)	115	ciento quince
17	diez y siete (diecisiete)	116	ciento diez y seis
18	diez y ocho (dieciocho)	200	doscientos,-as
19	diez y nueve (diecinueve)	300	trescientos,-as
20	veinte	400	cuatrocientos,-as
21	veinte y uno,-a, un	500	*quinientos,-as*
	(veintiuno,-a, veintiún)	600	seiscientos,-as
22	veinte y dos (veintidós)	700	*setecientos,-as*
23	veinte y tres (veintitrés)	800	ochocientos,-as
24	veinte y cuatro (veinticuatro)	900	*novecientos,-as*
25	veinte y cinco (veinticinco)	1,000	mil
26	veinte y seis (veintiséis)	2,000	dos mil
27	veinte y siete (veintisiete)	100,000	cien mil
28	veinte y ocho (veintiocho)	1,000,000	un millón (de)
29	veinte y nueve (veintinueve)	2,000,000	dos millones (de)
30	treinta	100,000,000	cien millones (de)

Note

A. The numbers 16 to 19 and 21 to 29 may also be written as one word. In such cases, the numbers 16, 22, 23, and 26 have a written accent mark on the last syllable.

B. The only numerals that vary with gender are **uno (una, un)** and the compounds of **ciento** (**doscientos,-as, trescientos,-as,** etc.).

un libro; *una* pluma	a (one) book; a (one) pen
trescient*os* **hombres**	three hundred men
cuatrocient*as* **mujeres**	four hundred women
veinte y *un* lápices	twenty-one pencils
cincuenta y *una* tarjetas	fifty-one cards

C. The conjunction **y** is used only between *tens* and *units*, that is, in numbers 16 to 99.

33   treinta **y** tres

but

109   ciento nueve

Ciento becomes **cien** before nouns and before the numbers **mil** and **millones**. In all other numbers, the full form **ciento** is used.

cien pesetas	*cien mil* soldados
cien buenos **libros**	*cien millones* de habitantes

but

ciento veinte y cinco dólares

Un is not used before **ciento** or **mil.** It is used before the noun **millón.** If another noun follows **de** is placed between **millón** and the other noun.

ciento dos alumnos

mil doscientos años

un millón *de* dólares

ARITHMETIC EXPRESSIONS

y, plus (+)
menos, minus (−)
por, (multiplied) by, "times" (×)
dividido por, divided by (÷)
son, equal (=)

ORDINAL NUMBERS

1st	primero,-a (primer)		6th	sexto,-a
2nd	segundo,-a		7th	séptimo,-a
3rd	tercero,-a (tercer)		8th	octavo,-a
4th	cuarto,-a		9th	noveno,-a
5th	quinto,-a		10th	décimo,-a

Ordinal numbers are used only through *tenth;* beyond that, the cardinal numbers are used.

la *tercera* fila	the third row
la *Quinta* Avenida	Fifth Avenue
Carlos *Quinto (quinto)*	Charles V
but	
el siglo diez y nueve	the 19th century
la página (número) cuarenta y uno	page 41

Note

A. When a cardinal number is used in place of an ordinal, it is always considered masculine, since **número** is understood.

B. The numerals **primero** and **tercero** drop the final **-o** before a masculine singular noun.

el *primer día*
el *tercer edificio*
but
la **primera** visita
el **siglo tercero**

TIME

¿Qué hora es?	What time is it?
Es la una.	It is one o'clock.
Son las dos (tres, cuatro, etc.**).**	It is two (three, four, etc.) o'clock.
Son las diez y veinte.	It is 10:20 (twenty after ten).
Son las ocho y cuarto (quince).	It is 8:15 (a quarter past eight).
Son las seis y media (treinta).	It is 6:30 (half past six).
Son las doce menos veinte (dos, cuarto, etc.**).**	It is 11:40 (11:58, 11:45, etc.).
¿A qué hora salió Vd.?	At what time did you leave?
a(l) mediodía	at noon
a (la) medianoche	at midnight
a eso de las siete	at about seven o'clock
Dio la una (Dieron las dos).	It struck one (It struck two).

Note

A. *It is* is expressed by **es** for one o'clock, and by **son** for the plural hours. *At* is expressed by **a.**

B. The article **la** (for **la hora**) is always used with one o'clock; **las** (for **las horas**) is used with the plural hours.

C. *After* or *past* is expressed by **y**; *to* or *of* by **menos.** After half past, time is expressed by the following hour minus **(menos)** the minutes.

Son las tres *y* veinte y cinco.	It is 3:25.
Es la una *menos* diez.	It is 12:50 (ten minutes to one).

D. **Media** is an adjective and agrees with **hora**; **cuarto** is a noun and does not vary.

The expressions **de la madrugada** and **de la mañana** correspond to the English *A.M.* (morning). The former refers to the hours before daylight, the latter to the daylight hours. **De la tarde** (afternoon) and **de la noche** (evening) correspond to *P.M.* **En punto** means *sharp*.

a las tres *de la madrugada*	at 3 A.M.
a las ocho y media *de la mañana*	at 8:30 A.M.
a las cuatro *de la tarde*	at 4 P.M.
Eran las nueve *en punto* de la noche.	It was 9 P.M. sharp.

DATES

¿Cuál es la fecha de hoy? ¿A cuántos estamos hoy?	What is today's date?
Es el primero de enero. Estamos a primero de enero.	It is January 1.
Es el dos (tres, cuatro) de febrero.	It is February 2 (3, 4).
Es el diez de marzo de mil novecientos sesenta y tres.	It is March 10, 1963.
Salió el tres de agosto.	He left on August 3.

Note

A. Cardinal numbers are used for all dates except **primero** (first).

B. The names of the months are written with small letters in Spanish.

C. The years are expressed in *thousands* and *hundreds*, not in *hundreds* alone, as in English. (1400 = **mil cuatrocientos**)

D. With dates, *on* is expressed by **el**.

EJERCICIOS

A. Escríbase lo siguiente en español.

1. $414 - 363 = 51$ _____

_____

2. $336 \times 12 = 4032$ _____

_____

3. $254 + 587 = 841$ _____

_____

4. $911 - 276 = 635$ _____

_____

5. $31,217 \div 31 = 1007$ _____

_____

6. $419 + 716 = 1135$ _____

_____

7. $1818 \div 18 = 101$ _____

_____

8. $345 + 577 = 922$ -

9. $864 \div 16 = 54$ -

10. $785 - 246 = 539$ -

11. $990 \div 9 = 110$ -

12. $93 \times 71 = 6603$ -

13. $119 \times 17 = 2023$ -

14. $63 \times 74 = 4662$ -

15. $13 \times 14 = 182$ -

16. $1,322,828 \div 52 = 25,439$ -

17. $810 + 597 = 1407$ -

18. $756,336 \div 48 = 15,757$ -

19. $613 + 715 = 1328$ -

20. $458 + 211 = 669$ -

B. Escríbanse en español las palabras en letra cursiva.

1. la *fifth* columna - - - - - - - - - - - - - -

2. la Avenida *Eighth* - - - - - - - - - - - - - -

3. el *ninth* día - - - - - - - - - - - - - -

4. Alfonso *XII* - - - - - - - - - - - - - -

5. el *fourth* párrafo - - - - - - - - - - - - - -

6. el siglo *XX* - - - - - - - - - - - - - -

7. la *third* fila - - - - - - - - - - - - - -

8. la *seventh* serie - - - - - - - - - - - - - -

9. la página *261* - - - - - - - - - - - - - -

10. el *tenth* aniversario - - - - - - - - - - - - - -

11. el *second* edificio - - - - - - - - - - - - - -

12. el *third* capítulo - - - - - - - - - - - - - -

13. el número *99* -

14. el tranvía *43* -

15. el *second* semestre - - - - - - - - - - - - - -

16. la *first* calidad - - - - - - - - - - - - - -

17. Carlos *V* - - - - - - - - - - - - - -

18. el *First* Congreso Panamericano - - - - - - - - - - - - - -

19. el *sixth* renglón - - - - - - - - - - - - - -

20. el *third* grado - - - - - - - - - - - - - -

C. Escríbanse en palabras españolas.

1. at 10:32 P.M. _____

2. It is 5:10 P.M. _____

3. It struck 10 o'clock. _____

4. at 6 P.M. sharp _____

5. It is midnight. _____

6. at 4:45 P.M. _____

7. It is 1:14 P.M. _____

8. at 1:18 P.M. _____

9. at 8:52 A.M. _____

10. It is 8:25 P.M. _____

11. at 12:55 P.M. _____

12. It is noon. _____

13. at about 1 o'clock _____

14. at 3:30 P.M. _____

15. at 1:40 P.M. _____

16. It is 2:15 A.M. _____

17. at about 4 P.M. _____

18. It is 7:15 A.M. _____

19. It is 10 A.M. sharp. _____

20. It is striking 3 o'clock. _____

D. Escríbanse en palabras españolas.

1. May 2, 1808 _____

2. December 20, 1910 _____

3. June 15, 1963 _____

4. October 12, 1492 _____

5. December 7, 1941 _____

6. July 4, 1776 _____

7. January 1, 1952 _____

8. March 31, 1519 _____

9. December 31, 1900 _____

10. August 9, 1913 _____

11. February 22, 1732 _____

12. April 1, 1649 _____

13. November 1, 1396 _____

14. September 16, 1810 _____

15. April 12, 1823 _____

E. Contéstense en frases completas en español.

1. ¿Cuánto tiempo dedica Vd. cada día a los estudios? _ _ _ _ _ _ _ _ _ _ _ _ _ _ _

_ _

2. ¿Cuántos estados componen los Estados Unidos? _ _ _ _ _ _ _ _ _ _ _ _ _ _ _

_ _

3. ¿En qué año nació Vd.? _

4. ¿Cuántos pies tiene un caballo? _

5. ¿A qué hora toma Vd. la cena? _

_ _

6. ¿Cuántos alumnos hay en esta escuela aproximadamente? _ _ _ _ _ _ _ _ _ _ _

_ _

7. ¿En qué año entraron los moros en España? (711) _ _ _ _ _ _ _ _ _ _ _ _ _ _

_ _

8. ¿Cuántas alas tiene el águila? _

9. ¿En qué año fundó Pizarro la ciudad de Lima? (1535) _ _ _ _ _ _ _ _ _ _ _ _

_ _

10. ¿En qué año conquistaron los españoles el reino moro de Granada? (1492) _ _ _ _

_ _

11. ¿Hay siete u ocho palabras en esta frase? _ _ _ _ _ _ _ _ _ _ _ _ _ _ _ _ _

12. ¿Cuántos ceros hay en el número "un millón"? _ _ _ _ _ _ _ _ _ _ _ _ _ _ _

_ _

13. ¿Cuántos lados tiene un cuadrado? _

14. ¿A cuántos estamos hoy? _

15. ¿Cuándo cae el Día de Año Nuevo? _

_ _

16. ¿Cuántas letras hay en el alfabeto inglés? _ _ _ _ _ _ _ _ _ _ _ _ _ _ _ _ _

_ _

17. ¿A qué hora anochece en el invierno? _ _ _ _ _ _ _ _ _ _ _ _ _ _ _ _ _ _ _

_ _

18. ¿Cuánto dinero tiene Vd. en el bolsillo? _ _ _ _ _ _ _ _ _ _ _ _ _ _ _ _ _ _

_ _

19. ¿En qué año terminó la Segunda Guerra Mundial? (1945) _ _ _ _ _ _ _ _ _ _ _

_ _

20. ¿A qué hora apagó Vd. la luz en su cuarto anoche? _ _ _ _ _ _ _ _ _ _ _ _ _

_ _

21. ¿Cuántos reales hay en una peseta? (4) _ _ _ _ _ _ _ _ _ _ _ _ _ _ _ _ _ _

22. ¿Cuántas ruedas tiene el coche de su familia? _ _ _ _ _ _ _ _ _ _ _ _ _ _ _ _

23. ¿Qué número es el doble de nueve? --------------------------------

----

24. De pies a cabeza, ¿cuántos pies de alto tiene Vd.? ----------------

----

25. ¿Cuántas personas hay en un equipo de fútbol? --------------------

----

26. ¿Cuántos años tiene Vd.? ---

27. ¿En qué fecha se firmó nuestra Declaración de Independencia? (1776) ----------

----

----

28. ¿Cuántos centavos hay en un dólar? ------------------------------

----

29. ¿Cuántos huevos hay en una docena? -----------------------------

----

30. ¿Cuántos habitantes tiene nuestro país? --------------------------

----

F. Escríbanse en español los números y las expresiones en inglés.

1. Dedicó *thirty-one* ----------------------- años a la enseñanza.

2. Alfonso *X* ----------------, hijo de Fernando *III* --------------, vivió en el siglo *XIII*

------------------.

3. Colón salió hacia el oeste *on August 3, 1492* --------------------

---.

4. La lámpara de vidrio se rompió en *a hundred* -------------- pedazos.

5. El pueblo consistía en *3,500* ------------------------------- seres humanos.

6. La única fecha que no ocurre todos los años es *February 29* ------------

------------- .

7. En el campo había espacio para más de *seven hundred* ---------------- vacas.

8. No tengo nada que hacer desde *noon* ------------------ hasta *5:45 P.M.* ------------

-----------------------------------.

9. Todas las mercancías, de un valor de *one hundred thousand* -------------- dólares, fueron
destruidas por el fuego.

10. Volvió sano y salvo a España en *1493* ------------------------------.

11. Fue necesario armar las tropas, un ejército de *two million* ----------------- soldados.

12. Para llegar al fondo de la mina, tuvo que bajar *1371* ----------------------

---------- pies.

13. Sus armas no bastaban; les quedaban solamente *twenty-one* ---------------- balas con
que defenderse de los bárbaros.

14. *At 3:20 A.M.* _____ sintió un dolor en el pecho.

15. Juan pesa más de *two hundred fifty-one* _____ libras.

16. No se aprende el uso del subjuntivo hasta el *third* _____ año.

17. Si se divide *144 by 2* _____, el resultado es 72 _____.

18. Al sentir la *third* _____ gota, se dio cuenta de que llovía.

19. Su sueño fue interrumpido *at 9 o'clock sharp* _____.

20. Mostró su disgusto al saber que las tiendas se cerrarían *at noon on July 4* _____
_____.

G. Tradúzcanse al español.

1. The sun is (at) ninety-three million miles from the earth. _____
_____

2. January 1 is the first day of the year. _____
_____

3. At midnight on December 24 they heard the church bells. _____
_____
_____

4. It is now 8:30; we have an hour and a half left. _____
_____

5. In the bookcase there was room for (caber) three hundred magazines. _____
_____

6. Peace was declared on November 11, 1918. _____
_____
_____

7. The 16th and 17th centuries were the Golden Age of Spanish literature. _____
_____
_____

8. The hospital employs thirty-one nurses and twenty-one doctors. _____
_____

9. In the 15th century many people believed that the earth was flat. _____
_____

10. The moon will appear at 8:43 P.M. _____
_____

11. The expedition left at noon on December 31, 1865. _____
_____
_____

12. The most important historical date for us is July 4, 1776. ----------------------------------

----

----

13. He waited forty-one minutes, but at 2 o'clock sharp he went away. ----------------------

----

14. The first girl did not answer well; the second answered correctly. ----------------------

----

----

15. The stenographer can write a hundred words per minute. --------------------------------

----

16. The contract was signed at 3:37 A.M. ---

----

17. Philip II, son of Charles V, was the most powerful monarch in (de) Europe. ------------

----

----

18. $14 + 76 \div 10 \times 21 = 189.$ ---

----

19. His action resulted in a loss of more than a hundred thousand dollars. ----------------

----

20. The bookkeeper discovered an error of a hundred twenty-one dollars. ----------------

----

Jai-alai es un juego que originó en las Provincias Vascongadas, en España. Es muy popular en toda España y en varias partes del mundo hispánico, sobre todo en México y en Cuba. Es algo semejante al "handball," pero en jai-alai las manos no tocan la pelota. Para coger y arrojar la pelota se emplea una cesta atada a la muñeca del jugador.

Grammar Lesson 11—PREPOSITIONS

Prepositions are used to relate two elements of a sentence, such as noun to noun, verb to noun, verb to infinitive, etc.

1. When a noun is modified by a preposition + noun, the prepositional phrase is equivalent to an adjective.

un anillo *de* oro	a gold ring (a ring of gold)
un vaso *de* agua	a glass of water
un vaso *para* agua	a water glass (a glass for water)

2. When a verb is modified by a preposition + noun, the prepositional phrase is equivalent to an adverb.

Sale *con* frecuencia.	He goes out frequently (with frequency).

3. The second element may be a pronoun or an infinitive.

Entra *en* él.	He enters it.
Comienza *a* leer.	He begins to read.

For a list of common prepositions, see page 176.

PREPOSITIONS BEFORE INFINITIVES

In Spanish, the only verb form that may follow a preposition is the infinitive, regardless of the English translation of the verb.

Cesó *de llover*.	It stopped raining.
Acaba *de entrar*.	He has just entered.
Se desayunó *después de vestirse*.	He ate breakfast after getting dressed.

I. Verbs Requiring *a* Before an Infinitive

Verbs expressing *beginning, motion, teaching,* or *learning,* and a number of other verbs, require the preposition **a** before an infinitive.

comenzar a ⎤ empezar a ⎥ to begin to ponerse a ⎥ principiar a ⎦	acertar a, to happen to (by chance) acostumbrarse a, to become accustomed to aspirar a, to aspire to atreverse a, to dare to
apresurarse a, to hasten (hurry) to ⎤ ir a, to go to ⎥ regresar a, to return to (to . . . again) ⎥ motion salir a, to go out to ⎥ venir a, to come to ⎥ volver a, to return to (to . . . again) ⎦	convidar a, to invite to decidirse a, to decide to dedicarse a, to devote oneself to disponerse a, to get ready to invitar a, to invite to negarse a, to refuse to
enseñar a, to teach to aprender a, to learn to	obligar a, to obligate, to compel to resignarse a, to resign oneself to

212

Comenzó a trabajar.	He began to work.
Saldré a saludarle.	I will go out to greet him.
El maestro les *enseñó a* hablar.	The teacher taught them to speak.
Los alumnos *aprenden a* leer.	The pupils learn to read.
Acertó a pasar por allí.	He happened to pass by there.
Me *obligó a* pagarle.	He compelled me to pay him.

II. VERBS REQUIRING *de* BEFORE AN INFINITIVE

acabar de, to have just	**dejar de,** to fail to, to stop
acordarse de, to remember to	**encargarse de,** to take charge of
alegrarse de, to be glad to	**olvidarse de,** to forget to
cesar de, to stop	**tratar de,** to try to

Acabamos de estudiar.	We have just studied.
Se alegran de estar aquí.	They are glad to be here.
A las tres *cesó de* llover.	At three o'clock it stopped raining.
Juanito *dejó de* preparar la lección.	Johnny failed to prepare the lesson.

III. VERBS REQUIRING *en* BEFORE AN INFINITIVE

consentir en, to consent to	**empeñarse en** ⎫
consistir en, to consist of	**insistir en** ⎬ to insist on
convenir en, to agree to	**tardar en,** to delay in, to be long in

Consintió en ir al baile.	She consented to go to the dance.
El verdadero estudio *consiste en* leer y repasar.	True study consists of reading and reviewing.
Se empeñó en vender la casa.	He insisted on selling the house.
El tren no *tardará en* llegar.	The train won't be long in coming.

IV. VERBS REQUIRING *con* BEFORE AN INFINITIVE

amenazar con, to threaten to	**soñar con,** to dream of
contar con, to count on, to rely on	

Le *amenazó con* pegarle.	He threatened to spank him.
Cuento con ganar el premio.	I count on winning the prize.
Sueña con ir a España.	He dreams of going to Spain.

V. Prepositions Commonly Used Before Infinitives

a, to, at	**en,** in, on, of
al + inf., upon	**en lugar de** ⎫
antes de, before	**en vez de** ⎬ instead of
con, with (sometimes *to* or *of*)	**hasta,** until
de, of, to	**sin,** without
después de, after	

Al entrar, vio a su hija.	Upon entering, he saw his daughter.
Antes de salir, prepárese.	Before going out, prepare yourself.
Después de descansar un rato, se levantó.	After resting a while, he got up.
Se acostó *en vez de estudiar.*	He went to bed instead of studying.
Salió *sin decir* nada.	He left without saying anything.

Note

A. Other uses of prepositions will be found in the section on idioms, pages 256–258.

B. Whenever prepositions are followed by the infinitive, the subject of both verbs (main verb and infinitive) is unchanged. If the subjects are different, **que** is required and a "conjugated" verb form is used instead of the infinitive.

Me alegro de **estar** aquí.	I am glad to be here.
Me alegro de *que Vd. esté* aquí.	I am glad that you are here.
Insiste en **vender** la casa.	She insists on selling the house.
Insiste en *que su marido venda* la casa.	She insists on her husband's selling the house.
Se desayunó después de **preparar** el café.	He ate breakfast after preparing the coffee.
Se desayunó después (de) *que su madre preparó* el café.	He ate breakfast after his mother prepared the coffee.

VI. Verbs That Do Not Require a Preposition Before an Infinitive

deber, ought to, must	**necesitar,** to need	**prometer,** to promise
dejar, to let, to allow	**oír,** to hear	**querer,** to want, to wish
desear, to wish, to desire	**pensar,** to intend	**saber,** to know (how)
esperar, to hope, to expect	**poder,** to be able, can	**soler,** to be accustomed to, usually
hacer, to make, to have (something done)	**preferir,** to prefer	**ver,** to see
lograr, to succeed in	**pretender,** to attempt	

Debo ir a la escuela hoy.	I ought to go to school today.
No me *dejan salir.*	They don't let me go out.
Hizo construir una casa.	He had a house built.
Pienso comenzar mañana.	I intend to begin tomorrow.
Suele volver a las doce.	He usually returns at twelve o'clock.

PERSONAL *A*

The personal **a** is used before the direct object of a verb if the direct object is a noun denoting a definite person or anything personified.

1. *Definite person*

Visita **a su amigo (a sus padres, a Roberto,** etc.).

He visits his friend (his parents, Robert, etc.).

2. *Domestic animals (pets, etc.)*

Quiere **a su perrito (a Fido, a su gato,** etc.).

She loves her little dog (Fido, her cat, etc.).

3. *Geographic names (unless preceded by the definite article)*

Desea ver **a España (a México, a Nueva York,** etc.).

He wants to see Spain (Mexico, New York, etc.).

    but

Desea ver **la Argentina (los Estados Unidos, el Perú,** etc.).

He wants to see Argentina (the United States, Peru, etc.).

4. *Pronouns referring to persons, even though used in a negative sense*

Veo **a alguien.**

I see someone.

No veo **a nadie.**

I see no one.

Note

A. The personal **a** is not translated into English.

B. The personal **a** is not used with the verb **tener.**

Tengo un amigo.

I have a friend.

PARA—POR

I. THE USES OF *para*

1. **Para** means *for* in the sense of purpose, use, destination, for (by) a time in the future, considering that (in spite of the fact that). It is also translated *in order to, to, by.*

Estudia ***para*** aprender.
(purpose)

He studies in order to learn.

Es una caja ***para*** dulces.
(use)

It is a candy box (a box *for* candy).

    but

Compré una caja **de** dulces.

I bought a box *of* candy.

Ayer salió ***para*** España.
(destination)

Yesterday he left for Spain.

Para el viernes estará completo.
(future time)

For (By) Friday it will be complete.

Para extranjero, habla bien el inglés.
(in spite of being)

For a foreigner, he speaks English well.

2. **Para** also means **para ser.**

Estudia ***para*** médico.

He is studying to be a doctor.

II. THE USES OF *por*

1. **Por** means *for* in the sense of in exchange for, period or extent of time, for the sake of.

Pagó un dólar **por** el cuchillo.   He paid a dollar for the knife.
        (exchange)

Fue al campo **por** dos meses.   He went to the country for two months.
        (period)

Todo lo hago **por** ti.   I do it all for you.
        (sake)

2. **Por** also means *for* after the verbs **ir, enviar, luchar, llamar, preguntar.**

Fue (Envió, Llamó, Preguntó) **por** el médico.   He went (sent, called, asked) for the doctor.

3. **Por** also means *during* and is often translated by *in*.

Por la tarde juego al tenis.   In the afternoon I play tennis.

4. **Por** expresses the idea of rate and is equivalent to *per*.

Gana cincuenta dólares **por** semana.   He earns fifty dollars per (a) week.

5. **Por** also means *by, through, along*.

Fueron atacados **por** sus enemigos.   They were attacked by their enemies.

El viajar **por** avión es más rápido.   Traveling by plane is faster.

Entraron **por** la ventana.   They entered through (by) the window.

Pasaré **por** esa calle.   I'll pass along (through) that street.

The following verbs are not followed by **por** or **para,** since the word *for* is part of the meaning of the verb.

buscar, to look for (to seek)
esperar, to wait for (to await)
pedir, to ask for (to request)

Buscaron un asiento.   They looked for a seat.

Quiero *pedir*le un favor.   I want to ask a favor of you.
        (I want to ask you for a favor.)

Esperó dos horas a su amiga.   He waited two hours for his girl friend.

EJERCICIOS

A. Complétense las expresiones siguientes:

EJEMPLO: a steel knife—un cuchillo ___*de acero*___

1. a wooden cross   una cruz _____
2. a cotton skirt   una falda _____
3. the German class   la clase _____
4. a silk cape   una capa _____
5. woolen socks   calcetines _____

6. family secrets   secretos _____

7. a straw mattress   un colchón _____

8. a stone house   una casa _____

9. silver bracelets   brazaletes _____

10. a gold chain   una cadena _____

EJEMPLO: a medical school—una escuela *para médicos* _____

11. a hair brush   un cepillo _____

12. a young ladies' school una escuela _____

13. a book case   un estante _____

14. letter paper   papel _____

15. ladies' handkerchiefs pañuelos _____

16. a fever remedy   un remedio _____

17. cigar tobacco   tabaco _____

18. wine grapes   uvas _____

19. window glass   vidrio _____

20. a candy box   una caja _____

B. Llénense los espacios con la preposición correcta, *si hace falta*. Si no hace falta una preposición, escríbase una raya (—).

1. No se atrevió _____ replicar.   He didn't dare to reply.

2. Asistió a un partido _____ béisbol.   He attended a baseball game.

3. Leyó el telegrama _____ entenderlo.   He read the telegram without understanding it.

4. El rey consintió _____ renovar el castillo. The king consented to remodel the castle.

5. Le ataron con una cadena _____ hierro.   They tied him with an iron chain.

6. Me enseñó _____ escribir.   He taught me to write.

7. Bebió un vaso _____ agua.   He drank a glass of water.

8. El detective piensa _____ registrar la casa. The detective intends to search the house.

9. No pudo _____ dominar su furia.   He could not overcome his fury.

10. Se decidieron _____ confesar.   They decided to confess.

11. Era pobre _____ realizar sus sueños. He was poor before realizing his dreams.

12. _____ partir, dio un abrazo a su madre. Upon leaving, he gave his mother a hug.

13. Acertó _____ pasar por allí.   He happened to be passing there.

14. En tales casos suele _____ consultar a sus amigos. In such cases he usually consults his friends.

15. Se marchó _____ distribuir los premios. He left after distributing the prizes.

16. No me encargaré _____ gobernar el país. I will not take charge of governing the country.

17. Cesó _____ llover a las tres.   It stopped raining at three o'clock.

18. Les amenazó _____ quemar su casa.   He threatened to burn their house.

19. El prisionero quiere _____ escaparse.   The prisoner wants to escape.

20. Las tropas tardaron _____ avanzar.   The troops delayed in advancing.

C. Subráyese la palabra o raya entre paréntesis que complete correctamente la frase.

1. El zapatero tropezó (con, en) el carnicero.

2. Desde el balcón miró (—, a) una escena alegre.

3. Querían ver (—, a) Francia.

4. El maestro no alabó (a, —) nadie.

5. La madre bañó (el, al) pequeño Diego.

6. Pizarro fundó (a, —) Lima.

7. Guardó (a, —) algo en el bolsillo.

8. Cincuenta estados forman (a, —) los Estados Unidos.

9. El dictador mató (—, a) sus adversarios.

10. Aguardaba (a, —) alguien en la esquina.

11. El agricultor buscó (a, —) su hijo Alfonso.

12. El dependiente buscó (a, —) otro empleo.

13. Se casó (a, con) la bonita rubia.

14. Vio (a, —) un animal en el bosque.

15. El rey condenó (el, al) traidor.

16. La niña abrazó (a, —) su querido perro Fido.

17. En la calle dio (con, a) un grupo de turistas.

18. Fueron a visitar (a, —) la Argentina.

19. El lobo nos espantó (—, a) todos.

20. La actriz conmovió (al, el) público.

D. Complétense estas frases con *para* o *por*.

1. Las naranjas son buenas _____ la salud.

2. Se porta muy mal _____ reina.

3. _____ sus movimientos se notaba su inquietud.

4. Permaneció fuera de la ciudad _____ dos años.

5. Encendió la luz _____ iluminar la sala.

6. En la tienda vio unas preciosas tazas _____ café.

7. Mi nieta siempre tiene una sonrisa _____ mí.

8. El prisionero ganó la libertad _____ engaño.

9. Al amanecer, salió _____ el mercado.

10. Siguió el curso de estudios _____ ingeniero.

11. Es necesario usar veneno _____ los insectos.

12. _____ la semana que viene, estaremos en camino.

13. _____ músico profesional, toca muy mal.

14. Se arrojó al agua _____ buscar el tesoro.

15. Estudia _____ médico.

16. _____ persona culta, no es muy cortés.

17. Armó un ejército _____ conquistar el país vecino.

18. La operación fue hecha _____ un médico hábil.

19. La zapatería quedó cerrada _____ cinco días.

20. Busca varios estantes _____ libros.

21. No voy a pagar tanto _____ las perlas.

22. Ese pintor no sirve _____ director de museo.

23. ¡Cuánto daría yo _____ una copa de vino!

24. En la batalla fue herido en la espalda _____ una mano misteriosa.

25. Sabían _____ el ruido que el cuarto estaba lleno de niños.

26. Aquí se entra _____ la puerta, no _____ la ventana.

27. Pasó _____ la plaza pública con paso rápido.

28. Llamó _____ un médico.

29. El trece de febrero salgo _____ Europa.

30. _____ el viernes estará terminado su chaleco.

E. Contéstense en español en frases completas.

1. ¿Ha visto Vd. alguna vez una explosión de dinamita? _____
_____

2. ¿Deja Vd. a su perrito correr por las calles? _____
_____

3. ¿Ha comprado Vd. alguna vez una caja de dulces para su mamá? _____
_____

4. ¿Se alegra Vd. de poder contestar perfectamente a estas preguntas? _____
_____

5. ¿Le gustaría a Vd. ayudar a las personas pobres? _____
_____

6. ¿Adónde va Vd. por la tarde? _____
_____

7. ¿Sueña Vd. con visitar a España? _____
_____

8. ¿Cuánto pagaría Vd. por un automóvil? _____
_____

9. ¿Piensa Vd. ir al Perú algún día? _____
_____

10. ¿Aprendió Vd. a ser justo(-a) en sus opiniones? _____
_____

11. Para pedir perdón, ¿prefiere Vd. decir "perdóneme" o "dispénseme"? _____
_____

12. ¿Tiene Vd. ocasión de visitar a menudo a sus parientes? _____
_____

13. ¿Suele Vd. burlarse de sus amigos? _____
_____

14. ¿Tarda Vd. generalmente en hacer lo que le piden sus padres? _____
_____

15. ¿Logró Vd. comprender la diferencia entre "ser" y "estar"? _____
_____

16. Para saludar a sus amigos, ¿prefiere Vd. decir "hola, amigo" o "buenos días, señor"? _____
_____
_____

17. ¿Ha viajado Vd. por avión? _____
_____

18. ¿Para qué se usa una bolsa? _____
_____

19. ¿Qué diferencia hay entre "taza de té" y "taza para té"? _____
_____
_____

20. ¿Se empeñan sus padres en que Vd. estudie mucho? _____
_____

F. Tradúzcanse al español las expresiones en inglés.

1. Mamá *delayed in* _____ dividir el pastel entre nosotros.

2. *They know how to* _____ contar hasta novecientos.

3. El viajero no vio *anyone* _____ en la iglesia.

4. Llamó a la puerta y *asked for* _____ su amigo.

5. Empujó la puerta, vio la sala desierta, y *entered it* _____.

6. *He wasn't able to* _____ limitar sus gastos.

7. *To visit Argentina* _____, es necesario viajar muchas millas.

8. El sastre me prometió que *by Saturday* _____ los pantalones estarían hechos.

9. Los contratos serán examinados *by* _____ el juez.

10. *In the morning* _____, brillaba un sol ardiente.

11. *Upon* _____ hundirse el vapor, no se salvó nadie.

12. Todos los amigos alabaron *Richard* _____.

13. *He succeeded in* _____ satisfacer todas sus necesidades.

14. Marco Polo salió *for* _____ el Extremo Oriente.

15. Salió corriendo *for* _____ el médico.

16. Me hace falta media docena de *dessert dishes* _____.

17. La novia *insisted on* _____ fijar pronto el día de la boda.

18. Llevaba un impermeable *in order to* _____ protegerse de la lluvia.

19. El niño *tried to* _____ salir *without washing* _____.

20. *For a singer* _____, tiene la voz muy débil.

21. Pasaron *through* _____ el pueblo a ochenta kilómetros *per* _____ hora.

22. Bolívar *dreamed of* _____ ganar la independencia de las colonias.

23. La semana que viene salgo *for* _____ España *for* _____ dos meses.

24. Sorprendió *the thieves* _____ en el acto.

25. *Don't fail to* _____ avisarme en cuanto se concluya el combate.

26. *He forgot to* _____ llevar el tocadiscos a la reunión.

27. El muchacho tiene *a mother* _____ muy buena y amable.

28. *He looked for* _____ un palo grande *to* _____ defenderse de sus enemigos.

29. Los patriotas hispanoamericanos odiaban *Spain* _____.

30. Pagué ocho pesos *for* _____ las dos entradas.

    G. Tradúzcanse al español.

1. For his wife he bought a beautiful pearl necklace as (an) anniversary gift. _____
_____
_____

2. They agreed to meet in a week to discuss the matter. _____
_____

3. The farmer's son loved his favorite cow, Lupe. _____
_____

4. His pride did not permit him to ask for a favor. _____
_____

5. Let's leave it all for tomorrow. _____
_____

6. For a sidewalk, it is very narrow. _____
_____

7. The child looked at the nurse curiously. _____
_____

8. During the ceremony an honor guard (guard of honor) surrounded the famous hero. _____

9. His father threatened to spank him. _____

10. I don't know whether he is studying to be a doctor or an architect. _____

11. The poetess had her poems printed. _____

12. Ferdinand VII followed Joseph I on (en) the throne of Spain. _____

13. This medicine is good for colds. _____

14. Some day I want to visit Spain and Argentina. _____

15. I am glad that the child shows so much talent. _____

16. He waited for the secret signal for three days. _____

17. The sculptor has just created a masterpiece. _____

18. He is quite poor; he earns only $5,000 a year. _____

19. He began to cut the meat with a steel knife. _____

20. Yesterday in the store I bought a pound of bird food. _____

21. He wanted ninety céntimos for the basket of cherries. _____

22. Upon getting up, he washed, dressed, and sat down to have breakfast. _____

23. He refused to pay a dollar for a phonograph needle. _____

24. He cast a pitying glance (glance of pity) at the wounded soldier, and, with a sigh, went away. _____

25. The philosopher inspired all his disciples. _____

Grammar Lesson 12—MASTERY EXERCISES

(LESSONS 7–11)

A. Tradúzcanse al español las palabras en inglés. (See Grammar Lesson 7, page 175.)

1. Sabía los detalles, pero tardó en *telling them to us* _____.

2. ¿Compró Vd. las violetas? *Do not send them to her* _____

   ahora; *do it* _____ mañana.

3. ¿Tienes un cuento para tu sobrinito? *Tell it to him* _____ ahora.

4. Hacía falta a la sopa un poco de sal. La cocinera *added it to it* _____.

5. Sacó los diamantes y estaba *showing them to him* _____ cuando entró el detective.

6. Al ver a los ciegos, el doctor bondadoso sacó una limosna y se apresuró a *give it to them* _____

   _____.

7. Ésta es la propina para el camarero; no te olvides de *give it to him* _____.

8. Estos claveles son para mi novia; ahora estoy dispuesto a *present them to her* _____

   _____.

9. Aquella muñeca es encantadora; *buy it for me* _____, papá.

10. El torero pidió la espada, y su criado *gave it to him* _____.

11. La reina admira la estatua; el escultor *will present it to her* _____.

12. El administrador desea ver el recibo, pero *don't show it to him* _____.

13. Antes de matar el toro, volvió a los aficionados y *dedicated it to them* _____.

14. Las niñas querían aprender el alfabeto, y la maestra estaba *teaching it to them* _____

    _____.

15. A los huéspedes no les gusta el vino; *don't serve it to them* _____.

B. Tradúzcanse al español las expresiones en inglés. (See Grammar Lesson 7, page 175, and Grammar Lesson 11, page 212.)

1. En la isla desierta, los exploradores descubrieron *many stone images* _____

   _____.

2. El viajar *by plane* _____ es muy rápido.

3. Mamá *called us* _____ y dividió el pastel *among us* _____.

4. *Upon entering* _____ la sala, le sorprendió el silencio que reinaba.

5. De rodillas, *they asked for* _____ justicia.

6. Se hizo construir una magnífica *brick house* _____.

7. Tengo *a friend* _____ que es periodista.

223

8. Salió al balcón, y *from it* _____ vio la plaza y la gente que se paseaba *through it* _____ .

9. *She tried to* _____ alcanzar la fruta en el árbol.

10. *He entered* _____ la tienda y *asked for* _____ el propietario.

11. *For an armchair* _____ , no es muy cómodo.

12. Abrió el baúl y metió *inside of it* _____ el chaleco y las camisas.

13. *By Friday* _____ , habrá olvidado la lección.

14. Compró un anillo *for his wife* _____ .

15. Mientras *he* _____ guardaba silencio, *she* _____ se puso a hablar de nuevo.

16. *He waited for* _____ una ocasión favorable.

17. El maestro hizo esfuerzos *to teach* _____ bien.

18. El dueño *insisted on* _____ que el servicio fuese perfecto.

19. *It stopped* _____ llover, y la noche siguió serena.

20. Luego que entró, vio *all his relatives* _____ .

21. *In the morning* _____ envolvió los paquetes, y *in the afternoon* _____ los llevó al correo.

22. Se aplicó a la tarea *enthusiastically* _____ . (two words)

23. Te has portado muy mal *with me* _____ ; por consiguiente no iré *with you* _____ al concierto esta noche.

24. *It is* _____ necesario seguir adelante; ya *it is* _____ mediodía.

25. Pagó catorce pesetas *for* _____ un ejemplar reciente de la revista.

C. Tradúzcanse al español las expresiones en inglés. (See Grammar Lesson 8, page 185.)

1. No puedo imaginarme *why* _____ Ricardo no quiere escucharme.

2. La contestación del maestro, *which* _____ era clara, fue escrita en la pizarra.

3. ¿*What* _____ es la carrera que Vd. piensa seguir?

4. *He who* _____ habla lenguas extranjeras tiene el mundo por su país.

5. ¿*What* _____ es un diccionario?

6. No sabe *who* _____ le envió el collar de perlas.

7. *What* _____ su sobrina le dijo no le preocupó.

8. La poesía *which* _____ leyó es *the one which* _____ escribió recientemente.

9. ¿*How many* _____ escenas y *how many* _____ actos tiene esa comedia?

10. ¡*How* _____ sabio es! Sabe tanto como un filósofo.

11. Hablando con sus amigos, ¿*how* _____ expresa Vd. la palabra "you"?

12. Rápidamente abrió la caja, *inside of which* _____ encontró el tesoro.

13. ¿*Where* _____ se venden comestibles?

14. *¿For whom* _ son las nueces que están en la mesa?

15. El cura habló con la pobre viuda, *whose* _ _ _ _ _ _ _ _ _ _ _ aspecto inspiraba lástima.

16. El maestro no llegó a la clase, *which* _ _ _ _ _ _ _ _ _ _ _ _ _ les gustó a los alumnos.

17. *¿Why* _ _ _ _ _ _ _ _ _ _ _ _ _ _ estudia Vd. este idioma? Para poder hablarlo.

18. El artista americano *whom* _ _ _ _ _ _ _ _ _ _ _ _ _ vieron era el hombre *with whom* _ _ _ _ _ _ _ _ _ _ _ _ _ _ _ _ _ _ _ habían hablado antes.

19. No me dijo *what* _ _ _ _ _ _ _ _ _ _ palabras escribió en los documentos.

20. *¡What a* _ _ _ _ _ _ _ _ _ _ lástima! No tiene conocidos en este pueblo.

D. Tradúzcanse al español las expresiones en inglés. (See Grammar Lesson 9, page 193.)

1. *No one has* _ el poder de saber el porvenir.

2. No quiere trabajar, *but* _ _ _ _ _ _ _ _ _ _ _ _ descansar.

3. No probó el desayuno, *nor lunch either* _ .

4. No encontraron *either lions or wolves* _ en el bosque.

5. El hierro es más duro *than anything* _ _ _ _ _ _ _ _ _ _ _ _ _ _ _ _ _ _ .

6. ¿Cómo van los negocios? Pues, *nothing new* _ _ _ _ _ _ _ _ _ _ _ _ _ _ _ _ _ _ _ .

7. Sonó la campana de la iglesia, pero *no one did anything* _ .

8. *No life* _ puede existir en la luna.

9. Juan quería acompañarnos, *but* _ _ _ _ _ _ _ _ _ _ _ _ _ _ tenía que quedarse en casa.

10. Quizás el maestro se marche *without giving any examination* _ .

11. *Upon seeing her* _ , quedó más enamorado *than ever* _ _ _ _ _ _ _ _ _ _ _ _ _ _ _ _ _ _ .

12. *¿Have you ever traveled* _ a un país lejano?

13. No escuchó más, *but* _ se marchó.

14. *Neither fortune nor happiness* _ logró en su vida.

15. ¿Tiene experiencia en actuar? *She has none* _ .

16. Defendió la ley *passionately (with passion)* _ pero *without anger* _ _ _ _ _ _ _ _ _ _

_ _ _ _ _ _ _ _ _ _ _ _ _ _ _ _ _ _ .

17. No va a cenar a las seis, *but* _ _ _ _ _ _ _ _ _ _ _ _ _ _ a las siete.

18. ¿Tienes ganas de dar un paseo? *Not now* _ .

19. ¿Todavía tienes ese resfriado? *No longer* _ _ _ _ _ _ _ _ _ _ _ _ _ _ _ .

20. *He not even* _ hace esfuerzos para buscar un puesto.

21. Ellos *not yet* _ han empleado un nuevo contador.

22. En el combate se mostró más heroico *than anyone* _ .

23. Don Quijote *never could stop* _ el movimiento de los molinos de viento.

24. Tu amiga no es bonita, *but* _ _ _ _ _ _ _ _ _ _ _ _ _ _ fea.

25. *¿Does the banker have left* _ muchas propiedades? *He has none* _ .

E. Escríbanse en palabras españolas las palabras en inglés y los números. (See Grammar Lesson 10, page 202.)

1. Isabel *II* _____

2. *21* pinturas _____

3. la Calle *42* _____

4. Fernando *VII* _____

5. *100* ovejas _____

6. *my first* obligación _____

7. *1,000,000* abejas _____

8. el siglo *14* _____

9. *the third* párrafo _____

10. *It is 11:28 A.M.* _____

11. *91* zapateros _____

12. *1,000* consejos _____

13. *600* vacas _____

14. *107* tarjetas _____

15. *at 3:45 P.M.* _____

16. *the fourth* letra _____

17. el piso *5* _____

18. *the first* ministro _____

19. Alfonso *XII* _____

20. *at 2:15 A.M.* _____

21. *July 4, 1776* _____

22. *February 21, 1487* _____

23. *May 18, 1962* _____

24. *October 1, 1543* _____

25. *November 10, 1338* _____

F. Tradúzcanse al español.

1. Which is the favorite sport in the United States? It is baseball. _____ _____

2. The sleeve of the jacket was too short, which did not please him. _____ _____

3. The first semester starts the third week of September. _____ _____

4. He waited for his fiancée an hour, but saw no one. _____ _____

5. He doesn't read well, but badly. _____

6. He who believes in civilization will combat injustice. _
_ _

7. He didn't have a coat, nor an umbrella either. _
_ _

8. He consented to speak to the curious journalist. _
_ _

9. It is very hot, and I want a cool drink; serve it to me quickly, please. _ _ _ _ _ _ _ _ _ _ _ _ _ _
_ _

10. The dictator's enemies, who were patriots, defeated his army. _ _ _ _ _ _ _ _ _ _ _ _ _ _ _ _ _ _
_ _

11. The room was empty; there wasn't even one piece of furniture. _ _ _ _ _ _ _ _ _ _ _ _ _ _ _ _ _ _
_ _

12. For an intelligent pupil, he is not very studious. _
_ _

13. Why (For what reason) does she wear that platinum bracelet? To show her wealth. _ _ _ _ _ _ _ _ _
_ _
_ _

14. Without teeth, the poor old man couldn't eat anything. _
_ _

15. He began with 121 dollars; with good luck, he created a fortune of 2,000,000 dollars. _ _ _ _ _ _ _
_ _
_ _

16. Which of those two painters is more skillful? _
_ _

17. She bought her granddaughter a doll, which was what the child wanted. _ _ _ _ _ _ _ _ _ _ _ _ _ _
_ _

18. Ferdinand VII and Isabel II reigned in the 19th century. _
_ _
_ _

19. For Christmas, his father bought a bicycle and gave it to him. _ _ _ _ _ _ _ _ _ _ _ _ _ _ _ _ _ _
_ _

20. I am saving a souvenir of Spain, whose capital I have visited. _ _ _ _ _ _ _ _ _ _ _ _ _ _ _ _ _ _
_ _

21. The room was dark, but they didn't turn on the light.
_ _

22. Why does she wear a woolen cape? Because it is cold. _
_ _

23. The continent of Asia is larger than any other. _____

_____

24. It isn't going to rain, but snow. _____

25. The author's style, which is simple, attracts many readers. _____

_____

_____

26. Upon advancing a few steps, he saw his friend. _____

_____

27. What a pretty skirt! Is it (of) cotton or wool? _____

_____

28. It struck one o'clock, and the musicians started to play. _____

_____

29. What a wedding! How happy everyone is! How many people there are here! _____

_____

_____

30. He began to walk when it stopped raining. _____

_____

31. Those who lack money will not be able to see the circus. _____

_____

32. He didn't dare to go out in the afternoon. _____

_____

33. The number of tourists was small, and he didn't see anyone he knew. _____

_____

34. What is a needle? A needle is an instrument for sewing. _____

_____

35. The architect constructed a large office building (building for offices). _____

_____

36. They signed the contract on December 1, 1914. _____

_____

_____

37. There are no longer any stars in the sky. _____

_____

38. The purse he found belonged to the girl with whom he had just spoken. _____

_____

_____

39. Why is he mistaken? I don't know why he's mistaken. _____

_____

40. He was at the top of the peak, from which he could see the valleys and rivers. ---------

----

----

41. I have only cheese and bread left. ---------------------------

----

42. He visited Spain last year, but now he wants to see Peru. ---------

----

43. Which was the most glorious period of Spanish literature? ---------

----

44. Around John was the jungle and, in it, ferocious and cruel animals. ---------

----

----

45. I hate you (*fam. sing.*); I don't want to speak to (con) you again. ---------

----

46. At about 5 o'clock they served tea with cherry pie. ---------

----

47. In the market he saw neither merchandise nor vendors. ---------

----

48. They agreed to depart at 3:30 A.M. sharp.

----

49. She was born to be an actress. ---------

50. He earns 10,000 dollars a year. ---------

La Dama de Elche es una estatua de mujer encontrada en 1897 en Elche, en España, en la provincia de Alicante. Se cree que es la representación de una antigua diosa o princesa ibérica.

MASTERY STRUCTURE DRILLS

MULTIPLE-CHOICE QUESTIONS

Each of the incomplete statements is followed by four suggested answers numbered 1 through 4. Underline the answer that best completes each.

A

1. Si _____ en España, veríamos muchas cosas interesantes.
   1 fuésemos   2 éramos   3 estuviéramos   4 estuvimos

2. No envíen Vds. el paquete a las muchachas; _____ .
   1 no se las envíen Vds.   3 no envíenselo Vds.
   2 no se lo envíen Vds.   4 no las lo envíen Vds.

3. Hace dos horas que _____ .
   1 ha jugado   2 ha estado jugando   3 jugaba   4 juega

4. Si le _____, se lo diré.
   1 viera   2 vería   3 veré   4 veo

5. _____ mucho comen, gordas serán.
   1 Cuyas   2 Ellas que   3 Los cuales   4 Quienes

6. Prohibió que _____ en la tienda.
   1 fumásemos   2 fumemos   3 fumamos   4 fumaríamos

7. Es un lago _____ aguas son claras.
   1 cuyos   2 del cual   3 cuyas   4 de que

8. Asistió a la clase el lunes, _____ el martes.
   1 sino no   2 sino que no   3 sino   4 pero no

9. Le vi cuando _____ .
   1 le visité   2 le visite   3 le visito   4 le visitara

10. Compró más sellos _____ necesitaba.
    1 de que   2 que   3 de los que   4 de

B

1. Se lo diré cuando _____ .
   1 volverá   2 vuelvo   3 vuelva   4 vuelve

2. Entró y preguntó:—¿ _____ es este paraguas?
   1 De las cuáles   2 De cuyo   3 De quién   4 Cuyo

3. El alcalde _____ por la gente.
   1 se le elegía   2 estaba elegido   3 se eligió   4 fue elegido

4. _____ ahora.
   1 No lo hagamos   2 No hagámoslo   3 No hágalo nosotros   4 No lo hayamos

5. No llevaba _____ la chaqueta.
   1 ni siquiera   2 ni tampoco   3 todavía no   4 también

6. No encontró a nadie que _____ la respuesta.
   1 sabía   2 supo   3 sabría   4 supiera

7. Volvió a recomendar _____ había recomendado antes.
   1 qué   2 lo que   3 lo cual   4 cuál

8. José y Pablo beben _____ su hermana.
   1 tanta leche que   2 tanta leche como   3 tan leche como   4 tan leche que

9. _____ charlar con los amigos.
   1 Gustamos   2 Nosotros gusta   3 Nos gustan   4 Nos gusta

10. ¿_____ de estas camisas prefiere Vd.?
    1 Cuál   2 Quién   3 Qué   4 Cuyas

C

1. No iba al cine los sábados, _____ los domingos.
   1 sin que   2 sino que   3 pero   4 sino

2. Alfredo y Rosa son hermanos; _____ es menor que aquél.
   1 aquélla   2 éste   3 ése   4 ésta

3. Tengo miedo de _____ sola de noche.
   1 saliendo   2 salir   3 saliera   4 salga

4. La noche era oscura, _____ les inspiró terror.
   1 la cual   2 el que   3 que   4 lo cual

5. Por mucho que _____, nunca será rico.
   1 trabajara   2 puede trabajar   3 trabaje   4 trabaja

6. Hacía un mes que _____ allí.
   1 vivía   2 había estado viviendo   3 había vivido   4 vivió

7. El camarero no sirvió la comida a los clientes; el camarero _____ .
   1 no se la sirvió   2 no los la sirvió   3 no les sirvió ella   4 no sirviósela

8. Vds. no pueden figurarse _____ son estas cerezas.
   1 las buenas que   2 cuán buenas   3 cómo buenas   4 cuántas buenas

9. Era cierto que la medicina _____ .
   1 le ayudaría   2 le ayudará   3 le ayudase   4 le hubiera ayudado

10. _____ los actores.
    1 Se aplaudieron   2 Se aplaudió   3 Se aplaudió a   4 Estaban aplaudidos

D

1. Sabe la historia mejor que _____ .
   1 cualquiera   2 alguna   3 nadie   4 alguien

2. _____ viaja, tanto más desea viajar.
   1 Cuanto más   2 Tanto más   3 Lo más   4 Más

3. Los aztecas trataban a sus víctimas _____ y cruelmente.
   1 severamente   2 severas   3 severa   4 severos

4. No pierda Vd. la pluma; _____ sería una lástima.
   1 ésa   2 eso   3 aquél   4 ésta

5. Los alumnos son menos serios _____ el maestro cree.
   1 de los que   2 de lo que   3 del que   4 que

6. No creía que el criminal _____ presentarse.
   1 se atreviera a   2 se atrevería a   3 se atrevía a   4 se atrevió a

7. Las bibliotecas _____ a las seis.
   1 son cerrado   2 están cerrado   3 cierran   4 se cierran

8. Prefiere una máquina que _____ bien.
   1 funcionará   2 funciona   3 funcionaría   4 funcione

9. Es posible que _____ su maleta.
1 él me prestará   2 él me preste   3 él me prestaría   4 él prestarme

10. _____ no hacer nada malo, hijos.
1 Prometáisme   2 Prometedme   3 Prométame   4 Me prometáis

E

1. Prefieren _____ de otro modo.
1 los niños divertirse   3 que los niños se divierten
2 que los niños se divertir   4 que los niños se diviertan

2. En caso de que _____ más, ven a verme.
1 necesitas   2 necesitaras   3 necesites   4 necesitarás

3. Te dije mil veces:—_____ con tu hermana.
1 No riña Vd.   2 No riñe   3 No reñís   4 No riñas

4. _____ busca aventuras, las encontrará.
1 Quienes   2 El que   3 El quién   4 Él que

5. El maestro habló despacio para que todos _____ .
1 comprendían   2 comprendan   3 comprenderían   4 comprendiesen

6. En mi casa hay un estante que _____ doscientos libros.
1 tiene   2 ha   3 tenga   4 tengo

7. La bicicleta de Jorge, _____ es nueva, corre bien.
1 la cual   2 quien   3 que   4 el que

8. _____ las alhajas y las flores.
1 Las señoras gustan   3 Las señoras las gustan
2 A las señoras les gustan   4 A las señoras ellas gustan

9. Si él _____ más temprano, habría llegado a tiempo.
1 saldría   2 saliera   3 hubiese salido   4 hubo salido

10. Recogió su baúl y _____ su hija.
1 eso de   2 el de   3 ése de   4 que de

Aunque forma parte de la catedral de Sevilla, la Giralda es una torre de origen árabe. En lo alto de la torre hay una estatua que hace de veleta (weather vane), girando con el viento. De ahí el nombre (girar = to turn).

JOINING SENTENCES

Rewrite the two sentences in each question as a single sentence in accordance with the instructions, making changes and omissions, and reversing the order of sentences, as necessary. Do *not* begin the sentence with the word or words in italics unless you are specifically told to do so.

SAMPLE QUESTION:
Join by using *si:* Juan irá a casa. No lloverá.

ANSWER:
Juan irá a casa si no llueve.

A

1. Join with *sin:*   Pablo entró. No tocó el timbre.

2. Begin with *Cuando:*   Vd. llegará a Monterrey. Vd. tendrá que visitar a mi primo.

3. Begin with *Los incas:*   Alguien conquistó a los incas. Fue Pizarro.

4. Join with *para:*   María canta. Ella se divierte.

5. Join with *que:*   Vd. lo hará en seguida. Será mejor.

6. Join with *cuyo:*   Allí está Juanito López. Su madre es actriz.

7. Join with *sino:*   No tengo cuatro dólares. Tengo tres.

8. Begin with *Al:*   Corrió a saludarme. Escuchó mi voz.

9. Join with *con tal que:*   Les pagaré bien. Vds. terminarán el trabajo pronto.

10. Begin with *Los que:*   Ellos estudian. Aprenderán mucho.

B

1. Begin with *Aunque:*   Daremos una vuelta por el parque. Lloverá esta tarde.

2. Join with *a menos que:*   No ayudaré a Diego. Él aceptará mi ayuda de buena gana.

3. Join with *para que:*   Papá le dará el dinero. Podrá comprar los libros.

4. Join with *sino:*   No voy a comprar una maleta. Voy a comprar un baúl.

5. Join with *antes de que:*   La Sra. Cárdenas limpió la casa. Su suegra la visitó.

6. Begin with *Aquellos cuadros:*   Alguien pintó aquellos cuadros. Fue Velázquez.

7. Begin with *Si:*   Quieres dinero. Tienes que ganarlo.

8. Join with *hasta que:*   Siguió estudiando. Aprendió bien sus lecciones.

9. Join with *que:*   Lea Vd. correctamente. Lo deseo.

10. Join with *sin que:*   Él entró en la sala. Yo no lo sabía.

C

1. Join with *si:* — Habló como abogado. No era abogado.

2. Join with *que:* — Lo haremos con cuidado. Ella nos lo pide.

3. Begin with *Para:* — Voy a la fiesta. Necesito un automóvil.

4. Join with *quienquiera:* — Alguien llamará. No abra Vd. la puerta.

5. Join with *hasta que:* — Estaré en esa esquina. Vendrá el ómnibus.

6. Join with *de:* — Estoy de vacaciones. Me alegro mucho.

7. Join with *a menos que:* — Mi novia irá al baile. Yo no asistiré.

8. Join with *sino:* — No voy al teatro. Voy al museo.

9. Join with *con tal que:* — Tendremos mucho dinero. Ganaremos el premio gordo.

10. Join with *para que:* — El padre trabaja. La familia podrá comer.

D

1. Join with *cuando:* — Vds. dirán la verdad. Yo escucharé.

2. Join with *si:* — Ganaría más dinero. Podría gastar más.

3. Join with *sin:* — Fue al parque ayer. No se divirtió.

4. Join with *como si:* — Ellos respondieron. No sabían las respuestas.

5. Join with *a menos que:* — Cumpliremos con nuestros deberes. No nos permitirán ir al parque.

6. Join with *hasta que:* — Caminaré mucho. Me cansaré.

7. Begin with *Aunque:* — Tenía mucho dinero. No hizo el viaje.

8. Join with *que:* — Vendrá temprano. Me dijo eso.

9. Join with *ni . . . ni:* — No iremos al concierto. No iremos al teatro.

10. Join with *que:* — Ellos volverían inmediatamente. Sería preciso.

E

1. Join with *antes de que:* — Estudie Vd. sus lecciones. Su madre volverá.

2. Begin with *Si:* — Saldremos bien en el examen. Estudiaremos mucho.

3. Begin with the Spanish form of *What:* — Es un vaso de agua. Lo quiero.

4. Join with *que:* — Yo sabía el camino. Ellos lo dudaban.

5. Join with *si:* — Habríamos visto esa película. Nos habríamos divertido mucho.

6. Join with the Spanish form of *than:* — Ganaba poco dinero. Gastaba más.

7. Join with *para:* — Es muy alto. Es un niño.

8. Join with *sin:* — Lo hizo. No dijo nada.

9. Join with *después de:* — Terminaré el trabajo. Volveré del teatro.

10. Join with *a fin de que:* — El presidente pronunció un discurso importante. El público sabría la situación.

Idiom Lesson 1—IDIOMS WITH *DAR*, *HABER*, *HACER*, AND *TENER*

IDIOMS WITH *DAR*

1. **dar a,** to face, to look out upon

   Las ventanas *dan a* la avenida.   The windows face the avenue.

2. **dar con,** to come upon, to find

   Dimos con Juan en el cine anoche.   We came upon John at the movies last night.

3. **dar cuerda (a),** to wind

   Cada mañana *doy cuerda a* mi reloj.   Each morning I wind my watch.

4. **dar de beber (comer) a,** to give a drink to (to feed)

   Pedro *dio de beber a* su perro.   Peter gave his dog a drink.

5. **dar en,** to strike against, to hit

   Se cayó y *dio en* el suelo.   He fell and hit the floor.

6. **dar gritos (voces),** to shout

   Los niños *dieron gritos* de alegría.   The children shouted with joy.
   Dio voces, pidiendo ayuda.   He shouted, asking for help.

7. **dar la hora (las siete),** to strike the hour (seven)

   El reloj *dio la una.*   The clock struck one.

8. **darse la mano,** to shake hands

   Al encontrarse, *se dieron la mano.*   Upon meeting, they shook hands.

9. **dar las gracias (a),** to thank

   Dio las gracias a sus padres por el regalo.   He thanked his parents for the gift.

10. **dar por** + past participle, to consider

    El profesor *dio por terminada* la lección.   The teacher considered the lesson ended.

11. **darse por** + past participle, to consider oneself

    Al fin el ejército *se dio por vencido.*   Finally, the army considered itself defeated.

12. **dar recuerdos (a),** to give regards to

    Dé mis *recuerdos a* sus padres.   Give my regards to your parents.

13. **darse cuenta de,** to realize

    No *se dio cuenta de* su error.   He did not realize his error.

14. **darse prisa,** to hurry

    ¡Dense prisa! Ya son las ocho.   Hurry! It is already eight o'clock.

15. **dar un abrazo,** to embrace

    Antes de salir, *dio un abrazo* a su madre.   Before leaving, he embraced his mother.

16. **dar un paseo,** to take a walk
dar un paseo en coche, to take a ride (in a car)

Daba un paseo cuando vio el accidente.   He was taking a walk when he saw the accident.

17. **dar una vuelta,** to take a stroll

Por la tarde *doy una vuelta* por el parque.   In the afternoon I take a stroll through the park.

IDIOMS WITH *HABER*

1. **hay,** there is, there are   **habrá,** there will be
había ⎫ there was, there were   **habría,** there would be
hubo ⎭   **ha habido,** there has (have) been

Había muchos clientes en la tienda.   There were many customers in the store.

2. **haber de** + infinitive, to be (supposed) to, to have to

He de salir a las nueve.   I am to leave at nine o'clock.

3. **haber sol,** to be sunny

No *hubo sol* ayer, y llovió.   It wasn't sunny yesterday, and it rained.

4. **haber (mucho) polvo,** to be (very) dusty

Había mucho polvo en el camino.   It was very dusty on the road.

5. **haber (mucho) lodo,** to be (very) muddy

Después de la lluvia *había lodo.*   After the rain it was muddy.

6. **haber neblina,** to be foggy, misty

Ayer fue un día claro; no *hubo neblina.*   Yesterday was a clear day; it was not foggy.

7. **hay luna,** there is moonlight

Habrá luna esta noche.   There will be moonlight tonight.

8. **hay que** + infinitive, one must, it is necessary

Habrá que salir temprano.   It will be necessary to leave early.

9. **hay** + noun + **que** + infinitive, there is (are) + noun + infinitive

Siempre *habrá problemas que resolver.*   There will always be problems to solve.

Lope Félix de Vega Carpio (1562–1635) fue el dramaturgo principal de España. Su obra dramática consiste en centenares (hundreds) de comedias, todas escritas en verso. También escribió varios poemas épicos. En la literatura española, se le considera superado sólo por Cervantes.

IDIOMS WITH *HACER*

1. **hace** + time expression + **que** + preterite, ago

   Hace una semana que vino a verme.   He came to see me a week ago.

   Note. Without **que,** the expression is reversed:

   Vino a verme *hace una semana.*

2. **hace poco,** a little while ago

   El tren salió *hace poco.*   The train left a little while ago.

3. **hacer buen (mal) tiempo,** to be good (bad) weather

   Ayer *hacía buen tiempo,* pero hoy llueve.   Yesterday the weather was good, but today it is raining.

4. **hacer (mucho) frío (calor),** to be (very) cold (warm)

   En el invierno *hace frío.*   It is cold in winter.

5. **hacer (mucho) viento,** to be (very) windy

   Aquel día no salí porque *hacía viento.*   I didn't go out that day because it was windy.

6. **hacer caso de,** to pay attention to, to heed, to notice

   Ese muchacho no *hizo caso de* mis consejos.   That boy didn't heed my advice.

7. **hacer de,** to work as, to act as

   En el juego, Diego *hacía de* capitán.   In the game, James acted as captain.

8. **hacer el papel de,** to play the role of

   La actriz se negó a *hacer el papel de* condesa.   The actress refused to play the role of countess.

9. **hacer pedazos,** to break to pieces, to tear (to shreds), to smash

   El muchacho *hizo pedazos* el papel.   The boy tore the paper to shreds.

10. **hacer una pregunta,** to ask a question

    Me *hizo una pregunta,* pero yo no contesté.   He asked me a question, but I did not answer.

11. **hacer una visita,** to pay a visit

    Anoche *hice una visita* a mi amigo.   Last night I paid a visit to my friend.

12. **hacer un viaje,** to take (make) a trip

    Hizo un viaje a México el año pasado.   He took (made) a trip to Mexico last year.

13. **hacerse,** to become (through effort)

    Para *hacerse* médico, es necesario estudiar.   In order to become a doctor, it is necessary to study.

14. **hacerse tarde,** to become (grow) late

    Se hacía muy *tarde,* y tenían que marcharse.   It was becoming very late, and they had to leave.

15. **hacer daño (a),** to harm, to damage

    El frío *hizo daño a* los árboles.   The cold damaged the trees.

16. **hacerse daño,** to hurt oneself

    Se cayó y *se hizo daño* en la cabeza.   He fell and hurt his head.

IDIOMS WITH *TENER*

1. **tener (mucho) calor (frío),** to be (very) warm (cold)

   Tenía calor y se quitó el sobretodo.   He was warm and took off his overcoat.

2. **tener cuidado,** to be careful

   Tengan Vds. *cuidado* al cruzar la calle.   Be careful when crossing the street.

3. **tener dolor de cabeza (de estómago,** etc.), to have a headache (stomach ache, etc.)

   Ayer *tuve dolor de estómago,* pero hoy estoy bien.   Yesterday I had a stomach ache, but today I feel well.

4. **tener éxito,** to be successful

   Él *tiene éxito* en todo lo que hace.   He is successful in everything he does.

5. **tener ganas de,** to feel like

   A veces *tengo ganas de* bailar.   At times I feel like dancing.

6. **tener (mucha) hambre (sed),** to be (very) hungry (thirsty)

   Tenemos mucha sed en el verano.   We are very thirsty in the summer.

7. **tener la culpa (de),** to be to blame (for)

   El muchacho *tiene la culpa de* haber roto la ventana.   The boy is to blame for having broken the window.

8. **tener lugar,** to take place

   ¿Cuándo *tendrá lugar* la fiesta?   When will the party take place?

9. **tener miedo de,** to be afraid of

   El niño *tiene miedo de* la oscuridad.   The child is afraid of the dark.

10. **tener por** + adjective, to consider

    Tenía por hecho el trabajo, y se fue.   He considered the work done, and left.

11. **tener prisa,** to be in a hurry

    Tenía prisa y no podía detenerse a hablar.   He was in a hurry and could not stop to talk.

12. **tener que ver con,** to have to do with

    No *tenía* nada *que ver con* el robo.   He had nothing to do with the robbery.

13. **tener razón (no tener razón),** to be right (to be wrong)

    ¿Tiene razón? No, *no tiene razón.*   Is he right? No, he's wrong.

14. **tener (mucho) sueño,** to be (very) sleepy

    María *tenía sueño* y se acostó.   Mary was sleepy and went to bed.

15. **tener (mucha) suerte,** to be (very) lucky

    No *tenía suerte,* y perdió el dinero.   He wasn't lucky, and he lost the money.

16. **tener vergüenza (de),** to be ashamed (of)

    El muchacho *tenía vergüenza de* sus acciones.   The boy was ashamed of his actions.

EJERCICIOS

A. Escójase de la lista una expresión *sinónima* de cada una de las expresiones en letra cursiva, y escríbase en la forma correcta.

dar con	hacer pedazos
dar las gracias	hay que
darse por	tener ganas de
darse prisa	tener lugar
dar una vuelta	tener miedo de

1. Mientras *daba un paseo* por la ciudad, se fijaba en la gente. --------------------

2. En el vestíbulo *se encontró con* el cartero, quien repartía las cartas. --------------------

3. La fiesta *se verificó* la víspera de su cumpleaños. --------------------

4. Al ver al detective, el traidor *se consideró* perdido. --------------------

5. *Deseaba* entrar en la capilla para rezar. --------------------

6. El dramaturgo *se apresuró* a terminar la comedia a tiempo. --------------------

7. La niña *temía* la oscuridad de medianoche. --------------------

8. Fernando e Isabel *agradecieron* a Colón. --------------------

9. Para conocer el mundo *es necesario* estudiar la geografía. --------------------

10. De un golpe, *rompió* el instrumento. --------------------

B. Contéstense en español en frases completas.

1. ¿Sabe Vd. responder cuando el maestro hace una pregunta? --------------------

2. ¿Qué toma Vd. cuando tiene sed? --------------------

3. ¿Cuántas veces al día da Vd. de comer a su perro? --------------------

4. ¿Tiene Vd. ambición de hacerse abogado? --------------------

5. ¿Qué hace Vd. cuando tiene sueño? --------------------

6. ¿Hay polvo o lodo en la calle cuando la tierra está seca? --------------------

7. Cuando hay ruido en la clase, ¿tiene Vd. la culpa? --------------------

8. ¿Hay sol o luna de noche? --------------------

9. Cuando Vd. tiene prisa, ¿se sienta Vd. a descansar? --------------------

10. ¿Hace Vd. visitas los domingos? ¿A quiénes? --------------------

11. ¿En qué estación del año hace mal tiempo? _ _ _ _ _ _ _ _ _ _ _ _

12. ¿Tiene Vd. éxito en los exámenes? _ _ _ _ _ _ _ _ _ _ _ _

_ _

13. ¿Tiene Vd. cuidado al pronunciar las palabras? _ _ _ _ _ _ _ _ _ _

_ _

14. ¿Hace Vd. caso de las enseñanzas de la experiencia? _ _ _ _ _ _ _

_ _

15. ¿Puede hacer daño el fuerte sol de mediodía? _ _ _ _ _ _ _ _ _ _

_ _

16. ¿Tiene Vd. razón siempre? _ _ _ _ _ _ _ _ _ _ _ _ _ _ _ _

17. ¿Se da Vd. cuenta de la bondad y del cariño de sus padres? _ _ _ _

_ _

18. ¿Qué hace Vd. cuando tiene dolor de dientes? _ _ _ _ _ _ _ _ _ _

_ _

19. ¿Qué hace Vd. cuando hace viento? _ _ _ _ _ _ _ _ _ _ _ _ _

_ _

20. ¿Cuántas veces al día da la hora un reloj? _ _ _ _ _ _ _ _ _ _ _

_ _

C. Tradúzcanse al español las expresiones en inglés.

1. No te olvides de *give my regards* a tu hermana. _ _ _ _ _ _ _ _

2. El muchacho más inteligente *will act as* guía. _ _ _ _ _ _ _ _

3. El museo *faces* la plaza. _ _ _ _ _ _ _ _ _ _ _ _ _ _ _ _

4. *They are to* estar allí a las ocho en punto. _ _ _ _ _ _ _ _ _

5. Después de la lucha, los dos niños *shook hands*. _ _ _ _ _ _ _ _

6. Mientras jugaban, *they shouted* de alegría. _ _ _ _ _ _ _ _ _

7. Al caer, Ramón *hurt himself* en la pierna. _ _ _ _ _ _ _ _ _ _

8. Lucía *embraced* a su madre. _ _ _ _ _ _ _ _ _ _ _ _ _ _

9. La bondad *has nothing to do with* la riqueza. _ _ _ _ _ _ _ _ _

10. Celebraron su aniversario *a little while ago*. _ _ _ _ _ _ _ _ _

11. *It is very foggy* y no se puede ver nada. _ _ _ _ _ _ _ _ _ _

12. Siempre *there will be illnesses to* curar. _ _ _ _ _ _ _ _ _ _

13. Mamá *was ashamed of* lo que hizo Paco. _ _ _ _ _ _ _ _ _ _

14. *We considered* acabada la tarea. _ _ _ _ _ _ _ _ _ _ _ _ _

15. Siempre me olvido de *to wind* mi reloj. _ _ _ _ _ _ _ _ _ _

16. *It's getting late* y tengo que volver a mi despacho. _ _ _ _ _ _ _

17. En el invierno *it is cold*, y el agua se hiela. _ _ _ _ _ _ _ _ _

18. La pelota se le escapó de las manos y *struck* la pared. _ _ _ _ _ _

19. Sabe mucho; yo le *consider* sabio. _____

20. *He is very lucky;* reunió una gran fortuna en tres años. _____

D. Tradúzcanse al español.

1. Although he was hungry, he was afraid to enter a restaurant. _____

_____

2. It is sunny, but it is still muddy in the streets. _____

_____

3. Be careful. Don't eat too much at the banquet. _____

_____

4. She was sleepy and cold, and scarcely noticed the beauty of the night. _____

_____

5. I strolled through the museum, looking at the marble statues. _____

_____

6. It was warm, but it was foggy, and they hurried to reach home. _____

_____

7. He knows when all the historic battles took place. _____

_____

8. Cortés smashed the stone figures of the Aztec gods. _____

_____

9. The manager considered the account settled. _____

_____

10. His granddaughter played the role of princess in the play. _____

_____

11. After the explosion, there were many victims to save. _____

_____

12. I don't feel like attending the circus this afternoon. _____

_____

13. The map indicates where we can find all the interesting buildings. _____

_____

14. Upon leaving the bath, he fell and hurt himself. _____

_____

15. The clock is striking five, and it is getting late. _____

_____

Idiom Lesson 2—MISCELLANEOUS VERBAL IDIOMS (PART I)

1. **acabar de** + infinitive, to have just

   Acabo de volver de la escuela. — I have just returned from school.

   Acababa de volver de la escuela. — I had just returned from school.

2. **acabar por** + infinitive, to end by, to finally . . .

   Cayó enfermo y *acabó por morir.* — He fell ill and finally died.

3. **acercarse a,** to approach

   Nos acercamos a la casa. — We approached the house.

4. **acordarse de,** to remember

   Se acordó de sus antiguos amigos. — He remembered his old friends.

5. **alegrarse de,** to be glad of (to)

   Se alegró de ganar el premio. — He was glad to win the prize.

6. **alejarse de,** to go away from

   El tren *se alejó de* la estación. — The train drew away from the station.

7. **apoderarse de,** to take possession of

   El ejército *se apoderó de* la fortaleza. — The army took possession of the fortress.

8. **apoyarse en,** to lean against (on)

   El viejo *se apoyó en* la pared. — The old man leaned against the wall.

9. **apresurarse a** + infinitive, to hurry to

   Se apresuró a escribir la carta. — She hurried to write the letter.

10. **arrepentirse de,** to repent

    Se arrepintió de su crimen. — He repented his crime.

11. **asomarse a,** to look out of, to appear at (a window)

    Al oír la música, *me asomé a* la ventana. — On hearing the music, I looked out of the window.

12. **atreverse a** + infinitive, to dare to

    Llovía y no *se atrevieron a salir.* — It was raining, and they did not dare to leave.

13. **burlarse de,** to make fun of

    No *se burlen* Vds. *de* los débiles. — Don't make fun of the weak.

14. **carecer de,** to lack

    Carece de sentido común. — He lacks common sense.

15. **casarse (con),** to marry, to get married (to)

    Se casó con Roberto. — She got married to Robert.

16. **consentir en,** to consent to

    Consienten en que salga hoy. — They consent to my going out today.

17. **consistir en,** to consist of

    El libro *consiste en* trescientas páginas. — The book consists of three hundred pages.

242

18. **contar con,** to rely on, to count on

Los niños siempre *cuentan con* su madre.   Children always rely on their mothers.

19. **convenir en,** to agree on (to)

Convinieron en reunirse al día siguiente.   They agreed to meet on the following day.

20. **cuidar a,** to take care of (a person)
    cuidar de, to take care of (a thing)

No *cuidó de* su bicicleta y la perdió.   He didn't take care of his bicycle and lost it.

21. **cumplir con,** to fulfill, to keep (a promise, one's word)

Siempre *cumplo con* mi palabra.   I always keep my word.

22. **dejar caer,** to drop

Juanito *dejó caer* el vaso de leche.   Johnny dropped the glass of milk.

23. **dejar de** + infinitive, to fail to, to stop, to neglect to

Dejó de estudiar y cerró el libro.   He stopped studying and closed the book.

24. **dirigirse a,** to address, to make one's way to

El policía *se dirigió a* casa del ladrón.   The policeman made his way to the thief's home.

25. **disponerse a** + infinitive, to get ready to

Cuando *nos dispusimos a salir,* comenzó a llover.   When we got ready to leave, it started to rain.

26. **echarse a** + infinitive, to start to, to begin to

Al ver el toro, el torero *se echó a correr.*   On seeing the bull, the bullfighter began to run.

27. **echar al correo,** to mail

Escribí la carta y la *eché al correo.*   I wrote the letter and mailed it.

28. **echar de menos,** to miss

Los niños *echaron de menos* a su vecino.   The children missed their neighbor.

29. **echar la culpa (a),** to blame

Echó la culpa a su hermana.   He blamed his sister.

30. **empeñarse en** + infinitive, to insist on, to persist in

El muchacho *se empeñó en arrancar* las flores.   The boy insisted on pulling out the flowers.

31. **enamorarse de,** to fall in love with

Al verla, *se enamoró de* ella locamente.   On seeing her, he fell madly in love with her.

32. **encogerse de hombros,** to shrug one's shoulders

Al saber la noticia, *se encogió de hombros.*   On learning the news, he shrugged his shoulders.

33. **enterarse de,** to become aware of, to find out about

Nunca *se enteró de* lo que había pasado.   He never found out what had happened.

34. **estar a punto de** + infinitive, to be about to

Espérame, *estoy a punto de terminar* el trabajo.   Wait for me, I'm about to finish the work.

35. **estar conforme (con)** ⎫
36. **estar de acuerdo (con)** ⎭ to be in agreement (with)

No *estoy conforme con* su opinión. ⎫
No *estoy de acuerdo con* su opinión. ⎭   I'm not in agreement with your opinion.

37. **estar de vuelta,** to be back

Estaré de vuelta el miércoles.   I'll be back on Wednesday.

38. **estar para** + infinitive, to be about to

Estoy para salir ahora.   I'm about to leave now.

39. **estar por,** to be in favor of

Yo *estoy por* ir al campo este verano.   I'm in favor of going to the country this summer.

40. **fiarse de,** to trust

Dice tantas mentiras que no *me fío de* él.   He tells so many lies that I don't trust him.

41. **fijarse en,** to stare at, to notice

Al entrar, *me fijé en* las obras de arte.   On entering, I noticed the works of art.

42. **gozar de,** to enjoy

En las montañas *gozó del* aire fresco.   In the mountains he enjoyed the fresh air.

43. **guardar cama,** to stay in bed

Tenía fiebre y *guardó cama* todo el día.   He had a fever and stayed in bed all day.

44. **insistir en,** to insist on

Insistió en dedicarse al arte.   He insisted on devoting himself to art.

45. **llegar a ser,** to become, to get to be

Después de años de estudio, *llegó a ser* médico.   After years of study, he became a doctor.

46. **llevar a cabo,** to carry out

El capitán *llevó a cabo* las órdenes del general.   The captain carried out the general's orders.

47. **negarse a** + infinitive, to refuse to

El niño *se negó a comer* el cereal.   The child refused to eat the cereal.

48. **oír hablar de,** to hear about

En clase *oí hablar del* gran héroe, Bolívar.   In class I heard about the great hero, Bolívar.

49. **oler a,** to smell of, to smell like

Esta flor *huele a* clavel.   This flower smells like a carnation.

50. **olvidarse de,** to forget

Nunca *me olvidaré de* ella.   I will never forget her.

EJERCICIOS

A. Escójase de la lista una expresión *sinónima* de cada una de las expresiones en letra cursiva, y escríbase en la forma correcta.

acordarse de	asomarse a	echarse a
alejarse de	casarse con	estar conforme con
apoderarse de	consentir en	llegar a ser
apresurarse a	disponerse a	llevar a cabo

1. Tenía esperanzas de *hacerse* jefe de la empresa. _____

2. Bajó del autobús y *comenzó a* correr a pie. _____

3. No tenía ganas de *ejecutar* los proyectos del amo. _____

4. No *estoy de acuerdo con* sus ideas sobre la enseñanza. _____

5. El viejo *recordó* la época de su juventud. _____

6. El capitán *permitió* que los marineros visitasen la isla desierta. _____

7. Se lavó, se vistió, y *se preparó para* salir. _____

8. *Se apartó del* lado de su nieto y se sentó en el banco. _____

9. Los patriotas *tomaron posesión de* la fortaleza. _____

10. *Se dio prisa a* cobrar su sueldo porque necesitaba dinero. _____

B. Escójase de la lista una expresión *antónima* de cada una de las expresiones en letra cursiva, y escríbase en la forma correcta.

acercarse a	atreverse a	dejar caer
acordarse de	carecer de	dejar de
alegrarse de	consentir en	estar de vuelta
asomarse a	convenir en	estar por

1. *Tiene miedo de* encontrar aventuras peligrosas. _____

2. *Se arrepintió de* haber dedicado tanto tiempo a los deportes. _____

3. Desde el andén vio que el tren *se alejaba de* la estación. _____

4. *No deseo* ir a la función esta noche. _____

5. Mamá *prohíbe* que juguemos con los fósforos. _____

6. A las dos *se echó a* trabajar. _____

7. *Tengo* mucho dinero y recursos. _____

8. *Se marchará de* aquí el catorce de mayo. _____

9. La cocinera *se olvidó de* echar sal en la sopa. _____

10. Mientras pasaba de la cocina al comedor, *levantó* la botella de vino. _____

C. Contéstense en español en frases completas.

1. ¿Cumple Vd. con todas sus obligaciones? _____

2. ¿Está Vd. por un examen mañana? _____

3. ¿Carece Vd. de fondos a veces? _____

4. Durante el invierno, ¿echa Vd. de menos los placeres de las vacaciones? _____

_____

_____

5. ¿Se empeña el maestro en que Vd. hable en voz alta? _____

_____

6. ¿Cuenta Vd. con la buena suerte para salir bien en los exámenes? _____

_____

7. ¿Se encoge Vd. de hombros al oír hablar de una catástrofe? _____

_____

8. ¿Se burla Vd. de sus amigos? _____

9. Al entrar en casa, ¿deja Vd. caer sus libros en el suelo? _____

_____

10. ¿Echa Vd. las cartas al correo antes de escribirlas? _____

_____

11. ¿Cuida Vd. a su hermanito(-a) cuando sus padres salen de noche? _____

_____

12. ¿Goza Vd. de buena salud? _____

13. ¿Está Vd. a punto de graduarse de la escuela? _____

_____

14. Cuando Vd. hace algo malo, ¿echa Vd. la culpa a otro? _____

_____

15. ¿Se niega Vd. a ir al dentista cuando tiene dolor de dientes? _____

_____

16. Cuando Vd. se dirige al profesor, ¿habla Vd. en tono cortés? _____

_____

17. En sus estudios, ¿se fija Vd. en los pequeños detalles? _____

_____

18. ¿Deja Vd. de cumplir con sus deberes a menudo? _____

_____

19. ¿Guarda Vd. cama cuando tiene fiebre? _____

_____

20. ¿Se atreve Vd. a hablar en la clase sin permiso? _____

_____

D. Tradúzcanse al español las expresiones en inglés.

1. Los trabajadores *agreed to* _____ volver al trabajo.

2. *They approached* _____ la máquina para ver por qué no funcionaba.

3. El muchacho que *took care of* _____ las ovejas había visto un lobo.

4. Subiendo la escalera, *he leaned against* _____ la pared varias veces para descansar.

5. Es bueno tener fieles amigos y poder *to trust* _____ ellos.

6. Los otros alumnos *made fun of* _____ mi modo de vestir.

7. *He ended by* _____ asegurarme que yo tenía razón.

8. Mi padre *insisted on* _____ establecer nuestra casa en una calle estrecha.

9. *I kept* _____ mi promesa, y compré una muñeca para mi sobrina.

10. Esa novela es larga; *it consists of* _____ sesenta capítulos.

11. *He hurried to* _____ llegar a casa antes de la medianoche.

12. En vez de abrir la puerta, *she appeared at* _____ la ventana para averiguar quién llamaba.

13. Según la ley el gobierno *will take possession of* _____ las propiedades del traidor.

14. Hechos los arreglos para la ceremonia, *she married* _____ el príncipe.

15. El médico *relied on* _____ una operación para curar al enfermo.

16. El padre *was about to* _____ castigar al niño cuando entró el abuelo.

17. *We had just* _____ entrar en la casa cuando sonó el teléfono.

18. Mi padre *makes his way to* _____ su despacho todos los días.

19. *Don't fail to* _____ llamar al plomero; no hay agua.

20. En el pueblo lejano, *she missed* _____ a sus queridas amigas y parientes.

21. *On finding out* _____ que el contador no estaba en casa, la policía *got ready to* _____ buscarle.

22. Algunos navegantes *repented* _____ haberse embarcado con Colón.

23. La conoció en el banquete y *fell in love with her* _____ en seguida.

24. En la primavera los jardines *smell of* _____ flores.

25. Los hispanoamericanos *were glad of* _____ haber ganado la independencia.

E. Tradúzcanse al español.

1. When they saw the broken eyeglasses, they blamed James. _____
_____

2. She fell in love with a clerk in her father's store. _____
_____

3. I have heard of the dignity and pride of the Spaniards. _____
_____

4. When the miser found out about the loss of his treasure, he fainted. _____
_____

5. Upon hearing the cries (gritos) of his victims, the tyrant shrugged his shoulders. _____
_____

6. The wounded soldier leaned on the arm of his companion. _____
_____

7. He told me that he would be back in a few minutes. _____

_____

8. He persisted in singing in the bath, although he had a bad voice. _____

_____

9. He stared at the spectacle that was unfolding before his eyes. _____

_____

10. Mary carried out her plan to make a trip to Peru. _____

_____

11. This soap smells like roses and violets. _____

12. My mother forgot to decorate the parlor for the party. _____

_____

13. I am not in agreement with the attitude of my parents. _____

_____

14. The child refused to take a bath after falling in the mud. _____

_____

15. Instead of going out to look for a job, he stayed in bed all day. _____

_____

16. With a firm hand he wrote the letter, put it in an envelope, and mailed it. _____

_____

_____

17. I have just seen the postman, and he gave me a letter for you. _____

_____

18. It is useless to trust false friends. _____

_____

19. He became a bullfighter and spent many years fighting bulls. _____

_____

20. She was a Spanish dancer who enjoyed world fame. _____

_____

Idiom Lesson 3—MISCELLANEOUS VERBAL IDIOMS (PART II); *GUSTAR*

1. **parecerse a,** to resemble

   La niña *se parece a* su tía.
   The child resembles her aunt.

2. **pensar** + infinitive, to intend

   ¿Qué *piensa* Vd. *hacer* este verano?
   What do you intend to do this summer?

3. **pensar de,** to think of (have an opinion about)

   ¿Qué *piensa* Vd. *del* nuevo maestro?
   What do you think of the new teacher?

4. **pensar en,** to think of (direct one's thoughts to)

   Siempre *piensa en* las vacaciones.
   He is always thinking about the vacation.

5. **perder cuidado,** not to worry

   Pierda Vd. *cuidado;* todo saldrá bien.
   Don't worry; everything will turn out well.

6. **perder de vista,** to lose sight of

   Le siguieron, pero pronto le *perdieron de vista.*
   They followed him, but they soon lost sight of him.

7. **ponerse** + adjective, to become (involuntarily)

   Al oír la noticia, el niño *se puso pálido.*
   On hearing the news, the child became pale.

8. **ponerse a** + infinitive, to begin to

   La alumna *se puso a llorar.*
   The pupil began to cry.

9. **ponerse de acuerdo,** to come to an agreement

   Por fin, *se pusieron de acuerdo.*
   Finally, they came to an agreement.

10. **quedarse con,** to keep

    Me quedaré con este lápiz.
    I'll keep this pencil.

11. **quejarse de,** to complain of (about)

    El joven *se quejaba de* un dolor.
    The young man complained of a pain.

12. **querer decir,** to mean

    ¿Qué *quiere decir* esta palabra?
    What does this word mean?

13. **reírse de,** to laugh at, to make fun of

    Todos *se rieron del* chiste.
    Everybody laughed at the joke.
    Todos *se rieron del* inventor.
    They all made fun of the inventor.

14. **reparar en,** to look at, to observe, to notice

    Al entrar, *reparó en* la muchacha rubia.
    On entering, he noticed the blond girl.

15. **(saber) de memoria,** (to know) by heart

    Sé de memoria la poesía.
    I know the poem by heart.

16. **sacar una fotografía,** to take a picture

    Me gusta *sacar fotografías.*
    I like to take pictures.

17. **ser aficionado(-a) a,** to be fond of

    Juan *es aficionado a* las corridas de toros.
    John is fond of bullfights.

18. **servir de,** to serve as

El Sr. Vásquez *sirvió de* intérprete. | Mr. Vásquez served as an interpreter.

19. **servir para,** to be useful for, to be good for

Los pies *sirven para* andar. | The feet are used for walking.

20. **soñar con,** to dream of

Soñó con hacerse rico. | He dreamed of becoming rich.

21. **tardar en** + infinitive, to be late in, to delay in

El tren *tardó en llegar.* | The train was late in arriving.

22. **tratar de** + infinitive, to try to

Trate Vd. *de mover* esa piedra. | Try to move that stone.

23. **tratarse de,** to be a question of, to be concerned with

Se trata de un asunto serio. | It concerns (is concerned with) a serious matter.

24. **tropezar con,** to come upon, to meet (unexpectedly)

Anoche *tropecé con* ella en el teatro. | Last night I met her in the theater.

25. **valer la pena,** to be worthwhile

Siempre *vale la pena* escuchar. | It is always worthwhile to listen.

26. **volver a** + infinitive, to . . . again

El cantor *volvió a cantar.* | The singer sang again.

27. **volver en sí,** to regain consciousness, to come to

El herido nunca *volvió en sí.* | The wounded man never regained consciousness.

GUSTAR

The verb **gustar** (to be pleasing) also expresses the meaning of the English verb *to like.* "They like the book" must be rephrased in Spanish: "The book is pleasing to them" **(Les gusta el libro).**

The thing *liked* in English becomes the subject in Spanish; the *one who likes* becomes the indirect object.

The verb **gustar** agrees with the Spanish subject. Note that the subject generally follows **gustar.**

1. *Me gusta* el libro. | I like the book. (The book is pleasing to me.)

2. *Me gustan* los libros. | I like the books. (The books are pleasing to me.)

3. *Le gusta* la flor. | You (He, She) like(s) the flower. [The flower is pleasing to you (him, her).]

4. *Le gustan* las flores. | You (He, She) like(s) the flowers. [The flowers are pleasing to you (him, her).]

5. *Nos gustó* la novela. | We liked the novel. (The novel was pleasing to us.)

6. *Nos gustaron* las novelas.

We liked the novels. (The novels were pleasing to us.)

7. *Les gusta* cantar.

They like to sing. (To sing is pleasing to them.)

8. *Les gustan* cantar y bailar.

They like to sing and dance. (To sing and dance are pleasing to them.)

9. **A María** no *le gusta* leer.

Mary doesn't like to read. (To read is not pleasing to Mary.)

10. **A los niños** *les gusta* ir a la escuela.

The children like to go to school. (To go to school is pleasing to the children.)

11. **A ellos** *les gusta* el nuevo profesor.

They like the new teacher. (The new teacher is pleasing to them.)

Note

If the thing liked is not a noun but an "action" (expressed by a verb or clause), **gustar** is used in the third person singular.

VERBS USED LIKE *GUSTAR*

1. **agradar,** to be pleasing (to be pleased with)

   Les agrada mi regalo.

They are pleased with my gift. (My gift is pleasing to them.)

2. **bastar,** to be enough, to suffice

   Me bastan tres dólares.

Three dollars are enough for me.

3. **doler,** to be painful, to cause sorrow

   Me duele el pie izquierdo.

My left foot hurts (is painful to) me.

4. **faltar**
5. **hacer falta** } to be lacking (to need)

   Le faltan cincuenta centavos.

He needs fifty cents. (Fifty cents are lacking to him.)

   Le hace falta dinero.

He needs money. (Money is lacking to him.)

6. **parecer,** to seem

   Me parece imposible.

It seems impossible to me.

7. **placer,** to be pleasing (to like)

   Me place ver el sol.

I am pleased to see the sun. (To see the sun is pleasing to me.)

8. **quedarle (a uno),** to remain (to someone), to have left

   Nos queda un día.

We have one day left. (One day remains to us.)

9. **sobrar,** to be left over, to have too much

   Me sobran tres.

I have three too many. [Three are left over (to me).]

10. **tocarle (a uno),** to be one's turn

   A mí me toca lavar los platos.

It is my turn to wash the dishes.

EJERCICIOS

A. Escójase de la lista una expresión *sinónima* de cada una de las expresiones en letra cursiva, y escríbase en la forma correcta.

burlarse de	fijarse en	significar
carecer de	guardar	soñar con
dar con	gustar	tardar en
echarse a	hacer de	tener dolor en

1. Al entrar, el atrevido galán *reparó en* las señoritas rubias. _____

2. Todos *se rieron de* su aspecto ridículo. _____

3. Un viejo *servía de* guía para los turistas. _____

4. *Me duele* la pierna derecha. _____

5. *Le hace falta* sentido común. _____

6. El alumno no sabe lo que *quiere decir* el párrafo. _____

7. Andando por la selva, *tropezó con* muchos mosquitos y abejas. _____

8. *Se puso a* leer con mucho interés. _____

9. Me *place* saber que he ganado el premio. _____

10. Decidió *quedarse con* la camisa más barata. _____

B. Subráyese la expresión que complete correctamente cada frase.

1. (Plazco, Me place) saber que Vds. se han hecho periodistas.

2. (Le gustan, Les gusta) los meses de mayo y junio.

3. A los burros (le bastan, les basta) una hora de descanso.

4. (Me agrada, Me agradan) el silencio y la paz del campo.

5. (Nos faltan, Nosotros faltamos) las llaves para abrir los cajones.

6. ¿(No te parece, No te parecen) que las armas son peligrosas?

7. (Te toca, Te tocan) dar unos centavos al pordiosero.

8. A ellas (les duelen, les duele) la miseria de sus amigos.

9. De todo el tesoro que le pertenecía, (le queda, le quedan) dos pesos.

10. (Nos sobra, Nos sobran) discos; lo que necesitamos es un tocadiscos.

C. Contéstense en español en frases completas.

1. ¿Sacó Vd. muchas fotografías durante las vacaciones pasadas? _____

2. ¿Se queja Vd. del trabajo que le da el profesor? _____

3. ¿Le duele a Vd. hoy la cabeza? _____

4. ¿Qué piensa Vd. de la última película que vio? _____

5. ¿De qué se trata en esta lección? _____

_____

6. ¿Qué dice Vd. cuando tropieza con un conocido? _____

_____

7. ¿Piensa Vd. hacer un viaje a la América Hispana algún día? _____

_____

8. ¿Vale la pena llevar un paraguas en un día de lluvia? _____

_____

9. Después de una noche de fiesta y baile, ¿le queda a Vd. mucho dinero? _____

_____

10. ¿Aprende Vd. de memoria las reglas de gramática? _____

_____

11. ¿Sueña Vd. con una carrera profesional? _____

_____

12. ¿Piensa Vd. algunas veces en el porvenir? _____

_____

13. ¿Repara Vd. en los pequeños detalles cuando estudia? _____

_____

14. ¿Se pone Vd. pálido(-a) al oír hablar de una catástrofe? _____

_____

15. ¿Le gusta leer cuentos de aventuras? _____

_____

16. ¿Trata Vd. de cumplir con todas sus obligaciones? _____

_____

17. ¿Se parece Vd. a sus hermanos(-as)? _____

_____

18. ¿Presta Vd. dinero a sus amigos, si le sobra? _____

_____

19. ¿Le toca a Vd. hablar mucho en esta clase? _____

_____

20. ¿Se ríe Vd. de los chistes de sus amigos? _____

_____

21. ¿Le parece a Vd. interesante esta clase? _____

_____

22. Después de la cena, ¿se pone Vd. a lavar los platos? _____

_____

23. ¿Tarda Vd. en contestar a las preguntas del maestro? _____

_____

24. ¿Es Vd. aficionado(-a) al béisbol? _____

_____

25. ¿Para qué sirve el jabón? _____

_____

D. Tradúzcanse al español las expresiones en inglés.

1. Para comer, *suffice for me* pan y leche. _____

2. *It is a question of* deshacer el mal que hizo don Juan. _____

3. La noche era oscura, y le *I lost sight of* inmediatamente. _____

4. Vd. no sabe lo que *means* aquel proverbio. _____

5. Es buena y diligente, pero *she lacks* imaginación. _____

6. Se desmayó, pero dentro de poco *she regained consciousness.* _____

7. La taza está rota y *is not good for* nada. _____

8. *I'll keep* este vestido; es más bonito que el otro. _____

9. Después del almuerzo, el jefe *again examined* las cuentas. _____

10. *It is worthwhile* ser generoso con los pobres. _____

11. *He never thought of* el peligro que corría en la nueva empresa. _____

12. *"Don't worry,"* dijo Colón para asegurar a sus marineros. _____

13. El tren andaba lentamente y *delayed in* llegar. _____

14. De todas las legumbres, *I like* más el arroz y los guisantes. _____

15. Todos *observed* el gran actor que acababa de entrar. _____

16. El navegante no sabía qué *to think of* la nueva estrella. _____

17. El dependiente *tried to* satisfacer al público, pero sin éxito. _____

18. *I intend to* facturar las maletas antes de subir al tren. _____

19. Sabe *by heart* todas las provincias de España. _____

20. El conferenciante *was fond of* la arquitectura antigua. _____

E. Tradúzcanse al español.

1. The father was pleased with his son's progress. _____

_____

2. On seeing the lion, the explorer began to tremble. _____

_____

3. The soldier knew that it was his turn to spy on the enemy. _____

_____

4. There are too many (sobrar) difficulties in this lesson. _____

_____

5. He hurt himself and fainted, but later he came to. _____

_____

6. The artist tried to win eternal glory with his work. _____

7. The dancer always complained of the attitude of the public. _____

8. "I have three tests left to correct," said the teacher. _____

_____

9. In the dry desert he dreamed of a cool bath. _____

_____

10. The lawyer laughed at his opponent's efforts. _____

_____

11. In a nearby bookstore I came upon John, my fellow pupil. _____

12. Many Spaniards still think of the era of Spain's greatness. _____

_____

13. We need a stenographer to copy the letters. _____

_____

14. It seems to me that the Greek philosophers were very wise. _____

_____

15. They came to an agreement, shook hands, and left. _____

_____

En la América Central se producen grandes cantidades de bananas. Las bananas son recogidas cuando aún están verdes, llevadas al puerto en carros tirados por burros, y exportadas a todas partes del mundo en buques refrigerados.

Idiom Lesson 4—IDIOMS WITH *A*, *DE*, AND *EN*

IDIOMS WITH *A*

1. **a causa de,** because of

   No salió *a causa del* frío. — He didn't go out because of the cold.

2. **a eso de,** at about + time

   Nos reuniremos *a eso de las cinco.* — We'll meet at about five o'clock.

3. **a fines de,** at the end of

   La primavera comienza *a fines de* marzo. — Spring begins at the end of March.

4. **a fondo,** thoroughly

   Sabe *a fondo* la lección para hoy. — He knows the lesson for today thoroughly.

5. **a fuerza de,** by dint of

   A fuerza de estudio, aprendió bien la historia. — By dint of study, he learned history well.

6. **a la derecha,** to the right, at the right

   Para llegar al museo, hay que ir *a la derecha.* — To get to the museum, it is necessary to go to the right.

7. **a la española,** in the Spanish style

   Sirvieron una comida *a la española.* — They served a meal in the Spanish style.

8. **a la izquierda,** to the left, at the left

   El edificio está allí, *a la izquierda.* — The building is there, on the left.

9. **a la vez,** at the same time

   Puede escribir y hablar *a la vez.* — He can write and speak at the same time.

10. **a lo lejos,** in the distance

    A lo lejos se veían unas montañas muy altas. — In the distance were seen some very high mountains.

11. **a lo (al) menos,** at least

    Esa señora tendrá *a lo menos* cuarenta años. — That lady must be at least forty years old.

12. **a menudo,** often

    A menudo se encuentran en la calle. — They often meet in the street.

13. **a mi (su,** etc.**) parecer,** in my (his, etc.) opinion

    A su parecer, la distancia es grande. — In his opinion, the distance is great.

14. **a pesar de,** in spite of

    A pesar de estar enfermo, se levantó. — In spite of being ill, he got up.

15. **a pie,** on foot

    Fueron de Madrid a Alcalá *a pie.* — They went from Madrid to Alcalá on foot.

16. **a principios de,** at the beginning of, early in

    Pienso estar allí *a principios de* julio. — I intend to be there at the beginning of July.

17. **a solas,** alone

    En la cárcel, se quedó *a solas* con su conciencia. — In prison, he remained alone with his conscience.

18. **a tiempo,** on time

Si quieres comer, vuelve *a tiempo.*   If you want to eat, return on time.

19. **a (al) través de,** through, across

Una barca los llevó *a través del* río.   A ferryboat took them across the river.

20. **al aire libre,** in the open air

En el campo, pasó mucho tiempo *al aire libre.*   In the country, he spent much time in the open air.

21. **al amanecer,** at daybreak

Se puso en marcha *al amanecer.*   He got started at daybreak.

22. **al anochecer,** at nightfall

Al anochecer volvió.   At nightfall he returned.

23. **al cabo (de),** at the end (of), finally

Al cabo de dos meses lo había aprendido todo.   At the end of two months he had learned it all.

24. **al fin,** finally

Al fin, consintió en que su hijo saliera.   Finally, he consented to his son's going out.

25. **al parecer,** apparently

Al parecer, se siente mejor.   Apparently, he feels better.

IDIOMS WITH *DE*

1. **de buena gana,** willingly

Me lo prestó *de buena gana.*   He lent it to me willingly.

2. **de cuando en cuando,** from time to time

De cuando en cuando lo veo en la escuela.   From time to time I see him at school.

3. **de día (noche),** by day (at night)

De día trabajo, *de noche* duermo.   By day I work, at night I sleep.

4. **de esta (esa) manera** ⎫
   de este (ese) modo ⎭ in this (that) way

Le dije que lo hiciese *de ese modo.*   I told him to do it in that way.

5. **de hoy en adelante,** from now on, henceforth

De hoy en adelante, estudiaré cada día.   From now on, I'll study every day.

6. **de mala gana,** unwillingly

Devolvió el dinero *de mala gana.*   He returned the money unwillingly.

7. **de manera que** ⎫
   de modo que ⎭ so that

Habló claramente, *de modo que* todos oyeran.   He spoke clearly, so that everyone would hear.

8. **de ninguna manera** ⎫
   de ningún modo ⎭ by no means

No lo creo; *de ninguna manera.*   I don't believe it; by no means.

9. **de nuevo,** again

Al día siguiente, atacaron **de nuevo.**   On the following day, they again attacked.

10. **de otro modo,** otherwise

Pague Vd. ahora; **de otro modo** llamo a la policía.   Pay now; otherwise I'll call the police.

11. **(abrir) de par en par,** (to open) wide

Las puertas estaban **abiertas de par en par.**   The doors were wide open.

12. **de pie,** standing

El alumno se levantó y se quedó **de pie.**   The pupil stood up and remained standing.

13. **de pronto** ⎫
    de repente ⎬ suddenly

De repente oyeron un gran ruido.   Suddenly they heard a loud noise.

14. **de rodillas,** kneeling

De rodillas, pidió perdón.   Kneeling, he begged pardon.

15. **de veras,** really, truly

¿La quieres **de veras?**   Do you really love her?

16. **de vez en cuando,** from time to time

De vez en cuando abría los ojos y miraba afuera.   From time to time he opened his eyes and looked out.

IDIOMS WITH *EN*

1. **en cambio,** on the other hand

Juan es perezoso; su hermano, **en cambio,** es diligente.   John is lazy; his brother, on the other hand, is studious.

2. **en cuanto,** as soon as

Llámame **en cuanto** vuelvas.   Call me as soon as you return.

3. **en cuanto a,** in regard to, as for

En cuanto al robo, el ladrón lo negó todo.   As for the robbery, the thief denied everything.

4. **en efecto,** in fact, actually, as a matter of fact

En efecto, lo compré ayer.   In fact, I bought it yesterday.

5. **en lugar (vez) de,** instead of

En vez de estudiar, fue al cine.   Instead of studying, he went to the movies.

6. **en ninguna parte,** nowhere, not anywhere

No encontraron el dinero **en ninguna parte.**   They did not find the money anywhere.

7. **en seguida,** at once, immediately

Se puso el abrigo y se marchó **en seguida.**   He put on his coat and left at once.

8. **en todas partes,** everywhere

Hay buena gente **en todas partes.**   There are good people everywhere.

EJERCICIOS

A. Escójase de la lista una expresión *sinónima* de cada una de las expresiones en letra cursiva, y escríbase en la forma correcta.

al mismo tiempo	desde ahora	otra vez
así	en mi opinión	por lo visto
a veces	inmediatamente	si no
de repente	de vez en cuando	tan pronto como

1. *De hoy en adelante,* el enfermo debe evitar los pasteles y el azúcar. _____

2. *De nuevo* subió al manzano para coger las frutas. _____

3. *A mi parecer* la gramática es muy importante. _____

4. La pobre viuda lloraba y gemía *a la vez.* _____

5. Atacaron con fuerza, y *de esta manera* triunfaron. _____

6. *De pronto,* apareció una neblina que lo cubrió todo. _____

7. *Al parecer,* el color rojo enoja a los toros. _____

8. Hay que pagar antes; *de otro modo,* los músicos no tocarán. _____

9. *En cuanto* probó el té se quemó los labios. _____

10. Sin reparar en nadie, se marchó *en seguida,* a paso rápido. _____

B. Escójase de la lista una expresión *antónima* de cada una de las expresiones en letra cursiva, y escríbase en la forma correcta.

a causa de	de ninguna manera	nunca
a la izquierda	de pie	por la tarde
al anochecer	en ninguna parte	sin querer
con entusiasmo	muy cerca	tarde

1. *De mala gana* subió la escalera y llamó a la puerta. _____

2. *De rodillas,* rezaba por la salud de su hijo. _____

3. Aquella mañana el amo llegó *a tiempo.* _____

4. En vez de seguir adelante hay que torcer *a la derecha.* _____

5. *Al amanecer* se asomó al balcón para hablar con su galán. _____

6. Comió la ensalada *de buena gana.* _____

7. *A pesar de* los críticos, la poetisa ganó fama. _____

8. *En todas partes* se encuentran aventuras. _____

9. *A lo lejos* vimos los campos de maíz. _____

10. *A menudo* menciona el nombre de su novio. _____

C. Contéstense en español en frases completas.

1. ¿Qué fiesta ocurre a fines de diciembre? _____

2. Al recibir buenas notas, ¿experimenta Vd. satisfacción de veras? _____

_____

_____

3. ¿Se pone Vd. de pie para hablar en la clase? _____

_____

4. ¿Le gusta a Vd. comer a la española? _____

_____

5. A su parecer, ¿sería bueno formar un club español? _____

_____

6. ¿Lleva Vd. paraguas a pesar del buen tiempo? _____

_____

7. ¿Puede Vd. mirar la televisión y leer a la vez? _____

_____

8. En una noche clara, ¿qué se ve a lo lejos en el cielo? _____

_____

9. ¿Viaja Vd. a menudo por ferrocarril? _____

_____

10. ¿Sabe Vd. a fondo la lección de hoy? _____

_____

11. ¿De vez en cuando piensa Vd. en las vacaciones? _____

_____

12. ¿Estudia Vd. de día o de noche? _____

_____

13. ¿Le gusta a Vd. estudiar a solas o con un compañero? _____

_____

14. ¿Prefiere Vd. subir la escalera a pie o usar el ascensor? _____

_____

15. ¿Le gusta a Vd. dar un paseo al aire libre? _____

_____

16. ¿Madrugaría Vd. de buena gana para ver salir el sol? _____

_____

17. Al anochecer, ¿le gusta a Vd. estar en casa o fuera? _____

_____

18. ¿Siempre llega Vd. a tiempo a una cita? _____

_____

19. En cuanto terminan las clases, ¿a dónde va Vd.? _____

_____

20. ¿Le gusta a Vd. recibir cosas en vez de regalarlas? _____

_____

D. Tradúzcanse al español las expresiones en inglés.

1. *Finally* _____, el cartero le trajo la carta que esperaba.

2. *In regard to* _____ la edad, las mujeres nunca la admiten.

3. El navegante tuvo que torcer *to the left* _____ para evitar otro barco.

4. El avaro poseía una fortuna del valor de un millón, *at least* _____.

5. ¿Es severo el maestro? *By no means* _____; es justo.

6. En el restaurante les sirvieron una comida *in the French style* _____.

7. *By dint of* _____ agitar las alas, el pajarito aprendió a volar.

8. La noche de la conferencia las puertas estaban abiertas *wide* _____.

9. Todos los días papá va a su trabajo *on foot* _____.

10. *At the end of* _____ diez años su marido le compró un brazalete de platino.

11. ¡Qué inteligente es! Sabe *thoroughly* _____ la lista de modismos.

12. *At the beginning of* _____ las vacaciones los estudiantes no saben qué hacer.

13. Es mejor empezar el viaje *by day* _____.

14. *Through* _____ las cortinas se veían los muebles de la sala.

15. *Because of* _____ sus méritos le ascendieron a jefe de la compañía.

16. Era muy cortés; *in that way* _____, ganó la amistad de todos.

17. El primer acto comienza *at about* _____ las ocho y media.

18. Tenía una verdadera pasión por hacer ejercicios *in the open air* _____.

19. Tienes que partir mañana; *otherwise* _____, no llegarás *on time* _____.

20. *At daybreak* _____ los pescadores salieron a la mar.

21. Ponga Vd. su dinero en el banco; *in this way* _____, estará seguro.

22. *Unwillingly* _____ se sentó a estudiar la lección de geografía.

23. *From time to time* _____ daba una vuelta por las calles cercanas.

24. La Sra. Álvarez es delgada; su esposo, *on the other hand* _____, es gordo.

25. *As a matter of fact* _____, ejecutó fielmente las órdenes del capitán.

E. Tradúzcanse al español.

1. Suddenly a cry of terror interrupted our conversation. _____
_____
_____

2. Instead of an easy victory, the explorers had to fight all day. _____
_____
_____

3. At the beginning of winter the lakes freeze over. _____
_____
_____

4. The teacher is by no means severe; she is very kind. --------------------------------

----

----

5. Cotton is cheap; on the other hand, silk is expensive. ----------------------------

----

----

6. At the right he saw a large lake and was able to get his bearings. -----------------

----

7. From time to time he stopped and leaned against the wall to rest. -----------------

----

----

8. As for Columbus, he deserves the admiration of everybody. -----------------------

9. It is a pity that he has to do the work alone. --------------------------------

----

10. At eight o'clock sharp, the doors were opened wide and everybody entered. ----------

----

----

11. At the end of the summer the days become shorter. ---------------------------

----

12. At night many stars can be seen in the sky. --------------------------------

----

13. At about three o'clock his right leg began to hurt (him). -----------------------

----

14. The inspector examined the documents again. ------------------------------

----

----

15. The artist painted at least a hundred portraits. ----------------------------

----

16. From now on I promise not to quarrel with my friends. ------------------------

----

17. Cover your face with oil; in this way you will avoid the bees. ------------------

----

----

18. At nightfall he went to bed because he had to get up at 3 A.M. -----------------

----

----

19. Finally he had left neither his money nor his home. _

20. Apparently, the sleeves of the jacket are short. _

21. Mr. Gallo really has patience; he explained the lesson three times. _

22. By dint of using their (la) intelligence, they made the machine work. _

23. Kneeling, he succeeded in entering through the small door. _

24. In fact, the catastrophe had serious results. _

25. Everywhere one finds diligent and lazy students. _

Cuzco, la antigua capital de los incas, es hoy una ciudad pintoresca situada a una altura de 11,000 pies en los Andes del Perú. Todavía hoy se encuentran en Cuzco las ruinas de muchos palacios y fortalezas de la civilización incaica. Muchos de estos edificios formaron la base para residencias e iglesias españolas.

Idiom Lesson 5—MISCELLANEOUS IDIOMS

1. **ahora mismo,** right now

   —Acuéstate *ahora mismo*—dijo mamá. | "Go to bed right now," said Mother.

2. **billete de ida y vuelta,** round-trip ticket

   Antes de marcharse, compró un *billete de ida y vuelta.* | Before leaving, he bought a round-trip ticket.

3. **cada vez más,** more and more

   El español se pone *cada vez más* difícil. | Spanish is becoming more and more difficult.

4. **con tal que** + subjunctive, provided that

   Leeré el libro *con tal que sea* interesante. | I'll read the book provided that it's interesting.

5. **conforme a,** according to, in accordance with

   Conforme a mis deseos, llegó temprano. | In accordance with my wishes, he came early.

6. **cuanto antes,** as soon as possible, without delay

   Escríbale una carta *cuanto antes.* | Write her a letter as soon as possible.

7. **dentro de poco,** in a little while

   Dentro de poco llegarán las vacaciones. | In a little while vacation time will come.

8. **desde luego,** of course, at once

   Desde luego, la máquina costó mucho. | Of course, the machine cost a great deal.

   Prometió hacerlo *desde luego.* | He promised to do it at once.

9. **dicho y hecho,** no sooner said than done

   El general mandó que avanzasen. *Dicho y hecho.* | The general ordered them to advance. No sooner said than done.

10. **fuera de sí,** beside oneself

    Al verla, estuvo *fuera de sí* de alegría. | On seeing her, he was beside himself with joy.

11. **hoy día,** nowadays, today, at present

    Hoy día los precios son muy altos. | Nowadays, prices are very high.

12. **hoy mismo,** this very day

    Tienes que entregarme los documentos *hoy mismo.* | You have to hand me the documents this very day.

13. **junto a,** next to, beside

    Estaba sentado *junto a* su novia. | He was seated beside his sweetheart.

14. **lo más pronto posible,** as soon as possible

    Trató de llegar *lo más pronto posible.* | He tried to arrive as soon as possible.

15. **mientras tanto,** meanwhile, in the meantime

    Los niños jugaban; *mientras tanto,* su madre preparaba la cena. | The children played; meanwhile, their mother prepared supper.

16. **no cabe duda,** doubtless, there's no doubt

    No cabe duda; la libertad es preciosa. | There's no doubt; liberty is precious.

17. **no hay remedio,** it can't be helped

Tenemos que esperar dos horas; *no hay remedio.*

We have to wait two hours; it can't be helped.

18. **no importa,** it doesn't matter

No importa el precio; quiero un reloj de oro.

The price doesn't matter; I want a gold watch.

19. **no obstante,** nevertheless, notwithstanding

No obstante mis esfuerzos, no pude llegar a tiempo.

Notwithstanding my efforts, I couldn't arrive on time.

20. **no poder menos de** + infinitive, not to be able to help

No pueden menos de admirar su belleza.

They can't help admiring her beauty.

21. **ocho días,** a week

Se casarán en *ocho días.*

They'll get married in a week.

22. **otra vez,** again

Dígalo Vd. *otra vez.*

Say it again.

23. **para sí,** to himself, to herself, to themselves

Abrió el libro y comenzó a leer *para sí.*

She opened the book and began to read to herself.

24. **pasado mañana,** the day after tomorrow

Pasado mañana es día de fiesta.

The day after tomorrow is a holiday.

25. **por consiguiente,** therefore, consequently

Estaba hablando; *por consiguiente,* no oyó la voz del maestro.

He was speaking; consequently, he did not hear the teacher's voice.

26. **por desgracia,** unfortunately

Por desgracia, la estatua estaba rota.

Unfortunately, the statue was broken.

27. **por escrito,** written, in writing

Preparen Vds. los ejercicios *por escrito.*

Prepare the exercises in writing.

28. **por eso,** therefore

Hace calor y sol; *por eso,* hay tantos insectos.

It is hot and sunny; therefore, there are so many insects.

29. **por lo común** ⎫
    por lo general ⎭ usually, generally

Por lo común, las joyas cuestan mucho.

Generally, jewels cost a great deal.

30. **por lo visto,** apparently

Por lo visto, todo está en orden.

Apparently, everything is in order.

31. **por supuesto,** of course

Por supuesto, es necesario trabajar.

Of course, it's necessary to work.

32. **puesto que,** since

Puesto que has sido malo, tengo que castigarte.

Since you have been bad, I have to punish you.

33. **quince días,** two weeks, a fortnight

Prometió volver en *quince días.*

He promised to return in two weeks.

34. **raras veces,** seldom, rarely

Raras veces hay nieve en septiembre.

Seldom is there snow in September.

35. **sano y salvo,** safe and sound

El vapor llegó al puerto **sano y salvo.**

The ship reached port safe and sound.

36. **sin duda,** doubtless, without doubt

Sin duda el clima es mejor allí.

Doubtless the climate is better there.

37. **sin embargo,** nevertheless, however

Estaba enfermo; **sin embargo,** se levantó al día siguiente.

He was ill; nevertheless, he got up the next day.

38. **sin novedad,** as usual, nothing new

¿Qué hay de nuevo? **Sin novedad.**

What's new? Nothing new.

39. **tal vez,** perhaps

Tal vez el prisionero confesará.

Perhaps the prisoner will confess.

40. **tan pronto como,** as soon as

Tan pronto como recibió el dinero, lo gastó.

As soon as he received the money, he spent it.

41. **todo el mundo,** everybody

Todo el mundo necesita comer para vivir.

Everybody needs to eat in order to live.

42. **unos cuantos (unas cuantas),** a few

Buscó en su bolsillo y no encontró sino **unas cuantas** monedas.

He looked in his pocket and found only a few coins.

43. **¡Vaya un (una) . . . !,** What a . . . !

¡Vaya una memoria! Sabe todas las fechas.

What a memory! He knows all the dates.

44. **¡Ya lo creo!,** Of course! I should say so!

¿Es verdad? *¡Ya lo creo!*

Is it true? I should say so!

45. **ya no,** no longer

Ya no asiste a la escuela.

He no longer attends school.

46. **ya que,** since

Ya que eres tan fuerte, levanta ese baúl.

Since you are so strong, lift that trunk.

La Alhambra, palacio moro en Granada, es el ejemplo más hermoso de la arquitectura morisca que existe en España. Fue construida en el siglo XIII. Entre sus muchos salones y patios uno de los más famosos es el Patio de los Leones.

EJERCICIOS

A. Escójase de la lista una expresión *sinónima* de cada una de las expresiones en letra cursiva, y escríbase en la forma correcta.

cada vez más   ocho días   unos cuantos
cuanto antes   por consiguiente   ¡Vaya un . . . !
desde luego   por lo común   ya no
no cabe duda   tal vez   ya que

1. Nos han robado; hay que avisar a la policía *lo más pronto posible.* _____

2. En el cielo se veían *varias* estrellas. _____

3. *Por lo general* lleva una cámara adondequiera que vaya. _____

4. Quería aprender; *por eso,* siempre prestaba atención en la clase. _____

5. *Quizás* la campaña dure todo el verano. _____

6. *Puesto que* es modesto, nunca habla de sus hazañas. _____

7. En *una semana* su aspecto había cambiado horriblemente. _____

8. *¡Qué* diccionario! No contiene las palabras que busco. _____

9. *Por supuesto* el aire fresco es bueno para la salud. _____

10. *Sin duda,* el gobierno piensa apoderarse de los bienes del traidor. _____

B. Escójase de la lista una expresión *antónima* de cada una de las expresiones en letra cursiva, y escríbase en la forma correcta.

ahora mismo   para sí   todo el mundo
fuera de sí   por desgracia   unos cuantos
junto a   por lo común   ¡Ya lo creo!
mientras tanto   sano y salvo   ya no

1. Después de su viaje tenía *muchas* fotografías y el bolsillo vacío. _____

2. Los críticos *raras veces* alaban la obra de aquel dramaturgo. _____

3. *Nadie* desea escuchar el discurso de aquel conferenciante. _____

4. *Lejos de* la carnicería estaba la botica del pueblo. _____

5. El ladrón tuvo que acompañar al guardia, echando maldiciones *en voz alta.* _____

6. *Más tarde* atacarán la fortaleza de los árabes. _____

7. Salió *herido* de la lucha. _____

8. Después de muchos años de miseria, *todavía* tiene fe en la humanidad. _____

9. —*¡De ningún modo!*—exclamó el propietario al oír el plan del empleado. _____

10. *Afortunadamente,* la provincia estaba lejos de la capital. _____

C. Contéstense en español en frases completas.

1. Viajando por ferrocarril, ¿le gusta sentarse junto a la ventana? _____
_____
_____

2. En esta clase, ¿sale bien en los exámenes todo el mundo? _____
_____

3. ¿Va Vd. a graduarse dentro de poco? _____

_____

4. ¿Cree Vd. que llueva pasado mañana? _____

_____

5. ¿Tiene Vd. muchos amigos o solamente unos cuantos? _____

_____

6. ¿Siempre se porta Vd. conforme a los deseos de sus padres? _____

_____

7. ¿Tienen Vds. examen en esta clase cada ocho días o cada quince días? _____

_____

8. ¿Le gustaría a Vd. estar fuera de la escuela ahora mismo? _____

_____

9. Al hacer un viaje, ¿compra Vd. un billete de ida y vuelta? _____

_____

10. Cuando comienza a tronar y llover, ¿vuelve Vd. a casa lo más pronto posible? _____

_____

_____

11. ¿Encuentra Vd. dificultad en preparar las traducciones por escrito? _____

_____

12. ¿Sale Vd. solo(-a) a menudo o raras veces? _____

_____

13. ¿Comienza Vd. a estudiar tan pronto como llega a casa? _____

_____

14. ¿Hace Vd. cosas peligrosas, no obstante el riesgo? _____

_____

15. Por lo general, ¿qué bebe Vd. cuando tiene sed? _____

_____

16. ¿Vale mucho un centavo hoy día? _____

_____

17. ¿Le gusta el campo cuando ya no hay hojas en los árboles? _____

_____

18. Por lo común, ¿son diligentes los alumnos de esta clase? _____

_____

19. ¿Piensa Vd. ir al cine hoy mismo? _____

_____

20. ¿Necesita Vd. estudiar estos modismos otra vez? _____

_____

D. Tradúzcanse al español las expresiones en inglés.

1. Sonaba la campana de la iglesia; *meanwhile* _____, la capilla se llenaba de gente.

2. *Unfortunately* _____, la enfermedad era grave, y el enfermo murió.

3. *Perhaps* _____ la neblina no nos permita navegar con seguridad.

4. Estás lleno de sudor y lodo; báñate *without delay* _____.

5. Al oír el chiste, *we couldn't help* _____ reír.

6. Se puede construir el edificio de madera; *nevertheless* _____, el mármol es más hermoso.

7. La bailarina prometió tomar parte en la función *provided that* _____ la pagasen bien.

8. Abrió la carta, y la leyó *to himself* _____.

9. —¡*What a* _____ respuesta ridícula!—exclamó el maestro.

10. Al encontrar en el cajón las joyas perdidas, *she was beside herself* _____ de alegría.

11. Su madre derramó lágrimas de alegría al verle *safe and sound* _____.

12. *Of course* _____, beso a mi mamá todos los días al salir para la escuela.

13. *Since* _____ don Quijote se imaginaba héroe, salió en busca de aventuras.

14. El libertador mandó quitar las cadenas al esclavo; *no sooner said than done* _____.

15. Aquel día, fue a su trabajo y volvió *as usual* _____.

16. *It doesn't matter* _____ que la distancia sea grande.

17. El público se ponía *more and more* _____ animado.

18. En el otoño no se ven sino *a few* _____ hojas secas en los árboles.

19. *Doubtless* _____, se puede comprar este libro en cualquier librería.

20. ¿Es interesante el tercer párrafo? *I should say so!* _____

21. *There is no doubt* _____ que a veces el castigo es necesario.

22. *Apparently* _____ la herida es leve y puede curarse pronto.

23. *No longer* _____ se preocupan por el porvenir.

24. Tenemos que escuchar la conferencia; *it can't be helped* _____.

25. Era muy rico; *therefore* _____, podía mostrarse generoso.

E. Tradúzcanse al español.

1. On reading the article, he was beside himself with anger. _____

_____

2. The "fans" couldn't help admiring the skill of the bullfighter. _____

_____

3. I greeted him and asked how he was; he answered, "As usual." _____

_____

4. I'll tell you the truth, provided that you don't become angry. _____

_____

5. I have to take care of my little sister this afternoon; it can't be helped. _____

_____

6. Every two weeks she has to buy a new pair of stockings. _____

_____

7. The army felt tired and advanced more and more slowly. _____

_____

8. It doesn't matter that he is tired; there's work to do. _____

_____

9. As soon as the shoemaker opened his shop, the people entered. _____

_____

10. The general ordered them to hinder the progress of the enemy; no sooner said than done. _____

_____

_____

11. Omit the seventh exercise, but prepare the eighth in writing. _____

_____

12. Every hour the nurse brought the medicine, in accordance with the doctor's orders. _____

_____

_____

13. The day after tomorrow neither you nor I will remember all the historical dates. _____

_____

14. In a little while the group will assemble in the living room. _____

_____

15. The danger had passed; nevertheless, the inhabitants were afraid to go out. _____

_____

_____

16. The teacher was speaking to the class; meanwhile, a pupil was erasing the blackboard. _____

_____

_____

17. He bought a round-trip ticket and went out to the platform to wait for the train. _____

_____

18. After his operation, he no longer wears eyeglasses. _____

_____

19. Usually, the first act begins at 8:40 P.M. _____

_____

_____

20. "Put on a white shirt right now," said my mother. --

----

21. "This very day, victory will be ours," shouted Cortés to his soldiers. -------------------

----

----

22. Apparently he has lost his patience and will now proceed with a firm hand. -----------------

----

----

23. Nowadays, the telephone is one of the most important instruments we have.

----

24. Notwithstanding his fever, he got up the next day and left the house. ----------------------

----

----

25. The tailor again measured the sleeve and saw that it was short. -------------------------

----

La Universidad de Salamanca es la universidad más vieja de España. Fue fundada en la Edad Media, en el siglo XIII. En los siglos XV y XVI, era una de las universidades principales de Europa.

Idiom Lesson 6—MASTERY EXERCISES

A. Escríbase la letra de la expresión del grupo *B* que traduzca correctamente la expresión del grupo *A*.

	A		*B*
_____	**1.** en lugar de	*a.*	to be sleepy
_____	**2.** conforme a	*b.*	since
_____	**3.** darse cuenta de	*c.*	suddenly
_____	**4.** hacer caso de	*d.*	instead of
_____	**5.** dar por	*e.*	to dream of
_____	**6.** tan pronto como	*f.*	therefore
_____	**7.** en seguida	*g.*	to feel like
_____	**8.** burlarse de	*h.*	to mean
_____	**9.** por consiguiente	*i.*	as soon as
_____	**10.** tener sueño	*j.*	to be successful
_____	**11.** tener ganas de	*k.*	immediately
_____	**12.** echar de menos	*l.*	to enjoy
_____	**13.** soñar con	*m.*	in accordance with
_____	**14.** volver en sí	*n.*	to pay attention to
_____	**15.** de veras	*o.*	to insist on
_____	**16.** tener éxito	*p.*	to realize
_____	**17.** querer decir	*q.*	to make fun of
_____	**18.** a través de	*r.*	to miss
_____	**19.** de repente	*s.*	through
_____	**20.** ya que	*t.*	to consider
		u.	to regain consciousness
		v.	really

B. En cada grupo, subráyese el modismo que signifique lo mismo que el modismo a la izquierda.

1. *fijarse en:*   reparar en, empeñarse en, enterarse de
2. *no obstante:*   tal vez, sin embargo, ya no
3. *dar gritos:*   dar recuerdos, dar voces, dar cuerda
4. *dar con:*   tropezar con, contar con, quedarse con
5. *hay que:*   tiene por, ha de, es necesario
6. *apresurarse:*   tener prisa, apoderarse, lo más pronto posible
7. *desde luego:*   hace poco, puesto que, por supuesto
8. *hacer de:*   haber de, hacerse, hacer el papel de
9. *por consiguiente:*   en efecto, por eso, de pronto
10. *estar a punto de:*   estar de vuelta, estar para, estar por

11. *conforme a:*   de acuerdo con, a eso de, en cambio

12. *gustar:*   agradecer, parecer, placer

13. *ponerse de acuerdo:* convenir en, dar cuerda, acordarse de

14. *echarse a:*   dar a, ponerse a, ponerse

15. *de nuevo:*   sin novedad, otra vez, a menudo

16. *dar las gracias:*   agradecer, agradar, alegrarse de

17. *dar una vuelta:*   dar un paseo, volver a, estar de vuelta

18. *por lo visto:*   perder de vista, por supuesto, al parecer

19. *tener lugar:*   llegar a ser, verificarse, en vez de

20. *hacer pedazos:*   romper, echar al correo, hacer falta

C. Subráyese el modismo que correctamente traduzca lo inglés.

1. *I am in favor of* ir en busca de un cochero que nos lleve a la fiesta. (Estoy para, Estoy por)

2. *Since* la puerta estaba cerrada, no pudieron entrar en el templo. (Ya no, Ya que)

3. El tintero cayó de sus manos y *hit* el suelo. (dio en, dio a)

4. Los espectáculos *are good for* divertir al público. (sirven de, sirven para)

5. El sol era fuerte, y andando por el camino, *he was warm.* (tenía calor, hacía calor)

6. El ladrón *ended by* admitir su crimen. (acabó por, acababa de)

7. Después de la lluvia, *there was mud* en las calles. (había polvo, había lodo)

8. Cuando vieron el vidrio roto, *they blamed* Vicente. (tuvieron la culpa de, echaron la culpa a)

9. A los cuatro meses el dramaturgo *considered* terminada su comedia. (dio por, se dio por)

10. Durante años, Colón *thought of* el descubrimiento de las Indias. (pensaba en, pensaba de)

11. Ponte el chaleco; *otherwise* es posible que te resfríes. (de otro modo, de ningún modo)

12. *Nowadays* se estudia el castellano en casi todas las escuelas. (Hoy mismo, Hoy día)

13. *Apparently*, la amistad de los dos políticos no va a durar mucho tiempo. (Al parecer, A su parecer)

14. El conquistador *tried to* establecer un pueblo en la selva. (trató de, se trató de)

15. *In regard to* la aritmética, la encuentro muy difícil. (En cuanto, En cuanto a)

16. Siempre tenía curiosidad; *in that way* aprendió mucho. (de esta manera, de ese modo)

17. El maestro *took care to* borrar la pizarra antes de salir. (cuidó de, cuidó a)

18. *Willingly* emprendió la construcción de la casa. (Tenía ganas de, De buena gana)

19. Al ver de cerca el león, *he became* pálido. (se puso, se hizo)

20. *Be careful*, señor; esas uvas no son maduras. (Pierda Vd. cuidado, Tenga Vd. cuidado)

D. En cada frase, escríbase una palabra o una expresión que correctamente complete la frase.

1. Si hoy es martes, _____ es jueves.

2. Estudió la poesía, y al día siguiente la sabía de _____.

3. Cuando llueve y hace frío decimos que hace _____ tiempo.

4. No sabía qué hacer; estaba _____ sí de alegría.

5. Me dijo algo que yo sabía, y le contesté,—¡Ya _____!

6. Mis amigos son fieles, y puedo _____ me de ellos.

7. Era valiente; no tenía _____ de los animales de la selva.

8. Cuando bebo agua es porque tengo mucha _____.

9. No puedo coser con esta aguja; compraré otra _____ poco.

10. Yo debía estar allí a las seis, y no llegué hasta las ocho; _____ mucho en llegar.

11. Si hay algo en la lección que no comprendo, hago _____ al profesor.

12. Los que tienen la vista débil por lo _____ llevan anteojos.

13. La escena le encantó y en seguida preparó la cámara para _____ una fotografía.

14. Si alguien me hace un favor, le doy las _____.

15. Juan tiene las mismas opiniones que yo; siempre está _____ conmigo.

16. Siempre llegaba tarde; nunca podía llegar a _____.

17. El peligro era grande, pero pude salir _____ y _____, sin heridas.

18. A _____ de cada mes esperamos el próximo mes.

19. Cuando me _____ el estómago, tengo dolor de estómago.

20. He gastado casi todo mi dinero; me _____ solamente once centavos.

E. Contéstense las preguntas siguientes empleando en cada respuesta una expresión que signifique *lo contrario* de la expresión en letra cursiva.

EJEMPLO: *¿Hay sol* de noche? No, señor, hay luna de noche.

1. ¿Le gusta a Vd. mirar la puesta del sol *a pesar de* su belleza? _____

2. ¿Duerme Vd. *de día?* _____

3. *¿Hace calor* en el invierno? _____

4. ¿Deben andar los coches *a la izquierda* del camino? _____

5. *¿Se da Vd. prisa a* volver a casa después de las clases? _____

6. *¿Se olvida Vd. de* limpiarse los dientes por la mañana? _____

7. ¿Es libre el oro *en todas partes?* _____

8. Al ver a sus amigos, *¿se aleja Vd. de* ellos? _____

9. Cuando alguien dice la verdad, ¿contesta Vd. *"De ninguna manera"?* _____

10. ¿Ocurre la Navidad *a principios del* año? _____

11. Si alguien tuviera hambre, ¿le *daría Vd. de beber?* _____

12. ¿Escucha Vd. *de mala gana* las explicaciones del maestro? _____

_____

13. ¿Habla Vd. *de rodillas* en la clase? _____

_____

14. ¿Contesta Vd. correctamente *raras veces?* _____

_____

15. ¿Desaparece el sol *al amanecer?* _____

_____

16. En el invierno, ¿pasa Vd. mucho tiempo *al aire libre?* _____

_____

17. *¿Le sobra* a Vd. dinero al fin de la semana? _____

_____

18. ¿Llega Vd. a la escuela *a pie?* _____

_____

19. *¿Hace buen tiempo* cuando llueve? _____

_____

20. *¿Tiene Vd. frío* en el verano? _____

    F. Tradúzcanse al español las expresiones en inglés.

1. *He approached the* _____ teatro, y vio que las puertas estaban *wide open*

_____.

2. Compramos *round-trip tickets* _____, y luego *we made*

our way to the _____ andén.

3. —¡*What a* _____ cantor!—exclamaron todos *at the same time* _____.

4. En la acera los dos norteamericanos *shook hands* _____ y prometieron

verse en *two weeks* _____.

5. El tirano *repented* _____ haber hecho una injusticia a los trabajadores,

pero *it couldn't be helped* _____.

6. *At the end of* _____ una hora, entró en su cuarto y *got ready to* _____

_____ estudiar la geografía.

7. Cuando el reloj de la iglesia *struck the hour* _____, *he embraced* _____

_____ a su esposa y salió del comedor.

8. Pedro *kept* _____ su promesa y *carried out* _____ los

deseos de su padre.

9. *I insist on* _____ un contrato *written* _____.

10. Su discurso *has nothing to do with* _____ la realidad,

pero, *unfortunately* _____, los alumnos tienen que escucharle.

11. *He dropped* _____ la servilleta, y al recogerla, *he hurt himself* _____ _____ en la cabeza.

12. Afuera *it was very cold* _____, pero adentro *it was warm* _____ _____.

13. El padre *consented* _____ que su hija *marry* _____ el andaluz.

14. *He was lucky* _____ en el comercio, y *by dint of* _____ trabajo, pudo aumentar su capital.

15. *She complained of* _____ fiebre y *stayed in bed* _____ todo el día.

16. *At nightfall* _____ vieron una fonda *in the distance* _____.

17. Los pícaros *lacked* _____ fondos y *were hungry* _____; así, robaron unas naranjas de los árboles.

18. En la aldea *everybody laughed at the* _____ pobre loco.

19. *It's worthwhile* _____ estudiar hasta saber *thoroughly* _____ la lección.

20. *She is right* _____; todos los hijos *resemble her* _____.

21. *From time to time she looked out of* _____ la ventana para ver si su novio todavía esperaba.

22. *He stopped* _____ contemplar la puesta del sol porque *there was work to do* _____.

23. El viejo no podía mantenerse *standing* _____, y *leaned on* _____ el hombro de su nieto.

24. *They heard about* _____ los encantos de aquel sitio, y el próximo verano *they paid a visit* _____ allí.

25. Nuestro perro *would not dare to hurt* _____ a nadie.

G. Tradúzcanse al español.

1. The policeman ordered him to turn to the right; no sooner said than done. _____
_____
_____

2. He sat down beside his friend and asked the waiter for rice and chicken in the Spanish style. _____
_____
_____

3. It was foggy and windy, but in the kitchen it was very warm. _____
_____

4. He was ill and lacked food; meanwhile, his rival was enjoying wealth and good health. _____
_____
_____

5. He bought a guitar and practiced at least three hours a day; in this way, he learned to play it well.
_____
_____

6. There is no doubt that his whole fortune consists of a few coins. _

_ _

_ _

7. It doesn't matter what I eat; a salad and a piece of bread and butter are enough for me. _ _ _ _ _ _ _

_ _

_ _

8. Because of her goodness and her beauty, the young man couldn't help falling in love with her.

_ _

_ _

9. She read the letter to herself, so that she might not annoy anyone. _

_ _

_ _

10. It was getting late, and they could not see a human being anywhere. _

_ _

11. He insists on becoming a dramatist in spite of not knowing how to write. _ _ _ _ _ _ _ _ _ _ _ _ _ _ _ _

_ _

12. Doubtless you can avoid a disaster, provided that you follow my advice. _ _ _ _ _ _ _ _ _ _ _ _ _ _ _ _

_ _

_ _

13. His mother was ashamed of his actions and refused to speak to him. _ _ _ _ _ _ _ _ _ _ _ _ _ _ _ _ _ _ _

_ _

14. He is fond of the theater; he goes there every week. _

_ _

15. Finally, she decided to buy the perfume because it smelled of violets. _ _ _ _ _ _ _ _ _ _ _ _ _ _ _ _ _ _

_ _

16. On falling, he hit the ground and never regained consciousness. _

_ _

17. Henceforth I intend to study alone. _

_ _

18. It is necessary to reach an agreement as soon as possible. _

_ _

19. Since it was my turn to mail the letters, I shrugged my shoulders and went out. _ _ _ _ _ _ _ _ _ _ _

_ _

_ _

20. Because of their interest in (por) music, their conversation became more and more lively. _ _ _ _ _ _

_ _

_ _

Part IV—*Civilization*

Civilization Lesson 1—LA GEOGRAFÍA DE ESPAÑA

EXTENSIÓN, CLIMA, Y POBLACIÓN

España está situada al sudoeste del continente europeo. Con Portugal, forma la **Península Ibérica.** Sus vecinos más cercanos son Francia al norte y Portugal al oeste. El resto del país está rodeado de las aguas del Mar Mediterráneo al este y del Océano Atlántico al oeste. El Estrecho de Gibraltar separa a España de Marruecos (Morocco), en el norte de África.

Su extensión, con las Islas Baleares, es de unas 195,000 millas cuadradas; es decir, algo menos que la del estado de Tejas, pero cuatro veces más grande que la del estado de Nueva York.

El clima de España es muy variado. En las mesetas del norte y del centro hay tierras frías; en la costa del Atlántico, tierras templadas; y en el sur y el este, tierras cálidas (hot). A causa de las grandes diferencias de temperatura, se ha dicho que Castilla tiene "nueve meses de invierno y tres de infierno (hell)."

España es una nación de unos 40 millones de habitantes. Madrid tiene una población de casi cuatro millones, y Barcelona, de unos dos millones.

CORDILLERAS PRINCIPALES

España tiene cinco grandes cordilleras. Con la excepción de Suiza, es el país más montañoso de Europa.

1. Los **Pirineos,** que marcan la frontera entre España y Francia, están en el norte del país.

2. Los **Montes Cantábricos** están en el noroeste del país. Esta cordillera está compuesta de muchas mesetas rodeadas de altas montañas.

3. La **Sierra de Guadarrama** está en el centro del país, al norte de Madrid.

4. La **Sierra Morena** está en el sur, y separa la meseta de La Mancha del valle del Guadalquivir.

5. La **Sierra Nevada** está aún más al sur. En esta sierra se encuentra, cerca de Granada, el **Cerro del Mulhacén,** el pico más alto de España, el cual tiene una altura de 11,400 pies.

RÍOS

Entre las mencionadas cordilleras corren los ríos más grandes del país, todos los cuales desembocan (empty) en el Océano Atlántico, excepto el Ebro.

1. El **Ebro,** en el norte, fluye hacia el este, pasa por la importante ciudad de Zaragoza, y desemboca en el Mar Mediterráneo.

2. El **Duero,** que nace cerca de la ciudad de Burgos en Castilla y León, pasa por Portugal y desemboca en el Atlántico.

3. El **Tajo,** el río más largo de España, pasa por la ciudad de Toledo y desemboca en el Atlántico, cerca de Lisboa, en Portugal.

4. El **Guadiana** está en el sur del país. Pasa por Mérida y por Badajoz, dos antiguos centros romanos, y entra en Portugal, desembocando en el Atlántico.

5. El **Guadalquivir** (palabra árabe que significa "río grande") se halla también en el sur del país. Es el río más navegable de España. En sus orillas se hallan las ciudades de Córdoba y Sevilla.

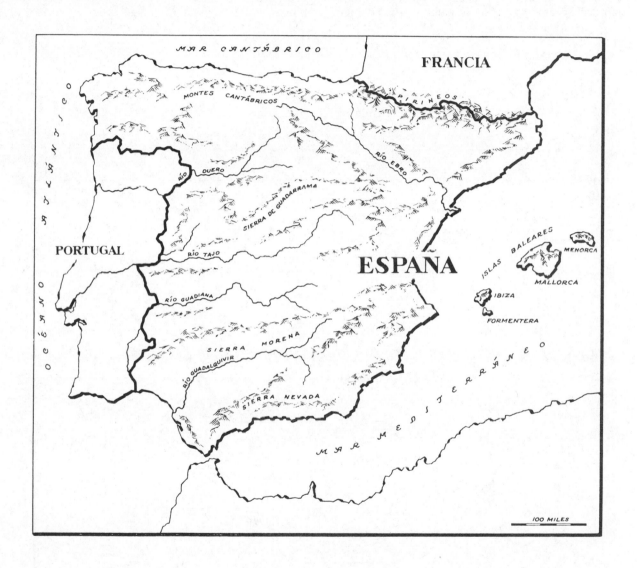

PRODUCTOS Y MINERALES PRINCIPALES

España es una nación industrial moderna. Sus industrias más importantes incluyen la fabricación de acero, automóviles y aparatos electrónicos. España es también un país agrícola. Son abundantes en el norte la madera y la pesca (fishing); en la parte central, el trigo y la ganadería; en el sur, la vid, de donde vienen los célebres vinos de Jerez (sherry) y de Málaga, aceitunas (olives), aceite de oliva (olive oil), y corcho (cork); en el sudeste, arroz, naranjas de Valencia, limones (lemons), dátiles (dates), y otras frutas tropicales.

España posee mucha riqueza minera. Se hallan las minas de hierro de Somorrostro en la provincia de Vizcaya (en el norte); en el sur del país, las minas de plomo (lead) de Linares; en el sudeste, las minas de cobre del Río Tinto; y, en la parte central del sur, las minas de mercurio de Almadén.

EJERCICIOS

A. Refiriéndose al mapa abajo, identifíquense los siguientes nombres geográficos, escribiendo a la izquierda de cada uno la letra correspondiente:

1. _____ el Estrecho de Gibraltar   4. _____ las Islas Baleares

2. _____ Portugal   5. _____ el Mar Mediterráneo

3. _____ Francia

B. Refiriéndose al mapa abajo, identifíquense los siguientes ríos y cordilleras, escribiendo a la izquierda de cada nombre el número correspondiente:

1. _____ la Sierra Nevada   6. _____ el Duero

2. _____ el Ebro   7. _____ la Sierra Morena

3. _____ el Guadalquivir   8. _____ los Pirineos

4. _____ la Cordillera Cantábrica   9. _____ la Sierra de Guadarrama

5. _____ el Guadiana   10. _____ el Tajo

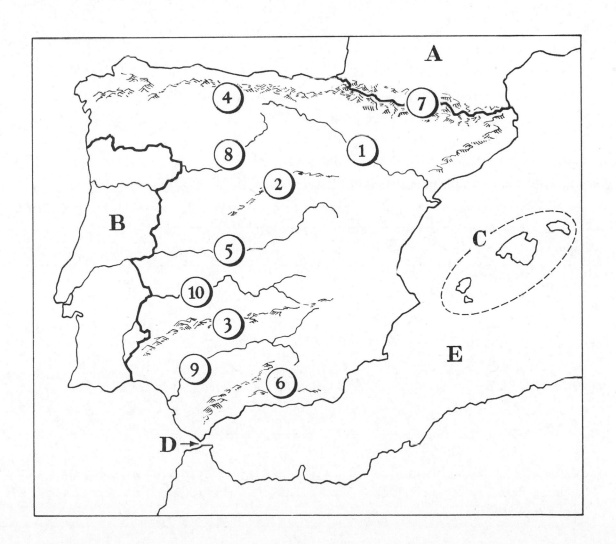

C. A la izquierda de cada expresión de la lista *A*, escríbase la letra de la expresión correspondiente de la lista *B*.

A	B
_____ 1. montañas cerca de Madrid	*a.* la Sierra de Guadarrama
_____ 2. río más navegable de España	*b.* Badajoz
_____ 3. pico más alto de España	*c.* el Ebro
_____ 4. montañas del sur de España	*d.* el Guadiana
_____ 5. montañas en el noroeste de España	*e.* el Duero
_____ 6. río más largo de España	*f.* Barcelona
_____ 7. río que desemboca en el Mar Mediterráneo	*g.* los Pirineos
_____ 8. ciudad de unos dos millones de habitantes	*h.* la Sierra Morena
_____ 9. río que nace en Castilla y León	*i.* Burgos
_____10. montañas entre Francia y España	*j.* el Mulhacén
	k. el Guadalquivir
	l. la Cordillera Cantábrica
	m. el Tajo

D. Complétense las siguientes frases en español:

1. Jerez y Málaga son célebres por sus _____.

2. La palabra *Guadalquivir* significa _____.

3. El metal que se saca de las minas de Linares es _____.

4. La ciudad de Zaragoza está a orillas del río _____.

5. Dos productos agrícolas del sudeste de España son _____ y _____.

6. España y Portugal forman la Península _____.

7. Se hallan las tierras cálidas en el _____ y en el _____ de España.

8. Con la excepción de Suiza, España es el país más _____ de Europa.

9. La Sierra _____ separa la meseta de la Mancha del valle del Guadalquivir.

10. Al este, España está rodeada del _____.

DIVISIÓN TERRITORIAL DEL PAÍS

Políticamente, España con sus posesiones está compuesta de cincuenta provincias. Históricamente, está dividida en quince regiones, cada una de las cuales tiene sus propias tradiciones y cultura.

El norte

1. **Galicia** está al norte de Portugal y tiene el Atlántico al norte y al oeste. Sus habitantes, que se llaman **gallegos,** son descendientes de la raza céltica. Los puertos principales de esta región son **Vigo** y **La Coruña.**

2. El País Vasco está cerca de los Pirineos, en la parte norte central de España. Es montañoso, bien irrigado (irrigated) y hermoso. Sus habitantes se llaman **vascos.** Son descendientes de un pueblo de origen desconocido. Son bilingües (es decir, hablan dos lenguas). Además del español, hablan **el vascuence,** un idioma también de origen muy antiguo y desconocido. Los vascos tienen un carácter muy independiente y un profundo sentimiento religioso. San Ignacio de Loyola, quien fundó la **Compañía de Jesús** (los jesuitas), nació allí. En esta región se halla la célebre playa de **San Sebastián.** Esta playa es conocida como el "Biarritz" o el "Lido" de España.

3. **Asturias** está entre el País Vasco y Galicia. Allí se halla Covadonga, donde el héroe, Pelayo, venció a los moros en el año 718, iniciando así la Reconquista de España. Las ciudades principales de esta región son **Oviedo** y **Gijón.**

4. **Navarra** está al este del País Vasco. En **Pamplona,** su capital, se celebra en julio una fiesta que atrae a muchos turistas.

5. La Rioja es famosa por sus vinos de calidad. Su capital es Logroño.

EL CENTRO

6. **Castilla y León** y **Castilla-La Mancha** están situadas en una alta meseta seca, casi sin ríos ni lagos. Ésta está al sur de aquella. El idioma nacional, **el castellano,** tuvo su origen en estas regiones. También se llaman **castellanos** los habitantes. Ninguna otra región ha influido tanto en la vida nacional como Castilla, que domina el país por sus ideales y su espíritu. La capital, **Madrid,** se halla en Castilla-La Mancha.

7. **Extremadura,** al sur de León, está llena de montes. El río Guadiana fluye por estas tierras, donde se hallan muchos monumentos de la época romana. Aquí nacieron los grandes conquistadores (Pizzaro, Cortés, y Balboa).

EL SUR

8. **Andalucía,** en el sur del país, recibió la influencia más profunda de la cultura árabe. Sus ciudades principales representan los distintos períodos de su historia. **Cádiz,** por ejemplo, fue el centro del comercio fenicio. Más tarde, durante la época musulmana (árabe), florecieron centros como **Córdoba, Granada,** y **Sevilla.** En Andalucía se hallan las típicas casas españolas, pintadas de vivos colores, con patio en el centro y con rejas y balcones que dan a la calle.

EL ESTE

9. **Cataluña** está en el nordeste del país, en la costa mediterránea al norte de Valencia. Es la región más industrial del país. Sus habitantes son bilingües, pues además del castellano hablan su propio idioma, **el catalán.** Su ciudad principal es **Barcelona.** Durante la Edad Media, los catalanes estaban unidos en su cultura con Provenza (Provence), provincia antigua del sur de Francia, la cual fue el centro de una gran cultura.

10. **Valencia,** conocida por la fertilidad de su tierra y su excelente sistema de riego, está al sur de Cataluña. Es llamada "la huerta (orchard) de España" a causa de sus numerosos productos agrícolas, entre los cuales son bien conocidas las deliciosas naranjas valencianas. Los campesinos todavía emplean la **noria,** primitiva máquina de riego introducida en España por los moros. Las costumbres de los valencianos, así como sus tradiciones, están bien representadas en algunas de las novelas del gran escritor Blasco Ibáñez.

11. **Murcia,** al sur de Valencia, es típicamente mediterránea. Tiene un cielo limpio y un clima semitropical. Los productos principales de esta región son dátiles, limones, y naranjas.

12. **Aragón** está en el nordeste del país, al oeste de Cataluña. Sus habitantes, los **aragoneses,** tienen fama de ser muy obstinados (stubborn). El terreno consiste en montañas y picos. El nombre de la capital, **Zaragoza,** viene del nombre del emperador romano César Augusto.

POSESIONES EXTRATERRITORIALES

1. Del gran imperio español hoy no quedan más que fragmentos. En el Mar Mediterráneo están las **Islas Baleares:** Mallorca, Menorca, Ibiza, y Formentera. La más grande es **Mallorca,** cuya capital es **Palma.**

2. En el Atlántico, cerca de la costa africana, se encuentran las **Islas Canarias,** que están divididas en dos provincias, **Santa Cruz de Tenerife** y **Las Palmas.**

3. España tiene también **Ceuta** y **Melilla,** dos puertos en la costa de Marruecos (Morocco).

EJERCICIOS

A. Refiriéndose al mapa abajo, identifíquense los siguientes nombres geográficos, escribiendo a la izquierda de cada uno el número correspondiente:

1. _____ Asturias
2. _____ Valencia
3. _____ Murcia
4. _____ Galicia
5. _____ Portugal
6. _____ Castilla-La Mancha
7. _____ Navarra
8. _____ Andalucía

9. _____ Extremadura
10. _____ las Islas Baleares
11. _____ La Rioja
12. _____ Castilla y León
13. _____ País Vasco
14. _____ Aragón
15. _____ Cataluña

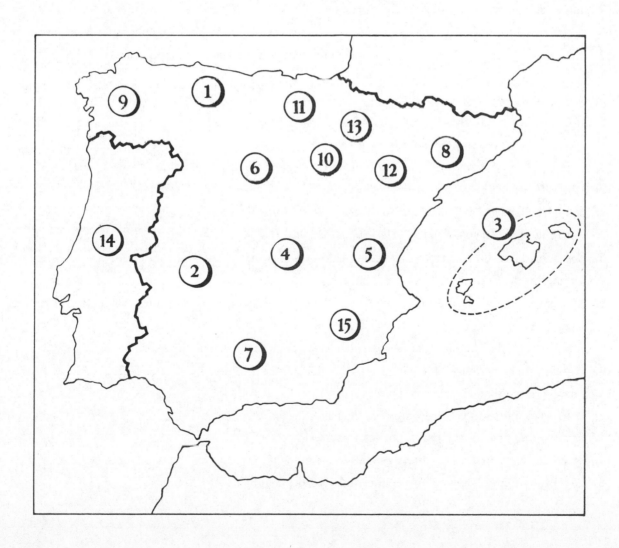

B. Complétense, escribiendo el nombre de la región.

1. _____ está directamente al norte de Portugal.

2. _____ es la región más industrial de España.

3. _____ es "la huerta de España."

4. _____ ha tenido más influencia que ninguna otra en la vida nacional.

5. _____ tiene una ciudad cuyo nombre viene del de un emperador romano.

6. En _____ se inició la Reconquista.

7. Los habitantes de _____ hablan el español y un idioma cuyo origen es desconocido.

8. _____ dio al mundo muchos conquistadores.

9. _____ todavía conserva mucho de la gran cultura árabe.

10. _____ dio a España su idioma nacional.

11. _____ es la posesión española situada cerca de África.

12. En _____ están las ciudades de Cádiz y Granada.

13. La famosa playa de San Sebastián se halla en _____.

14. _____ son la única posesión española en el Mediterráneo.

15. _____ tiene muchos monumentos de la época romana.

C. Indíquese si las frases siguientes son *verdad* o *mentira*. Si una frase es mentira, corríjase cambiando la expresión en letra cursiva.

1. Palma es la capital de *las Islas Canarias.* _____

2. *Los vascos* son descendientes de la raza céltica. _____

3. El gran héroe, *Pelayo*, inició la reconquista de España de la dominación de los moros. _____

4. Las Islas Canarias se hallan en el *continente de África.* _____

5. San Ignacio de Loyola fundó *la Compañía de Jesús.* _____

6. Los puertos de La Coruña y *Barcelona* están en la provincia de Galicia. _____

7. La capital de España está en Castilla *y León.* _____

8. En tiempos pasados Cataluña tenía relaciones culturales con *Provenza*, una provincia de Francia. _____

9. *Blasco Ibáñez* describe la vida de los valencianos en algunas de sus novelas. _____

10. Murcia está al *norte* de Valencia. _____

11. España *ya no* tiene un gran imperio. _____

12. Muchos extranjeros van a Pamplona en el mes de *julio.* _____

13. La noria fue llevada a España por los *franceses.* _____

14. La ciudad principal de *Cataluña* es Barcelona. _____

15. Cádiz fue un gran centro comercial establecido por los *romanos.* _____

CIUDADES PRINCIPALES

1. **Madrid,** la capital y ciudad más grande de España, está en el centro del país. Sus lugares de interés principales son los siguientes:

   a. El **Museo del Prado** tiene muchas obras de los grandes pintores españoles, como Velázquez y El Greco.

   b. El lujoso (luxurious) **Palacio Nacional** es uno de los palacios más grandes del mundo.

   c. El **Parque del Buen Retiro** es el parque principal de la capital.

   d. La plaza principal es la **Puerta del Sol,** de donde salen las calles más importantes. Allí se encuentran magníficos edificios, grandes hoteles, lujosas tiendas, y cafés elegantes.

   e. Cerca de la capital está **El Escorial,** un enorme monasterio que mandó construir Felipe II. De estilo severo, representa el carácter frío del rey. El edificio contiene el Panteón de los Reyes (burial place for kings), donde están enterrados (buried) muchos de los reyes de España. También hay en él una biblioteca y una iglesia. El arquitecto principal fue Juan de Herrera.

   f. Otro monumento enorme cerca de la capital es el **Valle de los Caídos,** dedicado en 1958. Fue construido en memoria de los soldados que murieron en la Guerra Civil española (1936–39). Encima de la ancha bóveda (dome) hay una cruz que tiene más de cuatrocientos pies de alto.

2. **Barcelona,** capital de **Cataluña,** es el puerto principal de España. **La Rambla,** uno de los paseos más hermosos de toda Europa, es la avenida más ancha de la ciudad. La **Plaza de Cataluña** es el centro comercial y social de la ciudad.

   En las afueras de Barcelona se halla el célebre **monasterio de Montserrat.** Todos los años miles de turistas y peregrinos (pilgrims) visitan este lugar sagrado.

3. **Sevilla,** ciudad principal de **Andalucía,** es un puerto del río Guadalquivir. Durante la época colonial era el único puerto de donde salían los buques para el Nuevo Mundo. La **Catedral de Sevilla** es la catedral gótica más grande del mundo. Allí se encuentra la gran tumba de Cristóbal Colón, descubridor del Nuevo Mundo. La **Giralda,** torre de la Catedral de Sevilla, es un admirable ejemplo de arquitectura árabe. Fue construida en el año 1184.

4. **Valencia** está en la costa del Mediterráneo. Es importante en la exportación de vinos, naranjas, y arroz.

5. **Granada,** situada al pie de la Sierra Nevada, fue la última fortaleza de los moros en España. Fue conquistada por los Reyes Católicos en 1492. Allí se encuentran los siguientes lugares de interés:

   a. El **Albaicín** es un barrio (neighborhood) pintoresco donde viven los gitanos desde principios del siglo XVI.

   b. La **Alhambra** es el antiguo palacio de los reyes moros, el cual fue inmortalizado por el escritor norteamericano Washington Irving en su libro *The Alhambra.* En este palacio se pueden ver el célebre **Patio de los Leones** y ejemplos preciosos del arte musulmana.

   c. El **Generalife,** otro palacio moro, es célebre por sus jardines encantadores. Este edificio servía de residencia de verano para los reyes moros.

6. **Toledo,** situada a orillas del río Tajo a poca distancia de Madrid, es conocida por sus productos de acero y metales preciosos. Fue inmortalizada en las pinturas del gran artista El Greco. Allí había el **Alcázar** de Toledo, un castillo moro que fue destruido durante la Guerra Civil en 1936.

7. **Cádiz,** en **Andalucía,** es un puerto del Atlántico. En tiempos primitivos fue una colonia de los fenicios.

8. **Bilbao,** centro de la industria minera del norte, es una ciudad importante conocida como el "Pittsburgh de España."

9. **Burgos,** antigua capital de **Castilla y León,** tiene la famosa catedral del mismo nombre, la cual es una de las maravillas de la arquitectura gótica en España. Allí se halla la tumba del Cid Campeador, el héroe nacional de España.

10. **Santiago de Compostela,** ciudad de **Galicia,** es visitada cada año por miles de peregrinos religiosos. Según la tradición, allí se encuentra la tumba del apóstol Santiago, santo patrón de España.

11. **Salamanca** es el sitio de una de las universidades más viejas de Europa, fundada en el siglo XIII.

12. **Córdoba,** a orillas del río Guadalquivir, fue, en los siglos X y XI, la capital del gobierno musulmán en España y el centro cultural más importante de toda Europa.

EJERCICIOS

A. A la izquierda de cada expresión de la lista *A*, escríbase la letra de la expresión correspondiente de la lista *B*.

A	*B*
_____ 1. Montserrat	*a.* plaza principal de Madrid
_____ 2. Museo del Prado	*b.* santo patrón de España
_____ 3. Puerta del Sol	*c.* el río Tajo
_____ 4. El Retiro	*d.* última fortaleza de los moros en España
_____ 5. Bilbao	*e.* monumento de la Guerra Civil
_____ 6. Santiago	*f.* el Cid Campeador
_____ 7. Burgos	*g.* parque público
_____ 8. Granada	*h.* paseo moderno
_____ 9. Toledo	*i.* Velázquez
_____ 10. Valle de los Caídos	*j.* el "Pittsburgh de España"
	k. monasterio famoso

B. Complétense las frases siguientes en español:

1. La Universidad de Salamanca fue fundada en el siglo _____.

2. El Albaicín se halla en la ciudad de _____.

3. El célebre Patio de los Leones está en _____, un edificio construido por los moros.

4. El puerto principal de España es _____.

5. La ciudad más grande de España es _____.

6. El santo patrón de España es _____.

7. Felipe II hizo construir _____.

8. _____, el hermoso castillo moro en Toledo, fue destruido durante la Guerra Civil española.

9. La tumba del Cid está en la catedral de _____.

10. _____ pintó muchas escenas de la ciudad de Toledo.

C. Identifíquese la persona o el lugar.

1. el arquitecto principal de El Escorial _____

2. un palacio moro en Granada que se usaba como residencia de verano _____

3. un lugar pintoresco donde viven muchos gitanos ------------------------------

4. paseo hermoso de Barcelona ------------------------------

5. torre alta en Sevilla ------------------------------

6. ciudad conquistada en 1492 ------------------------------

7. colonia fenicia ------------------------------

8. capital de los moros durante los siglos X y XI ------------------------------

9. ciudad donde se fabrican artículos de metales finos ------------------------------

10. palacio moro descrito por Washington Irving ------------------------------

Plaza de las Tres Culturas, Ciudad de México

En esta plaza se reúnen lo antiguo y lo moderno. Una iglesia española,
vestigio (relic) de la época colonial, domina las ruinas de un templo azteca.
La "tercera cultura" se ve en el fondo: casas de apartamentos modernas.

Civilization Lesson 2—LA HISTORIA DE ESPAÑA

ÉPOCA PRIMITIVA

La España de hoy es el producto de las diversas razas que se establecieron en ella y dejaron allí su cultura.

1. Los primitivos habitantes del país, los **iberos,** penetraron en España por el sur. No se sabe mucho de su historia. El mejor ejemplo de la escultura (sculpture) ibérica es una cabeza de mujer, **"La Dama de Elche."**

2. Los **celtas** entraron en la península por el norte unos siglos más tarde. De la unión de las dos razas (ibérica y celta), se formó la raza **celtíbera.**

3. Hace unos tres mil años, los **fenicios** establecieron colonias en todas las costas de la península ibérica con excepción de la del norte. Eran un pueblo de comerciantes de una cultura avanzada. Introdujeron en España el arte de escribir, el uso de la moneda, y el arte de trabajar los metales. Los fenicios fundaron muchos centros comerciales, entre ellos **Cádiz.**

4. Otro pueblo de comerciantes, los **griegos,** también habían fundado unas colonias en la península. Esta raza contribuyó a establecer en España la agricultura e introdujo nuevas plantas, tales como la vid y el olivo (olive tree).

5. Más tarde, entraron en la península ibérica los **cartagineses** (Carthaginians), para ayudar a los fenicios en sus guerras contra los celtíberos. Pero pronto los cartagineses emplearon sus armas contra los fenicios, los vencieron, y quedaron dueños de gran parte de la península. No obstante, no pudieron derrotar por completo a los celtíberos, quienes prefirieron morir antes que rendirse. Ejemplo de su heroísmo fue el **Sitio de Sagunto,** el cual duró nueve meses. Cuando los cartagineses, bajo el mando de Aníbal, su famoso general, entraron por fin en la ciudad, no hallaron más que muerte y ruinas.

6. Pero Cartago a su vez fue vencida por los **romanos** en el año 206 antes de Jesucristo (B.C.), en las **Guerras Púnicas.** Entonces Roma pudo dedicarse a la conquista de los españoles. Los habitantes de la península, bajo el mando de **Viriato,** ofrecieron dura resistencia a los romanos, sobre todo en el **Sitio de Numancia,** el cual duró más de quince meses. Fue otro ejemplo del heroísmo español.

   Los romanos permanecieron en España unos seis siglos. Contribuyeron mucho a la cultura española. Le dieron la base de su idioma actual, un magnífico sistema de leyes y muchas obras públicas, grandes carreteras, puentes, y acueductos.

7. La dominación romana en España terminó en el siglo V. Entre las tribus germánicas que invadieron a España había los **visigodos,** quienes lucharon contra las otras tribus, las derrotaron, y establecieron su propio gobierno en la península. Pero, a pesar de su dominación, que duró casi cuatro siglos, la gran influencia romana continuó en la península.

8. Los **moros** (o **árabes**), una raza del norte de África, entraron en España en el año 711. En la batalla de Guadalete, vencieron a los soldados del rey Rodrigo, el último rey visigodo. Los moros lograron dominar toda la península con excepción de unas regiones del norte. En 718, **Pelayo,** con un pequeño ejército de visigodos, venció a los moros en **Covadonga,** en Asturias. Así comenzó la **Reconquista,** una lucha constante entre moros y cristianos, la cual duró casi ocho siglos, hasta 1492.

   Gracias en gran parte a la influencia árabe, España llegó a ser el país más avanzado y más culto de toda Europa. Los moros construyeron lujosos palacios. Llevaron a España la noria, que aún hoy se usa para el riego. De toda Europa llegaron estudiantes a Córdoba (la capital de los moros) para estudiar las matemáticas, las ciencias, y la medicina. El rey cristiano de León, **Alfonso X** (llamado **el Sabio**), reunió en su corte a muchos sabios, entre los cuales había árabes, cristianos, y hebreos. Allí estudiaron y enseñaron, y a ellos se debe mucho de lo que hoy sabemos de la España medieval.

9. **El Cid Campeador** (**Rodrigo Díaz de Vivar**), el héroe nacional de España, vivió en el siglo XI. Se distinguió en las luchas entre moros y cristianos. Fue muy temido de los moros, quienes le dieron el título de **El Cid,** que significa "señor" en árabe. En el año 1094 venció a los moros de la ciudad de Valencia, y gobernó esta ciudad hasta su muerte, en 1099. Sobre sus hazañas se escribió un poema épico, *el Poema del Cid*, obra compuesta hacia 1140.

10. En 1469 se casó Isabel, princesa de Castilla, con Fernando, príncipe de Aragón. Más tarde, cuando ella llegó a ser reina de Castilla, y él rey de Aragón, la España cristiana quedó unificada por primera vez. Del gran imperio árabe, sólo quedaba el reino de Granada, gobernado por **Boabdil,** el último rey moro. **Fernando e Isabel** (**Los Reyes Católicos**) conquistaron a Granada en 1492, y la Reconquista quedó terminada.

GRANDEZA DE ESPAÑA

1. Bajo el reinado de **los Reyes Católicos,** España llegó a ser la primera nación de Europa. Fue la reina Isabel quien recibió a **Cristóbal Colón,** un navegante italiano, y resolvió ayudarle, dándole tres barcos, *la Santa María, la Niña, y la Pinta.* El día 3 de agosto de 1492, estos tres barcos partieron del puerto de Palos, en el sur de España. El día 12 de octubre del mismo año, Colón y sus marineros pisaron tierra en una isla que llamaron San Salvador (hoy día conocida con el nombre de Watling Island). Así Colón descubrió un nuevo mundo bajo la bandera española. Con el descubrimiento del Nuevo Mundo empezó el gran imperio español. Otro hecho importante que ocurrió durante el reinado de los Reyes Católicos fue la conquista de gran parte de Italia por **Gonzalo de Córdoba,** el "Gran Capitán."

2. Durante el reinado de **Carlos V** (1516–1556), la nación española tenía posesiones en Alemania, Austria, Italia, los Países Bajos (Netherlands), y América. Ésta fue la época de los grandes descubrimientos y conquistas.

3. **Felipe II,** hijo de Carlos V, reinó desde 1556 hasta 1598. Durante su reinado tuvo lugar la famosa **batalla de Lepanto,** contra los turcos. También ocurrió el mayor desastre naval que sufrió España, la destrucción de **la Gran Armada** en 1588 a manos de Inglaterra, rival religioso y político de España. Esta derrota (defeat) inició la decadencia de España.

DECADENCIA

Felipe III, que siguió a Felipe II, no sabía gobernar sus vastas tierras y, por consiguiente, España empezó a sufrir derrotas y a perder territorios. Además, el dominio del mar ya no pertenecía a España sino a Inglaterra. El reinado de **Felipe IV** fue tan débil como el de Felipe III. Había mucha corrupción en los asuntos del gobierno, y el pueblo sufría mucha miseria. España experimentaba la ruina económica a causa de las frecuentes guerras, la emigración al Nuevo Mundo, y la expulsión de los judíos (Jews) y de los moriscos (Moors). Durante el reinado de **Carlos II** la decadencia de la nación española llegó a ser casi completa. La muerte del rey en 1700 marca el fin de la dinastía (dynasty) de los Habsburgos en España.

En 1759 subió al trono **Carlos III,** el rey más activo y más patriótico que haya tenido España. Bajo su dirección, se nacionalizó la enseñanza y se estableció el servicio de correos. Carlos III fue el mejor rey de la dinastía de los Borbones.

ESPAÑA DESDE EL SIGLO XIX HASTA HOY

1. Desgraciadamente, el hijo de Carlos III, **Carlos IV,** era tan débil que deshizo toda la obra progresista (progressive) y liberal de su padre. Durante su reinado, en 1808, **Napoleón** invadió a España y nombró rey a su hermano José. El 2 de mayo del mismo año, los ciudadanos madrileños se rebelaron contra los soldados franceses, y así comenzó la **Guerra de Independencia,** que duró desde 1808 hasta 1814. Con la ayuda de Inglaterra, España logró finalmente expulsar de su territorio a las tropas francesas. Desde entonces, el 2 de mayo se ha considerado como la fiesta nacional del país.

2. El nuevo rey de España, **Fernando VII,** fue un monarca reaccionario. Reinó como rey absoluto, suprimiendo (suppressing) el espíritu liberal del país. Durante su reinado, España perdió casi todas sus colonias en el Nuevo Mundo.

3. Después de la muerte de Fernando VII en 1833, estalló una guerra civil entre los partidarios (partisans) del príncipe Don Carlos, hermano de Fernando (los carlistas), y los de Isabel II, hija del rey. Los carlistas representaban el espíritu más conservador (conservative). Ésta fue la primera **Guerra Carlista.** Hubo batallas e incidentes en 1848, 1855, y en 1873. La segunda Guerra Carlista fue ganada por los ejércitos liberales en 1876.

4. La primera república fue establecida en 1873 y duró solamente un año. **Alfonso XII,** hijo de Isabel II, volvió como rey en 1874. En 1902 **Alfonso XIII,** hijo del rey, subió al trono. Alfonso XIII fue expulsado en 1931 por haber permitido que el dictador **Primo de Rivera** gobernase en España de 1923 a 1930, y por haber actuado mal en la guerra de Marruecos.

5. La segunda república de España fue declarada en 1931 y duró solamente cinco años, a causa de muchas dificultades políticas. Bajo este nuevo gobierno España recibió una nueva constitución y muchas leyes liberales. Por desgracia, el gobierno no pudo mantenerse fuerte, y en 1936 estalló la Guerra Civil española. Después de muchas luchas sangrientas, el general **Francisco Franco** logró vencer las fuerzas de la República, y estableció una dictadura en 1939. Franco rigió (ruled) el país hasta su muerte en 1975.

6. El gobierno actual de España es una monarquía constitucional.

ALGUNAS OBSERVACIONES SOBRE LOS IDIOMAS DE LA PENÍNSULA

El idioma popular de los romanos durante su dominación de España era el latín vulgar. De este idioma se quedaron en España tres lenguas que se pueden llamar lenguas **romances.** Una de estas lenguas es el **gallego,** dialecto del portugués, el cual se habla en Galicia. Otra es el **castellano,** el idioma nacional, llamado generalmente el **español.** La tercera es el **catalán,** que se habla en Cataluña. El idioma que se habla en el País Vasco, llamado **vascuence,** es de origen desconocido.

El castellano tiene otros elementos lingüísticos además del latín. El árabe ha contribuido con casi mil palabras. La mayor parte de éstas empiezan con el artículo árabe "al," como, por ejemplo, "alcalde" y "álgebra." De los visigodos el idioma español recibió menos de cien palabras, la mayor parte de las cuales se refieren a la guerra, como "guardia" y "espía."

EJERCICIOS

A. A la izquierda de cada expresión de la lista *A*, escríbase la letra de la expresión correspondiente de la lista *B*.

A	B
_____ 1. La Dama de Elche	*a.* Guerra Carlista
_____ 2. el uso de monedas	*b.* último rey de los moros
_____ 3. el Sitio de Sagunto	*c.* la segunda república española
_____ 4. Numancia	*d.* la primera gramática española
_____ 5. Boabdil	*e.* Cristóbal Colón
_____ 6. Rodrigo Díaz de Vivar	*f.* los fenicios
_____ 7. Pelayo	*g.* invasión romana
_____ 8. La Gran Armada	*h.* Covadonga
_____ 9. Palos	*i.* estatua
_____10. Isabel II	*j.* cartagineses
	k. el héroe nacional de España
	l. Felipe II

B. Complétense las siguientes frases en español:

1. Además del castellano, se habla en Cataluña el _____.

2. _____ se hizo dictador durante el reinado de Alfonso XIII.

3. Los _____ introdujeron la vid y el olivo en España.

4. Bajo Felipe II, España venció a los turcos en la batalla de _____.

5. El mejor rey español de la dinastía de Borbón fue _____.

6. El gallego es un idioma muy semejante al _____.

7. Napoleón invadió a España en el año _____.

8. Los primeros habitantes de España fueron los _____.

9. La mayor parte de las palabras de origen visigodo que se hallan en el idioma español se refieren a _____.

10. La dominación romana terminó en el siglo _____.

C. Indíquese el orden cronológico de las personas siguientes escribiendo los números 1–10 en los espacios a la izquierda:

1. _____ Pelayo

2. _____ Carlos V

3. _____ Viriato

4. _____ Alfonso XII

5. _____ el rey Rodrigo

6. _____ Felipe II

7. _____ Fernando e Isabel

8. _____ Rodrigo Díaz de Vivar

9. _____ Isabel II

10. _____ Fernando VII

D. Identifíquese el personaje.

1. Fue el rey de España que perdió su trono en 1931. _____

2. Se hizo dictador de España en 1939. _____

3. Conquistó gran parte de Italia para los Reyes Católicos. _____

4. Durante su reinado se estableció el servicio de correos. _____

5. Durante su reinado la decadencia de España llegó a ser casi completa. _____

6. Se disputó con Isabel II el trono de España. _____

7. Se casó con la reina Isabel. _____

8. Los grandes descubrimientos y conquistas ocurrieron durante su reinado. _____

9. Fue hermano de Napoleón. _____

10. Durante su reinado España perdió la mayor parte de sus colonias. _____

Civilization Lesson 3—LA LITERATURA DE ESPAÑA

LITERATURA ANTES DEL SIGLO DE ORO

AUTORES Y OBRAS

1. El *Poema del Cid* es el mejor ejemplo de la poesía épica de España. En él se trata del héroe naciona de España, Rodrigo Díaz de Vivar. El poema, de autor anónimo, fue compuesto hacia el año 1140. Está dividido en tres partes ("cantares"), que tratan de tres distintas épocas de su vida.

2. **Alfonso X, el Sabio** (1252–1284) es la figura más prominente de la literatura española del siglo XIII. Además de escribir varias obras en prosa y en verso, reunió en su corte a los hombres más cultos del mundo entero, para estudiar, traducir, y escribir. Se debe a Alfonso *Las siete partidas*, una vasta colección de leyes y costumbres.

3. **Jorge Manrique** (1440–1478) es famoso por las *Coplas*, una poesía escrita en la ocasión de la muerte de su padre. Se considera tal vez la mejor poesía lírica escrita durante la Edad Media. Fue traducida al inglés, en verso, por el poeta norteamericano Henry Wadsworth Longfellow.

4. Antonio de **Nebrija** (1444–1522) escribió la primera gramática del idioma español, en 1492. Este libro fue la primera gramática escrita sobre cualquier idioma moderno.

SIGLO DE ORO

El Siglo de Oro comienza durante la primera mitad del siglo XVI y termina hacia fines del siglo XVII, con la muerte de Calderón. Es la época más gloriosa de la literatura española.

AUTORES Y OBRAS

1. **Garcilaso de la Vega** (1503–1536) era un verdadero representante del Renacimiento (Renaissance). Fue soldado y poeta. Introdujo en España nuevas formas de poesía lírica. Popularizó en España la forma poética llamada **soneto.**

2. La **novela picaresca** describe las aventuras de un **pícaro** que trata de vivir sin trabajar. Sus comentarios son una verdadera sátira de la vida y de la sociedad de su época. La primera y más típica de las novelas de esta clase es *Lazarillo de Tormes*, de autor anónimo, escrita durante la primera parte del siglo XVI.

3. Miguel de **Cervantes** Saavedra (1547–1616) es conocido en todo el mundo como el autor de *Don Quijote de la Mancha*, uno de los libros más leídos en todas las lenguas.

Cervantes fue un hombre extraordinario. Se distinguió como soldado en la batalla de Lepanto, donde perdió el uso del brazo izquierdo (se quedó manco—*one-armed*). Por eso se le llamaba "el manco de Lepanto." Su vida fue una serie de fracasos. Tuvo mala suerte en los negocios, y pasó algún tiempo en la cárcel. Tampoco tuvo éxito en su matrimonio.

Escribió poesías, novelas, obras de teatro, y una colección de doce novelas cortas, las *Novelas ejemplares*.

En 1605 publicó la primera parte de su obra maestra, *El ingenioso hidalgo, don Quijote de la Mancha*. En 1615 publicó la segunda parte. El libro trata de un hombre de edad avanzada que se imagina caballero, y que sale en su caballo, Rocinante, para buscar aventuras y combatir las injusticias del mundo, pero sin éxito. Lleva como escudero a Sancho Panza, un labrador ignorante pero de sentido práctico. Este libro, que Cervantes escribió para burlarse de los libros de caballerías (novels of chivalry), está lleno de episodios ridículos. Pero, además del humorismo de las aventuras, hay una base filosófica, el conflicto entre el idealismo y el materialismo.

Desde el día de su publicación, el libro logró un éxito tremendo que todavía no ha perdido.

4. Francisco de **Quevedo** (1580–1645) fue el escritor satírico sin igual en la literatura española. *Los sueños*, una serie de ensayos, son su obra maestra. También escribió una novela picaresca, *La vida del buscón*.

El teatro

5. **Lope de Vega** (1562–1635) fue un verdadero "monstruo (monster) de la naturaleza," como le llamó Cervantes, a causa de su gran producción literaria. Escribió toda clase de obras. Pero su fama se debe a sus obras dramáticas. Escribió muchísimas comedias, tal vez más de mil, todas en verso.

Se ha dicho de él que creó el teatro nacional. Estableció la técnica de escribir comedias (tres actos, en verso, etc.). Escogió temas de todas las épocas. Sus obras más famosas son las que tratan de la historia de España y de la dignidad humana. Se pueden mencionar entre éstas *Fuenteovejuna* y *Peribáñez y el comendador de Ocaña*. En estas dos, la gente del pueblo lucha contra las injusticias de los nobles.

6. Juan **Ruiz de Alarcón** (1581–1639) nació en México de padres españoles. Escribió más de veinte obras teatrales en las cuales castigaba el vicio y alababa la virtud. Entre sus obras principales deben mencionarse *Las paredes oyen*, contra la calumnia (slander), y *La verdad sospechosa* (contra la mentira).

7. **Tirso de Molina** (1583–1648) fue otro gran dramaturgo del Siglo de Oro. Su verdadero nombre fue Gabriel Téllez. Su fama principal consiste en haber creado en la literatura el personaje de **don Juan** en el drama *El burlador de Sevilla*. Desde la época de Tirso, la figura de don Juan ha inspirado las obras de muchos autores en muchos países. En la música, por ejemplo, el gran compositor Mozart empleó el tema de don Juan en su ópera *Don Giovanni*.

8. Pedro **Calderón** de la Barca (1600–1681) fue el último de los grandes dramaturgos del Siglo de Oro. El tema principal de sus obras es el honor. Sus dos obras principales son *El alcalde de Zalamea* y *La vida es sueño*. En la primera, un hombre del pueblo, elegido alcalde, manda matar a un noble para vengar (avenge) el honor de su hija. La segunda contiene profundas ideas filosóficas sobre la realidad y los sueños.

SIGLO XVIII

En el siglo XVIII hubo poca producción literaria de valor. La mayor parte de las obras fueron imitaciones en español del estilo francés.

SIGLO XIX

En 1833, con la muerte del reaccionario Fernando VII, volvieron a España muchos españoles que habían salido del país durante su reinado. Éstos trajeron consigo las ideas liberales que habían aprendido en otros países. Así empezó en España el **romanticismo,** movimiento literario que exaltaba al individuo (sus ideas y sentimientos), y que no se preocupaba por las reglas literarias del siglo XVIII.

Autores y obras

1. **Duque de Rivas** (1791–1865) escribió *Don Álvaro*, drama romántico que más tarde inspiró al compositor italiano Verdi, en su ópera *La forza del destino*.

2. Mariano José de **Larra** (1809–1837) fue un ensayista y crítico importante. Escribió bajo el seudónimo de "Fígaro."

3. José de **Espronceda** (1810–1842) fue un poeta romántico. Sus obras principales son *El estudiante de Salamanca* y *Canto a Teresa*. Se compara a Espronceda, en su vida y en sus obras, con el poeta inglés Byron.

4. José **Zorrilla** (1817–1893) escribió *Don Juan Tenorio*, drama basado en el tema de don Juan pero escrito desde el punto de vista romántico. Tan popular es este drama que se representa hasta hoy cada año el Día de los Difuntos, es decir, el 2 de noviembre.

5. Gustavo Adolfo **Bécquer** (1836–1870) escribió *Rimas,* una colección de unas setenta poesías líricas.

Realismo y regionalismo en la novela

El romanticismo fue seguido de una época de **realismo**. La novela del siglo XIX se caracteriza por el **realismo** y el **regionalismo** (el autor escribe acerca de la región donde nació, su "patria chica").

6. **Fernán Caballero** es el seudónimo de Cecilia Böhl de Faber (1796–1877). Esta autora inició la novela realista en España. Describió las costumbres de su época y de su región (Andalucía) en un estilo sencillo y natural. Su obra principal es *La Gaviota*.

7. Juan **Valera** (1827–1905) también describió a Andalucía. Lo que más le interesó fue la psicología de sus personajes. Su obra maestra es *Pepita Jiménez*.

8. Pedro Antonio de **Alarcón** (1833–1891) describió su región, Andalucía. Fue autor de la popularísima novela *El sombrero de tres picos*, la cual sirvió de tema para el *ballet*, del mismo título, del compositor español Manuel de Falla.

9. Benito **Pérez Galdós** (1843–1920) fue el novelista principal del siglo XIX. Fue liberal y crítico violento de la intolerancia religiosa y de la injusticia social. Su producción literaria es vasta. Entre sus obras deben mencionarse *Doña Perfecta* (contra la intolerancia religiosa) y *Episodios nacionales*, una serie de más de sesenta novelas históricas de la España del siglo XIX. No se limitó a ninguna región, sino que escribió sobre toda España.

10. Emilia **Pardo Bazán** (1852–1921) introdujo el **naturalismo** en la novela. Escribe acerca de su región, Galicia. Sus novelas principales son *Los pazos de Ulloa* y *La madre naturaleza*.

11. Armando Palacio **Valdés** (1853–1939) fue un novelista muy popular. Escribió *La hermana San Sulpicio* (sobre Andalucía) y *José* (sobre los pescadores de Asturias).

12. Vicente **Blasco Ibáñez** (1867–1928) escribe acerca de Valencia. Su obra principal es *La barraca*, que describe la vida de los campesinos valencianos. También escribió *Sangre y arena* (sobre la corrida de toros), y *Los cuatro jinetes del Apocalipsis* (sobre la primera Guerra Mundial).

"GENERACIÓN DEL '98" HASTA NUESTROS DÍAS

A fines del siglo XIX, como resultado de la guerra de 1898 con los Estados Unidos, España perdió lo poco que le quedaba de su imperio colonial. Debido a este desastre, los intelectuales (en su mayor parte jóvenes) se pusieron a examinar el estado cultural y espiritual de su país en el mundo moderno. Estos escritores se conocen hoy como la "Generación del '98."

El ensayo

1. Francisco **Giner de los Ríos** (1839–1915), filósofo y profesor, fue el gran educador de los intelectuales. Su influencia se ve en los escritores de la "Generación del '98." Fundó la Escuela Libre de Enseñanza, centro de ideas liberales.

2. Miguel de **Unamuno** (1864–1936) es la figura dominante de la "Generación del '98." Fue filósofo, crítico, y novelista. Su obra maestra es *Del sentimiento trágico de la vida*. Murió durante la Guerra Civil de España.

3. Ramón **Menéndez Pidal** (1869–1968) fue el erudito principal de la España del siglo XX. Hizo estudios profundos en la lengua y la literatura medievales de España.

4. José **Martínez Ruiz** ("**Azorín**") (1873–1967) escribió ensayos y novelas. En sus obras relacionó la España antigua con la moderna. Entre sus obras principales deben mencionarse *Castilla* y *Los valores literarios*. Fue tal vez el crítico literario más importante de la "Generación del '98."

5. José **Ortega y Gasset** (1883–1955), filósofo, buscó los valores espirituales de España en la tradición. Sus obras principales son *La rebelión de las masas* y *Meditaciones del Quijote*.

EL TEATRO

6. Jacinto **Benavente** (1866–1954) ganó el Premio.Nobel de Literatura en 1922. Sus obras principales son *La malquerida* y *Los intereses creados.*

7. Los hermanos **Quintero** (Serafín, 1871–1938, y Joaquín, 1873–1944) colaboraron (collaborated) en escribir sobre su "patria chica." Sus obras tienen la gracia y el encanto de Andalucía.

8. Federico **García Lorca** (1898–1936), notable poeta andaluz, escribió sobre temas folklóricos y tradicionales. Su teatro trata en gran parte de las pasiones humanas. Entre sus obras dramáticas deben mencionarse *Bodas de sangre* y *La casa de Bernarda Alba.*

9. Alejandro **Casona** (1903–1965), español que vivió muchos años en la Argentina después de la Guerra Civil, escribió con mucha fuerza dramática. Dos de sus obras principales son *La dama del alba* y *Los árboles mueren de pie.*

LA NOVELA

10. Ramón de **Valle-Inclán** (1869–1936) fue famoso por su estilo delicado. Por el lenguaje, su prosa casi puede llamarse poesía. Entre sus obras deben mencionarse las cuatro *Sonatas (de primavera, de estío, de otoño, y de invierno).*

11. **Pío Baroja** (1872–1956) fue tal vez el novelista principal de la "Generación del '98." En sus novelas hay mucha fuerza y acción. Dos de sus novelas importantes son *El árbol de la ciencia y Camino de perfección.*

12. Camilo José **Cela** (1916–   ) es tal vez el más famoso de los novelistas de la España contemporánea. Su novela *La familia de Pascual Duarte* lamenta la falta de dignidad personal que se nota hoy en España.

13. Carmen **Laforet** (1921–   ), en su novela *Nada,* trata del vacío espiritual de la España de hoy.

14. Juan **Goytisolo** (1931–   ), un novelista de renombre internacional, se burla de los valores de la sociedad occidental moderna en su novela *Paisajes después de la batalla.*

LA POESÍA

Además de García Lorca, deben mencionarse los siguientes poetas:

15. Antonio **Machado** (1875–1939) fue uno de los mejores poetas de este siglo. Introdujo en la poesía española el **modernismo** de Rubén Darío. Su obra *Campos de Castilla* tiene por tema el paisaje austero de su país.

16. **Juan Ramón Jiménez** (1881–1958) ganó el Premio Nobel de Literatura en 1956. Además de varias colecciones de poesías, escribió también libros en prosa. Su *Platero y yo* (en prosa), obra muy conocida, describe los recuerdos de su juventud.

EJERCICIOS

A. Identifíquense los siguientes:

1. _____ escribió *Las siete partidas.*

2. _____, una serie de ensayos, es la obra maestra de Quevedo.

3. _____ fue el último gran escritor del Siglo de Oro.

4. _____ escribió la primera gramática de la lengua española.

5. _____ escribió contra la mentira.

6. _____ es el mejor ejemplo de la poesía épica española.

7. _____ fue soldado y poeta; popularizó el soneto en España.

8. _____, de Jorge Manrique, es una obra poética importantísima.

9. _____ fue llamado "el manco de Lepanto."

10. Se le considera a _____ el héroe nacional de España.

B. Indíquese si las frases siguientes son *verdad* o *mentira*. Si una frase es mentira, corríjase cambiando la expresión en letra cursiva.

1. Mozart empleó un tema popular que se encuentra en una obra de *Tirso de Molina*. _____

2. *Don Quijote de la Mancha* fue escrito para burlarse de los libros de caballerías. _____

3. Los siglos *XVI y XVII* se llaman también el Siglo de Oro. _____

4. La vida de *Espronceda* fue semejante a la del poeta inglés Byron. _____

5. *Palacio Valdés* describe la vida diaria de Valencia en sus obras. _____

6. En su novela *Los cuatro jinetes del Apocalipsis*, Blasco Ibáñez describe los desastres de la guerra. _____

7. *La primera guerra carlista* causó la formación de un grupo de intelectuales llamado la "Generación del '98." _____

8. *Azorín* fue el mayor crítico de la "Generación del '98." _____

9. Camilo José Cela es un autor del siglo *XIX*. _____

10. En su obra *Platero y yo*, Juan Ramón Jiménez describe su juventud. _____

C. A la izquierda de cada expresión de la lista *A*, escríbase la letra de la expresión correspondiente de la lista *B*.

	A	B
_____ 1.	El Cid	*a.* Benavente
_____ 2.	Goytisolo	*b.* Calderón
_____ 3.	*Novelas ejemplares*	*c. La barraca*
_____ 4.	*Episodios nacionales*	*d. La Gaviota*
_____ 5.	Gustavo Adolfo Bécquer	*e.* Rodrigo Díaz de Vivar
_____ 6.	Blasco Ibáñez	*f.* Valle-Inclán
_____ 7.	*Los intereses creados*	*g. Paisajes después de la batalla*
_____ 8.	*La vida es sueño*	*h.* Cervantes
_____ 9.	*Sonatas*	*i. Rimas*
_____ 10.	Fernán Caballero	*j. Don Álvaro*
		k. Galdós

D. Identifíquense las obras siguientes, escribiendo por cada una:

> la *clase* de obra (drama, poesía, novela, ensayo)
> el *autor*
> la *época* (Siglo de Oro, romanticismo, realismo, Generación del '98)

EJEMPLO: *Don Quijote*   novela   Cervantes   Siglo de Oro

1. *Lazarillo de Tormes*

----

2. *Doña Perfecta*

----

3. *Don Álvaro*

----

4. *Los intereses creados*

----

5. *El estudiante de Salamanca*

----

6. *El sombrero de tres picos*

----

7. *Del sentimiento trágico de la vida*

----

8. *Don Juan Tenorio*

----

9. *Fuenteovejuna*

----

10. *El alcalde de Zalamea*

----

11. *La rebelión de las masas*

----

12. *El burlador de Sevilla*

----

13. *Las paredes oyen*

----

14. *Pepita Jiménez*

----

15. *La vida del buscón*

E. Subráyese el nombre correcto.

1. Dramaturgo del Siglo de Oro: Quevedo, Palacio Valdés, Tirso de Molina

2. Poeta romántico: Espronceda, Jorge Manrique, Fernán Caballero

3. Daba importancia al individuo: realismo, regionalismo, romanticismo

4. Ganó el Premio Nobel: Pérez Galdós, Juan Ramón Jiménez, Juan Valera

5. Escudero de don Quijote: Sancho Panza, Rocinante, Fígaro

6. Escribe acerca de la España contemporánea: Laforet, Palacio Valdés, Unamuno

7. Dramaturgo español que vivió en la Argentina: Pío Baroja, Alejandro Casona, José Martínez Ruiz

8. El gran maestro de los intelectuales de la Generación del '98: Ortega y Gasset, Valle-Inclán, Giner de los Ríos

9. Erudito principal del siglo XX: Alfonso el Sabio, Menéndez Pidal, el Duque de Rivas

10. Escribió sobre el tema de "don Juan": Duque de Rivas, Larra, Zorrilla

Miguel de Cervantes Saavedra (1547–1616) es el novelista más grande de España, y ocupa un lugar eminente entre los grandes escritores del mundo. Su obra maestra, *Don Quijote de la Mancha*, ha sido traducida a casi todos los idiomas del mundo. Esta novela presenta un vasto panorama de la sociedad española del siglo XVI, y además es un estudio penetrante de la naturaleza humana.

Civilization Lesson 4—LAS BELLAS ARTES Y LA CIENCIA

MÚSICA

España es muy rica en la música folklórica. Un buen ejemplo de esta clase de música es el **cante jondo** de Andalucía, llamado también **flamenco,** que es muy semejante a la música oriental (gitana y árabe).

El instrumento típico y tradicional de España es la **guitarra,** que se emplea tanto en la música clásica como en la música popular. Para acompañamiento se emplean la **pandereta** (tambourine) y las **castañuelas.** En Galicia el instrumento típico es la **gaita.**

España es importante en el género llamado **zarzuela,** que es una combinación de música, diálogo hablado, y baile. Es muy semejante a la "musical comedy." Uno de los mejores compositores de zarzuelas fue Francisco **Asenjo Barbieri** (1823–1894).

Compositores, instrumentistas, cantantes

1. Isaac **Albéniz** (1860–1909) escribió música para el piano. Entre sus composiciones principales son *Iberia* y *El Albaicín.*

2. Enrique **Granados** (1867–1916) también compuso música para el piano. Su obra maestra, *Goyescas,* fue inspirada por los cuadros del pintor Goya.

3. Manuel de **Falla** (1876–1946) fue el más célebre de los compositores del siglo XX. Como Albéniz y Granados, escribió sobre temas folklóricos. Pero Falla escribió principalmente para la orquesta. Escribió varios *ballets,* entre ellos *El amor brujo* (que tiene la popularísima *Danza ritual del Fuego*), y *El sombrero de tres picos,* basado en la famosa novela de Alarcón.

4. Pablo **Casals** (1884–1973) fue el mejor violoncelista (cellist) del mundo. Salió de España en 1939, después de la Guerra Civil, porque se oponía a la dictadura de Franco. En 1956 se estableció en Puerto Rico.

5. José **Iturbi** (1895–1980) fue pianista y director de orquesta sinfónica (symphony).

6. Andrés **Segovia** (1894–1987) fue un gran maestro de la guitarra.

7. **Victoria de los Ángeles** (1923–   ) es una de las mejores cantantes españolas. Cantó en la "Metropolitan Opera House" en Nueva York.

8. Plácido **Domingo** (1941–   ), un tenor de fama mundial, ha cantado en muchas óperas.

El baile

1. Hay grandes diferencias entre los bailes regionales. La región que tiene mayor variedad es **Andalucía.** De allí vienen el *bolero,* el *fandango,* la *seguidilla,* el *jaleo,* la *malagueña,* la *sevillana,* y el *flamenco.* Muchas veces el baile va acompañado de la pandereta y de las castañuelas.

2. La **jota** es el baile regional de **Aragón.**

3. La **sardana** es el baile regional de **Cataluña.** Se baila en grupo, en un gran círculo.

4. La **muñeira** es el baile regional de **Galicia.** Se baila en pareja, con música de la gaita.

5. Vicente **Escudero** (1892–1980) y Carmen **Amaya** (1913–1963), bailarines famosos, fueron grandes intérpretes del baile flamenco.

ARQUITECTURA, PINTURA, CIENCIA

La arquitectura

Romanos, moros, españoles, todos dejaron en España ejemplos magníficos de su manera de construir. De los romanos existen todavía puentes y acueductos (por ejemplo, el acueducto de Segovia); de los moros quedan mezquitas (mosques), alcázares (castles), y el exquisito palacio de la **Alhambra,** en Granada.

De la Edad Media hay también muchas catedrales de estilo **románico** (como la de Santiago de Compostela) y **gótico** (como las de Burgos, Sevilla, Toledo).

De los tiempos posteriores deben mencionarse el **Escorial,** cuyo arquitecto principal fue Juan de **Herrera,** y el estilo **barroco** (baroque), que fue introducido en España por José de **Churriguera,** y que se llama "estilo churrigueresco."

La pintura

España es muy rica en la pintura. Casi no hay en todo el mundo museo de importancia que no tenga varios cuadros de los maestros españoles. El museo principal de España es el del **Prado,** en Madrid.

1. **Doménico Theotocópuli** (1548–1625), llamado **el Greco,** nació en Grecia. Estudió en Italia, pasó a España, y se estableció en Toledo, donde se quedó hasta su muerte. Su obra se caracteriza por lo ascético y lo religioso. Sus obras más famosas son *El entierro del conde de Orgaz* y *Vista de Toledo.*

2. José de **Ribera** (1588–1656) nació en España pero pasó la mayor parte de su vida en Italia. Su cuadro más famoso es *El martirio de San Bartolomé.*

3. Francisco **Zurbarán** (1598–1662) pintó cuadros religiosos. Su *Monje en meditación* es representativo de su obra.

4. Diego **Velázquez** (1599–1660) fue el pintor más original y perfecto de la escuela española. Fue pintor de cámara del rey Felipe IV, y pintó muchos cuadros de la familia real. Su obra maestra es *Las meninas.* Otras son *La rendición de Bredá* (también llamada *Las lanzas*), *Los borrachos* (The Drunkards), y *Las hilanderas* (The Weavers).

5. Bartolomé Esteban **Murillo** (1617–1682) fue principalmente un pintor religioso, y es famoso por sus *Concepciones.* Además pintó tipos populares.

6. Francisco **Goya** (1746–1828) fue el pintor más famoso de su época. Fue pintor de cámara del rey Carlos IV. Tiene varios cuadros satíricos de la familia real, una colección de aguas fuertes (etchings), llamadas *Caprichos,* y unos cuadros sobre la Guerra de Independencia contra Napoleón (*Los desastres de la guerra, Los fusilamientos del dos de mayo*). Entre sus obras más conocidas son *La maja vestida* y *La maja desnuda.*

7. Joaquín **Sorolla** (1862–1923) es el pintor de "sol y color." Muchos de sus cuadros se encuentran en el Museo de la Sociedad Hispánica, en Nueva York.

8. Ignacio **Zuloaga** (1870–1946) pintó muchos tipos: toreros, pordioseros, gitanos, etc.

9. José María **Sert** (1876–1945) es famoso por una serie de cuadros que representan episodios del *Quijote.* Estos cuadros se hallan en el salón Sert del hotel Waldorf-Astoria, en Nueva York.

10. Pablo **Picasso** (1881–1973) nació y fue educado en Málaga, pero pasó la mayor parte de su vida en Francia. Es famoso como fundador del **cubismo,** estilo de pintura en que se emplean figuras geométricas para representar figuras humanas. Su obra *Guernica* pinta la destrucción de ese pueblo vasco durante la Guerra Civil española.

11. Salvador **Dalí** (1904–1989) pertenece a la escuela **surrealista.** Trata de pintar los pensamientos fantásticos de la imaginación.

Hombres de ciencia

1. Santiago **Ramón y Cajal** (1851–1934) ganó el Premio Nobel de Fisiología en 1906. Hizo muchos descubrimientos acerca de las funciones del sistema nervioso.

2. Juan **de la Cierva** (1896–1936) inventó el autogiro, precursor del helicóptero.

3. Severo **Ochoa** (1905–   ) ganó el Premio Nobel de Medicina en 1959 por sus estudios sobre la herencia (heredity).

EJERCICIOS

A. Subráyese la palabra o expresión que complete correctamente cada frase.

1. El compositor que escribió la música del ballet *El sombrero de tres picos* es
   (*a*) Albéniz   (*b*) Granados   (*c*) Iturbi   (*d*) Falla

2. Un baile regional de Aragón es
   (*a*) la malagueña   (*b*) la sardana   (*c*) la jota   (*d*) el fandango

3. Un tipo de obra teatral que corresponde a la "musical comedy" es
   (*a*) la zarzuela   (*b*) la seguidilla   (*c*) la pandereta   (*d*) el ballet

4. De los siguientes, el que no se emplea como instrumento de música es
   (*a*) la gaita   (*b*) la guitarra   (*c*) el flamenco   (*d*) la pandereta

5. Un famoso bailarín español fue
   (*a*) Granados   (*b*) Victoria de los Ángeles   (*c*) Casals   (*d*) Escudero

6. El mejor violoncelista del mundo fue
   (*a*) Iturbi   (*b*) Casals   (*c*) Segovia   (*d*) Albéniz

7. Un baile regional de Cataluña es
   (*a*) el flamenco   (*b*) la sardana   (*c*) la muñeira   (*d*) la sevillana

8. Un ejemplo de la música folklórica es
   (*a*) el cante jondo   (*b*) la zarzuela   (*c*) el ballet   (*d*) *Goyescas*

9. El gran maestro de la guitarra fue
   (*a*) Segovia   (*b*) Escudero   (*c*) Granados   (*d*) Asenjo Barbieri

10. La música que acompaña la muñeira se produce con
    (*a*) la guitarra   (*b*) el piano   (*c*) la gaita   (*d*) las castañuelas

B. Complétense correctamente las frases.

1. Un pintor español, famoso por sus *Concepciones*, es ----------------------------.

2. Un acueducto construido por los romanos está en la ciudad de ----------------------------.

3. *El entierro del conde de Orgaz* es una obra maestra del pintor ----------------------------.

4. La construcción más famosa de los moros es ----------------------------, en Granada.

5. *Las meninas* es una obra maestra del pintor ----------------------------.

6. El fundador del cubismo es ----------------------------.

7. El museo principal de España es el Museo ----------------------------, en Madrid.

8. *Los fusilamientos del dos de mayo* es una obra de ----------------------------.

9. El pintor español cuyas obras se hallan en un gran hotel de Nueva York es ----------------------------.

10. El arquitecto principal del Escorial fue ----------------------------.

C. ¿Qué o quién es (fue) _____?

1. el artista que creó *Los caprichos* _____

2. la bailarina conocida por sus interpretaciones de los bailes flamencos _____

3. el músico que compuso el ballet *El amor brujo* _____

4. la cantante española que cantó en la "Metropolitan Opera House" de Nueva York _____

5. un pintor extranjero que vino a España y se estableció en Toledo _____

6. el pintor contemporáneo, surrealista _____

7. el músico que compuso *Iberia* y *El Albaicín* _____

8. el pintor español que pasó la mayor parte de su vida en Italia _____

9. el científico conocido por sus estudios sobre la herencia _____

10. el compositor de música que se inspiró en las obras de un gran pintor español _____

11. una obra teatral, con música, diálogo, y baile _____

12. el inventor del autogiro _____

13. el pintor de "sol y color" _____

14. el gran científico español que hizo estudios sobre el sistema nervioso _____

15. el arquitecto que introdujo en España el estilo barroco _____

16. el baile regional que se baila en un gran círculo _____

17. la música gitana semejante a la música oriental _____

18. el estilo de pintura en que la figura humana se representa con formas geométricas _____

19. el cantante operático español que ha ganado fama mundial _____

20. el pintor que pintó tipos de toreros y gitanos _____

     Diego de Silva y Velázquez (1599-1660) es, tal vez, el pintor más grande de España. Expresó su teoría sobre la pintura con estas palabras: "verdad y no pintura" (es decir, el realismo). Velázquez fue pintor de cámara (court painter) del rey Felipe IV, y muchas de sus obras representan la familia real o temas patrióticos. Entre sus obras principales figuran *Las meninas* y *La rendición de Breda* (llamada también *Las lanzas*).

Civilization Lesson 5—LA VIDA Y LAS COSTUMBRES ESPAÑOLAS

CASA Y FAMILIA

1. **Casa:** En los pueblos de España, las casas están situadas en calles estrechas. Por lo general, son de un solo piso con balcones, ventanas con rejas, y patios pintorescos. En muchas casas las paredes están cubiertas de azulejos (glazed tiles).

2. **Nombres y Apellidos:** Además del nombre de pila, cada niño español lleva dos apellidos, el de su padre seguido del de su madre. A veces se pone "y" entre los dos apellidos. Por ejemplo, Carlos *Pérez* (y) *Gómez* se casa con María *Vega* (y) *González*. Tienen un hijo que se llama Juan *Pérez* (y) *Vega* (o Juan *Pérez*). La hermana de Juan se llama Adela *Pérez* (y) *Vega* (o Adela *Pérez*). Si Adela se casa con Leandro *Fernández* (y) *Álvarez*, ella se llamará Adela *Pérez* **de** *Fernández*.

3. **El Día del Santo:** Los españoles generalmente llevan el nombre de un santo, y, además de su propio cumpleaños, celebran el día de ese santo.

TIPOS PINTORESCOS

1. **El sereno** pasa la noche guardando las calles de su barrio. Lleva las llaves de todas las casas. Su deber principal es ayudar a los que vuelven a casa sin llave, por lo cual se le da una propina. También anuncia la hora:—¡Las tres y sereno! Es por eso que se le llama "el sereno."

2. **El pordiosero** es un mendigo que pide limosna "por Dios."

3. **Los gitanos** viven en los barrios pobres, sobre todo en el sur de España. Tienen fama de ser muy listos. Muchos de ellos se ganan la vida diciendo la buenaventura.

4. **El aguador** es un tipo muy común en las regiones secas. Lleva el agua por las calles y la vende en las varias casas.

ACTIVIDADES SOCIALES Y COSTUMBRES

1. El **ateneo** es un club intelectual (literario y científico) que existe en muchas ciudades.

2. **Pelando la pava** es la costumbre que tiene el novio de hablar con su novia a través de la reja. Él se queda fuera (de pie), y ella dentro (sentada).

3. La **tertulia** es una reunión informal, en casa, con el propósito de charlar y divertirse.

4. La **lotería** es dirigida por el gobierno. Ocurre tres veces al mes. Hay muchos premios. El premio gordo es muy grande.

5. La **siesta** es la costumbre que tienen los españoles de acostarse por la tarde durante las horas de mayor calor. Se cierran todas las tiendas y las casas comerciales. Después de la siesta se abren de nuevo, y quedan abiertas hasta muy tarde.

COMIDAS Y BEBIDAS

1. El **puchero** se puede llamar el plato nacional de España. Es un guisado (stew) que sirve de alimento diario, sobre todo entre los campesinos. Se llama también **olla** o **cocido.**

2. El **arroz con pollo** consiste en estos dos alimentos, bien sazonados con sal, pimientos, y **azafrán** (saffron). En Valencia añaden mariscos (sea food) al arroz con pollo, y lo llaman **paella.**

3. La **horchata** es una bebida fría que se toma en el verano como refresco. Consiste en almendras (almonds), agua, y azúcar.

4. El **chocolate** forma parte del desayuno de los españoles. Consiste en una taza pequeña de chocolate muy espeso y caliente, que se toma con panecillos o bizcochos (biscuits).

ROPA

En general, la ropa de los españoles es semejante a la del resto de Europa. Sin embargo, en varias partes todavía llevan ropa tradicional, sobre todo los días de fiesta.

1. La **mantilla** es un gran pañuelo de seda y encajes (lace) que la mujer lleva en la cabeza en vez de sombrero.

2. La **peineta** es un peine alto, ricamente adornado, que se lleva debajo de la mantilla.

3. El **mantón** es un chal (shawl) grande, ricamente bordado (embroidered) de flores.

4. La **boina** es una gorra redonda semejante al "beret" francés.

5. Las **alpargatas** son sandalias de lona (canvas). Son comunes entre los trabajadores en muchas partes de España.

DÍAS DE FIESTA

RELIGIOSOS

1. La **Navidad** cae el 25 de diciembre. La **Nochebuena** (Christmas Eve) la gente va a la iglesia para asistir a la **misa del gallo** (midnight mass). Grupos de personas andan por las calles cantando **villancicos.** No se ven arbolitos de Navidad. En cambio, cada casa tiene su **nacimiento,** que consiste en pequeñas figuras que representan el nacimiento de Jesucristo.

   Se dan regalos (llamados **aguinaldos**) a las personas que han servido a la familia durante el año (el cartero, el sereno, los criados, etc.). Los niños no reciben sus regalos hasta el **Día de los Reyes Magos,** que cae el 6 de enero. Los Reyes Magos son para los niños españoles lo que Santa Claus es para nosotros.

2. El **Carnaval** es un período de tres días de diversión y alegría antes de la **Cuaresma** (Lent).

3. La **Semana Santa** precede a la **Pascua Florida** (Easter). Se celebra con mucha solemnidad y devoción, sobre todo en Sevilla.

4. La **Pascua Florida.** El **Viernes Santo** es un día de gran solemnidad, que se celebra con procesiones religiosas. El **Domingo de Resurrección** es un día de alegría y diversión, de comer y beber bien, de ir al teatro, etc.

5. El **día del (santo) patrón.** Cada pueblo tiene su (santo) patrón, cuyo día se celebra con una fiesta. La víspera hay una **verbena** (evening festivity). El día mismo hay **romerías** (religious picnics) a la tumba del santo. La gente pasa el día comiendo, bebiendo, jugando, bailando, etc. Dos santos muy populares en España son **Santiago** (St. James), patrón de España, y **San Isidro,** patrón de Madrid.

6. El **Día de los Difuntos** cae el 2 de noviembre. Se celebra en memoria de los que han muerto. La gente visita los cementerios para adornar con flores las tumbas de parientes y amigos.

NACIONALES

1. El **Dos de Mayo** es el día de fiesta nacional de España. Conmemora un suceso patriótico, el principio de la resistencia contra los franceses en 1808.

2. El **Día de la Raza** cae el 12 de octubre, y corresponde a nuestro *Columbus Day.* Se celebra en todo el mundo hispánico.

DIVERSIONES Y DEPORTES

1. La **corrida de toros** es todavía el espectáculo favorito de España. Generalmente, en las ciudades grandes, hay corridas los domingos y los días de fiesta importantes. La corrida tiene tres partes, llamadas *suertes:*

1ª *suerte:* Los **picadores** entran, montados a caballo. Llevan picas (lances) largas, con las cuales castigan el toro en la cerviz (el cuello).

2ª *suerte:* Entran los **banderilleros,** a pie. Llevan **banderillas** (darts). Esperan la embestida (charge) del toro, y al pasar éste, le ponen las banderillas en la cerviz.

3ª *suerte:* El **matador,** armado de una espada de acero muy fino y llevando una pequeña **muleta** roja, exhibe su arte y su valor. Ejecuta varios pases con la muleta, hasta que llegue el momento ideal para matar el toro. Entonces, cara a cara con su adversario, le mete la espada y lo mata. Lo que el público estima y aplaude más es la valentía y el arte del matador.

2. **Jai-alai,** también llamado **pelota,** es un juego vasco. Tiene gran popularidad en toda España, y también en Cuba y en la Florida. Se juega en un gran **frontón** (court) de tres paredes, con una pelota dura. Es semejante al *handball,* pero en vez de tirar y coger la pelota con la mano, se emplea una cesta larga y estrecha, atada a la muñeca.

3. El **fútbol** no es semejante a nuestro *football.* El fútbol español se llama aquí *soccer.* Es muy popular, no sólo en España, sino también en el resto de Europa.

EJERCICIOS

A. En cada grupo subráyense las dos palabras o expresiones relacionadas.

1. santo, mantilla, peineta, banderilla

2. nacimientos, alpargatas, horchata, villancicos

3. siesta, premio gordo, lotería, tertulia

4. ateneo, reja, limosna, pordiosero

5. boina, arroz con pollo, mendigo, puchero

6. santo, matador, muleta, aguador

7. Dos de Mayo, franceses, mantón, pelar la pava

8. aguinaldo, siesta, romería, verbena

9. Semana Santa, Día de la Raza, Pascua Florida, Dos de Mayo

10. frontón, misa del gallo, picador, jai-alai

B. Complétense correctamente las frases siguientes:

1. En la tercera suerte de la corrida de toros, el torero importante es _____.

2. Los niños españoles reciben sus regalos de Navidad el Día de _____.

3. El que vigila las calles de noche se llama _____.

4. El apellido paterno (del padre) de Juan Díaz y Pérez es _____.

5. El _____ muy espeso y caliente se toma en el desayuno.

6. El día que nosotros llamamos *Columbus Day* se llama el Día de _____ en el mundo hispano.

7. En la corrida de toros, el torero que va montado se llama _____.

8. El santo patrón de España es _ .

9. El plato de arroz, pollo, y mariscos se llama _ .

10. La fiesta nacional de España se celebra el _ .

C. A la izquierda de cada expresión de la lista *A*, escríbase la letra de la expresión correspondiente de la lista *B*.

	A		B
_ _ _ _ _ _ _	**1.** tertulia	*a.*	aguador
_ _ _ _ _ _ _	**2.** Carnaval	*b.*	pelar la pava
_ _ _ _ _ _ _	**3.** gitano	*c.*	Domingo de Resurrección
_ _ _ _ _ _ _	**4.** ateneo	*d.*	descanso
_ _ _ _ _ _ _	**5.** reja	*e.*	reunión
_ _ _ _ _ _ _	**6.** Nochebuena	*f.*	sandalia
_ _ _ _ _ _ _	**7.** Pascua Florida	*g.*	la buenaventura
_ _ _ _ _ _ _	**8.** puchero	*h.*	villancicos
_ _ _ _ _ _ _	**9.** siesta	*i.*	club literario
_ _ _ _ _ _ _	**10.** alpargata	*j.*	Cuaresma
		k.	cocido

La corrida de toros es un espectáculo vistoso que ha atraído a los españoles a través de los siglos, desde sus comienzos en el siglo XII. Lo que emociona (thrills) a los españoles es la valentía y destreza (skill) demostradas por el torero al confrontarse con su adversario mortal: un toro fuerte, feroz y armado de cuernos (horns) grandes y puntiagudos (sharp-pointed).

Civilization Lesson 6—MASTERY EXERCISES ON SPAIN

A. Subráyese la expresión que complete correctamente cada frase.

1. La gaita es   (*a*) una bebida   (*b*) un baile   (*c*) una canción   (*d*) un instrumento músico

2. *El entierro del conde de Orgaz* es una obra de   (*a*) El Greco   (*b*) Velázquez   (*c*) Ribera   (*d*) Goya

3. El Escorial está cerca de   (*a*) Sevilla   (*b*) Barcelona   (*c*) Valencia   (*d*) Madrid

4. La obra mas famosa del Siglo de Oro es   (*a*) *El burlador de Sevilla*   (*b*) *Fuenteovejuna*   (*c*) *La vida es sueño*   (*d*) *Don Quijote de la Mancha*

5. La Semana Santa es un período   (*a*) de diversión y alegría   (*b*) que dura tres días   (*c*) que precede a la Pascua Florida   (*d*) que se llama también el Día de los Difuntos

6. El pico más alto de España es   (*a*) la Guadarrama   (*b*) la Mancha   (*c*) la Sierra Morena   (*d*) el Mulhacén

7. El romanticismo es un movimiento literario que floreció en España en el siglo   (*a*) XX   (*b*) XVI   (*c*) XIX   (*d*) XVII

8. Dos obras importantes de Calderón son   (*a*) *Peribáñez y Las paredes oyen*   (*b*) *Lazarillo de Tormes* y *El burlador de Sevilla*   (*c*) *Fuenteovejuna y Sangre y arena*   (*d*) *El alcalde de Zalamea y La vida es sueño*

9. El río más navegable de España es el   (*a*) Guadalquivir   (*b*) Tajo   (*c*) Ebro   (*d*) Guadiana

10. La ciudad donde se estableció el Greco es   (*a*) Madrid   (*b*) Segovia   (*c*) Toledo   (*d*) Sevilla

11. España es un país   (*a*) industrial   (*b*) agrícola   (*c*) industrial y agrícola   (*d*) sin recursos naturales

12. Menéndez Pidal hizo profundos estudios   (*a*) de la literatura medieval   (*b*) de la novela regional   (*c*) del romanticismo   (*d*) de la España contemporánea

13. Andalucía está en el   (*a*) centro   (*b*) norte   (*c*) sur   (*d*) oeste   de España

14. *Del sentimiento trágico de la vida* es una obra filosófica de   (*a*) Giner de los Ríos   (*b*) Unamuno   (*c*) Ortega y Gasset   (*d*) Azorín

15. Una boina se lleva en   (*a*) la cabeza   (*b*) los pies   (*c*) las manos   (*d*) el cuello

16. En la corrida de toros, el picador   (*a*) mata el toro   (*b*) emplea una muleta   (*c*) va montado   (*d*) emplea las banderillas

17. Los moros invadieron a España en el año   (*a*) 718   (*b*) 1492   (*c*) 711   (*d*) 1469

18. *La vida del buscón* es una novela picaresca de   (*a*) autor anónimo   (*b*) Cervantes   (*c*) Quevedo   (*d*) Ruiz de Alarcón

19. García Lorca escribió sobre temas   (*a*) picarescos   (*b*) filosóficos   (*c*) cómicos   (*d*) folklóricos

20. Fernando, esposo de Isabel, fue rey de   (*a*) Asturias   (*b*) León   (*c*) Aragón   (*d*) Castilla

21. De los bailes siguientes, el que no es andaluz es   (*a*) el jaleo   (*b*) la jota   (*c*) el flamenco   (*d*) el bolero

22. A la caída del imperio romano, entraron en España los   (*a*) visigodos   (*b*) moros   (*c*) griegos   (*d*) celtas

23. Juan de la Cierva inventó el   (*a*) aeroplano   (*b*) automóvil   (*c*) buque de vapor   (*d*) autogiro

24. La muñeira es un baile de los   (*a*) vascos   (*b*) gallegos   (*c*) catalanes   (*d*) andaluces

25. Durante el reinado de Carlos II, España   (*a*) era el país más poderoso de Europa   (*b*) sufrió una decadencia   (*c*) perdió la Armada Invencible   (*d*) inició muchas reformas sociales

26. El santo patrón de España es   (*a*) San Juan   (*b*) Santiago   (*c*) Santo Tomás   (*d*) San Isidro

27. El pintor de cámara de Carlos IV fue   (*a*) Goya   (*b*) Velázquez   (*c*) Zurbarán   (*d*) el Greco

28. *Guernica* es una obra de   (*a*) Dalí   (*b*) Sert   (*c*) Sorolla   (*d*) Picasso

29. La Alhambra está en   (*a*) Burgos   (*b*) Granada   (*c*) Toledo   (*d*) Málaga

30. Fernando e Isabel conquistaron a los moros de Granada en   (*a*) 1492   (*b*) 718   (*c*) 711   (*d*) 206

B. Complétense correctamente las frases siguientes:

1. El gran rival de España en tiempos de Felipe II fue _____.

2. La noria fue introducida en España por _____.

3. En vez del arbolito de Navidad, cada casa española tiene _____.

4. Una obra de Galdós que trata de la intolerancia religiosa es _____.

5. El mejor ejemplo de la poesía épica española es _____.

6. El gran monumento dedicado a los que murieron en la Guerra Civil es _____.

7. *Las meninas* es la obra maestra de _____.

8. Gonzalo de Córdoba tenía el apodo (nickname) de _____.

9. El día que conmemora la resistencia contra los franceses es _____.

10. *Los fusilamientos del dos de mayo* fue pintado por _____.

11. La ciudad principal de Cataluña es _____.

12. Un drama popular que se representa cada año el 2 de noviembre es _____.

13. El único río que fluye hacia el este es _____.

14. *Paisajes después de la batalla* es una especie de sátira (satire) escrita por _____.

15. Una bebida fría, hecha de almendras, es _____.

16. Las guerras civiles entre los partidarios del príncipe don Carlos y los de la reina Isabel II se llaman

_____.

17. En el jai-alai, para tirar la pelota se emplea _____.

18. En la corrida de toros, el torero que emplea la muleta y la espada es _____.

19. Los cartagineses pusieron sitio a la ciudad de _____.

20. Un poeta español que ganó el Premio Nobel fue _____.

21. Las tres partes de una corrida de toros se llaman _____.

22. Las catedrales de Burgos y de Sevilla son ejemplos del estilo _____ en la arquitectura.

23. El grupo de escritores que se inspiraron en el desastre de la guerra con los Estados Unidos se llama _____.

24. Las montañas que separan a España de Francia son _____.

25. El museo principal de España es _____.

Civilization Lesson 7—LA GEOGRAFÍA DE HISPANOAMÉRICA

Al sur de los Estados Unidos, y ocupando una extensión mucho más grande que nuestro país, viven más de doscientos cuarenta millones de personas que constituyen la América española. La América española comprende diez y nueve países situados en tres regiones distintas: (1) México y la América Central, (2) las Antillas, y (3) la América del Sur. Se excluyen países que no son hispánicos, como el Brasil (de habla portuguesa); Belice, Guyana, y Trinidad (de habla inglesa); Haití (de habla francesa); y Surinam (de habla holandesa).

MÉXICO Y LA AMÉRICA CENTRAL

1. **México** se halla en la América del Norte, limitado al norte por los Estados Unidos, al oeste por el Pacífico, al sur por Guatemala, y al este por el Golfo de México. El Río Bravo del Norte (que nosotros llamamos el Río Grande) lo separa de los Estados Unidos.

Es un país de contrastes. Dos cadenas de montañas, la **Sierra Madre Oriental** y la **Sierra Madre Occidental**, lo atraviesan de norte a sur. También hay muchos valles y mesetas. En las montañas florece la industria minera, de oro y de plata. En México se hallan varios grandes volcanes, tales como el **Orizaba**, el **Popocatépetl**, y el **Ixtaccíhuatl**, así como el **Paricutín**, el cual se formó en 1943.

La capital del país, la **Ciudad de México**, está situada en la meseta central a una altura de más de 7,000 pies. Fue fundada por Cortés sobre las ruinas de **Tenochtitlán**, la antigua capital azteca. En la capital se encuentra el **Castillo de Chapultepec**, un museo histórico que antes servía de residencia para los presidentes del país. Hay muchos otros puntos de interés: (1) el **Paseo de la Reforma**, la avenida más elegante de la capital; (2) el **Zócalo**, la plaza mayor; (3) el **Palacio de Bellas Artes**, teatro más grande de todo el país, el que contiene también una magnífica colección de pinturas mexicanas; (4) la **Ciudad Universitaria**; y (5) la **Basílica de Guadalupe**, la iglesia más famosa de México, la cual fue fundada en honor de la Virgen de Guadalupe, patrona del país. Los famosos **jardines flotantes** (floating) **de Xochimilco** se hallan a poca distancia de la capital:

Otras ciudades importantes son:

a. **Guadalajara,** la segunda ciudad de México, ciudad comercial e industrial, y centro principal de la agricultura y la ganadería.

b. **Veracruz** y **Tampico,** puertos importantes del Golfo de México.

c. **Acapulco,** playa famosa de la costa del Pacífico.

d. **Taxco,** ciudad antigua, conocida por su aspecto colonial.

e. **Mérida,** en la península de Yucatán, centro de la producción del henequén (hemp).

f. **Chichén-Itzá,** también en Yucatán, que tiene ruinas de la cultura maya.

La ciudad de **Chichén-Itzá,** en la península de Yucatán, es el centro tradicional de la gran civilización de los mayas. Hasta hoy día se pueden ver sus magníficas pirámides y las ruinas de sus templos.

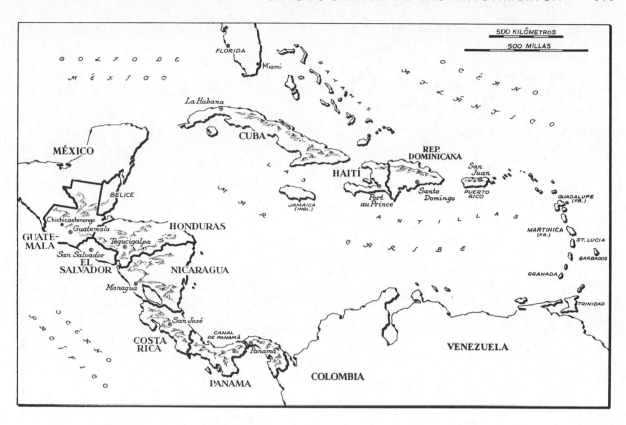

2. **Guatemala** es el país de mayor población de la América Central. Sus productos principales son café, bananas, y chicle, del cual se hace la goma de mascar. La capital del país es la **Ciudad de Guatemala.**

3. **Honduras** es el país más montañoso de Centroamérica. Su capital es **Tegucigalpa.** Honduras exporta bananas, café, y maderas finas.

4. **El Salvador** es la nación más pequeña de Centroamérica. Su capital, **San Salvador,** es una ciudad moderna. El Salvador exporta mucho café y minerales preciosos.

5. **Nicaragua** es la nación más grande de la América Central. Produce caña (cane) de azúcar, algodón, y café. Su capital es **Managua.**

6. **Costa Rica** es un país agrícola, y exporta mucho café y plátanos. También produce varios minerales. Su capital es **San José.**

7. **Panamá** es un istmo entre la América del Norte y la del Sur. La Zona del Canal, arrendada (leased) a los Estados Unidos, cruza el país y contiene el famoso **Canal de Panamá.** En 1978 los dos países convinieron en que Panamá tomaría posesión del Canal en el año 2000. La capital del país es la **Ciudad de Panamá.**

LAS ANTILLAS

Las Antillas son un grupo de islas en el Mar Caribe que incluye a Cuba, La Española, y Puerto Rico. La Española es una isla compartida (shared) por Haití y la República Dominicana.

1. **Cuba,** descubierta por Colón en su primer viaje, es la isla más grande de las Antillas. Debido a la fertilidad de la tierra se llama "la perla de las Antillas." Produce más azúcar que ningún otro país hispanoamericano. **La Habana,** capital de la nación, es la ciudad principal de toda la región del Caribe. De gran interés histórico es el **Castillo del Morro,** situado en el puerto de La Habana, el cual en tiempos coloniales servía de fortaleza para proteger la isla contra los piratas ingleses. En Guantánamo hay una base naval que pertenece a los Estados Unidos.

2. **La República Dominicana,** situada en una isla descubierta por Colón en 1492, es la nación más antigua del Caribe. Su capital es **Santo Domingo.** En la capital se encuentra la universidad más antigua del Nuevo

Mundo, la Universidad de Santo Tomás de Aquino, fundada en 1538, que hoy se llama la Universidad de Santo Domingo.

3. **Puerto Rico** es la única tierra descubierta por Colón que llegó a ser una posesión de los Estados Unidos. Su capital, **San Juan,** fue fundada por Ponce de León, el primer gobernador de la isla. Produce mucho café y caña de azúcar.

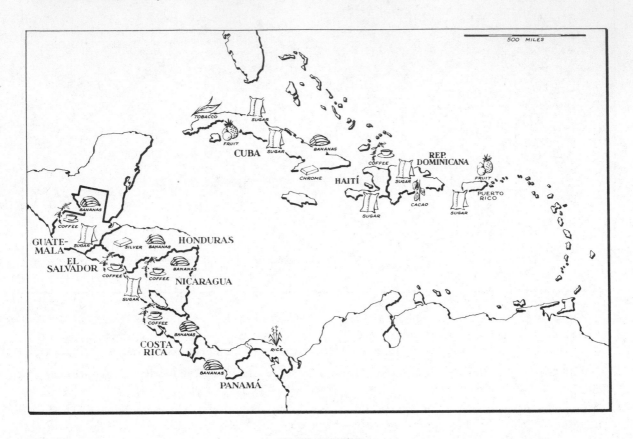

EJERCICIOS

A. A la izquierda de cada expresión de la lista *A*, escríbase la letra de la expresión correspondiente de la lista *B*.

A	B
_____ **1.** Yucatán	*a.* teatro grande
_____ **2.** Honduras	*b.* plaza mayor de la ciudad de México
_____ **3.** Xochimilco	*c.* Castillo de Chapultepec
_____ **4.** San José	*d.* henequén
_____ **5.** Río Bravo del Norte	*e.* Costa Rica
_____ **6.** Tampico	*f.* jardines flotantes
_____ **7.** chicle	*g.* frontera con los Estados Unidos
_____ **8.** Guatemala	*h.* puerto del Golfo de México
_____ **9.** Palacio de Bellas Artes	*i.* base de la goma de mascar
_____**10.** museo histórico	*j.* país más montañoso de Centroamérica
	k. país centroamericano de mayor población

B. Refiriéndose al mapa abajo, identifíquense los siguientes nombres geográficos, escribiendo a la izquierda de cada uno la letra correspondiente:

1. _____ Puerto Rico
2. _____ Guatemala
3. _____ Panamá
4. _____ Cuba
5. _____ Nicaragua
6. _____ Golfo de México
7. _____ Península de Yucatán
8. _____ República Dominicana

9. _____ México
10. _____ Mar Caribe
11. _____ El Salvador
12. _____ Canal de Panamá
13. _____ Océano Pacífico
14. _____ Costa Rica
15. _____ Honduras

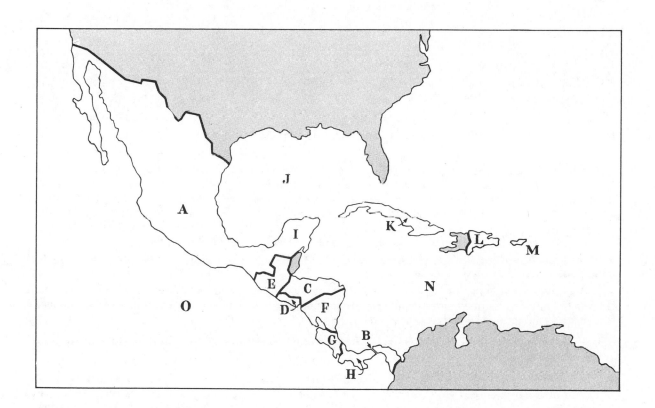

C. A la izquierda de cada expresión de la lista _A_, escríbase la letra de la expresión correspondiente de la lista _B_.

_A_

_____ 1. Morro
_____ 2. Ponce de León
_____ 3. La Española
_____ 4. Cuba
_____ 5. Guantánamo

_B_

_a._ base naval
_b._ "Perla de las Antillas"
_c._ capital de la República Dominicana
_d._ Puerto Rico
_e._ fortaleza
_f._ Haití y la República Dominicana

LA AMÉRICA DEL SUR

La mayor parte de Sudamérica está al sur del ecuador, y las estaciones del año caen en orden opuesto a las nuestras. Cuando nosotros estamos en invierno aquí, allí tienen el verano.

Volando en avión sobre la América del Sur, se ve que casi todos los países son montañosos. En el este están las tierras altas de las Guayanas y del Brasil, y al oeste la larga cordillera de los Andes. Estas montañas, con sus vastas mesetas, sus valles y majestuosos picos, han tenido gran influencia en el lento desarrollo (development) del continente sudamericano. Impiden el transporte y el comercio. La construcción de ferrocarriles y carreteras cuesta mucho. Hasta cierto punto, el transporte por avión ha mejorado las comunicaciones. Las montañas tienen separados no solamente a los diferentes países, sino también, a veces, a las regiones de un mismo país, como en el Perú, el Ecuador, y Colombia. Los Andes son ricos en minerales: el oro, la plata, el aluminio, el cobre, el platino, el hierro, y el estaño. Las mesetas son saludables (healthful), y allí vive la mayor parte de la gente.

Tres vastos llanos ocupan el interior del continente y se extienden hasta la costa del Atlántico. Estos son los valles del Orinoco, del Amazonas, y de los ríos Paraná y Paraguay. Aquí se encuentran bosques y pantanos (swamps), los cuales han hecho imposible la fácil navegación.

Países del este

Éstos incluyen la Argentina, el Uruguay, y el Paraguay. La economía de estos tres países depende principalmente de los ríos Paraná y Paraguay, y del Río de la Plata, los que se usan para el transporte.

1. **La Argentina,** que significa "de plata," recibió su nombre porque en tiempos coloniales era el portal que conducía (por medio de los ríos) a las tierras de la plata.

   La Argentina se extiende desde la región del Chaco, en el norte, hasta la Tierra del Fuego y el Estrecho de Magallanes, en el sur; y desde el Atlántico hasta los Andes. Por lo general, el país tiene un clima templado, aunque hay extremos de frío en el sur (en Tierra del Fuego), y de calor y humedad en las selvas del Chaco. En el extremo nordeste (northeast), entre la Argentina y el Brasil, están las famosas **cataratas del Iguazú.** En la región andina se halla el **Aconcagua,** pico que alcanza una altura de 23,000 pies, el pico más alto de todo el hemisferio occidental. La mayor parte del país es un llano extenso, llamado la *pampa,* que es la tierra del *gaucho,* y el centro de la agricultura y de la ganadería, de donde se exportan grandes cantidades de trigo y de carne. Aquí se halla el *ombú,* árbol grande típico de la pampa.

   Buenos Aires, la capital, es la ciudad más grande de Sudamérica, y su puerto figura entre los más activos del mundo. Es una ciudad moderna y cosmopolita, con grandes y elegantes avenidas, tiendas, y teatros. Los habitantes se llaman *porteños.*

   La segunda ciudad de la Argentina es **Rosario,** puerto a orillas del **río Paraná,** un centro industrial importante.

2. **El Uruguay,** llamado antes la Banda Oriental, es la nación hispana más pequeña de la América del Sur. Al norte del país se halla el Brasil, al oeste y al sur la Argentina, y al este el Océano Atlántico. **Montevideo,** capital y puerto principal de la nación, está al este de Buenos Aires, en la orilla opuesta del **Río de la Plata.** El clima del país es templado y por sus costas se extienden muchas playas elegantes, entre ellas la de **Punta del Este,** donde tuvo lugar en 1962 una sesión importante de la Organización de los Estados Americanos. El Uruguay es un país progresista donde existe muy poco analfabetismo (illiteracy). Las industrias principales son la agricultura y la ganadería. El **río Uruguay,** que forma parte de la frontera con la Argentina, es importante para el comercio.

3. **El Paraguay** es una de las dos repúblicas de la América del Sur que no tienen puerto de mar, pero el **río Paraná** le permite comunicarse con el Atlántico. Este país se halla entre Bolivia, el Brasil, y la Argentina. La región del **Gran Chaco** ocupa el oeste del país. En 1932 estalló una guerra entre Bolivia y el Paraguay para determinar a quién pertenecía este territorio. Duró hasta 1935, y el resultado fue que el Paraguay recibió dos terceras partes del territorio y Bolivia consiguió una salida al mar por medio del río Paraguay. La famosa *yerba mate,* una especie de té, es un producto importante del Paraguay, y también la madera de un árbol llamado *quebracho,* que se emplea para curtir el cuero. La capital es **Asunción.**

MAR CARIBE

CANAL DE PANAMÁ

La Guaira
Caracas
VENEZUELA

OCÉANO ATLÁNTICO

COLOMBIA

LLANOS

RÍO ORINOCO

GUYANA

SURINAM

GUAYANA FRANCESA

RÍO MAGDALENA

Bogotá

LOS ANDES

ECUADOR

Quito
COTOPAXI
Guayaquil
CHIMBORAZO

ECUADOR

RÍO AMAZONAS

Natal

PERÚ

LOS ANDES

BRASIL

Callao
Lima
Cuzco

LAGO TITICACA

La Paz
BOLIVIA
Sucre

Brasilia

Tacna
Arica

LOS ANDES

GRAN CHACO

PARAGUAY

Río de Janeiro

Santos

Asunción

IGUAZÚ

Tucumán

RÍO PARANÁ

Córdoba

OCÉANO PACÍFICO

Viña del Mar
Valparaíso
ACONCAGUA
ISLAS JUAN FERNÁNDEZ (CH.)
Santiago

PAMPAS

CHILE

Buenos Aires

Montevideo

URUGUAY

RÍO DE LA PLATA

OCÉANO ATLÁNTICO

ARGENTINA

LOS ANDES

PATAGONIA

ESTRECHO DE MAGALLANES

ISLAS MALVINAS
(Falkland Islands)
(ing.)

CABO DE HORNOS

▲ VOLCÁN O PICO

1000 KILÓMETROS

1000 MILLAS

EJERCICIOS

A. A la izquierda de cada expresión de la lista *A*, escríbase la letra de la expresión correspondiente de la lista *B*.

	A		B
_____	1. El Uruguay	*a.*	guerra entre el Paraguay y Bolivia
_____	2. Punta del Este	*b.*	pico muy alto
_____	3. ombú	*c.*	minerales
_____	4. Rosario	*d.*	se usa para curtir el cuero
_____	5. quebracho	*e.*	playa
_____	6. porteños	*f.*	Buenos Aires
_____	7. río Uruguay	*g.*	capital del Paraguay
_____	8. Gran Chaco	*h.*	Banda Oriental
_____	9. Aconcagua	*i.*	la pampa
_____	10. Asunción	*j.*	frontera entre el Uruguay y la Argentina
		k.	ciudad de la Argentina

B. Refiriéndose al mapa en la página siguiente, identifíquense los siguientes nombres geográficos, escribiendo a la izquierda de cada uno la letra correspondiente:

1. _____ Aconcagua
2. _____ río Paraná
3. _____ el Paraguay
4. _____ Buenos Aires
5. _____ cataratas del Iguazú

6. _____ el Uruguay
7. _____ Asunción
8. _____ pampa
9. _____ Estrecho de Magallanes
10. _____ Montevideo

Yerba mate es una planta de la cual se hace una bebida, un té llamado "mate." Es muy popular en el Paraguay y la Argentina. Se bebe en una calabaza, por medio de un tubo llamado "bombilla."

Países andinos

Éstos se encuentran en el oeste del continente, y comprenden Chile, Bolivia, el Perú, el Ecuador, Colombia, y Venezuela. La cordillera de los Andes atraviesa todos estos países de norte a sur.

1. **Chile** se encuentra entre la cordillera de los Andes y el Océano Pacífico. Chile se extiende casi 3,000 millas, desde la frontera con el Perú, en el norte, hasta Tierra del Fuego, en el sur, parte de la cual pertenece a Chile. El país no tiene más que 230 millas de ancho en ninguna parte, y en algunas partes se vuelve muy estrecho, hasta 50 millas.

El **desierto de Atacama,** en el norte, es uno de los desiertos más secos del mundo. Pasan años y no cae ni una gota de agua. Aquí se encuentran grandes depósitos de salitre (nitrates), cobre, y otros minerales.

Antofagasta es el puerto principal del norte.

El valle central tiene un clima excelente, y es el centro agrícola del país. Los productos principales son vinos y cereales. Aquí se encuentran las ciudades más importantes del país: **Santiago,** la capital, que está al pie de los Andes, y **Valparaíso,** el puerto principal de Chile. **Viña del Mar,** una playa famosa, está cerca de Valparaíso. En el sur hay una región de lagos que se llama la "Suiza chilena."

2. **Bolivia,** llamada así en honor de Simón Bolívar, se llamaba en tiempos coloniales el Alto Perú. Aunque está en la zona tórrida, Bolivia es, en algunas partes, el país más frío del continente sudamericano, debido a su gran altura. Tiene fronteras con el Brasil al norte y al este, con el Paraguay al sudeste, con la Argentina al sur, con Chile al sudoeste, y con el Perú al oeste. De esto se ve que Bolivia no tiene ningún contacto con el mar, y que depende de los países vecinos para exportar sus productos.

La Paz, capital de Bolivia, es la capital más alta del mundo, pues tiene una altura de más de 12,000 pies. El **lago Titicaca,** que está entre Bolivia y el Perú, es el lago navegable más alto del mundo; se encuentra a una altura de 12,500 pies. **Sucre** es la capital constitucional del país, pero La Paz es la capital de hecho.

Bolivia es un país rico en minerales. **Potosí** fue conocido en tiempos coloniales como el centro más importante de la producción de plata del Nuevo Mundo, y funciona todavía. Pero el producto más importante hoy es el estaño.

3. **El Perú** está casi totalmente en los Andes, menos la región de la costa y la del este. Este país, tres veces más grande que el estado de California, está limitado al norte, al este, y al sur por las repúblicas del Ecuador, Colombia, el Brasil, Bolivia, y Chile. El río principal del Perú es el **Marañón,** un tributario del Amazonas. La riqueza mineral del Perú consiste en plata y cobre. El guanaco, la alpaca, la llama, y la vicuña producen lana para los indios, y también para la exportación.

Antes de la llegada de los españoles florecieron grandes civilizaciones en el Perú. La más avanzada y mejor conocida fue la de los incas, la cual fue destruida por Pizarro. Su capital fue **Cuzco,** que es hoy el centro arqueológico del país. Cerca de Cuzco se hallan las ruinas incaicas de **Machu-Picchu.** Además del español, los indios hablan *quechua,* un idioma indio.

Lima, capital del país, es también el centro comercial y cultural. Pizarro la llamó la "Ciudad de los Reyes," porque la fundó el 6 de enero, Día de los Reyes Magos. En la capital se halla la Universidad de San Marcos, que fue fundada en 1551. **El Callao** sirve de puerto para Lima y está a ocho millas de la capital. **Arequipa,** situada al pie del volcán Misti, es el centro económico de la zona agrícola del sur.

4. **El Ecuador** se llama así porque la línea geográfica del mismo nombre lo atraviesa, en el norte. En este país se hallan dos picos que figuran entre los más altos del continente, el **Chimborazo** (de más de 20,000 pies de altura) y el **Cotopaxi** (de unos 19,500 pies).

Quito, la capital, está a una altura de 9,000 pies y tiene un clima bastante frío, a pesar de estar en el centro de la Zona Tórrida. Esta capital ha conservado mucho de su carácter colonial.

El puerto principal y centro comercial es **Guayaquil.** Los productos principales son cacao, tagua (de la cual se fabrican botones), y *sombreros de jipijapa,* que nosotros llamamos "Panama hats."

Lo que nosotros llamamos "Panama hats" no vienen de Panamá sino del Ecuador, donde se llaman sombreros de jipijapa. Se llaman así porque se tejen (are woven) de una paja obtenida cerca del pueblo de Jipijapa.

5. **Colombia** está limitada al norte por el Mar Caribe, al sur por el Ecuador y el Perú, al oeste por el Pacífico y Panamá, y al este por Venezuela y el Brasil. Esta república, nombrada en honor de Colón, es el único país de la América del Sur que tiene puertos en dos mares: en el Caribe (**Cartagena, Barranquilla**) y en el Pacífico (**Buenaventura**). El **Magdalena,** río principal del país, forma un importante medio de comunicación dentro del país.

Bogotá, capital de la nación, está en el interior, en las montañas. **Medellín** es la segunda ciudad del país y es el centro de la producción de café. El **salto** (falls) **de Tequendama,** situado a pocas millas de Bogotá, es mucho más alto que el Niágara, pero es menos ancho. Los principales productos de exportación son café, platino, y esmeraldas (emeralds).

6. **Venezuela,** patria del Libertador, Simón Bolívar, está situada en el extremo norte de Sudamérica. Esta república está bañada por las aguas del Mar Caribe al norte, y tiene fronteras con Colombia al oeste, con el Brasil al sur, y con la Guayana inglesa al este. Se encuentran extensos llanos en las orillas de los ríos Orinoco y Apure. Los llanos son el centro principal de la ganadería. El **Orinoco,** río principal de Venezuela, tiene más de mil quinientas millas de largo.

Caracas es la capital política y comercial de la nación. El puerto principal es **La Guaira,** y los productos principales son petróleo, café, y cacao.

EJERCICIOS

A. Refiriéndose al mapa abajo, identifíquense los siguientes nombres geográficos, escribiendo a la izquierda de cada uno la letra correspondiente:

1. _____ La Paz
2. _____ Venezuela
3. _____ Chile
4. _____ Bolivia
5. _____ Colombia

6. _____ el Perú
7. _____ Caracas
8. _____ Bogotá
9. _____ el Ecuador
10. _____ Lima

B. A la izquierda de cada expresión de la lista *A*, escríbase la letra de la expresión correspondiente de la lista *B*.

	A		*B*
_____	**1.** Barranquilla	*a.*	puerto principal de Chile
_____	**2.** Viña del Mar	*b.*	depósitos de salitre
_____	**3.** Titicaca	*c.*	sombreros
_____	**4.** Machu-Picchu	*d.*	Venezuela
_____	**5.** Bolivia	*e.*	puerto colombiano
_____	**6.** jipijapa	*f.*	Chimborazo
_____	**7.** Atacama	*g.*	"Ciudad de los Reyes"
_____	**8.** Valparaíso	*h.*	lago navegable más alto del mundo
_____	**9.** Lima	*i.*	estaño
_____	**10.** Simón Bolívar	*j.*	ruinas incaicas
		k.	famosa playa chilena

C. Subráyese la palabra o expresión que complete correctamente cada frase.

1. La antigua capital de los incas fue   (*a*) Cuzco   (*b*) Lima   (*c*) Arequipa   (*d*) La Paz

2. Antofagasta se halla en   (*a*) el Perú   (*b*) el Ecuador   (*c*) Chile   (*d*) Bolivia

3. El país nombrado en honor del Libertador es   (*a*) Chile   (*b*) el Perú   (*c*) Venezuela   (*d*) Bolivia

4. La capital hispanoamericana que Pizarro nombró en honor de un día de fiesta es   (*a*) Quito   (*b*) Bogotá   (*c*) Caracas   (*d*) Lima

5. La capital de Chile es   (*a*) Chimborazo   (*b*) Santiago   (*c*) el Callao   (*d*) La Paz

6. El país que tiene lagos como los de Suiza es   (*a*) Bolivia   (*b*) Venezuela   (*c*) Chile   (*d*) el Ecuador

7. El río Marañón se halla en   (*a*) el Perú   (*b*) Venezuela   (*c*) el Ecuador   (*d*) Bolivia

8. El país sudamericano que tiene dos capitales es   (*a*) Chile   (*b*) Bolivia   (*c*) Colombia   (*d*) el Ecuador

9. El país andino que no tiene puerto de mar es   (*a*) el Ecuador   (*b*) Venezuela   (*c*) Colombia   (*d*) Bolivia

10. El puerto principal del Ecuador es   (*a*) Guayaquil   (*b*) Arequipa   (*c*) Cartagena   (*d*) Bogotá

D. Complétense correctamente las frases siguientes:

1. En la ciudad de _____ se estableció la primera universidad del Nuevo Mundo.

2. La capital de Chile es _____.

3. El pico más alto de todo el hemisferio occidental es _____.

4. Tegucigalpa es la capital de _____.

5. El gaucho argentino vive en la región llamada _____.

6. _____ tiene casi 3,000 millas de largo.

7. La capital de Cuba es _____.

8. El puerto principal de Venezuela es _____.

9. El volcán formado en 1943 en México se llama _____.

10. _____ sirve de puerto para la ciudad de Lima.

11. Una famosa playa en la costa occidental de México es _____.

12. Bogotá es la capital de _____.

13. La capital de Puerto Rico es _____.

14. El país sudamericano que tiene puertos en el Pacífico y en el Mar Caribe es _____.

15. Las islas llamadas Tierra del Fuego tienen un clima _____.

16. La capital de Guatemala es _____.

17. El río principal de Venezuela es el _____.

18. Las ciudades de Buenos Aires y _____ están situadas a orillas del Río de la Plata.

19. _____ es la nación más pequeña de Centroamérica.

20. Nuestro país tiene un canal en la República de _____.

21. Un animal que produce lana para los indios peruanos es _____.

22. Entre el Brasil y la Argentina se hallan las cataratas del _____.

23. El país hispano más pequeño de Sudamérica es _____.

24. En tiempos coloniales el centro sudamericano más importante en la producción de plata era _____.

25. Las dos grandes cadenas de montañas de México son la Sierra Madre Occidental y _____ _____.

26. La avenida más elegante de la Ciudad de México es _____.

27. La mayor parte de la América del Sur se halla al _____ de la línea del ecuador.

28. _____ es una ciudad antigua que tiene interesantes ruinas mayas.

29. Punta del Este es una playa elegante de la costa de _____.

30. La capital del Ecuador es _____.

31. Haití y _____ comparten la isla llamada La Española.

32. Un producto importante del Paraguay es un té llamado _____.

33. Tenochtitlán es el nombre antiguo de la Ciudad de _____.

34. La isla más grande de las Antillas es _____.

35. La capital del Paraguay es _____.

CIVILIZACIONES INDIAS

1. Antes de la llegada de los españoles florecieron y cayeron varias civilizaciones en el Nuevo Mundo. En la América Central los **mayas** habían alcanzado una cultura muy avanzada. Conocían la arquitectura y la ciencia. Habían aprendido bastante astronomía para poder inventar un calendario y calcular los eclipses del sol. En Yucatán habían establecido una ciudad brillante, **Chichén-Itzá.** Fueron seguidos por los **toltecas,** y éstos por los **aztecas.** Hoy día queda muy poco de la civilización maya.

2. Cuando llegaron los españoles, bajo Cortés (en 1519), encontraron a los **aztecas,** un pueblo guerrero (warlike) que ya dominaba el territorio de lo que as hoy México y gran parte de la América Central. Su capital, **Tenochtitlán,** ocupaba el lugar donde se encuentra hoy la Ciudad de México. Allí llevaban a los prisioneros de guerra para servir de víctimas en los sacrificios humanos.

3. Los **incas** ocupaban las regiones andinas de la América del Sur, y se extendían por lo que son actualmente las repúblicas del Perú, Bolivia, el Ecuador, y parte de Colombia y de Chile. Tenían un imperio bien organizado, tal vez el más perfecto de todos los indígenas. Desde su capital, **Cuzco,** salían caminos en todas direcciones, los que se empleaban para comunicarse rápidamente con todas partes del imperio. En vez de escribir, usaban *quipus,* cuerdas de varios colores en las cuales hacían nudos (knots), que ellos sabían interpretar. Usaban la llama y la alpaca, que les servían para llevar las mercancías, y que también les proveían (provided) de lana y carne.

4. Los **caribes** habitaban las Antillas. Fueron casi exterminados por los primeros conquistadores.

5. Los **chibchas** y los **guaraníes** vivían en el norte y en el centro de la América del Sur, respectivamente.

6. En el sur vivían los **patagones** y los **araucanos.** Estos últimos eran muy feroces, y nunca fueron completamente conquistados por los españoles.

DESCUBRIMIENTO, EXPLORACIÓN, Y CONQUISTA

1. Cristóbal **Colón** fue el primero de los grandes descubridores, y se le conoce hoy como "el descubridor de América." Es interesante notar que no tocó el continente de Norteamérica en ninguno de sus cuatro viajes. Descubrió varias islas de las Antillas, las costas de la América del Sur (cerca del Orinoco), y parte de la América Central. La fecha de su primer descubrimiento (el 12 de octubre) se celebra en todo el mundo hispano como el "Día de la Raza."

   Estableció la primera colonia, **Navidad,** en la Española (Hispaniola), que es hoy la isla de Santo Domingo. Ésta fue la primera colonia fundada por europeos en el Nuevo Mundo. El siglo siguiente fue una época de conquista, colonización, y expansión.

2. Juan **Ponce de León** estableció una colonia española en 1508, en Puerto Rico, y fue su primer gobernador. En 1513, buscando la Fuente (Fountain) de la Juventud, descubrió la Florida.

3. Vasco Núñez de **Balboa** atravesó el istmo de Panamá y descubrió el Océano Pacífico, al que dio el nombre de *Mar del Sur.*

4. Fernando de **Magallanes,** navegante portugués, emprendió dar la vuelta al mundo. Fue un trabajo heroico, completado por Juan Sebastián **del Cano,** español, al morir Magallanes en las Islas Filipinas.

5. Hernán **Cortés** fue, tal vez, el más grande de los conquistadores. Conquistó a los aztecas de México (1519–1521), matando al rey azteca, **Moctezuma.** Dio a la nueva colonia el nombre de *Nueva España.*

6. Francisco **Pizarro** pudo destruir el imperio de los incas, en 1532, haciendo prisionero al rey inca, **Atahualpa,** y matándole después. Fundó la ciudad de Lima, llamándola "Ciudad de los Reyes" en honor de los Reyes Magos.

7. Francisco Vázquez de **Coronado,** saliendo de México en busca de las fabulosas "siete ciudades de Cíbola" en Nuevo México, exploró gran parte de lo que es hoy el sudoeste (southwest) de los Estados Unidos. Descubrió el Gran Cañón.

8. Álvar Núñez **Cabeza de Vaca** exploró gran parte del sur de los Estados Unidos, hasta México. Años más tarde fue nombrado gobernador de la región de la Plata, en la América del Sur.

9. Pedro de **Valdivia** conquistó a Chile, luchando con los feroces araucanos. Fundó la ciudad de Santiago (de Chile).

10. Bartolomé de **las Casas,** el "apóstol de los indios," fue un misionero que pasó la vida luchando en favor de los indios, que morían a causa del duro trabajo y de la crueldad de los conquistadores. Debido a sus esfuerzos, el gobierno español decidió importar esclavos de África para el trabajo. Otros países, en particular Portugal, Inglaterra, y Holanda, también tomaron parte en el comercio de esclavos.

11. Fray Junípero **Serra** fundó una serie de misiones en California, en lo que hoy se llama el "Camino Real."

ADMINISTRACIÓN DE LAS COLONIAS

Todas las colonias se consideraban posesiones del rey mismo. El **Consejo de Indias** las dirigía por medio de virreyes nombrados por el rey. Las colonias estaban divididas en cuatro virreinatos:

1. **Nueva España:** México, Centroamérica, parte de lo que es hoy los Estados Unidos, y las Antillas.

2. **Nueva Granada:** lo que es hoy el Ecuador, Colombia, y Venezuela.

3. **Nueva Castilla:** el Perú y Chile.

4. **Río de la Plata:** Bolivia, el Paraguay, el Uruguay, y la Argentina.

La intención del gobierno español era doble: (1) civilizar a los indios y enseñarles las religión cristiana; (2) sacar tesoros de las colonias con qué pagar las guerras que España hacía en Europa. El resultado fue la explotación (exploitation) de los indios y de las riquezas del Nuevo Mundo.

Al principio de la época colonial, Cádiz, en España, fue el centro del comercio con las colonias. Pero, a causa de los ataques (attacks) de los piratas de varias naciones, se trasladó (was transferred) el centro a Sevilla. Los piratas también atacaron las costas de las colonias, en el Mar Caribe y el Golfo de México. Dos de los piratas más famosos fueron los ingleses Francis Drake y John Hawkins.

LA INDEPENDENCIA

Las causas de las revoluciones contra España fueron las siguientes: (1) las restricciones comerciales que impuso (imposed) España; (2) la injusticia de la organización social y política—los **criollos** (personas nacidas en las colonias, de origen español) no tenían los mismos derechos que los españoles, y no tomaban parte en el gobierno; (3) el ejemplo de la revolución norteamericana contra Inglaterra; (4) la invasión de España, en 1808, por Napoleón, y el nombramiento (appointment) de un rey francés.

Francisco **Miranda,** venezolano, fue el más importante de los precursores de la revolución. En 1806, con una expedición libertadora atacó las costas de Venezuela. La expedición fracasó (failed), pero cuatro años más tarde, en 1810, cuando estalló la revolución, Miranda fue una de las figuras prominentes. Fue capturado por los españoles y murió en una cárcel española en 1816.

Aunque tres de las revoluciones estallaron en distintas partes en el mismo año (1810), se pueden dividir en cuatro movimientos distintos: México, Sudamérica (norte), Sudamérica (sur), Cuba.

México

1. El padre Miguel **Hidalgo,** cura del pueblo de Dolores, inició la revolución mexicana el 16 de septiembre de 1810 con el famoso "Grito de Dolores." Salió victorioso en varias campañas, pero unos meses más tarde fue capturado y condenado a muerte.

2. José **Morelos,** discípulo de Hidalgo y también sacerdote, continuó el trabajo de éste. Después de varias batallas declaró la independencia de México en 1813. Cayó prisionero y fue fusilado (shot) en 1815.

3. Agustín de **Iturbide** al principio luchó al lado de los españoles, pero después desertó y se unió a los revolucionarios. Su famoso *Plan de Iguala* convirtió a México en una monarquía independiente de España. En 1822 se declaró emperador (Agustín I). Pero tuvo que abdicar cuando estalló otra revolución, bajo el general **Santa Anna.** En 1824 México se declaró una república independiente.

Sudamérica (norte)

4. Simón **Bolívar,** el "Jorge Wáshington" de la América del Sur, es la figura dominante de la revolución del norte. Fue a la vez militar brillante y filósofo político. Luchó largos años, ganando victorias y sufriendo derrotas. Pero con las victorias de **Boyacá** (Colombia), **Carabobo** (Venezuela), y **Pichincha** (el Ecuador), se aseguró la independencia del norte. En 1822 se formó de estos territorios la República de la Gran Colombia. Se nombró presidente a Bolívar. Hasta hoy se conoce a Bolívar con el título de "El Libertador."

5. Antonio José de **Sucre** mandó las fuerzas venezolanas en las batallas de Pichincha y de **Ayacucho.** Ayacucho, escena de la última batalla de la revolución (1824), aseguró para siempre la independencia de la América del Sur.

Sudamérica (sur)

6. José de **San Martín,** el "santo de la espada," argentino, hizo para el sur lo que Bolívar hizo para el norte. Ganada la independencia de la Argentina, San Martín organizó un ejército, con la ayuda del chileno, Bernardo **O'Higgins,** para ganar la independencia de Chile. Derrotó a los españoles en las batallas de **Chacabuco** (1817) y **Maipú** (1818). O'Higgins fue nombrado primer presidente de Chile.

Después emprendió San Martín la liberación del Perú. Durante esta campaña San Martín y Bolívar arreglaron una entrevista en Guayaquil. No se sabe lo que pasó en esta entrevista, pero al salir San Martín dejó el mando de sus tropas, y se retiró (withdrew) del movimiento de la independencia. La libertad del Perú fue asegurada por Sucre en la batalla de Ayacucho (1824).

Cuba

7. Durante la época de las grandes revoluciones Cuba quedó leal (loyal) a España. Pero hacia el año 1850 comenzaron varios movimientos de independencia. José **Martí,** poeta y patriota cubano, fue el espíritu del movimiento. Hizo más que ningún otro para unificar los esfuerzos de los revolucionarios desterrados. Murió en 1895, en una invasión de la isla. Más tarde, en 1898, con la intervención de los Estados Unidos, Cuba se libró de la dominación española. Al mismo tiempo los Estados Unidos tomaron posesión de Puerto Rico y de las Islas Filipinas.

DESDE LA INDEPENDENCIA HASTA NUESTROS DÍAS

PATRIOTAS Y DICTADORES

La independencia trajo consigo graves problemas políticos, sociales, y económicos, muchos de los cuales todavía existen hoy. La gente no tenía experiencia en gobernarse, y el analfabetismo era común. En muchos países llegaron al poder los militares, que gobernaron como dictadores.

1. Juan Manuel de **Rosas** estableció en la Argentina una dictadura sangrienta que duró unos veinte años, terminando en 1852.

2. El Dr. José Gaspar de **Francia** gobernó en el Paraguay veinte y cinco años, hasta su muerte en 1840. Se hizo llamar "el Supremo." Durante su dictadura el Paraguay perdió contacto con el resto del mundo.

3. Vicente **Gómez,** dictador venezolano, gobernó veinte y cinco años, hasta su muerte en 1935. Invitó a los capitalistas extranjeros a invertir (invest) mucho dinero en la industria petrolera de su país.

4. Benito **Juárez** se llama el "Abrahán Lincoln de México." Era un indio que se educó y llegó a ser presidente. En 1864, durante su presidencia, México fue conquistado por las tropas francesas de Napoleón III, quien había mandado a **Maximiliano,** un archiduque austríaco (Austrian), a gobernar como emperador. Juárez organizó la resistencia contra Maximiliano, y éste fue derrotado y fusilado en 1867. Así Juárez logró libertar a su patria de la dominación francesa y restaurar la república.

5. Porfirio **Díaz** fue dictador en México treinta y cinco años, hasta 1911. Durante su dictadura vendió derechos comerciales a los capitalistas extranjeros, que llegaron a ser los verdaderos dueños de la política y economía mexicanas. Fue derrotado en 1911 por Francisco **Madero.**

Todavía hoy hay dictaduras en varios países de la América Hispana. Se espera, con el tiempo, y con mejores condiciones económicas y educativas, que estas dictaduras pasen, y que triunfe la democracia.

RELACIONES INTERAMERICANAS

En 1826 Simón Bolívar dio el primer paso hacia la unidad del hemisferio occidental, llamando a una conferencia en Panamá a los representantes de todos los países del Nuevo Mundo. Solamente cuatro naciones enviaron delegados a la conferencia. No obstante, la Conferencia de Panamá tuvo un resultado bueno. El ideal de Bolívar, la unidad de las Américas, tuvo sus comienzos allí.

En los años siguientes, el movimiento ganó fuerzas y creció. Se celebraron varias conferencias, comenzando con la de Washington, D.C., en 1889. En estas reuniones los participantes se interesaban por mantener la paz en el hemisferio y por mejorar las relaciones comerciales. En la conferencia de Buenos Aires de 1910, se fundó la **Unión Panamericana.** El propósito de esta organización fue establecer relaciones económicas y culturales entre las 21 repúblicas americanas.

En 1948, en Bogotá, la alianza fue reorganizada y recibió el nombre de **Organización de los Estados Americanos (O.E.A.;** en inglés, O.A.S.); la Unión Panamericana sería su secretaría (secretariat) permanente. El propósito principal de la O.E.A. es la amistad y el progreso de las naciones americanas por medio del desarrollo de sus recursos naturales. En una reunión que tuvo lugar en Punta del Este en 1962, los representantes expulsaron a Cuba, cuyo gobierno se había convertido en dictadura comunista.

En **Puerto Rico** en el año 1941 se inició un nuevo programa económico. El programa se llamaba "Manos a la Obra" (Operation Bootstrap). Su gran éxito es evidente en la prosperidad de que gozan los puertorriqueños.

Durante la presidencia de Franklin D. Roosevelt, los Estados Unidos mejoraron sus relaciones con Latinoamérica, iniciando un nuevo programa económico y político llamado "La Política del Buen Vecino."

En la Segunda Guerra Mundial, muchos países hispanoamericanos mostraron su fe en la democracia y su amistad con los Estados Unidos, declarando la guerra contra nuestros enemigos y proveyendo de materias primas (raw materials) a los aliados (Allies).

Cuba, antigua amiga de los Estados Unidos, ha sufrido varias dictaduras en los años pasados. En 1952, Fulgencio **Batista** suprimió la democracia y gobernó tiránicamente. Al fin del año 1958 Batista fue derrotado, y en enero de 1959 otro dictador, Fidel **Castro,** se apoderó del gobierno. Éste convirtió a Cuba en estado comunista. Ahora nuestro país se ve obligado a proteger el hemisferio occidental contra la penetración comunista.

EL CUERPO DE PAZ Y LA ALIANZA PARA EL PROGRESO

En 1961, John F. Kennedy, presidente de los Estados Unidos, inició dos programas, el del **Cuerpo** (Corps) **de Paz** y el de la **Alianza Para el Progreso,** para mejorar la condición de otros países. El **Cuerpo de Paz** envía maestros y técnicos a los varios países para ayudar a los habitantes a mejorar su condición, en lo económico y lo educativo.

La Alianza Para el Progreso ofrecía ayuda financiera (financial) y técnica a los países latinoamericanos. Para recibir ayuda, un país tenía que iniciar cambios en su manera de cobrar impuestos y, en general, debía asegurar de una manera más justa el bienestar de los habitantes.

EJERCICIOS

A. A la izquierda de cada expresión de la lista *A*, escríbase la letra de la expresión correspondiente de la lista *B*.

A	*B*
_____ 1. Ponce de León	*a.* capital azteca
_____ 2. Nueva España	*b.* araucanos
_____ 3. Coronado	*c.* apóstol de los indios
_____ 4. Tenochtitlán	*d.* siete ciudades de Cíbola
_____ 5. Balboa	*e.* misiones en California
_____ 6. Chichén-Itzá	*f.* gobernador de Puerto Rico
_____ 7. Junípero Serra	*g.* Mar del Sur
_____ 8. Bartolomé de las Casas	*h.* ciudad maya
_____ 9. Cuzco	*i.* México, Centroamérica, y Antillas
_____10. Valdivia	*j.* capital incaica

B. Subráyese la palabra o expresión que complete correctamente cada frase.

1. El primer navegante que dio la vuelta al mundo fue

   (*a*) Cabeza de Vaca   (*b*) del Cano   (*c*) Colón   (*a*) Balboa

2. Los españoles nunca pudieron dominar completamente a los

   (*a*) incas   (*b*) caribes   (*c*) aztecas   (*d*) araucanos

3. El rey azteca matado por Cortés se llamaba

   (*a*) Tenochtitlán   (*b*) Moctezuma   (*c*) Cabeza de Vaca   (*d*) Atahualpa

4. La primera colonia del Nuevo Mundo fue establecida en

   (*a*) el Perú   (*b*) Chile   (*c*) Nueva España   (*d*) la Española

5. La ciudad de Santiago de Chile fue fundada por

   (*a*) Valdivia   (*b*) los incas   (*c*) Cortés   (*d*) Colón

6. El imperio incaico fue destruido por

   (*a*) Pizarro   (*b*) Cortés   (*c*) Valdivia   (*d*) Colón

7. Las colonias españolas eran gobernadas por

   (*a*) piratas   (*b*) misioneros   (*c*) virreyes   (*d*) reyes indios

8. Los indios de Centroamérica de cultura más avanzada eran los

   (*a*) toltecas   (*b*) aztecas   (*c*) guaraníes   (*d*) mayas

9. La Ciudad de México está hoy donde antes estaba situada la ciudad de

   (*a*) Tenochtitlán   (*b*) Chichén-Itzá   (*c*) Cíbola   (*d*) Santiago

10. La Florida fue descubierta por

   (*a*) Coronado   (*b*) Ponce de León   (*c*) Cabeza de Vaca   (*d*) Balboa

C. Complétense correctamente las frases siguientes:

1. En 1910, en Buenos Aires, se organizó _____.

2. La famosa entrevista entre San Martín y Bolívar se verificó en _____.

3. El Plan de Iguala estableció en México una _____.

4. El discípulo de Hidalgo, el que continuó su obra, fue _____.

5. La última gran batalla de las guerras por la independencia en Sudamérica tuvo lugar en _____
   _____ en 1824.

6. En 1959 se estableció en Cuba un gobierno comunista bajo _____.

7. El dictador mexicano que reinó hasta 1911 fue _____.

8. Los dos programas establecidos por los Estados Unidos en 1961 para mejorar la condición de otros países eran el del Cuerpo de Paz y el de _____.

9. El primer paso hacia la unidad del hemisferio fue dado por _____.

10. El precursor más importante de la lucha por la independencia fue _____.

D. A la izquierda de cada expresión de la lista *A*, escríbase la letra de la expresión correspondiente de la lista *B*.

	A	*B*
_____	**1.** Bolívar	*a.* Chile
_____	**2.** Martí	*b.* Ayacucho
_____	**3.** Unión Panamericana	*c.* Grito de Dolores
_____	**4.** Agustín I	*d.* el Libertador
_____	**5.** Rosas	*e.* Cuba
_____	**6.** Hidalgo	*f.* Maximiliano
_____	**7.** Juárez	*g.* O.E.A.
_____	**8.** O'Higgins	*h.* Iturbide
_____	**9.** Gómez	*i.* Venezuela
_____	**10.** Sucre	*j.* la Argentina

E. Complétense correctamente las frases siguientes:

1. Cortés dio a México el nombre de _____.

2. Los _____ son personas de origen español nacidas en la América Hispana.

3. "Manos a la Obra" fue un proyecto económico de la isla de _____.

4. Los incas habían establecido su capital en _____.

5. Fray Junípero Serra estableció _____ en California.

6. Los dos héroes principales de la guerra sudamericana de independencia fueron Bolívar en el norte y _____ en el sur.

7. En tiempos de Cortés, los _____ dominaban la mayor parte de México.

8. La región de Bolivia, la Argentina, el Uruguay, y el Paraguay se llamaba el virreinato de _____.

9. Ponce de León, buscando la Fuente de la Juventud, descubrió _____.

10. La gran época de la colonización española fue el siglo _____.

11. Santiago, capital de Chile, fue fundada por _____.

12. En vez de escribir, los incas usaban _____.

13. El primero que atravesó el istmo de Panamá fue _____.

14. Colón estableció la primera colonia del Nuevo Mundo en la isla de _____.

15. _____ siguió a Batista como dictador de Cuba.

16. Los araucanos vivieron en el _____ de Sudamérica.

17. Chichén-Itzá fue la ciudad principal de los _____.

18. Las colonias fueron administradas por el Consejo de _____.

19. El misionero que luchó más que ningún otro en favor de los indios fue _____.

20. Después de ganar la independencia, México tuvo dos emperadores, Agustín y _____.

21. El Gran Cañón fue descubierto por _____.

22. En la guerra contra los Estados Unidos, España perdió las Islas Filipinas, Cuba, y _____.

23. El rey inca matado por Pizarro fue _____.

24. Tres de las revoluciones contra España estallaron en el año _____.

25. O'Higgins fue el primer presidente de _____.

Civilization Lesson 9—LA LITERATURA DE HISPANOAMÉRICA

DESDE LA ÉPOCA COLONIAL HASTA LA REVOLUCIÓN

1. Bernal **Díaz del Castillo,** un compañero de Cortés, fue uno de los grandes historiadores de la época colonial. Su célebre *Historia verdadera de la conquista de la Nueva España* describe la conquista de México por Cortés.

2. Alonso de **Ercilla** (1533–1594) escribió el primer gran poema épico del Nuevo Mundo, *La araucana*. Este poema trata de las guerras entre los conquistadores españoles y los indios araucanos de Chile. A pesar de ser Ercilla un soldado español, los héroes son dos caciques (chieftains) araucanos, **Caupolicán** y **Lautaro.** *La araucana* sirvió de modelo para otros poemas épicos de la época colonial.

3. Sor **Juana Inés de la Cruz** (1651–1695), de México, representa la cumbre de la poesía americana de la época colonial. Se la llamaba la "décima musa." Su estilo es sencillo y lírico.

4. José Joaquín **Fernández de Lizardi** (1774–1827), mexicano, fue el primer novelista de Hispanoamérica. Fue conocido con el seudónimo de "El Pensador Mexicano." Su obra maestra, *El periquillo sarniento* (The Itching Parrot), es una novela picaresca que describe de una manera realista la sociedad mexicana de su época.

5. Andrés **Bello** (1781–1865), abogado, poeta, y filólogo (philologist), nació en Caracas, Venezuela. Pasó muchos años en Inglaterra, y después fue a Chile, donde escribió la constitución del nuevo país y fundó la Universidad de Santiago. Escribió una gramática que todavía se considera una de las mejores y más completas de la lengua castellana.

6. Simón **Bolívar** (1783–1830), "El Libertador," reveló una visión extraordinaria en sus documentos, como en la *Carta de Jamaica*, en la que habló de una América unificada económica y políticamente.

POST-REVOLUCIÓN

1. Domingo Faustino **Sarmiento** (1811–1888), argentino, fue presidente de su país de 1868 a 1874. *Facundo*, su obra maestra, es un ensayo biográfico sobre la barbarie (cruelty) gauchesca. Durante su presidencia, Sarmiento inició muchas reformas en el sistema educativo de la Argentina.

2. José **Mármol** (1817–1871) escribió *Amalia*, una novela trágica de la época del tirano Juan Manuel de Rosas, en la Argentina. Esta obra describe el terror que reinaba en Buenos Aires durante la dictadura de Rosas.

3. Ricardo **Palma** (1833–1919), del Perú, escribió sobre el pasado de su país. En su obra, *Tradiciones peruanas*, cuenta historias divertidas (amusing) de la época colonial.

4. José **Hernández** (1834–1886), argentino, escribió *Martín Fierro*, el gran poema épico del gaucho. El héroe es un gaucho que canta su propia historia.

5. Jorge **Isaacs** (1837–1895), de Colombia, escribió *María*, la novela más popular de Sudamérica. Es una obra sumamente sentimental, con descripciones exquisitas del paisaje.

6. Florencio **Sánchez** (1875–1910), uruguayo, fue el mejor dramaturgo de Sudamérica. Escribió del campo y de la ciudad. Entre otras obras, escribió *La gringa*, drama que trata de los conflictos entre los criollos y los inmigrantes.

EL MODERNISMO HASTA NUESTROS DÍAS

El modernismo apareció hacia fines del siglo XIX. Fue un movimiento literario de reacción contra el realismo. Dio énfasis (emphasis) al estilo y a la forma. Fue más importante en la poesía que en la prosa. El modernismo duró hasta bien entrado (well into) el siglo XX. Una multitud de poetas, españoles e hispanoamericanos, eran modernistas.

1. José **Martí** (1853–1895), cubano, además de ser uno de los precursores del modernismo, luchó y murió por la independencia de Cuba. Entre sus obras poéticas figuran *Versos sencillos*.

2. Manuel **Gutiérrez Nájera** (1859–1895), mexicano, escribió poesías y prosa llenas de dulzura y gracia. Una obra típica suya es *Cuentos de color de humo*.

3. Rubén **Darío** (1867—1916), de Nicaragua, fue el padre del modernismo y el mejor poeta de la América Hispana. Dejó también una profunda impresión en la poesía de España. Sus mejores obras son *Cantos de vida y esperanza* y *Prosas profanas.*

4. José Enrique **Rodó** (1872—1917), del Uruguay, fue el ensayista más célebre de Hispanoamérica. En su obra maestra, *Ariel*, hace una comparación entre el materialismo de los Estados Unidos y la cultura artística de la América Hispana.

NOVELISTAS DEL SIGLO XX

1. Mariano **Azuela** (1873—1952), mexicano, describe las luchas sangrientas de la revolución mexicana de 1910. Su obra más famosa es *Los de abajo*, traducida al inglés bajo el título de *The Underdogs.*

2. Horacio **Quiroga** (1878—1937), uruguayo, es el mejor escritor de cuentos de Hispanoamérica. Escribió *Cuentos de la selva* y *Cuentos de amor, de locura y de muerte.*

3. Hugo **Wast** (1883—1962), también de la Argentina, fue uno de los novelistas más populares de Hispanoamérica. Entre sus novelas más populares figuran *La casa de los cuervos* y *Desierto de piedra.*

4. Rómulo **Gallegos** (1884—1969), que fue una vez presidente de Venezuela, llegó a ser el mejor novelista de su país. En *Doña Bárbara* describió la vida de los llaneros venezolanos.

5. Ricardo **Güiraldes** (1886—1927), argentino, fue el mejor novelista de la literatura gauchesca. En su novela *Don Segundo Sombra*, describió la vida y las costumbres de los gauchos.

6. Martín Luis **Guzmán** (1887—1977), novelista mexicano, describió la revolución mexicana en su obra *El águila y la serpiente.*

7. José Eustasio **Rivera** (1889—1928), de Colombia, escribió *La vorágine*, una novela de la vida trágica de los caucheros (rubber workers).

8. Ciro **Alegría** (1909—1967), peruano, describió los problemas de los indios del Perú en su obra *El mundo es ancho y ajeno.*

9. Gabriel **García Márquez** (1928—   ), de Colombia, escribió la novela *Cien años de soledad*, que cuenta la historia de un pueblo colombiano ficticio (fictitious). García Márquez ganó el Premio Nobel de Literatura en 1982.

10. Mario **Vargas Llosa** (1936—   ), peruano, se interesa principalmente por los problemas sociales de su país. Una de sus novelas más populares es *La guerra del fin del mundo*, que trata de una sublevación (uprising) en el Brasil en 1896.

POETAS DEL SIGLO XX

1. Gabriela **Mistral** (1889—1957), de Chile, ganó el Premio Nobel de Literatura en 1945. Su mejor obra es *Desolación*, una colección de poesías.

2. Jorge Luis **Borges** (1899—1986), argentino, fue uno de los poetas principales de Hispanoamérica. Entre sus obras figura *Fervor de Buenos Aires.*

3. Pablo **Neruda** (1904—1973), chileno, fue uno de los mejores poetas de Hispanoamérica. Escribió *La canción de la fiesta.* Ganó el Premio Nobel de Literatura (1971).

EJERCICIOS

A. Identifíquense las siguientes obras, indicando por cada una: la *clase* de obra (drama, poesía, novela, ensayo); el *autor;* y su *país.*

EJEMPLO: *María*   novela   Isaacs   Colombia

1. *La gringa* ---

2. *Desolación* ---

3. *La casa de los cuervos* --

4. *El águila y la serpiente* ---

5. *La guerra del fin del mundo* --

6. *Amalia* --

7. *Martín Fierro* --

8. *Fervor de Buenos Aires* ---

9. *Facundo* --

10. *Ariel* --

B. A la izquierda de cada expresión de la lista *A*, escríbase la letra de la expresión correspondiente de la lista *B*.

A	B
-------- **1.** Sor Juana Inés de la Cruz	*a.* Ricardo Palma
-------- **2.** Bernal Díaz del Castillo	*b.* la "décima musa"
-------- **3.** *Carta de Jamaica*	*c.* la conquista de México
-------- **4.** Ricardo Güiraldes	*d.* Gabriel García Márquez
-------- **5.** Gabriela Mistral	*e.* *La vorágine*
-------- **6.** José Eustasio Rivera	*f.* Bolívar
-------- **7.** *Cien años de soledad*	*g.* *Don Segundo Sombra*
-------- **8.** Mariano Azuela	*h.* escritor de cuentos
-------- **9.** *Tradiciones peruanas*	*i.* *Ariel*
-------- **10.** Horacio Quiroga	*j.* Premio Nobel
	k. *Los de abajo*

C. Subráyese la expresión que mejor complete cada una de las frases siguientes:

1. El padre del modernismo fue   (*a*) Hugo Wast   (*b*) Martín Luis Guzmán   (*c*) Alonso de Ercilla   (*d*) Rubén Darío

2. El primer novelista de Hispanoamérica fue   (*a*) José Mármol   (*b*) Jorge Isaacs   (*c*) Fernández de Lizardi   (*d*) Florencio Sánchez

3. Una obra que trata de la conquista de Chile es   (*a*) *El periquillo sarniento*   (*b*) *Cantos de vida y esperanza*   (*c*) *La araucana*   (*d*) *Cuentos de color de humo*

4. Bernal Díaz del Castillo escribió acerca de la conquista   (*a*) de Cuba   (*b*) de México   (*c*) de la Argentina   (*d*) del Perú

5. La "décima musa" fue   (*a*) Sor Juana Inés de la Cruz   (*b*) Florencio Sánchez   (*c*) Gabriela Mistral   (*d*) Rubén Darío

6. Un dramaturgo importante de la América del Sur fue   (*a*) Manuel Gálvez   (*b*) José Enrique Rodó   (*c*) Florencio Sánchez   (*d*) Manuel Gutiérrez Nájera

7. Las *Tradiciones peruanas* fueron escritas por   (*a*) Ricardo Palma   (*b*) José Eustasio Rivera   (*c*) Ciro Alegría   (*d*) Horacio Quiroga

8. Domingo Faustino Sarmiento   (*a*) hizo reformas educativas en la Argentina   (*b*) murió por la independencia de Cuba   (*c*) escribió novelas de la revolución mexicana   (*d*) nació en Nicaragua

9. El mejor cuentista de Hispanoamérica fue   (*a*) Pablo Neruda   (*b*) Gutiérrez Nájera   (*c*) Alonso de Ercilla   (*d*) Horacio Quiroga

10. Rómulo Gallegos, además de ser novelista, fue presidente de   (*a*) México   (*b*) Colombia   (*c*) Venezuela   (*d*) la Argentina

D. Complétese cada una de las frases siguientes escribiendo el título de la obra o el nombre del autor:

1. El gran poema épico de los gauchos es --

2. *El mundo es ancho y ajeno* fue escrita por --

3. *Doña Bárbara* fue escrita por --.

4. El erudito venezolano que escribió una gramática famosa fue --

5. *Facundo,* un estudio de los gauchos, fue escrito por --

6. La novela que describe la vida de los caucheros es --

7. Rodó escribió un libro de ensayos llamado --

8. -- es el autor de una novela famosa acerca de un pueblo colombiano que nunca existió.

9. *Cantos de vida y esperanza* es la mejor obra de --

10. Un poema épico de la conquista de Chile es --

    Simón Bolívar (1783–1830), llamado "El Libertador" y "El Jorge Wáshington de Sudamérica," fue uno de los grandes héroes de la guerra de independencia. Ganó de España la independencia de Colombia, Venezuela, el Ecuador y el norte del Perú.

    Bolívar soñó con la unión fraternal de todos los países americanos. Años después de su muerte esta visión fue realizada con la formación de la Unión Panamericana, que es hoy la Organización de Estados Americanos (O.E.A.).

Civilization Lesson 10—EL ARTE Y LA MÚSICA DE HISPANOAMÉRICA

PINTORES

1. Diego **Rivera** (1886—1957) fue el más importante de los pintores mexicanos. En la primera parte de su vida, Rivera pintó escenas del paisaje mexicano. Más tarde se dedicó a la pintura mural. Gran parte de su obra representa temas políticos y sociales.

2. José Clemente **Orozco** (1883—1949), mexicano, también fue muralista. Pintó los frescos del Palacio de Bellas Artes, en la Ciudad de México. Muchos de sus cuadros representan escenas de la revolución mexicana de 1910.

3. David Alfaro **Siqueiros** (1898—1974) fue otro gran pintor y muralista de México. Sus obras, como las de Rivera y Orozco, tratan de problemas políticos y sociales.

4. Miguel **Covarrubias** (1904—1957), también mexicano, fue famoso, tanto en México como en los Estados Unidos, como pintor de caricaturas de personas célebres.

5. José **Sabogal** (1888—1956), peruano, fue el pintor más célebre de su país. Representó en sus cuadros la cultura indígena. Vio el porvenir de su patria en la civilización de los mestizos (half-breeds).

6. Cesáreo Bernaldo de **Quirós** (1879—1968), argentino, representó en sus cuadros lo pintoresco de la vida de los gauchos. Sus numerosos cuadros constituyen un recuerdo importante de la vida de la pampa.

7. Tito **Salas** (1889—1974), de Venezuela, fue el más famoso de los pintores modernos de su país. Pintó retratos de Bolívar y escenas de la lucha por la independencia.

MÚSICA Y BAILE

Gran parte de la música hispanoamericana está basada en temas folklóricos e indígenas. Hay gran variedad en la música popular de los diversos países. Por ejemplo, en México es muy popular el **corrido,** una clase de canción narrativa con baile, mientras que en Bolivia y en el Perú el **yaraví,** una canción triste, es muy común.

COMPOSITORES

1. Manuel **Ponce** (1886—1948), compositor de la popularísima canción *Estrellita,* inició el movimiento nacionalista de la música mexicana. En sus composiciones hay mucha influencia folklórica.

2. Ernesto **Lecuona** (1896—1963), cubano, fue un compositor de música popular. Compuso *Siboney* y *Malagueña.*

3. Carlos **Chávez** (1899—1978), mexicano, fue el compositor contemporáneo más famoso de su país. Su obra más conocida es *Sinfonía India.* Chávez fue también un famoso director de orquesta.

4. Agustín **Lara** (1900—1970) fue un compositor célebre de México, famoso por la bien conocida canción *Granada.*

INSTRUMENTOS MÚSICOS

1. La **quena** es una flauta (flute) inca que produce sonidos melancólicos. Se usaba aún antes de la época de los conquistadores.

2. Las **claves** son dos palitos de madera dura. Sirven para marcar el ritmo (rhythm). Son muy populares en Cuba y en otros países de las Antillas.

3. El **güiro** es una calabaza (gourd) seca que se frota (is rubbed) con un palito. Se usa mucho en Cuba y Puerto Rico.

4. Las **maracas** son calabazas secas con granos de maíz dentro. Son muy populares en las Antillas.

5. La **marimba,** usada en México y la América Central, se parece mucho al *xylophone.*

6. La **guitarra** es un instrumento de seis cuerdas. Es muy popular en Hispanoamérica y en España.

CANTANTES, INSTRUMENTISTAS, ACTORES DE CINE

1. Ramón **Vinay,** tenor chileno, es un gran cantante de ópera.

2. Yma **Sumac,** peruana, es conocida por su excelente voz, que la coloca entre las mejores cantantes del mundo.

3. Claudio **Arrau** es un famoso pianista de Chile que toca la música de los grandes compositores clásicos.

4. **Cantinflas** es el seudónimo de Mariano Moreno, el gran cómico mexicano.

5. Pedro **Armendáriz** fue un gran actor mexicano de cine. Hizo muchas películas en México y en nuestro país.

BAILES

1. La **rumba** es un baile afro-cubano, de movimientos acentuados, que se baila con maracas en las manos.

2. El **tango** es un baile argentino en que las parejas se mueven con mucho garbo (grace).

3. El **jarabe tapatío,** el baile nacional de México, se conoce aquí como *The Mexican Hat Dance.*

4. La **zamacueca** (o **cueca**) es un baile típico de Chile.

5. El **joropo** es un baile venezolano que se baila en grupo o en pareja.

EJERCICIOS

A. A la izquierda de cada expresión de la lista *A*, escríbase la letra de la expresión correspondiente de la lista *B*.

A	B
_____ **1.** Tito Salas	*a. Estrellita*
_____ **2.** Bernaldo de Quirós	*b. Sinfonía India*
_____ **3.** marimba	*c.* yaraví
_____ **4.** Manuel Ponce	*d. Granada*
_____ **5.** Covarrubias	*e.* pintor del Perú
_____ **6.** corrido	*f.* pintor venezolano
_____ **7.** Agustín Lara	*g.* caricaturas
_____ **8.** Siqueiros	*h.* xylophone
_____ **9.** Carlos Chávez	*i.* gauchos
_____ **10.** Sabogal	*j.* canción mexicana
	k. pintura mural

B. Subráyese la palabra o expresión que complete correctamente cada frase.

1. El tango es un baile   (*a*) argentino   (*b*) venezolano   (*c*) chileno   (*d*) mexicano

2. Un célebre actor mexicano es   (*a*) Lecuona   (*b*) Vinay   (*c*) Orozco   (*d*) Cantinflas

3. Claudio Arrau es un   (*a*) compositor cubano   (*b*) pianista chileno   (*c*) actor mexicano (*d*) pintor cubano

4. (*a*) La guitarra   (*b*) La quena   (*c*) El güiro   (*d*) El yaraví   es una flauta incaica

5. Un famoso pintor mexicano de murales fue   (*a*) Ernesto Lecuona   (*b*) José Sabogal   (*c*) Pedro Armendáriz   (*d*) Diego Rivera

C. Complétese correctamente cada frase.

1. Un baile típico de Chile es _____.

2. _____ es un famoso cantante chileno de ópera.

3. El _____ es una canción triste del Perú.

4. El _____ es el baile típico de México.

5. _____ pintó los murales del Palacio de Bellas Artes.

6. _____ es un instrumento músico muy popular en todo el mundo hispano.

7. _____, músico cubano, compuso *Malagueña*.

8. _____ son dos palitos que se emplean para marcar el ritmo.

9. _____, del Perú, es una de las mejores cantantes del mundo.

10. _____, pintor peruano, describió en sus cuadros la cultura indígena de su país.

El fútbol ("soccer" en inglés) es el deporte más popular del mundo hispánico. (El béisbol es también popular en varios países hispanos—especialmente en Puerto Rico, Cuba, la República Dominicana, Nicaragua y Venezuela.)

Civilization Lesson 11 — LAS COSTUMBRES HISPANOAMERICANAS

DÍAS DE FIESTA

1. La **Navidad** empieza en México (y también en otras partes del mundo hispánico) con *Las Posadas*, que consisten en visitas a varias casas vecinas durante los nueve días que preceden a la **Nochebuena.** Durante la fiesta que sigue a Las Posadas, la gente baila alrededor de la *piñata*, un jarro (jar) vivamente decorado, que contiene dulces y regalos. Después, rompen la piñata y cogen los dulces.

2. El **dieciséis de septiembre** es la fiesta nacional de México. Conmemora el principio de la guerra de independencia contra España.

3. El **cinco de mayo** conmemora la lucha de los mexicanos contra la dominación de Francia y del emperador Maximiliano.

4. El **catorce de abril** se celebra el **Día Panamericano.**

5. El **doce de octubre** se celebra el **Día de la Raza,** el cual corresponde a nuestro *Columbus Day.*

BEBIDAS

1. **Mate** es una especie de té, hecho de la planta **yerba mate.** Se bebe principalmente en la Argentina y en el Paraguay. Generalmente se toma en una calabaza por medio de un tubo llamado *bombilla*.

2. **Pulque** y **tequila** son bebidas intoxicantes hechas del *maguey*, una planta de México.

COMIDAS MEXICANAS

1. La **tortilla** se hace de maíz. Es semejante al "pancake."

2. El **tamal** es una tortilla arrollada (rolled) que contiene carne.

3. **Tacos** son tortillas llenas de carne picada (chopped), legumbres, y tomates.

4. **Enchiladas** son tortillas arrolladas servidas con salsa de ají (chile sauce).

5. **Chile con carne** es un plato que contiene carne picada, pimientos picantes, y salsa de ají.

TIPOS PINTORESCOS

1. El **charro** es el jinete típico de México. Lleva un traje tradicional.

2. La **china poblana** es la compañera del charro. Su vestido consiste en falda ancha y larga, de color rojo y verde, y blusa blanca.

3. Los **mariachis** son grupos de cantantes callejeros de México.

4. El **peón** es un campesino mexicano.

5. El **roto** es una persona de la clase baja de Chile.

6. El **gaucho** es el vaquero (cowboy) argentino, que vive en la pampa.

7. El **llanero** es el vaquero de los llanos de Venezuela.

TRAJES TÍPICOS

1. El **poncho** es una capa con una abertura (opening) en el centro, por la cual entra la cabeza. Se usa en la pampa para protegerse de la lluvia.

2. El **sarape** es una manta de colores vivos que el mexicano lleva en los hombros.

3. Los **huaraches (guaraches)** son sandalias mexicanas.

4. El **rebozo** es un chal usado por las mujeres mexicanas.

5. El **sombrero de jipijapa** es de paja, hecho a mano. Se fabrica en el Ecuador, pero se conoce en los Estados Unidos como "Panama hat."

MONEDAS

En siete países de Hispanoamérica, la moneda nacional se llama el *peso*. Se usa en Cuba, la República Dominicana, México, Bolivia, Colombia, Chile y el Uruguay. Se debe notar que los pesos de estos países no son del mismo valor. Las monedas corrientes de los demás países son:

la Argentina: el *austral*	Honduras: el *lempira*	el Perú: el *sol*
Costa Rica: el *colón*	Nicaragua: el *córdoba*	el Salvador: el *colón*
el Ecuador: el *sucre*	el Panamá: el *balboa*	Venezuela: el *bolívar*
Guatamala: el *quetzal*	el Paraguay: el *guaraní*	

EJERCICIOS

A. A la izquierda de cada expresión de la lista *A*, escríbase la letra de la expresión correspondiente de la lista *B*.

	A		*B*
_____	1. lempira	*a.*	sombrero
_____	2. Las Posadas	*b.*	tortilla
_____	3. 16 de septiembre	*c.*	Día de la Raza
_____	4. yerba mate	*d.*	fiesta nacional
_____	5. china poblana	*e.*	moneda
_____	6. 12 de octubre	*f.*	sarape
_____	7. enchilada	*g.*	pampas
_____	8. gaucho	*h.*	té
_____	9. jipijapa	*i.*	charro
_____	10. mariachi	*j.*	Navidad
		k.	cantante

B. En cada grupo, subráyese la palabra que se relacione más directamente con cada país.

1. Venezuela: charro, llanero, gaucho

2. el Perú: sucre, peso, sol

3. México: Las Posadas, yerba mate, roto

4. Guatemala: mariachi, balboa, quetzal

5. el Ecuador: poncho, jipijapa, sarape

6. México: guaraní, taco, lempira

7. México: china poblana, sucre, colón

8. el Paraguay: tamal, yerba mate, tequila

9. Bolivia: bolívar, córdoba, peso

10. México: mariachi, roto, llanero

C. Identifíquese cada uno, (*A*) clasificándolo como *bebida*, *comida*, *moneda*, *tipo*, o *traje*, y (*B*) nombrando el país de su origen.

1. roto _____
2. pulque _____
3. chile con carne _____
4. rebozo _____
5. poncho _____
6. tequila _____
7. gaucho _____
8. peón _____
9. enchilada _____
10. charro _____
11. guaraní _____
12. sarape _____
13. balboa _____
14. austral _____
15. huarache _____

Una estatua del padre Hidalgo está enfrente de la Biblioteca Central de la Universidad Nacional de México. La Biblioteca está decorada de mosaicos de piedra hechos por Juan O'Gorman, el famoso arquitecto y muralista mexicano. Los mosaicos cuentan en símbolos la historia de la cultura mexicana. O'Gorman usó unos 7½ millones de piedras para hacerlos.

Civilization Lesson 12 — MASTERY EXERCISES ON SPANISH AMERICA

En los ejercicios siguientes, subráyese la palabra o expresión que complete correctamente cada frase.

A. GEOGRAFÍA

1. Una famosa playa de la costa occidental de México es   (*a*) Veracruz   (*b*) Monterrey   (*c*) Acapulco   (*d*) Tampico

2. El país más grande de la América Central es   (*a*) Nicaragua   (*b*) Guatemala   (*c*) Costa Rica   (*d*) el Salvador

3. El producto más importante de Bolivia es   (*a*) el café   (*b*) el cobre   (*c*) la plata   (*d*) el estaño

4. El puerto principal del Ecuador es   (*a*) Valparaíso   (*b*) Guayaquil   (*c*) el Callao   (*d*) Montevideo

5. La Universidad de San Marcos está en la ciudad de   (*a*) Cuzco   (*b*) Quito   (*c*) Lima   (*d*) Guayaquil

6. La capital de Costa Rica es   (*a*) Tegucigalpa   (*b*) San José   (*c*) San Juan   (*d*) Managua

7. El río Orinoco está en   (*a*) Venezuela   (*b*) el Ecuador   (*c*) Bolivia   (*d*) Colombia

8. Los sombreros de jipijapa se fabrican en   (*a*) el Perú   (*b*) Venezuela   (*c*) el Ecuador   (*d*) el Panamá

9. El producto principal del Paraguay es   (*a*) esmeraldas   (*b*) plata   (*c*) yerba mate   (*d*) cobre

10. El río principal de Colombia es el   (*a*) Paraná   (*b*) Orinoco   (*c*) Magdalena   (*d*) Plata

B. HISTORIA

1. El gran precursor de las guerras de independencia fue   (*a*) Cristóbal Colón   (*b*) Francisco Miranda   (*c*) Miguel Hidalgo   (*d*) Vicente Gómez

2. El patriota mexicano que derrotó a Maximiliano fue   (*a*) Juárez   (*b*) Iturbide   (*c*) Santa Anna   (*d*) Díaz

3. Las naciones americanas fundaron la Unión Panamericana en   (*a*) 1898   (*b*) 1890   (*c*) 1910   (*d*) 1824

4. El general que ayudó a San Martín a ganar la independencia de Chile fue   (*a*) Miranda   (*b*) Bolívar   (*c*) O'Higgins   (*d*) Sucre

5. Durante la época colonial México se llamaba   (*a*) La Perla de las Antillas   (*b*) Nueva España   (*c*) Nueva Granada   (*d*) la Banda Oriental

6. Un misionero que luchó en favor de los indios fue   (*a*) Cabeza de Vaca   (*b*) las Casas   (*c*) Rosas   (*d*) Balboa

7. José Martí luchó por la independencia de   (*a*) Chile   (*b*) México   (*c*) Puerto Rico   (*d*) Cuba

8. México fue conquistado por   (*a*) Cortés   (*b*) Pizarro   (*c*) Colón   (*d*) Valdivia

9. Los indios que ocupaban las regiones andinas del Perú eran los   (*a*) aztecas   (*b*) incas   (*c*) mayas   (*d*) araucanos

10. El 14 de abril se celebra   (*a*) la independencia de México   (*b*) el nacimiento de Simón Bolívar   (*c*) el Día de la Raza   (*d*) la unidad de los países americanos

C. Literatura

1. La novela *María* fue escrita por   (*a*) José Martí   (*b*) Jorge Isaacs   (*c*) Rubén Darío   (*d*) Hugo Wast

2. El mejor escritor hispanoamericano de cuentos fue   (*a*) Florencio Sánchez   (*b*) Horacio Quiroga   (*c*) Hugo Wast   (*d*) Ciro Alegría

3. Fernández de Lizardi escribió la primera novela picaresca del Nuevo Mundo, llamada   (*a*) *El águila y la serpiente*   (*b*) *El periquillo sarniento*   (*c*) *Ariel*   (*d*) *Prosas profanas*

4. José Hernández escribió el gran poema épico del gaucho,   (*a*) *La araucana*   (*b*) *La gringa*   (*c*) *Fervor de Buenos Aires*   (*d*) *Martín Fierro*

5. El autor de una gramática famosa es   (*a*) Martín Luis Guzmán   (*b*) Domingo Faustino Sarmiento   (*c*) Andrés Bello   (*d*) Rómulo Gallegos

6. Un estudio de los gauchos, escrito por Sarmiento, es   (*a*) *Los de abajo*   (*b*) *Facundo*   (*c*) *Ariel*   (*d*) *Desierto de piedra*

7. El autor de *La araucana* fue   (*a*) Ercilla   (*b*) Lizardi   (*c*) Sarmiento   (*d*) Hernández

8. Un libro que describe la conquista de México fue escrito por   (*a*) Mariano Azuela   (*b*) Ricardo Palma   (*c*) Bernal Díaz del Castillo   (*d*) José Enrique Rodó

9. El padre del modernismo fue   (*a*) Jorge Luis Borges   (*b*) Pablo Neruda   (*c*) José Martí   (*d*) Rubén Darío

10. Una novela que describe la vida de los llaneros de Venezuela es   (*a*) *Doña Bárbara*   (*b*) *La vorágine*   (*c*) *Don Segundo Sombra*   (*d*) *El mundo es ancho y ajeno*

D. Arte y música

1. Un instrumento músico muy popular en España y en la América hispana es   (*a*) la quena   (*b*) la zamacueca   (*c*) el güiro   (*d*) la guitarra

2. Un baile venezolano es   (*a*) el jarabe tapatío   (*b*) el joropo   (*c*) el tango   (*d*) la cueca

3. Un famoso director de orquesta y compositor mexicano fue   (*a*) Diego Rivera   (*b*) Tito Salas   (*c*) Carlos Chávez   (*d*) David Alfaro Siqueiros

4. El gran pintor mexicano de murales fue   (*a*) Salas   (*b*) Armendáriz   (*c*) Rivera   (*d*) Quirós

5. Los frescos del Palacio de Bellas Artes en México fueron pintados por   (*a*) Orozco   (*b*) Salas   (*c*) Siqueiros   (*d*) Lara

6. La rumba es un baile   (*a*) argentino   (*b*) chileno   (*c*) mexicano   (*d*) cubano

7. Un pintor mexicano que se distinguió por sus caricaturas fue   (*a*) Cantinflas   (*b*) Siqueiros   (*c*) Covarrubias   (*d*) Sabogal

8. Un pintor peruano que se interesó por la cultura de los indios de su país fue   (*a*) Manuel Ponce   (*b*) José Sabogal   (*c*) Tito Salas   (*d*) Claudio Arrau

9. *Malagueña* fue compuesta por   (*a*) Lecuona   (*b*) Ponce   (*c*) Lara   (*d*) Chávez

10. Un cantor chileno muy célebre es   (*a*) Ramón Vinay   (*b*) Yma Sumac   (*c*) Claudio Arrau   (*d*) Cantinflas

Complétense correctamente las frases siguientes:

1. San Juan es la capital de _____.

2. Los picos de Cotopaxi y Chimborazo están en _____.

3. Ricardo Palma escribió historias de la época colonial, llamadas _____.

4. En la fiesta de Las Posadas se rompe _____ .

5. Un presidente de la Argentina que hizo muchas reformas educativas fue _____ .

6. La capital más alta del Hemisferio Occidental es _____ .

7. Las grandes montañas que cruzan a Sudamérica de norte a sur son _____ .

8. El conquistador de Chile fue _____ .

9. Un baile popular mexicano es _____ .

10. El Plan de Iguala convirtió a México en una _____ .

11. Xochimilco es famoso por _____ .

12. En Chile se encuentran grandes depósitos de _____ .

13. El mejor poeta de Hispanoamérica fue _____ .

14. En muchos países de Hispanoamérica se emplea como moneda el _____ .

15. Los cantantes callejeros de México son _____ .

16. Las grandes extensiones de tierra llana de la Argentina se llaman _____ .

17. La Florida fue descubierta por _____ .

18. Un baile típico de Chile es _____ .

19. El pico más alto del Hemisferio Occidental es _____ .

20. El rey de los aztecas fue _____ .

21. Un baile típico venezolano es _____ .

22. Para protegerse del frío y de la lluvia el gaucho lleva _____ .

23. *La araucana* trata de la conquista de _____ .

24. La capital de Chile es _____ .

25. La poetisa chilena que ganó el Premio Nobel fue _____ .

26. Tres de las revoluciones contra España comenzaron en el año _____ .

27. Las cataratas del Iguazú están entre el Brasil y _____ .

28. La última batalla de la guerra de independencia en Sudamérica fue la de _____ en 1824.

29. El misionero que fundó misiones en California fue _____ .

30. El país que produce más azúcar que ningún otro en Hispanoamérica es _____ .

31. La vida de los indios del Perú se describe en _____ , de Ciro Alegría.

32. Una obra que compara las culturas norteamericana e hispanoamericana es _____ , por Rodó.

33. Un árbol del Paraguay, que se emplea para curtir cuero, es _____ .

34. Un instrumento músico que se parece al xylophone es _____ .

35. Un producto importante de la Argentina es _____ .

36. La capital del imperio de los incas fue _____ .

37. Una cantante peruana muy famosa es _____ .

38. El río Orinoco pasa por el país de _____ .

39. El Gran Cañón fue descubierto por --

40. El río principal de Colombia es --

41. Los dos centros principales de comercio con las colonias eran Cádiz y --

42. Los indios que dominaban el territorio de México cuando llegó Cortés eran --

43. El más pequeño de los países hispanos de Sudamérica es --

44. Bernaldo de Quirós pintó cuadros de la vida de --

45. La capital del Uruguay es --

46. -- ganó el Premio Nobel de Literatura en 1982.

47. El "Grito de Dolores" inició la guerra de independencia en --

48. Una novela que trata de los gauchos es --, por Ricardo Güiraldes.

49. Caracas es la capital de --

50. Bolivia, el Uruguay, la Argentina, y el Paraguay formaban el virreinato de --

51. Los tres grandes pintores mexicanos de murales son Rivera, Siqueiros, y --

52. La moneda del Paraguay se llama --

53. El lago Titicaca está entre el Perú y --

54. La capital del Perú es --

55. El cómico mexicano Mariano Moreno se conoce con el apodo de --

56. La capital del Paraguay es --

57. Un plato mexicano de carne, pimientos, y salsa de ají es --

58. Una playa famosa de la costa occidental de México es --

59. La capital de Honduras es --

60. La capital de la Argentina es --

Los indios de Guatemala son muy hábiles en tejer (weave) paños. Para ellos es más que una industria comercial. Es una verdadera arte. Tejidos a mano, los paños son famosos por sus detalles y la gran variedad de colores.

Part V—*Practice in Composition*

SUGGESTIONS FOR WRITING COMPOSITIONS IN SPANISH

1. Make an outline of your main ideas and arrange them in a logical order. In a guided composition, the outline is presented to you.

2. Use vocabulary, expressions, and idioms that you have mastered thoroughly.

3. Be careful in your use of verb tenses, verb endings, and agreement of adjectives.

4. Begin with a good topic sentence. Your closing sentence should be an appropriate conclusion.

5. Strive for variety by using synonyms.

6. In order to make transitions smoothly, make use of common connectives such as *no obstante, luego que, por lo general, por eso, a causa de, puesto que, después, más tarde, y, pero,* etc.

7. Reread your composition after you have written it. Check for any errors in agreement, spelling, and accentuation. Suggested check list:

   (a) Agreement: adjective — noun   (e) *Por — Para*

   (b) Agreement: subject — verb   (f) Subjunctive

   (c) Tense   (g) Use of connectives

   (d) *Ser — Estar*   (h) Use of idioms

EXAMPLE OF A GUIDED COMPOSITION

Write a composition telling how you spend the day. The composition must consist of at least *ten* grammatically complete sentences in Spanish, containing the information given in the instructions below. Together these sentences are to form a unified composition.

a. at what time you get up

b. what you do before breakfast (wash, get dressed, etc.)

c. what you have for breakfast

d. how you go to school (by bus, with friends, etc.)

e. your classes (which you like best, the most difficult, the easiest, etc.)

f. at what time you leave school

g. what you do before supper (play, study, etc.)

h. at what time you have supper (with whom, etc.)

i. what you do after supper (study, watch television programs, etc.)

j. at what time you go to bed

SUGGESTED ANSWER

Generalmente me levanto a las siete. Después de lavarme y vestirme, me siento a tomar el desayuno. Mi desayuno favorito consiste en huevos, pan tostado, y café.

A las ocho salgo de casa para reunirme con mis amigos. Juntos tomamos el autobús para ir a la escuela.

Paso cinco horas y media en la escuela, asistiendo a mis clases. Mi clase favorita es el español, y la más difícil es la química. Salgo a las tres, y vuelvo directamente a casa. Al llegar a casa, tomo un vaso de leche, y me pongo a estudiar en seguida. Tengo tanto trabajo que no tengo tiempo para jugar.

A las seis cenamos, mis padres, mi hermano, y yo. Después me siento a mirar algunos programas de televisión. A las diez me acuesto, porque al día siguiente hay clases.

347

EXERCISES IN GUIDED COMPOSITION

Each of the following compositions must consist of at least *ten* grammatically complete sentences in Spanish, containing the information given in the instructions. Together these sentences are to form a unified composition.

A. Write a composition telling about the house in which you live.

a. where your house is located

b. whether it is large or small

c. whether it is a brick or wooden house

d. how many rooms it has, and what they are

e. the principal articles of furniture of the living room

f. who prepares the meals, and where

g. a description of your room

h. the principal articles of furniture of your room

i. in which room you receive your friends when they visit you

j. how you spend the time with them

Vocabulario útil

la **alcoba,** bedroom

la **alfombra,** carpet

el **aparato de televisión,** television set

el **armario,** closet

una **casa particular,** private house

la **cocina,** kitchen

el **comedor,** dining room

el **cuarto de baño,** bathroom

la **dirección,** address

el **escritorio,** desk

los **ladrillos,** bricks

la **madera,** wood

la **mesa,** table

la **pared,** wall

la **sala,** parlor

la **silla,** chair

el **sótano,** cellar

la **ventana,** window

Expresiones útiles

casa de piedra (ladrillos), stone (brick) house

estar situada en . . . , to be (located) in . . .

luz eléctrica, electric light

B. Write a composition telling what you will do this summer.

a. that classes are now over

b. what the weather is like in summer

c. what you will do during the week (work, read, go to school, etc.)

d. how you will spend the evenings with your friends

e. where you will go Saturday and Sunday (picnic, beach, etc.)

f. what you will do there (play, swim, etc.)

g. what you will do when it rains

h. that you plan to spend two weeks traveling before the vacation ends

i. what places you will visit

j. that in September you must go back to school

Vocabulario útil

la **arena,** sand

la **brisa,** breeze

el **calor,** heat

el **campo,** country

los **deportes,** sports

despejado, clear (day)

divertirse, to have a good time

la **jira,** picnic

llueve, it rains

mojado, wet

nadar, to swim

la **piscina,** swimming pool

la **playa,** beach

las **vacaciones,** vacation

Expresiones útiles

a fines de, at the end of

al aire libre, in the open air

echar una siesta, to take a nap

estar a mis anchas, to be at my ease, to be relaxed

hacer buen (mal) tiempo, to be good (bad) weather

hacer calor (viento), to be warm (windy)

jugar a la pelota (al tenis), to play ball (tennis)

el **traje de baño,** bathing suit

C. Write a composition telling about your first visit to the theater.

a. when you went to the theater for the first time

b. how old you were then

c. with whom you went

d. when you arrived at the theater

e. at what time the performance began

f. what kind of work was presented

g. what impressed you most

h. at what time the play ended

i. at what time you returned home

j. whether or not you liked the play, and why

Vocabulario útil

aburrido, boring

el **acto,** act

el **actor,** actor

la **actriz,** actress

el **aplauso,** applause

la **comedia,** comedy

cómico, funny, comical

la **función,** performance

impresionar, to impress

la **orquesta,** orchestra

la **pieza,** play

el **programa,** program

el **público,** audience

la **salida,** exit

el **telón,** curtain

Expresiones útiles

hacer el papel de, to play the role of

salir del teatro, to leave the theater

soltar una carcajada, to burst out laughing

tener una cita, to have a date

D. Write a composition telling about a party you attended.

a. when it took place (day and time)

b. where it took place

c. how many guests there were

d. with whom you went

e. what occasion was being celebrated

f. what type of music was there (records, radio, etc.)

g. how you spent the time

h. what refreshments were served

i. at what time you returned home

j. that you enjoyed yourself

Vocabulario útil

celebrar, to celebrate

el **cumpleaños,** birthday

charlar, to chat

el **disco,** record

los **dulces,** candy

¡Felicitaciones!, Congratulations!

las **frutas,** fruit

los **helados,** ice cream

el **invitado,** guest

el **juego,** game

la **limonada,** lemonade

la **naranjada,** orangeade

el **pastel,** pie, pastry

los **refrescos,** refreshments

la **tertulia,** party

el **tocadiscos,** phonograph, record player

Expresiones útiles

despedirse de, to take leave of, to say goodbye to

saludar a los amigos, to greet one's friends

ser presentado(-a) a, to be introduced to

¡Tanto gusto!, Glad to meet you!

tener lugar, to take place

E. Write a composition about a trip that you intend to take to Spain.

a. why you want to go to Spain

b. when you intend to go

c. how you intend to go (ship, plane, etc.)

d. how much time you will spend in Spain

e. what cities you wish to visit

f. how you will travel from one city to another

g. what you will see in each city

h. what dishes you will order in the Spanish restaurants

i. what gifts you will bring for your family

j. when you will return to the United States

Vocabulario útil

el **avión,** airplane

la **catedral,** cathedral

la **costumbre,** custom

desembarcarse, to disembark

embarcarse, to embark

el **ferrocarril,** railroad

el **monumento,** monument

el **museo,** museum

la **provincia,** province

el **vapor,** steamship

Expresiones útiles

asistir a, to attend

cambiar de tren, to change trains

la **corrida de toros,** bullfight

pensar + inf., to intend

sacar el pasaporte, to get a passport

el **servicio aéreo,** airplane service

F. Write a composition telling about a picnic you are planning.

a. where and when you intend to have the picnic

b. what the weather forecast is

c. who is going to accompany you

d. how you plan to get to the picnic area

e. the food and beverages you are going to bring

f. how you are going to cook the food

g. what facilities are available in the picnic area

h. the games and other activities you have planned

i. what time you intend to get home

j. what you will do if it rains

G. Write a composition about the profession (carrera) you have chosen, or the work you intend to follow.

a. the profession you intend to follow

b. why you chose it (interest, ability, etc.)

c. the studies you still have to finish

d. the time necessary to finish your studies

e. the opportunities this profession offers

f. how much money you expect to earn

g. why you think you will be successful

h. what your parents think of your choice

i. what your friends think of your choice

j. where you intend to settle down (establecerse)

H. Write a composition about your favorite sport.

a. what its name is

b. whether it is an indoor or outdoor activity

c. what special skills are required

d. how long it has been your favorite sport

e. in what season it is popular

f. whether it is popular in other countries also

g. whether it is a team sport or can be played individually

h. whether this activity takes time away from your studies

i. whether it is possible to earn a living at this sport

j. how long you expect to participate in it

I. Write a composition about a birthday party you attended recently.

a. whose birthday it was

b. where the party was held

c. in what room it was held

d. when the party began

e. how many guests were present

f. whom you danced with

g. what kind of music was played

h. what type of gift you brought

i. whether you enjoyed yourself

j. when the party ended

SUGGESTED TOPICS FOR FREE COMPOSITION

1. Mi primer baile

2. El hombre (La mujer) más interesante que conozco

3. Una aventura que tuve

4. El día más importante de mi vida

5. Cómo pienso pasar las vacaciones de Navidad (o del verano)

6. Un cuento de mi perro o de otro animal doméstico

7. Si yo tuviese más tiempo libre

8. Una comida que preparé

9. La importancia de la radio en la vida moderna

10. Lo que espero hacer en el futuro

11. Cómo celebré mi cumpleaños

12. Mi posesión más querida

13. Un recuerdo de mi niñez

14. El día del semestre pasado que me gustó más

15. Mi primer día en esta escuela superior

16. Una visita al circo

17. Un viaje que pienso hacer (a un país hispanoamericano)

18. La importancia de la televisión en la vida moderna

19. Una carta importante que acabo de recibir

20. Una visita a las Naciones Unidas

SUGGESTIONS FOR WRITING LETTERS IN SPANISH

A. Heading

The date line is written as follows:

Caracas, 15 de agosto (1° de mayo)
or
Caracas, agosto 15 (mayo 1°)

B. Salutations

1. Intimate letter, that is, to relatives or friends

Querido Juan,   Querida hermana,
Querida Luisa,   Queridísima tía,

2. Formal personal letter

(Mi) distinguido señor Gómez:
Mi distinguido (estimado) amigo:

C. Conclusion or closing phrases

Un abrazo de tu hermano,   Con el cariño de tu buena amiga,
Tu hijo que no te olvida,   Su amigo y seguro servidor,
Tuya afectísima (afma.),   Su amiga y segura servidora,
Tuyo afectísimo (afmo.),

EXAMPLE OF A GUIDED LETTER

Write a letter to a friend living in Quito, Ecuador, telling him that you intend to visit that city soon. The letter must consist of *nine* grammatically complete sentences in Spanish, containing the information given in the instructions below. Together these sentences are to form a unified letter.

Be sure to include in your letter the date, the salutation, and the complimentary close.

a. when you expect to get there
b. how you plan to get there
c. that you will bring appropriate clothing with you
d. that you doubt you will be able to stay more than a month
e. that you expect to improve your knowledge of spoken Spanish
f. that you are anxious to meet your friend's family
g. that you intend to visit places of interest in the capital
h. that you know this will be an unforgettable experience
i. that you hope your friend will answer soon

SUGGESTED ANSWER

Nueva York, 6 de julio

Querido Carlos,

El domingo, 14 de julio, partiré por avión para Quito a las dos y veinte de la tarde, y te veré al día siguiente en Quito.

Pienso tomar el vuelo número 231 de la Línea Aérea Avianca. He decidido llevar conmigo dos maletas con la ropa necesaria para el clima de Quito, el cual es muy frío, según me dicen.

Espero pasar allí un mes. Dudo que mis padres me permitan quedarme más tiempo.

Pienso practicar el español, y llevaré un cuaderno y un diccionario de bolsillo.

Tengo vivos deseos de conocer a tu familia. También quiero ver los puntos de interés de la capital.

Estoy seguro de que estas vacaciones serán una experiencia que no olvidaré nunca.

Deseo que me contestes pronto, porque salgo de aquí dentro de una semana.

Con el cariño de tu buen amigo,
Juanito

EXERCISES IN GUIDED LETTER WRITING

Each of the following letters must consist of at least *nine* grammatically complete sentences in Spanish, containing the information given in the instructions. Together these sentences are to form a unified letter.

Be sure to include in your letter the date, the salutation, and the complimentary close.

A. Write a letter to a "pen pal" (amigo) in Barcelona, Spain, telling him about your school life.

a. where your school is located

b. when your school day begins and ends

c. how you get to school

d. why you like (or don't like) school

e. what subjects (asignaturas, materias) you are taking

f. the subject you like best and why

g. the marks (notas) you received last term

h. the friends you have made

i. the sport(s) you like best in school

B. Write a letter to your "pen pal" (amigo) in Monterrey, Mexico, telling him how you spend the day.

a. what time you get up in the morning

b. how many hours you spend in school each day

c. how much time you spend doing your homework

d. what special chores (tareas) you do around the house

e. what your favorite radio and television programs are

f. what your favorite pastime is

g. if you have younger (or older) brothers and sisters

h. if you spend much time with your friends during the week

i. what time you go to bed during the week

C. Write a letter to a friend, inviting him (or her) to go on a shopping trip and to spend the day with you.

a. when you want to go

b. what you have to buy for yourself

c. the gifts you have to buy

d. where you would like to meet your friend

e. how much time you plan to spend in the stores

f. where you will have lunch

g. what you can do after lunch (visit a movie, theater, museum, etc.)

h. where you expect to have dinner

i. how you both can spend the evening

D. Write a letter to your cousin, telling him (or her) about the new automobile your father has just bought.

a. the make (marca) and color

b. how old the previous car was

c. how many passengers fit (caber) in the new car

d. how much it cost

e. the members of your family who can drive (manejar) it

f. Your father has given you permission to use it on Saturdays.

g. You must get good marks in your studies to keep this privilege.

h. where you intend to go with it

i. how you plan to keep it clean and shiny

E. Write a letter to a friend, telling him about another friend who is ill and is in the hospital.

a. when he became ill

b. what his illness is

c. in what hospital he is

d. how long he is going to remain in the hospital

e. He is often bored in the hospital.

f. how often you visit him

g. Suggest that your friend try to see him.

h. what the visiting hours are

i. what present would be appropriate to bring him

F. Write a letter to a friend, describing in detail a fire (incendio) you have seen.

a. where the fire took place

b. what kind of building was burned

c. how the fire happened

d. how long the firemen (bomberos) took in (tardar en) coming

e. what the firemen did to extinguish the fire

f. how long the building burned

g. the damage the fire caused

h. what you saw while passing by the building the following day

i. how fires can be avoided

Part VI—*Reading Comprehension*

Below each of the following passages you will find five questions or incomplete statements. Each statement or question is followed by four suggested answers *a* through *d*. Underline the answer that most satisfactorily completes each *in accordance with the meaning of the passage.*

A

Yo estaba absorta en mis oraciones cuando maquinalmente alcé la cabeza y mi vista se dirigió al altar. No sé por qué mis ojos se dirigieron a la imagen en ese momento, digo mal, a la imagen no; se dirigieron a un objeto que hasta entonces no había visto, un objeto que, sin poder explicármelo, llamaba sobre sí toda mi atención. No te rías; aquel objeto era el brazalete de oro que tiene la Madre de Dios en uno de sus brazos. Yo aparté la vista y quise volver a mis pensamientos religiosos. ¡Imposible! Mis ojos se volvían involuntariamente al mismo punto. Las luces del altar reflejaban en los claros diamantes haciéndolos brillar de una manera estupenda.

Salí de la iglesia, vine a casa; pero vine con una idea fija en la imaginación. Me acosté pero no pude dormirme. Pasé la noche que me pareció eterna con aquel pensamiento.

1. Cuando la mujer rezaba,

    a. bajó la cabeza involuntariamente
    b. cerró los ojos
    c. espontáneamente levantó la cabeza
    d. se asustó

2. Su mirada se dirigió

    a. a un objeto que había en el suelo
    b. al techo
    c. a unas joyas brillantes
    d. a la cara de la Virgen

3. Cuando ella quiso continuar meditando,

    a. no pudo hacerlo
    b. lo hizo sin deseos
    c. le dio sueño
    d. lo hizo arrodillándose

4. ¿Qué pudo observar la mujer?

    a. La Virgen movió la cabeza.
    b. Las luces del altar brillaban en la cara de la Virgen.
    c. Las luces del altar hacían resplandecer los diamantes.
    d. El brazalete cayó al suelo.

5. Cuando la mujer se acostó,

    a. se durmió con dificultad
    b. no pudo dormirse pensando en lo que había visto
    c. se alegró de lo que había visto
    d. se sintió enferma

B

Siempre se ha dicho que cuando un hombre inteligente hace una tontería, es casi siempre una tontería enorme. Y como el talento del abuelo Antonio era muy grande, la tontería que hizo fue grandísima también. ¿Tal vez se casó de edad tan avanzada? No, hizo algo todavía mucho peor.

Un hermoso día de primavera, llamó a tres hijos y a una hija que tenía, todos mayores de edad y casados, y distribuyó sus bienes entre ellos con la sola condición de que sus hijos habían de cuidar de él hasta su muerte, que no podía tardar mucho en llegar. Después de haber dado a sus hijos todo lo que tenía, quedó el bondadoso abuelo muy pobre y muy satisfecho, aunque no tanto como sus hijos.

El abuelo Antonio fue sublime modelo de todos los padres imaginables. Sus hijos le querían más que nunca y disputaban por ver quién sería el primero que lo llevara a su casa para cuidarlo. Finalmente se convino en que pasaría algunos meses en casa del mayor; luego en la del segundo; después en la del tercero, y últimamente en casa de su hija, que era la más joven de todos. El abuelo estaba completamente satisfecho del gran amor que le tenían sus hijos.

1. Se ha dicho que cuando un hombre de talento comete un error, este error es

   a. lógico
   b. ilegal
   c. muy grande
   d. insignificante

2. Después de haber dado a sus hijos todo lo que tenía, el abuelo quedó

   a. poco satisfecho
   b. arrepentido
   c. enfermo
   d. más pobre que nunca

3. Al principio sus hijos querían

   a. olvidarlo completamente
   b. devolverle todo el dinero que les había dado
   c. disputarse el dinero que les había dado
   d. invitarlo a sus casas

4. ¿Qué se hizo finalmente para resolver el conflicto?

   a. Mandaron a su padre a su propia casa.
   b. Todos se fueron a vivir juntos.
   c. Decidieron que Antonio visitaría a cada hijo en su turno.
   d. El viejo se quedó a vivir solo.

5. El abuelo se sentía

   a. completamente desilusionado
   b. solo y sin familia
   c. contento del amor de sus hijos
   d. temeroso de que sus hijos lo abandonasen

C

Entre los muebles de la nueva casa había una enorme caja, cerrada con tres llaves, que le había prestado el señor cura. Por ser muy grande y sólida, por su venerable apariencia, y por estar cerrada con tres llaves, la caja llamó la atención a todos los que visitaban al abuelo Antonio y especialmente la de sus avariciosos hijos. ¿Estaría llena de monedas? ¿Qué habría dentro de ella? Nadie había recordado haberla visto antes. Cierto día, uno de los más curiosos quiso levantarla pero no pudo ni moverla, aunque era un hombre robusto.

Aquel mismo día corrió por el pueblo la noticia de que el abuelo en su casa tenía una caja llena de oro, bastante para comprar todas las casas y tierras del vecindario. Naturalmente, sus hijos se alegraron muchísimo, calculando la suma que iba a tocarles cuando muriera el viejo, el cual por ley natural no podría vivir muchos años. No es necesario decir que le visitaban frecuentemente, tratándole con mucho cariño.

1. En la casa había una caja que

    a. había obtenido de un sacerdote
    b. el abuelo había comprado
    c. fue robada por uno de los hijos de Antonio
    d. el viejo había prestado al cura

2. La caja era

    a. muy baja y ancha
    b. inmensa y pesadísima
    c. nueva
    d. de poco valor

3. El que trató de levantar la caja

    a. pudo levantarla sin dificultad
    b. era muy débil
    c. la abrió
    d. no pudo hacerlo

4. ¿Qué noticia corrió por todo el pueblo?

    a. El abuelo iba a comprar todas las casas del pueblo.
    b. En la caja había un gran secreto.
    c. El anciano tenía la caja llena de riquezas.
    d. Antonio sacaba dinero de la caja a menudo.

5. Desde aquel momento sus hijos esperaban

    a. el día de la muerte de Antonio
    b. poder ayudar al padre
    c. heredar las casas que poseía Antonio
    d. que su padre les dijese el secreto

D

Los esposos, que estaban en la cocina, vieron cruzar por delante de la ventana una sombra enorme que eclipsó momentáneamente el sol. Al mismo tiempo las gallinas se pusieron a cacarear ruidosamente: parecía que un animal feroz había entrado en su corral para hacerles daño.

—¿Qué es eso?—preguntó la mujer.

—Será el águila que ha tomado especial interés en nuestras gallinas. Ya se ha llevado dos; pero yo te juro que no se ha de llevar la tercera—dijo el marido, cogiendo el fusil y dirigiéndose a la puerta de la cocina.

La mujer fue también; pero al ver lo que pasaba en el corral, dio un grito imposible de imitar, uno de esos gritos que sólo una madre sabe dar cuando ve a su hijo en peligro de muerte.

El hombre no gritó, pero su cara se puso tan pálida como la de un muerto.

—¡Mi hija! ¡Mi Quiqueta! ¡Mi alma!—gritó la madre corriendo al corral como una tigre.

El hombre corrió también y se puso la escopeta a la cara.

—¡No tires, no tires!—exclamó la mujer.

1. ¿Qué llamó la atención de esta pareja?

    a. la luz del sol
    b. el ruido de los pollos
    c. la repentina negrura del cielo
    d. la apariencia de un animal feroz

2. Ellos creían que un animal

    a. salía del corral
    b. estaba persiguiendo a alguna persona
    c. andaba buscando algo que comer
    d. buscaba refugio en su casa

3. ¿Qué juró el marido?

    a. que no tenía fusil
    b. que no mataría el animal
    c. no perder otra gallina
    d. no hacer daño a su mujer

4. ¿Cuál fue la reacción de la madre?

    a. Salió para espantar el águila.
    b. Dio un grito de dolor.
    c. Se cayó desmayada.
    d. Comenzó a imitar el ruido de las gallinas.

5. ¿Qué hizo el hombre?

    a. Quería disparar el fusil, pero no lo hizo.
    b. Calmó a su esposa lo mejor que pudo.
    c. Dio a su mujer un golpe en la cara.
    d. Corrió tras el tigre.

E

En aquel entonces había por las cercanías de Montserrat un castillo, ya olvidado, cuyos últimos señores fueron tres hermanos a cuál más gallardo en aspecto y más diestro en armas. Se llamaban, según el orden de su nacimiento, Ramón, Bernardo, y Guillermo. Los tres andaban muy enamorados de la misma dama. Era ésta una mujer muy hermosa y dura de corazón, que tenía placer más en ser amada de los hombres que en amar, y cuya constancia y seriedad eran mucho menos que su hermosura.

Los tres hermanos cayeron a sus pies y le confesaron su amor, pidiéndole su corazón y su mano. La dama les contestó que era imposible que los tres se casasen con ella, que su corazón y su mano sólo podrían pertenecer a uno, y como los tres le eran perfectamente iguales, en la imposibilidad de elegir entre ellos, se casaría con aquel que mostrara mayores méritos para ganar su mano. Los tres hermanos se miraron uno a otro, y cada uno pensó que los otros constituían el único estorbo para su felicidad. La desunión estalló entre ellos, se maldijeron en secreto el uno al otro, se afrentaron en público. Cada uno quería quitar de su camino la figura de los otros hermanos.

1. ¿Qué se sabe del castillo?

   a. Todavía existe.
   b. No se sabe dónde está.
   c. Pertenecía a unos hermanos.
   d. Era un castillo hermoso.

2. ¿Cómo se llamaba el hermano mayor?

   a. No se sabe.
   b. Bernardo
   c. Guillermo
   d. Ramón

3. ¿Cómo era la mujer?

   a. frívola
   b. bastante seria
   c. sentimental
   d. constante y fiel

4. La mujer consintió en casarse con

   a. el mejor
   b. el mayor
   c. los tres
   d. el que la amaba más

5. ¿Qué efecto tuvieron las palabras de la dama?

   a. Hicieron felices a los hermanos.
   b. Los hermanos llegaron a ser enemigos.
   c. La unión entre los hermanos se hizo más firme.
   d. Los tres decidieron hacer un viaje.

F

De un salto salí a la calle y me puse a correr, pero de pronto me di cuenta de que no tenía mi sombrero y me volví. Entré de nuevo en el portal con gran miedo. Encendí un fósforo y eché una mirada a la víctima, esperando verle mover, pero se quedaba inmóvil en el mismo sitio. Busqué el sombrero, me lo puse, y salí a la calle.

Pero esta vez no corrí porque el instinto de conservación me dominaba y pensaba solamente en los medios de evadir la cárcel. Caminé a la sombra de la pared y haciendo el menor ruido con los pasos entré en la calle de San Joaquín. Pero cuando yo ya había llegado cerca de mi casa, se me acercó un guardia y me dijo:

—Don Elías, ¿me hará usted el favor de decirme . . . ?

No oí más. Eché a correr por las calles de la ciudad como un loco hasta llegar a las afueras de la ciudad. Allí me paré y empecé a pensar en lo que acababa de hacer. Me dije ¡Qué estúpido había sido! Aquel guardia me conocía. Pensaría que estaba loco; pero a la mañana siguiente se sabría en la ciudad el crimen y el guardia tendría sospechas de mí. Yo estaba cogido de terror.

1. ¿Por qué volvió don Elías al portal?

   a. La víctima se había movido del sitio.
   b. Se dio cuenta de que había olvidado algo.
   c. Quería hallar unos fósforos perdidos.
   d. Quería saber si conocía al hombre.

2. Cuando don Elías salió a la calle por segunda vez, caminó

   a. más apresuradamente que antes
   b. fumando un cigarrillo
   c. sin hacer mucho ruido
   d. hacia la cárcel

3. Cuando don Elías vio al policía,

   a. le pidió un favor
   b. se puso a correr
   c. le hizo una pregunta
   d. se puso nervioso pero siguió su camino

4. Don Elías se creyó tonto porque

   a. el guardia sabía quién era
   b. tenía el corazón débil
   c. nadie había visto el crimen que había cometido aquella noche
   d. el guardia podría dispararle un tiro

5. Cuando don Elías se dio cuenta de lo que había hecho,

   a. se echó a réir
   b. se fue a otro pueblo
   c. tenía miedo
   d. no le importaba

G

Las golondrinas pueden moverse de un lado a otro con toda rapidez para atrapar cualquier insecto que trate de evitarlas. También pueden bajar del cielo y cambiar en seguida el vuelo vertical en horizontal. El punto flaco en la anatomía de la golondrina son sus patas, tan pequeñas, que apenas le permiten posarse. Los alambres del telégrafo parecen ser sus perchas más cómodas; y se ve con frecuencia cómo dan de comer a sus polluelos mientras se mantienen agarradas a los alambres.

De muy antiguo los campesinos consideran a estos pájaros valiosos para pronosticar el tiempo. Si vuelan bajo, anuncian frío y lluvia; si alto, sol y calor. Esta creencia no carece de base, pues las golondrinas siempre están buscando insectos para comerlos. Los insectos acomodan su vuelo a las variaciones atmosféricas; y por donde van los insectos, por allí vuelan las golondrinas.

1. La golondrina puede cambiar su vuelo

    a. con bastante dificultad
    b. volando al revés
    c. al instante
    d. para evitar los insectos

2. Las patas de la golondrina son

    a. fuertes y prominentes
    b. muy chicas
    c. muy útiles para coger insectos
    d. útiles para volar

3. Las golondrinas se agarran a los alambres porque

    a. pueden mantenerse allí fácilmente
    b. encuentran allí la comida
    c. tienen polluelos
    d. son flacas

4. ¿Cómo ayudan las golondrinas a los campesinos?

    a. Comen los insectos que hacen daño a las plantas.
    b. Les indican cómo va a ser el día.
    c. Les dicen la hora.
    d. Cantan alegremente.

5. Por lo general, ¿dónde van las golondrinas?

    a. donde no hay base sólida
    b. donde hay seres humanos
    c. donde hay clima favorable
    d. dondequiera que hallen comida

H

Dos niños, llamados Pablo y Juan, eran vecinos de un mismo pueblo. Aquél vivía en una casa elegante; tenía caballos, coches, y criados, y su única ocupación era ir a la escuela y estudiar sus lecciones.

El padre del segundo niño, por el contrario, era pobre y no tenía más que un pequeño terreno que le producía apenas para sostener a su familia. Su hijo le ayudaba; pero siempre que sus ocupaciones se lo consentían, el padre le enviaba a la escuela, según se lo había aconsejado el cura del lugar.

La primera vez que Juan se presentó en la escuela, los niños de familias ricas se burlaron de su pobre traje. Juan, comparando su vestido con los de sus condiscípulos, comprendió que era su pobre aspecto la causa de tanto desprecio, y se le saltaron las lágrimas a los ojos.

Pablo, viendo llorar al pobre niño, sintió compasión, y acercándosele le dijo:

—No te aflijas; yo me sentaré siempre a tu lado.

Esta muestra de bondad hizo a Juan derramar lágrimas de gozo.

—No puedo verte llorar así—continuó Pablo—vamos, y te prometo ser tu amigo; jugaremos siempre juntos y te defenderé de los compañeros si intentan maltratarte.

Juan, tomando la mano del compasivo niño, le dijo:

—Yo también seré tu amigo, y ¡ojalá pueda algún día pagarte el bien que hoy me haces!

1. Pablo vivía

    a. en una casa ordinaria
    b. en una casa muy cómoda
    c. en un pueblo elegante
    d. cerca de la escuela

2. El padre de Juan trataba de

    a. vivir como los ricos
    b. poner a su hijo en el monasterio
    c. educar a su hijo
    d. asistir a la escuela

3. ¿De qué se rieron los niños ricos cuando vieron a Juan?

    a. Era pequeño.
    b. No comprendía nada.
    c. No llevaba ropa elegante.
    d. Lloraba con frecuencia.

4. ¿Qué hizo Pablo?

    a. Le dio una bofetada a Juan.
    b. Le prometió ayuda y amistad.
    c. Se puso a llorar también.
    d. No hizo caso a Juan.

5. ¿Cuál fue la reacción de Juan?

    a. Maltrató a Pablo.
    b. Defendió a los que eran menos fuertes que él.
    c. No quiso volver a la escuela.
    d. Aceptó el ofrecimiento de Pablo.

I

Una noche, para mí memorable, mi madre, que sin duda me esperaba, hízome sentar junto al fuego y me habló así:

—Hijo mío, tienes diecisiete años. Yo soy vieja y tú no eres rico; menester es que pensemos en tu porvenir y tratemos de asegurarte el mañana. Hace unos días le escribí a Braulio, el hermano de tu padre, proponiéndole que te admitiese en su casa, prometiéndole yo, por supuesto, una pensión. Me contestó que estaba conforme en recibirte, y a vuelta de correo quedó cerrado nuestro negocio. Nada te había dicho hasta ahora, porque la sola idea de la separación me causa dolor. Pero como al fin es preciso, me decidí a hacerte sabedor del proyecto y a preparar tu partida. Deseo que aproveches la juventud que nunca vuelve. Sé bueno . . . y no te olvides de que aquí estará tu madre que te adora y rezará por ti a la Virgen Santísima.

Apenas se habían secado mis lágrimas cuando se me ocurrió la idea de que tenía que separarme de Juana. Aquella misma noche referí a mi novia la conversación de mi madre. Juana se entristeció también y me preguntó la fecha del viaje.

1. ¿Qué había hecho la madre?

   a. Había escrito a su hijo.
   b. Se había comunicado con su cuñado.
   c. Había pedido dinero al hermano de su padre.
   d. Había prometido su casa a Braulio.

2. ¿Qué causaba dolor a la madre?

   a. la necesidad de alejarse de su hijo
   b. la idea de separarse de su dinero
   c. la muerte de su esposo
   d. su avanzada edad

3. La madre quería que su hijo

   a. rezase a la Virgen por ella
   b. fuese bueno
   c. se olvidase de su juventud
   d. se despidiese de su tío

4. ¿Qué preocupaba al hijo?

   a. la falta de dinero
   b. su falta de experiencia en la vida
   c. su tío Braulio
   d. tener que dejar a su novia

5. Al recibir la noticia, Juana le preguntó

   a. si podría acompañarle
   b. adónde iba
   c. cuándo se iba
   d. si estaba triste

J

Lagartera es un pueblo de la provincia de Toledo. Sus trajes, sus fiestas, sus costumbres hablan de un pasado que se conserva casi intacto. Lo más curioso que tiene Lagartera es la ceremonia de las bodas.

Una boda de Lagartera rompe la monotonía de la vida del pueblo. No es una ocasión íntima, sino una fiesta popular. Dura cuatro días y cada uno de ellos tiene su ceremonia y su nombre especiales.

El primer día, que es la víspera de la boda, se llama el "día de la carne." Se llama así por el número de gallinas, pavos, y ovejas que las familias de los novios matan ese día en honor de los novios.

Ese día cuatro muchachos elegidos por la novia, que forman su corte, van a visitar al novio, llevándole el regalo que le hace la novia. Después de recibirlo, el novio viene a visitar a la novia y a convidar a los hombres que estén con ella para que ellos le acompañen a la peluquería y así, parientes e invitados, hacen afeitarse a costa del novio.

1. ¿Qué es Lagartera?

   a. un lugar lejos de Toledo
   b. una ciudad moderna
   c. un pueblo de gente habladora
   d. una población toledana

2. Lo más notable de Lagartera son

   a. los trajes
   b. los matrimonios
   c. las bodegas
   d. las fiestas

3. ¿Cuál es "el día de la carne"?

   a. el día en que se casan los novios
   b. el día en que los novios comen carne
   c. el primer día de la fiesta
   d. el día en que no se sirve carne

4. ¿Quiénes visitan al novio?

   a. unos jóvenes escogidos por la novia
   b. los padres de la novia
   c. unos amigos del novio
   d. el barbero del lugar

5. El novio tiene que pagar

   a. toda la fiesta
   b. los regalos que le hace la novia
   c. al barbero
   d. al padre de la novia

K

Al hablar de las ilusiones y esperanzas que tenemos, pero que nunca podremos realizar, es costumbre decir, en muchas diferentes lenguas, que esos deseos son nuestros "castillos en España."

Y hoy día, cuando en España van desapareciendo algunos castillos como uno de los resultados de la terrible guerra civil, esta expresión parece más apta que nunca.

Pero a pesar de eso, existen todavía castillos en España, y muchos: castillos de origen remoto, monumentos a la Edad Media y a los tiempos subsiguientes. Algunos de estos castillos están bien conservados. Otros están en ruinas. Todos están llenos de recuerdos históricos de gran interés.

Los castillos españoles no se pueden llamar ni bellos ni refinados. Son fuertes, austeros y sencillos, con la sencillez y la austeridad que amenazan más bien que encantan. Traducen a la actualidad el espíritu inquieto y bélico de los tiempos pasados. Se levantan en medio del paisaje como inmensos centinelas que lo dominan todo. ¡Lo que pudieran contar esas torres que van desapareciendo!

1. Para nosotros, la expresión "castillos en España" se refiere a

    a. edificios antiguos de la Edad Media
    b. esperanzas imposibles
    c. castillos históricos
    d. monumentos de arquitectura medieval

2. Algunos castillos desaparecen a causa de

    a. su mala construcción
    b. una guerra entre los españoles mismos
    c. el gran interés por parte del gobierno
    d. estar bien conservados

3. Los castillos que todavía quedan en la península

    a. son modernos
    b. son del tiempo de los romanos
    c. son pocos
    d. son de la época medieval y después

4. Los castillos españoles son

    a. bellos
    b. encantadores
    c. rascacielos
    d. severos

5. En estos castillos podemos darnos cuenta

    a. del espíritu militar de la época medieval
    b. de la grandeza de la España de hoy
    c. de la vida pacífica y tranquila de las épocas pasadas
    d. de que nunca se realizan las esperanzas

L

Carlos, a los veinticinco años de edad, fue a reunirse con su padre, un médico que vivía en las selvas con una tribu de salvajes. De bonísimo corazón y clara inteligencia, fue tierno y dulce poeta casi desde niño. A los veinticinco años había visto más vida que otros a los cincuenta. El drama del mundo había comenzado demasiado pronto para él, y vio sus variadas escenas con la clara mirada del talento, comprendiéndolas y apreciándolas más correctamente que los mismos que hacían un papel más activo en ellas. Para él la esencia de la vida estaba en el pensamiento, y como pensaba mucho vivía más aprisa.

El joven Carlos frecuentemente se ponía triste en la ciudad y buscaba la soledad y el silencio. Cuando se halló en el corazón de las selvas, creyó hallarse en su elemento; tenía soledad, silencio, cierta misteriosa grandeza que le rodeaba por todas partes, y una libertad que nunca hasta entonces había gozado.

Como su padre, Carlos supo hacerse querer en su nuevo pueblo, y se complacía del título de "hermano" que le daban los salvajes y la familiaridad que, conforme con ese trato, empleaban siempre con él. Se apresuró a comprar una canoa y aprendió a manejarla con sorprendente habilidad.

1. Carlos a los 25 años

    a. había adquirido mucha experiencia

    b. consideraba terminada su vida

    c. se había graduado de médico

    d. era amante del teatro

2. Carlos vivía a paso rápido porque

    a. le gustaba escribir poesías

    b. era inteligente y meditativo

    c. creía que su vida sería corta

    d. veía los horrores de la selva

3. Cuando se encontró en medio del bosque,

    a. se sintió muy triste

    b. quería volver a la vida del pueblo

    c. fue muy temido de los salvajes

    d. se acostumbró fácilmente a la nueva vida

4. ¿Qué pudo apreciar Carlos?

    a. la vida libre

    b. la frialdad de la nueva atmósfera

    c. la vida amarga de los salvajes

    d. la ansiedad manifestada por los desgraciados

5. ¿Cómo le recibieron los habitantes de la selva?

    a. con desprecio

    b. con enemistad

    c. con placer

    d. con tristeza

M

En toda la vega se observaba rigurosamente la fiesta del domingo, y como había cosecha reciente y no poco dinero, todos participaban con alegría en las festividades. No se veía un solo hombre trabajando en los campos ni una caballería en los caminos. Pasaban las viejas por los caminos con la reluciente mantilla sobre los ojos y la cesta al brazo, como si tirase de ellas la campana que sonaba lejos, muy lejos, sobre los techos del pueblo. En los campos gritaba un numeroso grupo de niños. Sobre el verde de los prados se destacaban los pantalones rojos de algunos soldaditos que aprovechaban la fiesta para pasar una hora en sus casas. Sonaban a lo lejos, como tela que se rompe, los escopetazos contra las bandadas de golondrinas que volaban de un lado a otro en contradanza caprichosa, con un suave silbido, como si cortasen con sus alas el azul cristal del cielo.

1. ¿Por qué había festividades?

   a. Los campesinos habían recibido regalos.
   b. Se habían celebrado unas fiestas.
   c. La gente tenía dinero.
   d. Los precios eran bajos.

2. ¿Qué se podía notar en la vega?

   a. Nadie trabajaba.
   b. Nadie se movía de su casa.
   c. Los caminos estaban desiertos.
   d. Dominaba el silencio.

3. Las viejas

   a. llevaban joyas ricas
   b. llevaban traje de domingo
   c. gritaban a sus hijos
   d. llevaban regalos para los soldados

4. ¿Dónde estaban los soldados?

   a. en el campo de batalla
   b. descansando sobre la hierba
   c. con sus familias
   d. tocando la guitarra

5. Los pájaros volaban

   a. ruidosamente, sin dejar dormir a nadie
   b. espantados por los tiros
   c. destruyendo las banderas
   d. luchando unos contra otros

N

Seis años pasaron allí padre e hija, retirados del mundo. Ella recibió en la soledad la más brillante educación, gracias al cuidado del padre, ayudado por Miss Fanny, una profesora que el doctor había hecho venir de Londres para que se encargara de enseñar a Sofía todo lo que debe saber una señorita de los tiempos modernos. Su hija era para él la recompensa de una vida dedicada al bien de la humanidad y al servicio de su patria. Sabían por los periódicos que aún existía Madrid, y que allí las gentes se divertían, se amaban o se odiaban; y lo mismo el viejo que la niña sonreían al leer la relación de una fiesta, de una discusión política, de un suceso cualquiera, con indiferencia completa.

Sofía tenía quince años y no sentía la necesidad de conocer el mundo. Era un pájaro que no quería salir del nido.

Cuando Miss Fanny dio por terminada su misión, volvió a Inglaterra, entregando al padre una joven cuya educación podía competir con la de cualquier princesa europea.

1. ¿Qué hicieron durante seis años padre e hija?

  a. Perdieron contacto directo con el mundo exterior.
  b. Viajaron por Inglaterra.
  c. Vagaron por el mundo.
  d. Se establecieron en la capital.

2. ¿Cómo fue educada Sofía?

  a. Estudió en un convento.
  b. Su padre la envió a Madrid.
  c. Una maestra extranjera le enseñó todo lo que necesitaba saber.
  d. Se educó en una escuela de Londres.

3. Sofía sabía

  a. cuidar a su padre
  b. lo que leía en los periódicos
  c. mucho acerca de las costumbres de los pájaros
  d. mucho acerca de la vida de Londres

4. El padre y la hija

  a. iban a algunas fiestas
  b. discutían la política
  c. se odiaban
  d. estaban contentos lejos del mundo elegante

5. Sofía podría compararse con

  a. un pájaro que quería dejar el nido
  b. un pájaro contento de quedarse en el nido
  c. Miss Fanny
  d. todas las princesas europeas

O

En los quince días que don Ramón estuvo en Madrid, yo no tuve razón para arrepentirme de compartir con él mi cuarto. Si volvía a casa más tarde que yo, entraba y se acostaba con tal cautela, que nunca me despertó; si se retiraba temprano, me aguardaba leyendo para que yo pudiese acostarme sin temor de hacer ruido. Por la mañana nunca se despertaba hasta que me oía moverme en la cama. Vivía cerca de Valencia, en una casa de campo, y sólo venía a Madrid cuando algún asunto urgente lo exigía. A pesar de que su hijo tenía la misma edad que yo, don Ramón no pasaba de los cincuenta años, lo cual hacía presumir que se había casado bastante joven. Aún ahora, con su elevada estatura, la barba gris y bien cortada, y los ojos animados y brillantes, sería aceptado por muchas mujeres con preferencia a otros galanes.

1. Los dos hombres vivieron por dos semanas

   a. arrepintiéndose de su crimen
   b. en la misma habitación
   c. sin verse en Madrid
   d. disputándose todo lo que tenían

2. Ramón no le molestaba a su compañero porque

   a. nunca llegaba tarde
   b. entraba cuidadosamente
   c. le gustaba acostarse temprano
   d. le gustaba leer en silencio

3. ¿Por qué leía Ramón?

   a. No quería que su amigo tuviera miedo de hacer ruido.
   b. De esta manera podía dormirse más fácilmente.
   c. No quería despertar a su compañero.
   d. Tenía miedo de la oscuridad.

4. Ramón venía a Madrid porque

   a. quería visitar a su hijo
   b. no le gustaba su casa de campo
   c. la vida madrileña le gustaba
   d. le llamaban unos negocios importantes

5. Las mujeres preferirían a don Ramón porque

   a. era rico
   b. tenía un hijo
   c. era alto y de buen aspecto
   d. era inteligente

P

Martín llegó a las doce y pico a casa de su protector y encontró cerrada la puerta. Dio algunos ligeros golpes que nadie, al parecer, oyó en el interior de la casa, y se retiró sin atreverse a hacer otra tentativa para entrar. Se armó de paciencia y se resolvió a pasar la noche recorriendo las calles sin alejarse mucho de la casa de don Dámaso.

Santiago era entonces una ciudad silenciosa desde temprano; así fue que Martín no tuvo más espectáculo durante sus correrías que las fachadas de las casas y los serenos que quedaban inmóviles en cada esquina, los ojos cerrados en pacífico sueño, velando así por la seguridad de la población.

Al día siguiente pudo Martín entrar en la casa cuando se abrió la puerta para dar paso al criado que iba a la plaza. Éste le miró con una sonrisa burlona que entristeció al joven.

1. ¿Cuándo llegó Martín a casa de su protector?

   a. cuando el reloj daba las doce
   b. poco antes de cerrarse la casa
   c. poco después de la medianoche
   d. al anochecer

2. Martín decidió

   a. quedarse detrás de la puerta
   b. pasar la noche cerca de la casa de don Dámaso
   c. seguir su viaje
   d. despertar al sereno

3. Mientras caminaba Martín por las calles,

   a. no ocurrió nada de particular
   b. las casas parecían tener caras
   c. había espectáculos en las calles
   d. no vio a nadie

4. ¿Qué hacían los serenos?

   a. Se paseaban por las calles.
   b. Gritaban para despertar a la gente.
   c. Hablaban entre sí para pasar el tiempo.
   d. Dormían.

5. Martín pudo entrar en la casa porque

   a. el criado volvió de la plaza
   b. el criado tenía que salir
   c. el criado le invitó a entrar
   d. el criado tuvo lástima de él

Q

Batiste estaba sereno y firme, sin arrogancia. Se reía de la inquietud de su familia y se ponía cada vez más atrevido conforme transcurría el tiempo desde la famosa riña.

Se consideraba seguro porque mientras llevase pendiente del brazo el magnífico "pájaro de dos voces," como él llamaba su rifle, podía marchar por toda la huerta. Y como iba en tan buena compañía, sus enemigos fingían no conocerle. Hasta algunas veces había visto a su mayor enemigo, Pimentó. Éste paseaba por la huerta como bandera de venganza, su cabeza envuelta en un paño rojo a pesar de que estaba repuesto de su herida. En estas ocasiones, Pimentó parecía huir, temiendo el encuentro tal vez más que Batiste.

Todos le miraban a Batiste, pero jamás se oyó una palabra de insulto. Le volvían la espalda con desprecio; se inclinaban sobre la tierra y trabajaban febrilmente hasta perderle de vista.

1. ¿De qué se reía Batiste?

   a. de la ansiedad de su mujer e hijos
   b. de la arrogancia de su familia
   c. del valor de sus enemigos
   d. del cantar de sus pájaros

2. ¿Cómo salía de casa?

   a. de prisa, volando como los pájaros
   b. sin ser visto por sus enemigos
   c. protegido por una arma
   d. llevando su instrumento músico

3. ¿Qué hacían sus enemigos?

   a. No le hacían caso.
   b. Llevaban un rifle.
   c. Le insultaban.
   d. Se le acercaban con cuidado.

4. Pimentó parecía huirse porque

   a. tenía la cabeza envuelta en un paño
   b. quería vengarse de su enemigo, Batiste
   c. había destruido la huerta
   d. tenía miedo de encontrar a Batiste

5. ¿Cómo fingían sus enemigos no conocerle a Batiste?

   a. Le evitaban la mirada directa.
   b. Le decían palabras de insulto.
   c. Se pusieron de pie al verle.
   d. Le maldecían.

R

Cumandá, la joven india, siente hambre; busca con ávidos ojos algún árbol frutal, y no tarda en descubrir uno de uva a corta distancia; se dirige a él, y aún alcanza a divisar por el suelo algunos racimos de la exquisita fruta; mas cuando va a tomarlos, advierte al pie del tronco y medio escondido entre unas ramas un tigre. La uva atrae a varios animales, y éstos atraen a su vez al tigre que los espera, especialmente en las primeras horas de la mañana. La joven, que felizmente no ha sido vista por la fiera, se aleja de puntillas y luego se escapa en rápida carrera.

Se le ha aumentado la sed y no halla arroyo donde apagarla. El sol abrasador y los pétalos más frescos van secándose como los sedientos labios de la joven; en vano prueba repetidas veces las aguas del río Palora; este río no es querido de las aves, y los indios creen que el beberlas mata a uno.

1. Cumandá buscaba el árbol porque

    a. quería hallar comida
    b. deseaba ver todo el paisaje
    c. tenía que descansar
    d. estaba cansada de ver las uvas

2. ¿Por qué estaba el tigre cerca del árbol frutal?

    a. Quería descansar entre las ramas.
    b. Había oído los pasos de Cumandá.
    c. Buscaba protección contra otros animales feroces.
    d. Esperaba coger algún animal.

3. ¿Qué hizo Cumandá?

    a. Se comió las frutas.
    b. Se apartó del lugar y se puso a correr.
    c. Se sentó debajo del árbol.
    d. Mató al tigre.

4. Los labios de la india

    a. estaban más frescos que los pétalos de una flor
    b. eran bellos como un arroyo
    c. estaban abrasados por el sol y la falta de agua
    d. eran del color de las uvas

5. ¿Dónde trata de apagar la sed?

    a. en un arroyo que halla por allí
    b. en la sombra donde no hay sol
    c. en las aguas del río favorito de los pájaros
    d. en cierto río de aguas impuras

S

El gitano siguió hablando:—Ayer por la tarde caímos mi burro y yo en poder de unos ladrones. Me llevaron a su campamento y allí me quedé hasta la noche. Durante todo el camino pensaba yo: ¿serán estos bandidos de Parrón? Si lo son, me matan, porque ese maldito asesina a todos los que le han visto la cara. Mi terror iba creciendo. Llegada la noche, se presentó un hombre vestido con mucho lujo, y sonriendo con gracia me dijo:—¡Yo soy Parrón!

Al oír esto me puse de rodillas temblando y exclamé:—¡Bendita sea su alma, rey de los hombres! Yo soy amigo suyo. ¿Quiere que le diga la buenaventura? ¿Quiere que le enseñe a cambiar burros muertos por burros vivos? ¿Quiere que le enseñe francés a una mula?

Al decir esto, el gitano le tomó la mano a Parrón para decirle la suerte. De repente dejó caer la mano y gritó:—Aunque me quite la vida, Parrón, no puedo cambiar la suerte que veo en su mano. Morirá ahorcado.

—Ya lo sé—respondió el bandido con toda tranquilidad. —Dime cuándo.

—El mes que viene—respondió el gitano.

Parrón pensó un momento. —Bueno—dijo. —Vas a quedarte aquí. Si no me ahorcan en un mes, yo te ahorco a ti.

Diciendo esto, el bandido se fue por entre unos árboles.

1. ¿Qué le pasó al gitano?

   a. Se cayó del burro.
   b. Perdió su burro.
   c. Capturó a unos ladrones.
   d. Fue preso por unos bandidos.

2. Parrón acostumbraba matar a

   a. sus hombres
   b. los gitanos
   c. los que pudieran reconocerle
   d. los ladrones

3. Cuando se presentó Parrón al gitano, éste

   a. le atacó
   b. no pudo hablar
   c. dijo a Parrón que se pusiera de rodillas
   d. se arrodilló

4. El gitano dejó caer la mano de Parrón porque

   a. quería cambiar burros muertos por burros vivos
   b. tenía miedo de decirle la verdad
   c. vio en ella la muerte de Parrón
   d. vio en la mano la buena fortuna de Parrón

5. Si dentro de un mes no moría Parrón, el gitano

   a. recibiría muchas riquezas
   b. estaría libre
   c. sería matado
   d. podría considerarse bandido también

T

Había cierto rey que era un gran monarca, pero que se enojaba a menudo, haciendo temblar a todos. Amaba mucho a su caballo, animal que se había ganado el cariño de su amo por su belleza y por su inteligencia.

Un día que el rey estaba muy enojado, le dijeron que su caballo estaba muy enfermo. Llamó a los más célebres médicos, pero el caballo se ponía cada día más enfermo. Furioso por no poder salvar, a pesar de su grandeza, la vida de un caballo, les dijo a sus criados:

—¡Mandaré ahorcar al primero que me traiga la noticia de la muerte de mi caballo!

El animal murió y nadie se atrevió a darle al rey la fatal noticia. Cuando el rey llamó a todos para pedirles informes, un criado contestó:

—Señor, el animal continúa en el mismo lugar, acostado, sin moverse; no come, ni bebe, ni duerme, ni ve, ni respira . . .

—¡Desgraciado!—interrumpió el rey, —¡el caballo está muerto!

—Es verdad, señor, —respondió el criado, —pero Su Majestad es el primero que lo dice.

1. Todos tenían miedo al rey cuando

    a. se enfadaba
    b. le veían pasar montado a caballo
    c. hablaba de su caballo
    d. le veían temblar

2. Cuando supo que el caballo se había enfermado, el rey declaró que

    a. mataría al que le anunciara la muerte del animal
    b. haría matar a los médicos
    c. él mismo salvaría la vida del caballo
    d. él mismo mataría al caballo

3. ¿Qué ocurrió cuando el animal se murió?

    a. Todos sus súbditos le trajeron la noticia al rey.
    b. Nadie le informó al rey de lo ocurrido.
    c. Los médicos huyeron del palacio.
    d. Le trajeron otro caballo semejante.

4. El criado le dio la mala noticia

    a. sin mirarle
    b. francamente
    c. sin moverse
    d. indirectamente

5. Lo cómico del caso es que

    a. los médicos pudieron salvarle la vida al caballo
    b. el criado dijo una mentira
    c. el rey mismo pronunció las palabras fatales
    d. el rey echó la culpa a los médicos desgraciados

Part VII—*Auditory Comprehension*

QUESTIONS AND ALTERNATIVES

After the reading of each paragraph by the Teacher, write the *number* of the alternative that best answers each question. Base your answers only on the content of the paragraph.

1. ¿De dónde era Fernando?

   1 del campo   2 de la capital   3 de la universidad   4 de la ciudad

2. ¿Dónde tuvo el teniente que pasar una noche?

   1 en el colegio   2 en una casa de locos   3 en el hotel   4 en prisión

3. ¿Qué había hecho el padre?

   1 Había mirado a los indios sin hablar.   3 Había sacado el mercurio de la mina.
   2 Había comprado el mercurio.   4 Había averiguado dónde estaba la mina.

4. ¿Qué parte del día era?

   1 el anochecer   2 el mediodía   3 el amanecer   4 la medianoche

5. ¿Por qué vino el hombre a la casa?

   1 Se había perdido.   3 Quería pasar el invierno.
   2 Tenía fiebre.   4 Estaba en el bosque.

6. ¿Qué creía el autor?

   1 que el hombre estaba dormido   3 que el hombre estaba muerto
   2 que el hombre se había ido   4 que el hombre se movía

7. ¿Qué debió hacer la comisión?

   1 controlar los precios de artículos esenciales
   2 investigar cómo México arregla los precios de las necesidades
   3 estudiar el gobierno de México
   4 escribir leyes

8. ¿Por qué no estaba la señorita Inés al lado de David?

   1 Estaba triste.   3 Iba a morir.
   2 Cuidaba a una mujer enferma.   4 Estaba muerta.

9. ¿Qué es una tertulia?

   1 un grupo de artistas   3 una serie de conferencias
   2 una reunión informal   4 una persona interesante

10. ¿En qué pone más atención el indio?

    1 en la producción de los artículos
    2 en vender los artículos
    3 en la hermosura y en la utilidad de lo que hace
    4 separar sus productos según el precio

11. ¿Qué se describe aquí?

    1 una sala de conferencias   2 una taberna   3 un restaurante   4 una confitería

12. ¿Cuándo se puso en marcha para su casa?

   1 por la mañana   2 una hora antes del anochecer   3 por la tarde   4 a las ocho

13. ¿A dónde iban las personas?

   1 a Madrid   2 a la estación   3 a sus ciudades   4 a la clase

14. ¿Qué deseaba la mayor parte de los hidalgos pobres?

   1 eliminar a sus rivales   3 acusar falsamente a Balboa
   2 enriquecerse en el Nuevo Mundo   4 trabajar mucho en el Nuevo Mundo

15. ¿Cómo es el clima de la América latina?

   1 como el de la Florida   2 tropical   3 muy variado   4 subantártico

16. ¿Qué se sabe del buque?

   1 Iba a salir pronto.   2 Acababa de llegar.   3 Ya había salido.   4 No iba a salir.

17. ¿De qué tenía miedo el muchacho?

   1 del mar   2 de la tempestad   3 de una lancha   4 del tiempo que pasaba

18. ¿Para qué tenía que ir a Aljama?

   1 para pasar el invierno   3 para ver al médico
   2 para curarse   4 para coger un ataque de reuma

19. ¿Cuál fue un resultado del viaje de Marco Polo?

   1 Se creyó que era difícil llegar al Oriente navegando por el Atlántico.
   2 La gente supo que el mundo era grande.
   3 Los europeos llegaron a conocer una ruta marítima a la India.
   4 La gente llegó a conocer nuevas riquezas.

20. ¿Qué tipo de persona era el gaucho?

   1 obediente a la ley   2 triste   3 independiente   4 actor

21. ¿Cómo se sentía el hombre?

   1 fuerte   2 agitado   3 enojado   4 débil

22. ¿En qué situación se hallaba este hombre?

   1 enfermo pero rico   3 con salud pero pobre
   2 enfermo y pobre   4 con salud y rico

23. ¿Cuándo ocurrió la discusión?

   1 temprano por la mañana   3 durante la noche
   2 al mediodía   4 cerca del anochecer

24. ¿Qué comió el caballo?

   1 las alforjas   2 nada   3 el almuerzo   4 hierba

25. ¿Dónde está Taxco?

   1 en un valle   2 en la cumbre de una montaña   3 en la costa   4 en una meseta

26. ¿Cuándo era pobre el amigo?

   1 nunca   2 algún tiempo   3 un día   4 el jueves

27. ¿Por qué se proyectó una película de Carlos Gardel?

1 Fue el aniversario de su muerte.
2 Había sido premiada.

3 Estaba en seis teatros.
4 Era una nueva película del cantor.

28. ¿Qué contiene el puchero?

1 todo lo bueno
2 todo, con excepción de garbanzos

3 solamente garbanzos
4 una antología

29. ¿Qué acostumbraban hacer las amigas de Soledad?

1 tocar la guitarra
2 bailar los bailes andaluces

3 pedir que ella bailase
4 cantar, acompañadas en la guitarra

30. ¿Por qué no había vendido la vaca?

1 Llegó tarde al mercado.
2 Nadie se había acercado.

3 La vaca se había alejado.
4 Quería demasiado dinero.

31. ¿De qué color tenía esta mujer el pelo?

1 pardo   2 rojo   3 blanco   4 negro

32. ¿Qué fiesta se acercaba?

1 una verbena   2 el dos de mayo   3 la Navidad   4 la Pascua Florida

33. ¿Por qué cree este señor que los perros son fieles?

1 Las familias son ingratas.
2 Nunca ha leído nada sobre los perros.

3 Ha observado la conducta de muchos perros.
4 Se levantan cuando sale el sol.

34. ¿Dónde ocurrió este incidente?

1 en el campo   2 en Guadalupe   3 en España   4 en la iglesia

35. ¿Cómo se sentía Manuel?

1 Estaba confuso, sin saber qué hacer.
2 Deseaba entrar en el pueblo.

3 Estaba alegre.
4 Estaba cansado.

36. ¿Quién era el recién llegado?

1 un cabo de ejército   2 Juan Rodríguez   3 No se sabía.   4 Villalta

37. ¿Cómo llegaron los tres caudillos?

1 resueltos a discutir
2 detrás de sus soldados

3 dispuestos a rendirse
4 listos para luchar

38. ¿Con qué motivo se reunieron los expertos?

1 para protestar ante una sesión de UNESCO
2 para ver cómo sería posible conseguir más agua para París
3 para encontrar una solución para la futura sed mundial
4 para discutir las industrias nacionales

39. ¿Qué interrupción ocurrió?

1 Estudiábamos en voz alta.
2 Entró alguien que no conocíamos.

3 El maestro se quitó el sombrero.
4 Mirábamos a las chicas.

40. ¿Dónde estaban?

1 en el campo   2 en el desierto   3 en la mar   4 en una ciudad grande

41. ¿Dónde estaba el autor?

   1 en un hospital   2 en la fiesta   3 en la montaña   4 en la calle

42. ¿Cuánto tiempo hace que trabaja en el banco este señor?

   1 veinte y tres años   2 más de un año   3 un año   4 unos meses

43. ¿Cuál es el día que precede a la Navidad?

   1 la Nochebuena   2 la misa del gallo   3 la medianoche   4 el nacimiento

44. ¿Quién estaba herido?

   1 un viejo   2 el capitán   3 el cura   4 los dos soldados

45. ¿Qué hacía el hombre?

   1 Registraba las casas de la vecindad.   3 Cerraba la puerta.
   2 Entraba en una casa.   4 Robaba una cerradura.

46. ¿Por qué no comía Pepe?

   1 No tenía trabajo.   3 Era difícil conseguir un título de abogado.
   2 No tenía hambre.   4 Defendía pleitos.

47. ¿Qué quería el director?

   1 que el muchacho se fuera   3 que interrumpiera la carrera
   2 que el padre tuviera cuidado de la familia   4 que el muchacho no se fuera

48. ¿Qué hacía el señor Frutos?

   1 Escuchaba con interés.   3 No escuchaba las palabras de su amigo.
   2 Comía con poco apetito.   4 Escribía de las maravillas de la ciudad.

49. ¿Por qué se honra a Artigas en la Argentina y en el Uruguay?

   1 Luchó por la independencia del Uruguay.
   2 Luchó por la monarquía.
   3 Es un héroe de los dos países.
   4 Trató de unir el Uruguay a la monarquía argentina.

50. ¿Cuándo conoció este señor a su tía?

   1 a la edad de once años   3 cuando él la visitó
   2 hace unos meses cuando ella vino a Madrid   4 al cumplir su tía los veinte años

Part VIII—*A Guide to the College Board Achievement Test in Spanish*

The scope of the College Board Achievement Test in Spanish is a wide one. The questions are graded, ranging from easy to difficult. The test is designed to measure the candidate's mastery of both the spoken and the written language. Although the types of questions may vary from year to year, the following types illustrate what the candidate may generally expect.

SITUATION QUESTIONS

These questions are intended to test familiarity with the spoken language used in conversation or in everyday situations.

In each of the sample situations below, underline the word or expression (A, B, C, D, or E) that most appropriately completes the sentence.

1. Juana fue al comedor para   (A) limpiarse la cara   (B) estudiar sus lecciones   (C) almorzar   (D) buscar su vestido nuevo   (E) preparar la cena

2. Un martillo es un instrumento empleado para   (A) coser   (B) arreglar la ropa   (C) cortar   (D) peinarse   (E) clavar

3. Ayer vimos a Elsa en la iglesia. Estaba   (A) nadando alegremente   (B) leyendo los anuncios   (C) hablando con un desconocido   (D) bailando   (E) rezando con mucho recogimiento

4. Este verano vamos a   (A) la misma montaña que el año pasado para esquiar   (B) quedarnos en casa todo el día   (C) ponernos el sobretodo   (D) la playa   (E) volver a la escuela

5. En cuanto comenzó la música,   (A) la orquesta dejó de tocar   (B) todos saludaron a la reina   (C) todo el mundo se puso a bailar alegremente   (D) todos dejaron de bailar   (E) reinó el silencio

6. Los campesinos son trabajadores dedicados   (A) a trabajar en las fábricas   (B) a la tierra   (C) a la vida fácil   (D) al cuidado de la ciudad   (E) a servir a Dios

7. Cuando Eduardo entró en el taller, preguntó por   (A) el mecánico especializado en los frenos   (B) el profesor Téllez   (C) su madre   (D) el dueño de la tienda   (E) el abogado

8. Mañana voy a ver al peluquero para que me   (A) arregle la radio   (B) corte el pelo   (C) diga la buenaventura   (D) venda una casa   (E) pinte el apartamiento

9. Miles de jóvenes se alistaron en el ejército para   (A) librarse de la casa   (B) aprender el inglés   (C) luchar por su patria   (D) enriquecer el país   (E) cobrar un buen sueldo

10. Ella sacó un lápiz y se puso a   (A) leer   (B) hacer dibujos   (C) sacar brillo al anillo   (D) escribir en máquina   (E) disparar

11. Para disminuir la velocidad, es necesario   (A) dar vuelta al timón   (B) poner en marcha el motor   (C) encender las luces   (D) aplicar los frenos   (E) poner gasolina en el tanque

12. Vamos a México para ver   (A) la torre inclinada   (B) las cataratas del Niágara   (C) El Gran Cañón   (D) una corrida de toros   (E) la Alhambra

13. Cuando llegué a la taquilla   (A) pregunté la hora de la función   (B) me detuve a observar los trajes vistosos   (C) me di cuenta de que estaba completamente perdido   (D) compré un periódico   (E) hablé con el tendero

14. Cuando me siento sumamente cansado   (A) me pongo a correr   (B) me echo boca abajo en el sofá   (C) miro qué hora es   (D) me pongo a estudiar   (E) me levanto de la mesa

15. Le oí preguntar en la biblioteca: (A) —¿Quién es la profesora de piano?   (B) —¿Dónde está la librería?   (C) —¿Se venden ejemplares de la Biblia aquí?   (D) —¿Hay un tomo sobre la psicología de Freud?   (E) —¿Cuánto cuesta una libra de carne?

16. Antes de acostarse, Pepito se dirigió   (A) a la piscina   (B) al sótano   (C) al baño para limpiarse los dientes   (D) al jardín   (E) al campo de béisbol

17. Llegó temprano a la fiesta porque   (A) no había nadie allí   (B) su reloj estaba adelantado   (C) el despertador estaba roto   (D) el tren tardó en llegar   (E) su reloj era nuevo

18. Al levantarse de la mesa, dijo a los demás: (A) —Tengo muchísima hambre.   (B) —Buen provecho.   (C) —Voy a comer.   (D) —Hola, compañeros.   (E) —Convido a Vds. a comer conmigo.

19. Cuando el taxi se detuvo delante de Liliana, ella dijo: (A) —¿Qué hora es?   (B) —Tengo dolor de cabeza.   (C) —¿Me podría llevar al Zócalo?   (D) —No tengo que pagar nada.   (E) —Hasta mañana.

20. Acabamos de visitar a nuestro tío. Al despedirnos dijimos: (A) —¿Qué tal, tío Paco? ¿Cómo estás?   (B) —¿Dónde está la tía Lola?   (C) —¿Me quieres traer un vaso de agua?   (D) —¿Qué día es hoy?   (E) —Nos hemos divertido mucho, tío.

21. Un pasajero bajó del ómnibus. Como hacía mucho frío, llevaba   (A) una americana   (B) una camisa de algodón   (C) una chaqueta de lana   (D) un abrigo   (E) un sombrero de paja

22. Mi hijo tiene muchos deseos de sacar la licencia para poder   (A) manejar un coche   (B) llegar tarde a casa   (C) comprar una casa   (D) bailar con su novia   (E) asistir a la escuela

23. Cuando se ve arder una casa, se debe   (A) llamar a los bomberos   (B) pegarle fuego   (C) quemar la basura   (D) alejarse sin hacer caso   (E) impedir el paso de los bomberos

24. Cuando viajaba en avión, oí una voz que anunciaba: (A) —¡Todos bajen en la próxima estación!   (B) —El viaje cuesta setenta y cinco centavos.   (C) —¡Viajeros al tren!   (D) —¡Abran Vds. los paraguas!   (E) —¡Abrochen la cintura!

25. Luego que se sentó en una de las mesas del restaurante, el hombre   (A) pidió la lista   (B) llamó al portero   (C) dejó una propina   (D) pidió el postre   (E) terminó de comer

26. Ese hombre tiene muchos planes, pero no puede llevarlos   (A) fuera   (B) a cabo   (C) en camino   (D) a fin   (E) al resultado

27. Era evidente que iba a afeitarse, porque en la mano tenía   (A) un lápiz   (B) una navaja   (C) dos monedas   (D) unas tijeras   (E) una cuchara

28. En el invierno todos los jóvenes iban al lago para   (A) nadar   (B) aprovecharse del calor del sol   (C) beber agua   (D) salir en bote   (E) patinar

29. La sala de lectura _____ al patio.   (A) llevaba   (B) se encaramaba   (C) ponía la vista   (D) miraba   (E) daba

30. El agua no está ni fría ni caliente; está   (A) tibia   (B) tranquila   (C) limpia   (D) sucia   (E) clara

31. Era sordo; no podía _____ bien.   (A) ver   (B) comer   (C) hablar   (D) oír   (E) gritar

32. Preparándose para el viaje, se puso a   (A) quitarse el abrigo   (B) hacer el tronco   (C) dar la hora   (D) hacer el baúl   (E) hacer una bala

33. Para caminar, se emplean   (A) las piernas   (B) las orejas   (C) las piedras   (D) los labios   (E) los brazos

34. El automóvil de mi padre tiene cuatro   (A) pasajeros   (B) muebles   (C) ruedas   (D) ventanas   (E) máquinas

35. La calle no era ancha, sino   (A) grande   (B) estrecha   (C) desierta   (D) pequeña   (E) directa

36. En la frontera tuve que mostrar mi pasaporte al   (A) aduanero   (B) huésped   (C) ferrocarril   (D) marinero   (E) camarero

37. Durante toda su vida soñaba _____ viajar a países lejanos.   (A) de   (B) por   (C) a   (D) con   (E) en

38. Pidió dinero a su _____, porque éste, el padre de su esposa, era muy rico.   (A) yerno   (B) padre   (C) suegro   (D) cuñado   (E) tío

39. Me preguntó si podría darle una cerilla porque quería   (A) encender su cigarro   (B) salir de paseo   (C) limpiar su cuarto   (D) comprar dulces   (E) beber vino

40. Preguntó: —¿A cuántos estamos? Nosotros comprendimos que quería averiguar   (A) el precio   (B) la hora   (C) cuántos había en el grupo   (D) la distancia que nos quedaba   (E) la fecha

41. Al entrar en casa, _____ el abrigo con cuidado.   (A) rompió   (B) tiró   (C) quemó   (D) colgó   (E) se puso

42. Se declaró en bancarrota porque   (A) tenía muchas deudas   (B) era muy rico   (C) no le interesaba el dinero   (D) era banquero   (E) ganaba un buen sueldo

43. Cubrieron el suelo con una _____ azul.   (A) alforja   (B) alfombra   (C) sombra   (D) tertulia   (E) almohada

44. Además de gasolina, hice poner en el motor un poco de   (A) acero   (B) vapor   (C) vidrio   (D) aceite   (E) aire

45. Adoptó un plan para ahorrar su dinero; cada semana   (A) pagó lo que debía   (B) cenó en restaurantes lujosos   (C) lo llevó al banco   (D) lo gastó   (E) lo repartió entre sus amigos

46. Agasajaron al nuevo director,   (A) dándole un banquete suntuoso   (B) negándose a hablarle   (C) sonriéndole con amistad   (D) trabajando mal   (E) hablándole en tono brusco

47. Era agosto; y los labradores estaban ocupados con   (A) sus buques   (B) los deportes   (C) el ajedrez   (D) la costura   (E) la cosecha

48. A causa del frío bebió   (A) café caliente   (B) jugo de limón   (C) una gaseosa   (D) agua fría   (E) té helado

49. Por la mañana se despejó; es decir,   (A) todo iba bien   (B) aparecieron nubes   (C) se perdió toda esperanza   (D) cesó de llover   (E) se miró en el espejo

50. Elogiaron al actor; lo   (A) lamentaron   (B) enterraron   (C) alabaron   (D) criticaron   (E) lloraron

GRAMMAR QUESTIONS

The following questions test your ability to distinguish between correct and incorrect usage in Spanish. You are generally given an incomplete sentence in Spanish and are asked to underline the word or expression which, when inserted in the blank, makes the sentence grammatically correct. The completed sentence must correspond to the English equivalent. Occasionally a whole sentence is to be translated.

1. Loud shouts were heard in the streets.

   Gritos agudos _____ en las calles.
   (A) se oyó   (B) oyeron   (C) estaban oídos   (D) se oyeron

2. He had been working in that office for a year.

   Hacía un año que _____ en esa oficina.
   (A) trabajó   (B) hubo trabajando   (C) había trabajado   (D) trabajaba

3. They were glad that the soldier was returning home.

   Se alegraron de que el soldado _____ a casa.
   (A) regresaba   (B) estaba regresando   (C) volviera   (D) estaba de vuelta

4. Which one is your nephew?

¿_____ es su sobrino?
(A) Quién   (B) Cuál   (C) Qué   (D) Cuáles

5. Raphael doesn't want to accompany her. Neither do I.

Rafael no quiere acompañarla. _____
(A) Ni yo también.   (B) Ni yo tampoco.   (C) Ni a mí.   (D) Lo mismo me da.

6. Don't leave until your parents come.

_____ tú hasta que lleguen tus padres.
(A) No salgas   (B) No sal   (C) No te vaya   (D) No entres

7. Joe was the oldest in the class.

Pepe era _____ la clase.
(A) el mayor de   (B) el mayor en   (C) el mejor de   (D) el menor de

8. It's a shame that they do not sing well.

Es lástima que no _____ bien.
(A) cantasen   (B) cantaran   (C) canten   (D) cantan

9. As soon as I had eaten, I left the house.

Así que _____, salí de la casa.
(A) comía   (B) comiera   (C) hube comido   (D) hubiese comido

10. Lincoln was born on the twelfth of February, 1809.

Lincoln nació _____ de febrero de 1809.
(A) en el doce   (B) al doce   (C) el doce   (D) doce

11. The one who is reading is Albert's cousin.

_____ está leyendo es el primo de Alberto.
(A) El cual   (B) Él que   (C) El que   (D) Lo que

12. He is the South American hero whom we admire.

Es el héroe sudamericano _____ admiramos.
(A) quien   (B) al que   (C) que   (D) al cual

13. My uncle knows it better than anyone.

Mi tío lo sabe mejor que _____.
(A) nadie   (B) alguien   (C) todos   (D) nada

14. There are more than a hundred persons here.

Hay más _____ cien personas aquí.
(A) que   (B) de   (C) de lo que   (D) del que

15. He is very fat; he eats more than two ordinary men.

Es muy gordo; come más _____ hombres ordinarios.
(A) de dos   (B) que dos   (C) que los dos   (D) de los dos

16. I have a book and a pencil; the former is red and the latter is blue.

Tengo un libro y un lápiz; _____.
(A) aquello es rojo y esto es azul   (B) ése es rojo y aquél es azul   (C) éste es azul y aquél es rojo   (D) el uno es rojo y el otro es azul

17. It didn't rain yesterday, which pleased me very much.

No llovió ayer, _____ me agradó mucho.
(A) el cual   (B) que   (C) el que   (D) lo cual

18. Thomas denied that Mary had lost the watch.

Tomás negó que María _____ el reloj.
(A) había perdido   (B) hubiera perdido   (C) haya perdido   (D) perdiera

19. I did not see any neckties that I liked.

No vi ningunas corbatas que _____.
(A) me gustan   (B) me gusten   (C) me gustarán   (D) me gustasen

20. Speak to him so that he may know the truth.

Háblele para que él _____ la verdad.
(A) supiera   (B) sepa   (C) puede saber   (D) conozca

21. If I were rich, I would buy an automobile.

Si yo fuera rico, _____ un automóvil.
(A) habría comprado   (B) hubiera comprado   (C) comprase   (D) comprara

22. You cannot help enjoying yourself.

_____ divertirse.
(A) Vd. no puede menos de   (B) No se puede evitar   (C) No te ayudes de   (D) No puede ayudarse

23. I am thinking about the summer vacation.

_____ las vacaciones de verano.
(A) Estoy pensando de   (B) Pienso   (C) Pienso en   (D) Pienso de

24. It was probably 12 o'clock when he entered.

_____ las doce cuando él entró.
(A) Serán   (B) Habrá sido   (C) Serían   (D) Habrían sido

25. After a half hour, she regained consciousness.

Después de media hora, _____.
(A) ganó su conocimiento de nuevo   (B) reconoció el ambiente   (C) volvió en sí   (D) supo lo que le rodeaba

Another type of grammar question has recently been included in the Spanish examination. This question eliminates all use of English. It consists of a complete sentence in Spanish with one or more words underlined. Of the five choices that follow, four may be substituted for the underlined words to form sentences that are grammatically correct but may differ in meaning from the original sentence. You are asked to choose the one answer that does *not* fit grammatically into the original sentence.

26. Después de visitar a nuestros padres por dos horas y media, estábamos para salir.

(A) estábamos dispuestos a ir   (B) queríamos regresar a nuestra casa   (C) pensábamos de ir   (D) estábamos por irnos   (E) decidimos irnos

27. Se puede ver el capitolio desde muy lejos.

(A) a lo lejos   (B) en lo lejos   (C) allá arriba   (D) en la distancia   (E) desde aquí

28. Creían que nosotros visitaríamos a nuestros amigos.

(A) nos faltaría   (B) echaríamos de menos a   (C) nos despediríamos de   (D) no tendríamos nada que ver con   (E) hablaríamos con

29. Estoy seguro; no cabe duda de que él es el ladrón.

   (A) no hay duda alguna de   (B) no hay ninguna duda de   (C) no dudo   (D) sabemos   (E) se lo dirán

30. Así que él llegue, díganoslo.

   (A) En cuanto a   (B) Tan pronto como   (C) Luego que   (D) Cuando   (E) En caso de que

31. Su compañero de clase le dijo:—Háblame de la partida.

   (A) Deja hablarme de   (B) No me hables más de   (C) Deja de hablar de   (D) Continúa hablando de   (E) No sigas hablando de

32. Estaré allí dentro de dos meses.

   (A) por   (B) como   (C) por lo menos   (D) para   (E) más de

33. Mientras tanto mi madre se puso a preparar la comida.

   (A) Entretanto   (B) Hace media hora   (C) En un dos por tres   (D) Sin decir esta boca es mía   (E) Pasado mañana

34. Carlos es el más alto de todos.

   (A) en la clase   (B) de la clase   (C) de la escuela   (D) que yo he visto   (E) del equipo

35. Él insistió en que yo aceptara el dinero.

   (A) deseaba   (B) se empeñó en   (C) quiso   (D) sabía   (E) aconsejó

36. Ellos no quisieron hacerlo.

   (A) rehusaron   (B) no sabían   (C) se negaron a   (D) trataron de   (E) conocieron

37. Se dice que ese hombre es muy rico.

   (A) Dicen   (B) Se sabe   (C) Creen   (D) Se ven   (E) No dudamos

38. Al verle la cara, me di cuenta de que era inocente.

   (A) supe   (B) me enteré de   (C) creí   (D) me dije   (E) realicé

39. Todos llegaron a casa a la vez.

   (A) temprano   (B) servidor de Vd.   (C) juntos   (D) dentro de media hora   (E) sanos y salvos

40. Cuando llegué a la fiesta, me saludaron cariñosamente.

   (A) Así que   (B) Luego que   (C) Antes de que   (D) Apenas   (E) En cuanto

41. Mi hermana va a la iglesia todas las noches.

   (A) una noche sí y otra no   (B) de vez en cuando   (C) cuando se le antoja   (D) hace poco   (E) a menudo

42. Él entró en la casa sin decir nada.

   (A) saludando a su madre   (B) mí   (C) mirarme   (D) sus libros   (E) hacer ruido

43. Yo tengo mi bicicleta. Juanito no tiene la suya.

   (A) suya   (B) la de él   (C) la de su hermano   (D) la que recibió el año pasado   (E) ninguna

44. ¿Cree Vd. que María lo lea?

   (A) Espera   (B) Sabe   (C) Pide   (D) Desea   (E) Aconseja

45. Yo tengo <u>mucho</u> que hacer esta noche.

(A) demasiado   (B) menos   (C) poco   (D) muchísimo   (E) muy pequeño

46. Llegamos a las seis y <u>cinco</u>.

(A) pico   (B) dos   (C) un poco   (D) quince   (E) cuarto

47. <u>Quien</u> estudia, aprende.

(A) El que   (B) Los que   (C) La que   (D) Cuando   (E) El hombre que

48. Nuestro perro y <u>el suyo</u> son fieles.

(A) la de él   (B) el tuyo   (C) el de él   (D) el vuestro   (E) el de ella

49. Estamos tristes porque nuestro padre <u>murió</u>.

(A) partió   (B) llora   (C) se divirtió   (D) se fuese   (E) se puso enfermo

50. <u>Carezco de</u> mis lentes.

(A) Me falta   (B) Me hacen falta   (C) Necesito   (D) Perdí   (E) Rompí

VOCABULARY QUESTIONS

Although all questions are, in a sense, vocabulary questions, there are generally some questions that aim directly at testing mastery of vocabulary. Sometimes the candidate is asked to select an acceptable definition of a word; at other times, he is to select a word or phrase that completes a statement in a meaningful way.

Underline the correct definition.

1. navío: (A) buque de guerra   (B) escuadra de guerra   (C) grupo de marineros   (D) donde se puede navegar   (E) piscina

2. posada: (A) asiento   (B) hotel   (C) pájaro   (D) foto   (E) antes

3. colina: (A) enfermedad   (B) fruta   (C) bebida   (D) monte   (E) medicina

4. nata: (A) natación   (B) crema   (C) grado   (D) absolutamente nada   (E) insecto

5. lectura: (A) disertación pública   (B) acción de leer   (C) entrevista   (D) una reunión   (E) discurso religioso

6. éxito: (A) puerta   (B) lo que sucede   (C) un acontecimiento importante   (D) salida   (E) resultado feliz

7. reírse de: (A) mofarse de   (B) sonreír   (C) gozar de   (D) divertirse   (E) entretenerse

8. la orden: (A) mandato   (B) números   (C) fila   (D) arreglo   (E) método

9. occidente: (A) oeste   (B) este   (C) septentrional   (D) meridional   (E) casualidad

10. trapo: (A) verdad   (B) mentira   (C) tela rota   (D) trampa   (E) derrota

11. melocotón: (A) fruta   (B) instrumento músico   (C) canción   (D) película   (E) vendedor de dulces

12. desaire: (A) falta de aire   (B) ventilación   (C) falta de cortesía   (D) voluntad   (E) goce

13. necio: (A) sobrino   (B) abuelo   (C) tonto   (D) nieto   (E) necesidad

14. anhelo: (A) estado helado   (B) bien iluminado   (C) sin esperanza   (D) afán   (E) anillo

15. arder: (A) enamorarse   (B) quemarse   (C) ser valiente   (D) amar   (E) tomar demasiado

16. cumbre: (A) abismo   (B) sima   (C) cubierta   (D) cima   (E) cueva

17. ingenuo: (A) astuto   (B) gentil   (C) franco   (D) engañador   (E) mentiroso

18. postrero: (A) anterior   (B) último   (C) fruta   (D) puerta   (E) dulces

19. desmayarse: (A) dar miedo   (B) asustar   (C) volver en sí   (D) perder el conocimiento   (E) hacer mucho frío

20. espantar: (A) dar miedo   (B) extender   (C) desalentarse   (D) vestirse   (E) respirar

21. semilla: (A) mitad   (B) semejante   (C) igual   (D) sencillo   (E) origen

22. sendero: (A) silla   (B) camino   (C) destino   (D) correo   (E) delgado

23. mentar: (A) inhalar   (B) mentir   (C) profesor   (D) mencionar   (E) pensar

24. juramento: (A) voto   (B) burro   (C) juicio   (D) corte   (E) juego

25. hazaña: (A) héroe   (B) acción heroica   (C) espada   (D) alimentación   (E) cobarde

READING COMPREHENSION QUESTIONS

The following passages require comprehension of words in context. Read each passage for comprehension. Note that some words or phrases are in italics; these words are repeated at the end of the passage, each followed by five English words or phrases. Underline the *one* English word or phrase that is the best and most appropriate translation, considering the context in which it appears.

I

Sentado frente al escritorio, trataba de contraer mi atención sobre el cuaderno de cuentas, que tenía abierto ante mí; pero al mirar por la ventana el día *brumoso* y oscuro, los húmedos *ramajes* de los pinos y naranjos del jardín, que *se destacaban* sobre un cielo de leche, volví a sumergirme en mi triste somnolencia, en mi inmotivado *abatimiento*.

—Hoy no hago más, no puedo hacer nada—pensé levantándome bruscamente de mi asiento y *desperezándome.*

En ese instante, la puerta del escritorio se abrió y mi perro de caza se lanzó con su acostumbrada violencia sobre mí, haciéndome las más exageradas *caricias.*

—¿Qué haré hoy?—pensaba, conteniendo de las orejas y las *patas* al nervioso animal que me *manchaba* el traje con su piel mojada por el *rocío* de la mañana. Por un instante me regocijó la idea de salir a cazar; pero me sentía demasiado fatigado para emprender una marcha, y, además, el *pasto* estaría demasiado húmedo aún.

1. *brumoso:*   (A) sweeping   (B) foggy   (C) gray   (D) clear   (E) heavy

2. *ramajes:*   (A) outlines   (B) fruit   (C) trunks   (D) branches   (E) bark

3. *se destacaban:*   (A) moved   (B) shone   (C) blended   (D) stood out   (E) were hidden

4. *abatimiento:*   (A) depression   (B) energy   (C) home   (D) den   (E) bedroom

5. *desperezándome:*   (A) falling asleep   (B) going out   (C) stretching   (D) walking about   (E) shouting

6. *caricias:*   (A) harm   (B) expressions   (C) dearness   (D) movements   (E) caresses

7. *patas:*   (A) pats   (B) claws   (C) stroking   (D) ducks   (E) paws

8. *manchaba:*   (A) tore   (B) took off   (C) soiled   (D) put on   (E) stole

9. *rocío:*   (A) sun   (B) pool   (C) rain   (D) dew   (E) light

10. *pasto:*   (A) pasture   (B) passage   (C) past   (D) paste   (E) pastry

II

Llegó hasta las primeras calles de la ciudad, y en una de ellas encontró una *lechería*. Era un negocito muy claro y limpio, lleno de mesitas con cubierta de *mármol*. Detrás de un *mostrador* estaba de pie una señora rubia, con un *delantal* blanquísimo.

Eligió ese negocio. La calle era poco transitada. Habría podido comer en uno de los *figones* que estaban junto al *muelle*, pero continuamente se encontraban llenos de gente que jugaba y bebía.

En la lechería no había sino un solo cliente. Era un vejete de anteojos, que con la nariz metida entre las hojas de un periódico, leyendo, permanecía inmóvil, como *pegado* a la silla. Sobre la mesita había un vaso de leche a medio consumir.

Esperó que se retirara, paseando por la acera, sintiendo que poco a poco *se le encendía* en el estómago la *quemadura* de antes, y esperó cinco, diez, hasta quince minutos. Se cansó y paróse a un lado de la puerta, desde donde lanzaba al viejo unas miradas que parecían *pedradas*.

1. *lechería:*   (A) nut   (B) theater   (C) milk bar   (D) dairy maid   (E) insect
2. *mármol:*   (A) navy blue   (B) snow-white   (C) tablecloth   (D) tabletop   (E) marble
3. *mostrador:*   (A) stage   (B) demonstration   (C) lights   (D) salesman   (E) counter
4. *delantal:*   (A) uniform   (B) apron   (C) overcoat   (D) in front of   (E) glove
5. *figones:*   (A) rooms   (B) warehouses   (C) benches   (D) chophouses   (E) fruit shops
6. *muelle:*   (A) tavern   (B) avenue   (C) beach   (D) dock   (E) park
7. *pegado:*   (A) next to   (B) glued   (C) beaten   (D) paid   (E) on top of
8. *se le encendía:*   (A) was flaring up   (B) was listening   (C) was hearing   (D) was empty   (E) understood
9. *quemadura:*   (A) cinders   (B) ripeness   (C) heat   (D) burning   (E) hardness
10. *pedradas:*   (A) loving   (B) caresses   (C) stone-throwing   (D) large stones   (E) intense

III

En la cabecera del puerto de Barcelona, al frente de los edificios de la *aduana*, se encuentra el monumento a Colón, el cual es tenido por el más hermoso que se ha levantado en Europa o América a la memoria del descubridor. Es una soberbia obra de arte, *digna* de Colón y del primer puerto de España.

Se compone de una base ricamente *historiada* y decorada y de una *airosa* columna de sesenta metros de altura que termina en un globo que soporta la estatua colosal del navegante.

Colocado sobre su *excelso* pináculo, el genovés contempla, reflejada del cielo, la *cerúlea* expansión del Mediterráneo, el mar de la raza latina, en cuyas orillas pasó su adolescencia y sobre cuyas olas se formó su educación de marino. Su mano derecha *señala* con su amplio ademán el camino de acercamiento al nuevo mundo; su mano izquierda sostiene una carta geográfica *a medio desplegar*.

A espaldas del puerto se extiende un vasto anfiteatro de *colinas* cubierto de quintas y palacios, y en el puerto se ve una selva de *mástiles* de navíos.

1. *aduana:*   (A) museum   (B) department store   (C) custom house   (D) pier   (E) fish market
2. *digna:*   (A) dedicated   (B) dainty   (C) built   (D) worthy   (E) dignified
3. *historiada:*   (A) historical   (B) engraved   (C) fabulous   (D) legendary   (E) storied
4. *airosa:*   (A) spirited   (B) exalted   (C) tall   (D) aerial   (E) graceful
5. *excelso:*   (A) high   (B) excellent   (C) surpassing   (D) expensive   (E) extraordinary
6. *cerúlea:*   (A) blue   (B) waxen   (C) stormy   (D) glazed   (E) calm
7. *señala:*   (A) teaches   (B) indicates   (C) distinguishes   (D) signifies   (E) signs
8. *a medio desplegar:*   (A) in the midst of unfurling   (B) half unrolled   (C) by way of showing   (D) half torn   (E) slightly displaced
9. *colinas:*   (A) streets   (B) plazas   (C) avenues   (D) hills   (E) meadows
10. *mástiles:*   (A) prows   (B) wild dogs   (C) keels   (D) mackerel   (E) masts

IV

Lin de la Carbayeda marchó desde su aldea a la ciudad cercana un día claro y hermoso del otoño de mil ochocientos sesenta. Acompañábale un hijo suyo, que *contaría a lo sumo* trece años, un rapaz morenillo y colorado, con ojos negros y muy brillantes, que caminaba *junto a* su padre por la carretera *sin cuidarse de salvar* los *charcos* en que metía los *descalzos* pies. El mozuelo llevaba *a la espalda* un baulillo, de cuyo peso le *aliviaba* su padre muchas veces, sobre todo cuando subían una *cuesta*. El padre caminaba triste y con los ojos bajos; el hijo con la cabeza *erguida* y *fijándose en* el horizonte. Así llegaron a la ciudad, de cuyo puerto debía salir aquella tarde el buque que conduciría al rapaz a las Américas, donde un tío suyo le esperaba para hacerle hombre.

Al anochecer de aquella tarde, *aprovechando* el pleamar, zarpó el buque en que emigraba el muchacho con otros cuarenta y *tantos* de su misma edad, cuyas familias los miraban desde el muelle. Sobre *cubierta* todos los jovenzuelos dirigían las miradas a sus parientes, llorando unos, *haciéndose los valientes* otros. Nuestro chicuelo solamente miraba al suyo con los ojos muy abiertos mientras *agitaba* un pañolito blanco. Por fin partió el buque; oyéronse gemidos y lloros, y poco a poco *se fue alejando, achicándose* allá entre las sombras de la noche que se acercaba, hasta no verse más que una nubecilla de humo negro en la línea ya poco luminosa del horizonte.

1. *contaría:*   (A) was probably   (B) country   (C) accounted   (D) would encounter   (E) counted

2. *a lo sumo:*   (A) at the summit   (B) at the sum of   (C) at the low sum of   (D) at the most   (E) soon

3. *junto a:*   (A) jauntily   (B) joined to   (C) beside   (D) in front of   (E) in back of

4. *sin cuidarse de:*   (A) without bothering to   (B) without cities   (C) without cares   (D) without caring for himself   (E) but in caring

5. *salvar:*   (A) to soothe   (B) to save   (C) to land   (D) to salvage   (E) to leap over

6. *charcos:*   (A) charcoal   (B) sharks   (C) rocks   (D) puddles   (E) mud

7. *descalzos:*   (A) bare   (B) well-groomed   (C) dirty   (D) discolored   (E) without callouses

8. *a la espalda:*   (A) to the side   (B) on his head   (C) on his shoulders   (D) on his side   (E) alongside of him

9. *aliviaba:*   (A) allied   (B) relieved   (C) attested   (D) added   (E) commented

10. *cuesta:*   (A) cost   (B) coast   (C) bill   (D) story   (E) hill

11. *erguida:*   (A) down   (B) on the side   (C) urging   (D) urgent   (E) erect

12. *fijándose en:*   (A) gazing at   (B) fixing   (C) fidgeting   (D) finding   (E) walking in single file

13. *Al anochecer:*   (A) During the night   (B) At dusk   (C) At daybreak   (D) Spending the night   (E) Early in the morning

14. *aprovechando:*   (A) protecting   (B) approving   (C) availing itself of   (D) proceeding   (E) steaming for

15. *tantos:*   (A) some odd   (B) as many   (C) fools   (D) aunts   (E) many more

16. *cubierta:*   (A) covering   (B) blanket   (C) deck   (D) hideout   (E) stowaway

17. *haciéndose los valientes:*   (A) acting cowardly   (B) showing their worth   (C) feigning indifference   (D) assuming good upbringing   (E) plucking up courage

18. *agitaba:*   (A) was getting angry   (B) waved   (C) threw away   (D) ripped to shreds   (E) threw overboard

19. *se fue alejando:*   (A) came nearer and nearer   (B) went away complaining   (C) went into outer space   (D) went away   (E) went east

20. *achicándose:*   (A) becoming younger   (B) going away   (C) growing smaller   (D) becoming insignificant   (E) was sinking

Irregular Verb Forms

Note. (1) Verbs that are similar in structure to the verbs in the following chart are listed alphabetically at the end of the chart.

(2) The only verbs that are irregular in the imperfect indicative are:

ir: iba, ibas, iba, íbamos, ibais, iban
ser: era, eras, era, éramos, erais, eran
ver: veía, veías, veía, veíamos, veíais, veían

Infinitive, Present Part., Past Part.	INDICATIVE			SUBJUNCTIVE		*Command*
	Present	*Preterite*	*Future*	*Present*	*Imperfect*	
1. abrir abriendo **abierto**						
2. almorzar	**almuerzo** **almuerzas** **almuerza** almorzamos almorzáis **almuerzan**	**almorcé** almorzaste almorzó etc.		**almuerce** **almuerces** **almuerce** **almorcemos** **almorcéis** **almuercen**		**almuerza**
3. andar		**anduve** **anduviste** **anduvo** **anduvimos** **anduvisteis** **anduvieron**			**anduviera(-se)** **anduvieras(-ses)** **anduviera(-se)** **anduviéramos(-'semos)** **anduvierais(-seis)** **anduvieran(-sen)**	
4. averiguar		**averigüé** averiguaste averiguó etc.		**averigüe** **averigües** **averigüe** **averigüemos** **averigüéis** **averigüen**		
5. buscar		**busqué** buscaste buscó etc.		**busque** **busques** **busque** **busquemos** **busquéis** **busquen**		
6. caber	**quepo** cabes cabe etc.	**cupe** **cupiste** **cupo** **cupimos** **cupisteis** **cupieron**	**cabré** **cabrás** **cabrá** **cabremos** **cabréis** **cabrán**	**quepa** **quepas** **quepa** **quepamos** **quepáis** **quepan**	**cupiera(-se)** **cupieras(-ses)** **cupiera(-se)** **cupiéramos(-'semos)** **cupierais(-seis)** **cupieran(-sen)**	
7. caer **cayendo** **caído**	**caigo** caes cae etc.	caí caíste **cayó** caímos caísteis **cayeron**		**caiga** **caigas** **caiga** **caigamos** **caigáis** **caigan**	**cayera(-se)** **cayeras(-ses)** **cayera(-se)** **cayéramos(-'semos)** **cayerais(-seis)** **cayeran(-sen)**	
8. cocer	**cuezo** **cueces** **cuece** cocemos cocéis **cuecen**			**cueza** **cuezas** **cueza** **cozamos** **cozáis** **cuezan**		**cuece**

Infinitive, *Present Part.,* *Past Part.*	INDICATIVE			SUBJUNCTIVE		
	Present	*Preterite*	*Future*	*Present*	*Imperfect*	*Command*
9. conocer	conozco			conozca		
	conoces			conozcas		
	conoce			conozca		
	etc.			conozcamos		
				conozcáis		
				conozcan		
10. continuar	continúo			continúe		continúa
	continúas			continúes		
	continúa			continúe		
	continuamos			continuemos		
	continuáis			continuéis		
	continúan			continúen		
11. creer		creí			creyera(-se)	
creyendo		creíste			creyeras(-ses)	
creído		creyó			creyera(-se)	
		creímos			creyéramos(-'semos)	
		creísteis			creyerais(-seis)	
		creyeron			creyeran(-sen)	
12. dar	doy	di		dé	diera(-se)	
	das	diste		des	dieras(-ses)	
	da	dio		dé	diera(-se)	
	damos	dimos		demos	diéramos(-'semos)	
	dais	disteis		deis	dierais(-seis)	
	dan	dieron		den	dieran(-sen)	
13. decir	digo	dije	diré	diga	dijera(-se)	di
diciendo	dices	dijiste	dirás	digas	dijeras(-ses)	
dicho	dice	dijo	dirá	diga	dijera(-se)	
	decimos	dijimos	diremos	digamos	dijéramos(-'semos)	
	decís	dijisteis	diréis	digáis	dijerais(-seis)	
	dicen	dijeron	dirán	digan	dijeran(-sen)	
14. dirigir	dirijo			dirija		
	diriges			dirijas		
	dirige			dirija		
	etc.			dirijamos		
				dirijáis		
				dirijan		
15. distinguir	distingo			distinga		
	distingues			distingas		
	distingue			distinga		
	etc.			distingamos		
				distingáis		
				distingan		
16. dormir	duermo	dormí		duerma	durmiera(-se)	duerme
durmiendo	duermes	dormiste		duermas	durmieras(-ses)	
dormido	duerme	durmió		duerma	durmiera(-se)	
	dormimos	dormimos		durmamos	durmiéramos(-'semos)	
	dormís	dormisteis		durmáis	durmierais(-seis)	
	duermen	durmieron		duerman	durmieran(-sen)	
17. elegir	elijo	elegí		elija	eligiera(-se)	elige
eligiendo	eliges	elegiste		elijas	eligieras(-ses)	
elegido	elige	eligió		elija	eligiera(-se)	
	elegimos	elegimos		elijamos	eligiéramos(-'semos)	
	elegís	elegisteis		elijáis	eligierais(-seis)	
	eligen	eligieron		elijan	eligieran(-sen)	
18. empezar	empiezo	empecé		empiece		empieza
	empiezas	empezaste		empieces		
	empieza	empezó		empiece		
	empezamos	etc.		empecemos		
	empezáis			empecéis		
	empiezan			empiecen		

Infinitive, Present Part., Past Part.		INDICATIVE			SUBJUNCTIVE		
	Present	*Preterite*	*Future*		*Present*	*Imperfect*	*Command*
19. enviar	envió				envíe		envía
	envías				envíes		
	envía				envíe		
	enviamos				enviemos		
	enviáis				enviéis		
	envían				envíen		
20. escribir escribiendo **escrito**							
21. estar	estoy	estuve			esté	estuviera(-se)	está
	estás	estuviste			estés	estuvieras(-ses)	
	está	estuvo			esté	estuviera(-se)	
	estamos	estuvimos			estemos	estuviéramos(-'semos)	
	estáis	estuvisteis			estéis	estuvierais(-seis)	
	están	estuvieron			estén	estuvieran(-sen)	
22. gozar		gocé			goce		
		gozaste			goces		
		gozó			goce		
		etc.			gocemos		
					gocéis		
					gocen		
23. haber	he	hube	habré		haya	hubiera(-se)	
	has	hubiste	habrás		hayas	hubieras(-ses)	
	ha	hubo	habrá		haya	hubiera(-se)	
	hemos	hubimos	habremos		hayamos	hubiéramos(-'semos)	
	habéis	hubisteis	habréis		hayáis	hubierais(-seis)	
	han	hubieron	habrán		hayan	hubieran(-sen)	
24. hacer haciendo **hecho**	hago	hice	haré		haga	hiciera(-se)	haz
	haces	hiciste	harás		hagas	hicieras(-ses)	
	hace	hizo	hará		haga	hiciera(-se)	
	etc.	hicimos	haremos		hagamos	hiciéramos(-'semos)	
		hicisteis	haréis		hagáis	hicierais(-seis)	
		hicieron	harán		hagan	hicieran(-sen)	
25. huir **huyendo** huido	huyo	huí			huya	huyera(-se)	huye
	huyes	huiste			huyas	huyeras(-ses)	
	huye	huyó			huya	huyera(-se)	
	huimos	huimos			huyamos	huyéramos(-'semos)	
	huís	huisteis			huyáis	huyerais(-seis)	
	huyen	huyeron			huyan	huyeran(-sen)	
26. imprimir imprimiendo **impreso**							
27. ir **yendo** ido	voy	fui			vaya	fuera(-se)	ve
	vas	fuiste			vayas	fueras(-ses)	
	va	fue			vaya	fuera(-se)	
	vamos	fuimos			vayamos	fuéramos(-'semos)	
	vais	fuisteis			vayáis	fuerais(-seis)	
	van	fueron			vayan	fueran(-sen)	
28. jugar	juego	jugué			juegue		juega
	juegas	jugaste			juegues		
	juega	jugó			juegue		
	jugamos	etc.			juguemos		
	jugáis				juguéis		
	juegan				jueguen		
29. llegar		llegué			llegue		
		llegaste			llegues		
		llegó			llegue		
		etc.			lleguemos		
					lleguéis		
					lleguen		

Infinitive, Present Part., Past Part.	INDICATIVE			SUBJUNCTIVE		
	Present	*Preterite*	*Future*	*Present*	*Imperfect*	*Command*
30. morir	muero	morí		muera	muriera(-se)	muere
muriendo	mueres	moriste		mueras	murieras(-ses)	
muerto	muere	murió		muera	muriera(-se)	
	morimos	morimos		muramos	muriéramos(-'semos)	
	morís	moristeis		muráis	murierais(-seis)	
	mueren	murieron		mueran	murieran(-sen)	
31. mostrar	muestro			muestre		muestra
	muestras			muestres		
	muestra			muestre		
	mostramos			mostremos		
	mostráis			mostréis		
	muestran			muestren		
32. mover	muevo			mueva		mueve
	mueves			muevas		
	mueve			mueva		
	movemos			movamos		
	movéis			mováis		
	mueven			muevan		
33. negar	niego	negué		niegue		niega
	niegas	negaste		niegues		
	niega	negó		niegue		
	negamos	etc.		neguemos		
	negáis			neguéis		
	niegan			nieguen		
34. **oír**	oigo	oí	oiré	oiga	oyera(-se)	oye
oyendo	oyes	oíste	oirás	oigas	oyeras(-ses)	
oído	oye	oyó	oirá	oiga	oyera(-se)	
	oímos	oímos	oiremos	oigamos	oyéramos(-'semos)	
	oís	oísteis	oiréis	oigáis	oyerais(-seis)	
	oyen	oyeron	oirán	oigan	oyeran(-sen)	
35. oler	huelo			huela		huele
	hueles			huelas		
	huele			huela		
	olemos			olamos		
	oléis			oláis		
	huelen			huelan		
36. pedir	pido	pedí		pida	pidiera(-se)	pide
pidiendo	pides	pediste		pidas	pidieras(-ses)	
pedido	pide	pidió		pida	pidiera(-se)	
	pedimos	pedimos		pidamos	pidiéramos(-'semos)	
	pedís	pedisteis		pidáis	pidierais(-seis)	
	piden	pidieron		pidan	pidieran(-sen)	
37. pensar	pienso			piense		piensa
	piensas			pienses		
	piensa			piense		
	pensamos			pensemos		
	pensáis			penséis		
	piensan			piensen		
38. perder	pierdo			pierda		pierde
	pierdes			pierdas		
	pierde			pierda		
	perdemos			perdamos		
	perdéis			perdáis		
	pierden			pierdan		
39. poder	puedo	pude	podré	pueda	pudiera(-se)	puede
pudiendo	puedes	pudiste	podrás	puedas	pudieras(-ses)	
podido	puede	pudo	podrá	pueda	pudiera(-se)	
	podemos	pudimos	podremos	podamos	pudiéramos(-'semos)	
	podéis	pudisteis	podréis	podáis	pudierais(-seis)	
	pueden	pudieron	podrán	puedan	pudieran(-sen)	

Infinitive, Present Part., Past Part.	INDICATIVE			SUBJUNCTIVE		
	Present	*Preterite*	*Future*	*Present*	*Imperfect*	*Command*
40. poner poniendo **puesto**	**pongo** pones pone etc.	**puse** pusiste **puso** pusimos pusisteis **pusieron**	**pondré** **pondrás** **pondrá** pondremos pondréis pondrán	**ponga** pongas ponga pongamos pongáis pongan	pusiera(-se) pusieras(-ses) pusiera(-se) pusiéramos(-'semos) pusierais(-seis) pusieran(-sen)	**pon**
41. querer	**quiero** quieres quiere queremos queréis quieren	**quise** quisiste quiso quisimos quisisteis quisieron	**querré** querrás querrá querremos querréis querrán	**quiera** quieras quiera queramos queráis quieran	quisiera(-se) quisieras(-ses) quisiera(-se) quisiéramos(-'semos) quisierais(-seis) quisieran(-sen)	**quiere**
42. reír **riendo** **reído**	**río** ríes ríe reímos reís **ríen**	reí reíste rió reímos reísteis rieron	**reiré** reirás reirá reiremos reiréis reirán	**ría** rías ría riamos riáis rían	riera(-se) rieras(-ses) riera(-se) riéramos(-'semos) rierais(-seis) rieran(-sen)	**ríe**
43. reñir **riñiendo** reñido	**riño** riñes riñe reñimos reñís **riñen**	reñí reñiste **riñó** reñimos reñisteis **riñeron**		**riña** riñas riña riñamos riñáis riñan	riñera(-se) riñeras(-ses) riñera(-se) riñéramos(-'semos) riñerais(-seis) riñeran(-sen)	**riñe**
44. reunir	**reúno** **reúnes** **reúne** reunimos reunís **reúnen**			**reúna** **reúnas** **reúna** reunamos reunáis **reúnan**		**reúne**
45. rezar		**recé** rezaste rezó etc.		**rece** reces rece recemos recéis recen		
46. rogar	**ruego** **ruegas** **ruega** rogamos rogáis **ruegan**	**rogué** rogaste rogó etc.		**ruegue** **ruegues** **ruegue** roguemos roguéis **rueguen**		**ruega**
47. romper rompiendo **roto**						
48. saber	**sé** sabes sabe etc.	**supe** supiste supo supimos supisteis supieron	**sabré** sabrás sabrá sabremos sabréis sabrán	**sepa** sepas sepa sepamos sepáis sepan	supiera(-se) supieras(-ses) supiera(-se) supiéramos(-'semos) supierais(-seis) supieran(-sen)	
49. salir	**salgo** sales sale etc.		**saldré** saldrás saldrá saldremos saldréis saldrán	**salga** salgas salga salgamos salgáis salgan		**sal**
50. seguir **siguiendo** seguido	**sigo** sigues **sigue** seguimos seguís **siguen**	seguí seguiste **siguió** seguimos seguisteis **siguieron**		**siga** sigas siga sigamos sigáis sigan	siguiera(-se) siguieras(-ses) siguiera(-se) siguiéramos(-'semos) siguierais(-seis) siguieran(-sen)	**sigue**

Infinitive, *Present Part.,* *Past Part.*	INDICATIVE			SUBJUNCTIVE		
	Present	*Preterite*	*Future*	*Present*	*Imperfect*	*Command*
51. sentir **sintiendo** sentido	siento sientes siente sentimos sentís sienten	sentí sentiste sintió sentimos sentisteis sintieron		sienta sientas sienta sintamos sintáis sientan	sintiera(-se) sintieras(-ses) sintiera(-se) sintiéramos(-'semos) sintierais(-seis) sintieran(-sen)	siente
52. ser	soy eres es somos sois son	fui fuiste fue fuimos fuisteis fueron		sea seas sea seamos seáis sean	fuera(-se) fueras(-ses) fuera(-se) fuéramos(-'semos) fuerais(-seis) fueran(-sen)	sé
53. tener	tengo tienes tiene tenemos tenéis tienen	tuve tuviste tuvo tuvimos tuvisteis tuvieron	tendré tendrás tendrá tendremos tendréis tendrán	tenga tengas tenga tengamos tengáis tengan	tuviera(-se) tuvieras(-ses) tuviera(-se) tuviéramos(-'semos) tuvierais(-seis) tuvieran(-sen)	ten
54. tocar		toqué tocaste tocó etc.		toque toques toque toquemos toquéis toquen		
55. traducir	traduzco traduces traduce etc.	traduje tradujiste tradujo tradujimos tradujisteis tradujeron		traduzca traduzcas traduzca traduzcamos traduzcáis traduzcan	tradujera(-se) tradujeras(-ses) tradujera(-se) tradujéramos(-'semos) tradujerais(-seis) tradujeran(-sen)	
56. traer **trayendo** **traído**	traigo traes trae etc.	traje trajiste trajo trajimos trajisteis trajeron		traiga traigas traiga traigamos traigáis traigan	trajera(-se) trajeras(-ses) trajera(-se) trajéramos(-'semos) trajerais(-seis) trajeran(-sen)	
57. vencer	venzo vences vence etc.			venza venzas venza venzamos venzáis venzan		
58. venir **viniendo** venido	vengo vienes viene venimos venís vienen	vine viniste vino vinimos vinisteis vinieron	vendré vendrás vendrá vendremos vendréis vendrán	venga vengas venga vengamos vengáis vengan	viniera(-se) vinieras(-ses) viniera(-se) viniéramos(-'semos) vinierais(-seis) vinieran(-sen)	ven
59. ver viendo **visto**	veo ves ve etc.			vea veas vea veamos veáis vean		
60. volver volviendo **vuelto**	vuelvo vuelves vuelve volvemos volvéis vuelven			vuelva vuelvas vuelva volvamos volváis vuelvan		vuelve

Other Verbs With Irregular Forms

acercarse (*See* buscar)
acertar (*See* pensar)
acordarse (*See* mostrar)
acostarse (*See* mostrar)
actuar (*See* continuar)
adquirir (*See* sentir)
afligir (*See* dirigir)
agradecer (*See* conocer)
alcanzar (*See* gozar)
apagar (*See* llegar)
aparecer (*See* conocer)
apretar (*See* pensar)
atraer (*See* traer)
atravesar (*See* pensar)
castigar (*See* llegar)
cerrar (*See* pensar)
coger (*See* dirigir)
colocar (*See* buscar)
comenzar (*See* empezar)
componer (*See* poner)
conducir (*See* traducir)
confiar (*See* enviar)
conseguir (*See* seguir)
consentir (*See* sentir)
contar (*See* mostrar)
contener (*See* tener)
contribuir (*See* huir)
convencer (*See* vencer)
convenir (*See* venir)
corregir (*See* elegir)
costar (*See* mostrar)

crecer (*See* conocer)
cruzar (*See* gozar)
cubrir (*See* abrir)
defender (*See* perder)
demostrar (*See* mostrar)
desaparecer (*See* conocer)
describir (*See* escribir)
descubrir (*See* abrir)
deshacer (*See* hacer)
despedirse (*See* pedir)
despertarse (*See* pensar)
destruir (*See* huir)
detener (*See* tener)
devolver (*See* volver)
disponer (*See* poner)
distribuir (*See* huir)
divertirse (*See* sentir)
ejercer (*See* vencer)
encontrar (*See* mostrar)
entender (*See* perder)
entregar (*See* llegar)
equivocarse (*See* buscar)
escoger (*See* dirigir)
esparcir (*See* vencer)
espiar (*See* enviar)
establecer (*See* conocer)
exigir (*See* dirigir)
exponer (*See* poner)
fiarse (*See* enviar)
fingir (*See* dirigir)
fluir (*See* huir)

gemir (*See* pedir)
gobernar (*See* pensar)
graduarse (*See* continuar)
guiar (*See* enviar)
helar (*See* pensar)
hervir (*See* sentir)
impedir (*See* pedir)
imponer (*See* poner)
incluir (*See* huir)
indicar (*See* buscar)
influir (*See* huir)
introducir (*See* traducir)
leer (*See* creer)
llover (3rd-person forms
   only. *See* mover)
mantener (*See* tener)
medir (*See* pedir)
mentir (*See* sentir)
merecer (*See* conocer)
nacer (*See* conocer)
nevar (3rd-person forms
   only. *See* pensar)
obedecer (*See* conocer)
obligar (*See* llegar)
obtener (*See* tener)
ofrecer (*See* conocer)
oponer (*See* poner)
pagar (*See* llegar)
parecer (*See* conocer)
pegar (*See* llegar)
permanecer (*See* conocer)

perseguir (*See* seguir)
pertenecer (*See* conocer)
poseer (*See* creer)
preferir (*See* sentir)
probar (*See* mostrar)
producir (*See* traducir)
proponer (*See* poner)
proseguir (*See* seguir)
proteger (*See* dirigir)
recoger (*See* dirigir)
reconocer (*See* conocer)
recordar (*See* mostrar)
referir (*See* sentir)
repetir (*See* pedir)
resfriarse (*See* enviar)
resolver (*See* volver)
sacar (*See* buscar)
satisfacer (*See* hacer)
sentarse (*See* pensar)
servir (*See* pedir)
soler (Present and imperfect
   tenses only. *See* mover)
sonreír (*See* reír)
soñar (*See* mostrar)
sustituir (*See* huir)
torcer (*See* cocer)
tropezar (*See* empezar)
valer (*See* salir)
verificarse (*See* buscar)
vestirse (*See* pedir)
volar (*See* mostrar)

a, to, at; **al + *inf.***, upon . . .

abajo, below; **escalera abajo**, downstairs

abandonar, to abandon, to desert

abeja, *f.*, bee

abierto,-a, open; **abierto de par en par**, wide open

abogado, *m.*, lawyer

aborrecer (zc), to hate, to detest

abrazar (c), to embrace, to hug

abrazo, *m.*, embrace, hug

abrigo, *m.*, coat, overcoat

abril, *m.*, April

abrir, to open

absoluto,-a, absolute

abuelo, *m.*, grandfather; **abuela**, *f.*, grandmother

abundante, abundant

aburrir, to bore; **aburrirse**, to become bored

acabar, to finish, to end; **acabar de + *inf.***, to have just . . .; **acabar por + *inf.***, to end by, to finally . . .

acaso, perhaps

accidente, *m.*, accident

acción, *f.*, action

acento, *m.*, accent

aceptar, to accept

acera, *f.*, sidewalk

acerca de, about, concerning

acercarse (qu) a, to approach

acero, *m.*, steel

acertar (ie), to hit the mark, to guess right; **acertar a + *inf.***, to happen to

acompañar, to accompany

aconsejar, to advise

acordarse (ue) de, to remember

acostar (ue), to put to bed; **acostarse**, to go to bed

acostumbrar, to be accustomed to; **acostumbrarse a**, to become accustomed to

acto, *m.*, act

actor, *m.*, actor; **actriz**, *f.*, actress

actual, present, present-day; **actualmente**, at present, nowadays

actuar (ú), to act

acueducto, *m.*, aqueduct

acuerdo, *m.*, agreement; **de acuerdo con**, in accordance with, **estar de acuerdo**, to be in agreement; **ponerse de acuerdo**, to come to an agreement

acusar, to accuse

adelantar(se), to advance, to progress

adelante, ahead, forward; **de hoy en adelante**, from now on, henceforth

ademán, *m.*, gesture

además, besides, moreover; **además de**, besides

adentro, inside

adiós, goodbye

adjetivo, *m.*, adjective

administrador, *m.*, manager, administrator

admiración, *f.*, admiration

admirar, to admire

admitir, to admit

adonde, (to) where; **¿adónde?**, (to) where?

adondequiera, (to) wherever

adornar, to decorate, to adorn

adquirir (ie, i), to acquire

adverbio, *m.*, adverb

adversario, *m.*, adversary, opponent, rival

advertir (ie, i), to notify, to warn

afecto, *m.*, affection

afeitar, to shave; **afeitarse**, to shave oneself

aficionado,-a (a), devoted (to); *m.* or *f.*, "fan"

afirmar, to state, to affirm

afligir (j), to afflict, to grieve; **afligirse**, to feel aggrieved

afortunado,-a, fortunate; **afortunadamente**, fortunately

afuera, outside; **afueras**, *f. pl.*, outskirts

agitar, to agitate, to stir, to wave; **agitarse**, to become upset

agosto, *m.*, August

agradable, pleasant, agreeable

agradar, to be pleasing

agradecer (zc), to thank (for), to be grateful (for)

agregar (gu), to add

agrícola, agricultural

agricultor, *m.*, farmer

agua (el), *f.*, water

aguador, *m.*, water seller

aguardar, to wait (for), to await

agudo,-a, sharp

águila (el), *f.*, eagle

aguja, *f.*, needle

ahí, there

ahora, now; **ahora mismo**, right now

aire, *m.*, air

ajedrez, *m.*, chess

ajeno,-a, foreign, alien, another's

ala (el), *f.*, wing

alabar, to praise

alba (el), *f.*, dawn

alcalde, *m.*, mayor

alcanzar (c), to reach, to overtake

alcoba, *f.*, bedroom

aldea, *f.*, village

alegrarse (de), to be glad (of, to)

alegre, merry, gay, happy

alegría, *f.*, joy, merriment

alejarse (de), to move away, to withdraw (from)

alemán, alemana, German; *m.*, German (language)

Alemania, *f.*, Germany

alfabeto, *m.*, alphabet

alfiler, *m.*, pin, brooch

alfombra, *f.*, carpet, rug

algo, something, somewhat

algodón, *m.*, cotton

alguien, someone

alguno,-a (algún), some; **alguna vez**, some time

alhaja, *f.*, jewel

alimento, *m.*, food

alma (el), *f.*, soul

almohada, *f.*, pillow

almorzar (ue, c), to eat lunch

almuerzo, *m.*, lunch

alrededor de, around

altar, *m.*, altar

alto,-a, high, tall; **en voz alta**, aloud; **de alto**, in height

altura, *f.*, height

alumbrar, to illuminate, to light up

alumno,-a, pupil, student

alzar (c), to raise, to lift

allí, allá, there

amable, kind, amiable

amanecer (zc), to dawn; **al amanecer**, at daybreak

amante, *m.* or *f.*, lover, suitor

amar, to love

amargo,-a, bitter

amargura, *f.*, bitterness

amarillo,-a, yellow

ambición, *f.*, ambition

ambos,-as, both

amenazar (c) (con), to threaten (to)

América, *f.*, America; **la América Hispana**, Spanish America

americano,-a, American; **americana**, *f.*, jacket (of a man's suit)

amigo,-a, friend

amistad, *f.*, friendship

amo, *m.*, master, owner, boss

amor, *m.*, love

ancho,-a, wide

andaluz,-a, Andalusian

andar, to walk, to go

andén, *m.*, station platform

andino,-a, Andean

ángel, *m.*, angel

anillo, *m.*, ring

animado,-a, lively, excited

animar, to encourage

aniversario, *m.*, anniversary

anoche, last night

anochecer (zc), to grow dark; **al anochecer**, at nightfall

ante, before (in the presence of)

anteayer, day before yesterday

anteojos, *m. pl.*, eyeglasses

anterior, previous, preceding

antes, previously, beforehand; **antes de**, before; **cuanto antes**, as soon as possible, without delay

antiguo,-a, ancient, old

anunciar, to announce

añadir, to add

año, *m.*, year; **el Año Nuevo**, New Year; **el año que viene**, next year; **tener . . . años**, to be . . . years old

apagar (gu), to put out, to extinguish

aparato, *m.*, apparatus, set; **aparato de televisión**, television set

aparecer (zc), to appear

apartamiento, *m.*, apartment

apartar, to separate, to place apart; **apartarse (de)**, to draw apart (from), to leave

aparte, aside, separate

apellido, *m.*, surname

apenas, scarcely, hardly

apetito, *m.*, appetite

aplaudir, to applaud

aplicado,-a, studious, diligent, industrious

aplicar (qu), to apply

apoderarse de, to take possession of, to get control of

apodo, *m.*, nickname

apóstol, *m.*, apostle

apoyar, to support, to aid; **apoyarse en**, to lean on

aprender, to learn

apresurarse (a), to hurry (to)

apretar (ie), to tighten, to squeeze, to be tight

aprovecharse de, to take advantage of

aproximadamente, approximately

apurarse, to worry

aquel: en aquel entonces, at that time

aquí, acá, here

árabe, Arab, Arabic; *m.*, Arabic (language)

árbol, *m.*, tree

arder, to burn

ardiente, ardent, burning

arena, *f.*, sand
la **Argentina**, Argentina
aritmética, *f.*, arithmetic
arma (el), *f.*, weapon, arm
armada, *f.*, fleet
armar, to arm
armario, *m.*, closet
arquitecto, *m.*, architect
arquitectura, *f.*, architecture
arrancar (qu), to pull out
arreglar, to arrange, to settle
arreglo, *m.*, arrangement
arrepentirse (ie, i) de, to repent
arriba, above, up, upstairs
arrojar, to throw
arroz, *m.*, rice
arte, *m.* or *f.*, art
artículo, *m.*, article
artista, *m.* or *f.*, artist
ascender (ie), to ascend
ascensor, *m.*, elevator
asegurar, to assure
así, thus, so, in this way; así que, as soon as; así como, as well as
asiento, *m.*, seat
asistir (a), to attend
asomarse a, to look out of, to appear at (a window)
asombrado,-a, astonished
asombrar, to astonish; asombrarse (de), to be astonished (at), to wonder (at)
aspecto, *m.*, appearance, aspect
aspirar (a), to aspire (to)
asunto, *m.*, matter, affair
asustar, to frighten; asustarse, to be frightened
atacar (qu), to attack
atar, to tie
atención, *f.*, attention; con atención, attentively; prestar atención, to pay attention
atento,-a, attentive
atraer (atraigo), to attract
atrás, in back, behind
atravesar (ie), to cross
atreverse (a), to dare (to)
atrevido,-a, daring, bold
aula (el), *f.*, classroom
aumentar, to increase
aún (aun), even, still, yet
aunque, although, even though
ausente, absent
autobús, *m.*, bus
automóvil (auto), *m.*, automobile
autor, *m.*, author
autoridad, *f.*, authority
avanzar (c), to advance
avaro,-a, miserly, miser
ave (el), *f.*, bird
avenida, *f.*, avenue

aventura, *f.*, adventure
averiguar (gü), to find out, to verify
avión, *m.*, airplane
avisar, to notify, to warn
¡ay!, alas!
ayer, yesterday
ayuda, *f.*, aid, help
ayudar, to help
azteca, *m.* or *f.*, Aztec
azúcar, *m.*, sugar
azul, blue

bailar, to dance
bailarín, bailarina, dancer
baile, *m.*, dance
bajar, to descend, to go down
bajo,-a, low, short; *adv.*, under
bala, *f.*, bullet
balcón, *m.*, balcony
banco, *m.*, bank, bench
banda, *f.*, edge; la **Banda Oriental**, Eastern Edge (former name of Uruguay)
bandera, *f.*, banner, flag
banquero, *m.*, banker
banquete, *m.*, banquet
bañar, to bathe; bañarse, to take a bath
baño, *m.*, bath, bathroom
barato,-a, cheap
bárbaro,-a, barbarous, barbarian
barco, *m.*, ship
base, *f.*, base, basis
bastante, enough, quite
bastar, to suffice, to be enough
batalla, *f.*, battle
baúl, *m.*, trunk
beber, to drink; dar de beber, to give a drink
bebida, *f.*, beverage, drink
béisbol, *m.*, baseball
belleza, *f.*, beauty
bello,-a, beautiful
besar, to kiss
beso, *m.*, kiss
biblioteca, *f.*, library
bicicleta, *f.*, bicycle
bien, well; *m.*, good, welfare; *m. pl.*, property; llevarse bien (con), to get along well (with); salir bien, to pass (an examination)
billete, *m.*, ticket; billete de ida y vuelta, round-trip ticket
blanco,-a, white
blando,-a, soft
blusa, *f.*, blouse
boca, *f.*, mouth
boda, *f.*, wedding
bolsa, *f.*, purse, stock market

bolsillo, *m.*, pocket
bondad, *f.*, kindness
bondadoso,-a, kind
bonito,-a, pretty
borrador, *m.*, eraser
borrar, to erase
bosque, *m.*, forest, woods
botella, *f.*, bottle
botica, *f.*, drugstore
botón, *m.*, button
bravo,-a, fierce, brave
brazalete, *m.*, bracelet
brazo, *m.*, arm
breve, short, brief
brillante, shining, brilliant
brillar, to shine
broma, *f.*, joke, jest; en broma, in jest
brotar, to sprout
bueno,-a (buen), good; de buena gana, willingly
buque, *m.*, ship
burlarse de, to make fun of, to laugh at
burro, *m.*, donkey
busca, *f.*, search; en busca de, in search of
buscar (qu), to look for, to seek

caballero, *m.*, gentleman, knight
caballo, *m.*, horse
cabello, *m.*, hair
caber (quepo), to fit; no cabe duda, doubtless, there is no doubt
cabeza, *f.*, head; de pies a cabeza, from head to foot
cabo, *m.*, end, corporal; llevar a cabo, to carry out
cabra, *f.*, goat
cada, each; cada vez más, more and more
cadena, *f.*, chain
caer (caigo, y), to fall; dejar caer, to drop
café, *m.*, coffee, café
cafetería, *f.*, cafeteria
caída, *f.*, fall
caja, *f.*, box
cajón, *m.*, drawer
calcetín, *m.*, sock
calendario, *m.*, calendar
calentar (ie), to heat
calidad, *f.*, quality
caliente, hot, warm
calma, *f.*, calm
calor, *m.*, heat, warmth; hacer calor, to be warm (weather); tener calor, to be warm (person)
callarse, to be silent, to keep still
calle, *f.*, street
cama, *f.*, bed; guardar cama, to stay in bed

cámara, *f.*, camera; pintor de cámara, court painter
camarero, *m.*, waiter; camarera, *f.*, waitress
cambiar, to change
cambio, *m.*, change, exchange; en cambio, on the other hand
caminar, to walk
camino, *m.*, road, highway; camino de, on the way to; en camino, on the road; proseguir el camino, to continue on one's way
camisa, *f.*, shirt
campana, *f.*, bell
campaña, *f.*, campaign
campesino, *m.*, farmer, peasant
campo, *m.*, country, field
canción, *f.*, song
cansado,-a, tired, tiresome
cansar, to tire; cansarse, to become tired
cantante, singer; cantante callejero, street singer
cantar, to sing
cantidad, *f.*, quantity
canto, *m.*, song, singing
cantor, *m.*, singer
cañón, *m.*, cannon, canyon; el **Gran Cañón**, the Grand Canyon
capa, *f.*, cape
capaz, capable
capilla, *f.*, chapel
capital, *f.*, capital (city); *m.*, capital (money)
capitán, *m.*, captain
capítulo, *m.*, chapter
cara, *f.*, face
cárcel, *f.*, prison
carecer (zc) de, to lack
cargar (gu), to load
caridad, *f.*, charity
cariño, *m.*, affection, love
cariñoso,-a, affectionate
carne, *f.*, meat
carnicería, *f.*, butcher shop
carnicero, *m.*, butcher
caro,-a, expensive, dear
carpintero, *m.*, carpenter
carrera, *f.*, profession, career
carreta, *f.*, cart
carretera, *f.*, highway
carretero, *m.*, truckman
carta, *f.*, letter
cartero, *m.*, letter carrier, postman
casa, *f.*, house, home; casa de correos, post office; a casa, (to) home; en casa, (at) home; mudar de casa, to move
casamiento, *m.*, marriage, wedding
casar, to marry; casarse (con), to get married (to)
casi, almost

caso, *m.*, case; **en caso de que**, in case; **en todo caso**, in any case; **hacer caso de**, to heed, to pay attention to

castañuelas, *f.*, castanets

castellano,-a, Castilian, Spanish

castigar (gu), to punish

castigo, *m.*, punishment

castillo, *m.*, castle

catalán, catalana, Catalonian

catarata, *f.*, waterfall

catarro, *m.*, cold (illness)

catástrofe, *f.*, catastrophe

catedral, *f.*, cathedral

caucho, *m.*, rubber

causa, *f.*, cause; **a causa de**, because of

ceder, to yield

celebrar, to celebrate; **celebrarse**, to be celebrated

célebre, famous, celebrated

cena, *f.*, supper

cenar, to have supper

centavo, *m.*, cent

centro, *m.*, center, downtown

cepillo, *m.*, brush

cerca de, near; **de cerca**, nearby

cercano,-a, nearby, neighboring

ceremonia, *f.*, ceremony

cereza, *f.*, cherry

cero, *m.*, zero

cerrado,-a, closed

cerrar (ie), to close

cesar (de), to stop, to cease

cesta, *f.*, basket

ciego,-a, blind

cielo, *m.*, sky, heaven

ciencia, *f.*, science

cierto,-a, certain, a certain

cigarro, *m.*, cigar

cine, *m.*, movies, movie theater

circo, *m.*, circus

círculo, *m.*, circle, club

cita, *f.*, appointment, date

ciudad, *f.*, city

ciudadano,-a, citizen

civil, civil, civilian

civilización, *f.*, civilization

claridad, *f.*, clarity, clearness

claro,-a, light, clear

clase, *f.*, class, classroom

clavel, *m.*, carnation

clima, *m.*, climate

cobrar, to collect, to charge

cobre, *m.*, copper

cocer (ue, z), to cook

cocina, *f.*, kitchen

cocinero,-a, cook

coche, *m.*, car

cochero, *m.*, coachman, driver

coger (j), to seize, to grasp, to catch

colchón, *m.*, mattress

colgar (ue, gu), to hang

colocar (qu), to place, to put

colonia, *f.*, colony

color, *m.*, color

columna, *f.*, column

collar, *m.*, necklace

combate, *m.*, combat

combatir, to combat, to fight

comedia, *f.*, (theatrical) play, comedy

comedor, *m.*, dining room

comenzar (ie, c), to begin, to commence

comer, to eat; **dar de comer**, to feed

comercial, commercial

comerciante, *m.*, merchant

comercio, *m.*, commerce, trade

comestibles, *m. pl.*, groceries

comida, *f.*, meal, dinner, food

como, as, like; **como si**, as if, as though; **¿cómo?**, how?; **así como**, as well as; **tan pronto como**, as soon as

cómodo,-a, comfortable

compañero,-a, companion, friend

compañía, *f.*, company

compilar, to compile

completar, to complete

completo,-a, complete

componer (compongo), to compose, to repair

compositor, *m.*, composer

compra, *f.*, purchase; **ir de compras**, to go shopping

comprar, to buy

comprender, to understand, to comprise

común, common; **por lo común**, usually, generally

comunicar (qu), to communicate

con, with; **con tal que**, provided that

conceder, to concede

concierto, *m.*, concert

concluir (y), to end, to conclude

conde, *m.*, count; **condesa**, *f.*, countess

condenar, to condemn

condicional, conditional

condiscípulo, *m.*, fellow pupil

conducir (zc), to conduct, to lead, to drive (an automobile)

conferencia, *f.*, lecture, talk

conferenciante, *m.*, lecturer

confesar (ie), to confess

confianza, *f.*, confidence

confiar (í) en, to rely on, to confide in

conforme, in agreement; **conforme a**, according to,

in accordance with; **estar conforme (con)**, to be in agreement (with)

confundir, to confuse; **confundirse**, to become confused

confusión, *f.*, confusion

congreso, *m.*, congress

conjunto, *m.*, entirety, whole

conmemorar, to commemorate

conmigo, with me

conmover (ue), to move (emotionally)

conocer (zc), to know (a person), to meet (make the acquaintance of)

conocido,-a, known; *m.* or *f.*, acquaintance

conquista, *f.*, conquest

conquistador, *m.*, conqueror

conquistar, to conquer

consecuencia, *f.*, consequence

conseguir (i, g), to get, to obtain; **conseguir + *inf.***, to succeed in

consejo, *m.*, advice, council

consentir (ie, i) (en), to consent (to)

conservar, to preserve, to save

considerar, to consider

consigo, with him (self), with her (self), with you (yourself), with them(selves)

consiguiente: **por consiguiente**, consequently, therefore

consistir (en), to consist (of)

constante, constant

constitución, *f.*, constitution

construcción, *f.*, construction

construir (y), to construct, to build

consuelo, *m.*, consolation

consultar, to consult

contador, *m.*, accountant, bookkeeper

contar (ue), to count, to relate; **contar con**, to rely on

contemplar, to contemplate

contemporáneo,-a, -contemporary, present-day

contener (ie, contengo), to contain

contento,-a, content, happy

contestación, *f.*, answer

contestar, to answer

contigo, *fam.*, with you

continente, *m.*, continent

continuar (ú), to continue

contra, against

contrario,-a, contrary

contrato, *m.*, contract

contribuir (y), to contribute

convencer (z), to convince

convenir (ie, convengo) (en), to agree (to)

conversación, *f.*, conversation

conversar, to converse

convertir (ie, i) (en), to convert (to)

copa, *f.*, goblet, cup

copiar, to copy

corazón, *m.*, heart

corbata, *f.*, necktie

cordillera, *f.*, mountain range

correcto,-a, correct

corregir (i, j), to correct

correo, *m.*, mail; **casa de correos**, post office; **echar al correo**, to mail

correr, to run

corresponder, to correspond, to belong, to be suitable

correspondiente, corresponding

corrida, *f.* (de toros), bullfight

corriente, current, present; *f.*, current

cortar, to cut

cortés, courteous, polite

cortesía, *f.*, courtesy

cortina, *f.*, curtain

corto,-a, short

cosa, *f.*, thing

cosecha, *f.*, harvest

coser, to sew

costa, *f.*, coast, cost

costar (ue), to cost

costumbre, *f.*, custom

crear, to create

crecer (zc), to grow

creer (y), to believe; **¡ya lo creo!**, of course!, I should say so!

criado, *m.*, servant; **criada**, *f.*, servant, maid

crimen, *m.*, crime

criollo,-a, Creole

cristiano,-a, Christian

crítico, *m.*, critic

cruz, *f.*, cross

cruzar (c), to cross

cuaderno, *m.*, notebook

cuadrado,-a, square; *m.*, square

cuadro, *m.*, picture

¿cuál?, which?

cualquier(a), any, whatever

¡cuán . . . !, how . . . !

cuando, when; **de vez en cuando**, from time to time; **¿cuándo?**, when?

cuandoquiera, whenever

cuanto,-a, as much as; **cuanto antes**, as soon as possible, without delay; **en cuanto**, as soon as; **en cuanto a**, in regard to, as for; **unos cuantos (unas cuantas)**, a few; **¿cuánto, -a?**, how much?; **¿cuántos, -as?**, how many?;

¿cuánto tiempo?, how long?; ¿a cuántos estamos?, what is today's date?

cuarto,-a, fourth; m., room, quarter

cubano,-a, Cuban

cubrir, to cover

cuchara, f., spoon

cuchillo, m., knife

cuello, m., neck, collar

cuenta, f., account, bill; darse cuenta (de), to realize, to become aware (of)

cuento, m., story, tale

cuerda, f., cord, rope, string; dar cuerda (a), to wind

cuero, m., leather

cuidado, m., care; con cuidado, carefully; perder cuidado, not to worry; tener cuidado, to be careful

cuidar (a), to take care of (a person); cuidar (de), to take care of (something)

culpa, f., blame, fault; echar la culpa a, to blame; tener la culpa (de), to be to blame (for)

culto,-a, cultured; m., cult, worship

cumbre, f., top, peak

cumpleaños, m., birthday

cumplir (con), to fulfill, to keep (a promise)

cura, m., priest; f., cure

curar, to cure

curiosidad, f., curiosity

curioso,-a, curious

cursivo,-a, italic (letter)

curso, m., course

curtir, to tan

cuyo,-a, whose

chaleco, m., vest

chaqueta, f., jacket

charlar, to chat

cheque, m., check

chicle, m., chewing gum

chico,-a, small, child

chileno,-a, Chilean

chiste, m., joke

dama, f., lady

daño, m., damage, harm; hacer(se) daño, to hurt (oneself), to cause damage

dar (doy), to give; dar a, to face; to look out upon; dar con, to come upon, to find; dar de beber (comer), to give a drink (to feed); dar en, to strike against (to hit); dar la hora, to strike the hour; dar la vuelta a, to

circumnavigate; dar las gracias, to thank; dar recuerdos (a), to give regards (to); dar un grito, dar gritos, to shout; dar un paseo, to take a walk, to ride; dar una vuelta, to take a stroll; dar voces, to shout; darse cuenta (de), to realize, to become aware (of); dar(se) por + past participle, to consider (oneself); darse prisa, to hurry

de, of, from, by, than; del, of the

debajo, underneath; debajo de, under

deber, to owe, should, ought to; m., duty; deber de, must, probably; debido a, due to

débil, weak

decadencia, f., decadence

decidir, to decide; decidirse (a), to decide (to)

decir (i, digo), to say, to tell; querer decir, to mean; es decir, that is to say; decir la buenaventura, to tell one's fortune; decir que sí (no), to say yes (no)

declaración, f., declaration

declarar, to declare

decorar, to decorate

dedicar (qu), to dedicate, to devote; dedicarse (a), to devote oneself (to)

dedo, m., finger, toe

defecto, m., defect

defender (ie), to defend

defensa, f., defense

definido, a, definite

dejar, to leave, to let; dejar caer, to drop; dejar de + inf., to fail to, to stop, to neglect to

delante de, in front of

delgado,-a, slender, thin

demás: los (las) demás, the remainder, the remaining

demasiado,-a, too much; adv., too

demostrar (ue), to show, to demonstrate

demostrativo,-a, demonstrative

dentista, m., dentist

dentro (de), within, inside (of); dentro de poco, in a little while

dependiente, m., clerk

deporte, m., sport

derecho,-a, right; m., right, law; a la derecha, to (at) the right

derramar, to spill, to shed

derrotar, to defeat

desagradable, disagreeable, unpleasant

desaparecer (zc), to disappear

desarrollar(se), to unfold, to develop

desastre, m., disaster

desayunarse, to have breakfast

desayuno, m., breakfast

descansar, to rest

descanso, m., rest

descender (ie), to descend

desconocer (zc), to be unaware of

describir, to describe

descubrimiento, m., discovery

descubrir, to discover

desde, from, since; desde luego, of course, at once

desear, to want, to wish

deseo, m., wish, desire

desgracia, f., misfortune; por desgracia, unfortunately

desgraciado,-a, unfortunate; desgraciadamente, unfortunately

deshacer (deshago), to undo

desierto,-a, deserted; m., desert

deslizarse (c), to glide

desmayarse, to faint

despacio, slowly

despacho, m., office

despedirse (i) (de), to take leave (of), to say goodby (to)

despertar (ie), to awaken (someone); despertarse, to wake up (oneself)

después, afterwards; después de, after; después que, after

destino, m., destiny, fate, destination

destruir (y), to destroy

detalle, m., detail

detener (ie, detengo), to stop, to detain; detenerse, to stop (oneself)

detrás de, behind

deuda, f., debt

devolver (ue), to return, to give back

día, m., day; día de fiesta, holiday; al día siguiente, on the following day; de día, by day; Día de los Difuntos, All Souls' Day; algún día, some day; hoy día, nowadays; ocho días, a week; quince días, two weeks; todo el día, all day; todos los días, every day

diamante, m., diamond

diario,-a, daily; m., newspaper

diccionario, m., dictionary

diciembre, m., December

dictado, m., dictation; escribir al dictado, to write at dictation

dictador, m., dictator

dictadura, f., dictatorship

dichoso,-a, fortunate, happy, blessed

diente, m., tooth

diferencia, f., difference

diferente, different

difícil, difficult

dificultad, f., difficulty

dignidad, f., dignity

diligente, diligent

dinamita, f., dynamite

dinero, m., money

Dios, God

dirección, f., address, direction

directo,-a, direct

director, m., director, principal

dirigir (j), to direct, to manage; dirigirse a, to make one's way toward, to address

discípulo, m., pupil, disciple

disco, m., (phonograph) record

discreto,-a, discreet

discurrir, to speak, to discourse, to run about

discurso, m., speech, lecture, discourse

discusión, f., discussion

discutir, to discuss

disgusto, m., displeasure

dispensar, to excuse

disponer (dispongo) de, to dispose of, to have; disponerse a + inf., to get ready to

dispuesto,-a, ready

distancia, f., distance

distinguir (g), to distinguish

distinto,-a, different

distribuir (y), to distribute

diverso,-a, diverse, different; pl., several

divertir (ie, i), to amuse; divertirse, to enjoy oneself, to have a good time

dividir, to divide

doblar, to fold; doblar la esquina, to turn the corner

doble, double

docena, f., dozen

documento, m., document

dólar, m., dollar

doler (ue), to be painful, to cause sorrow

dolor, m., pain, ache, sorrow; dolor de cabeza, headache; tener dolor, to have a pain (ache)

dominar, to dominate

domingo, m., Sunday; Domingo de Resurrección,

Easter Sunday

don, *m.*, doña, *f.*, (title used before the given name of a gentleman or lady)

donde, where; ¿dónde?, where?

dondequiera, wherever

dormido,-a, asleep

dormir (ue, u), to sleep; dormirse, to fall asleep

drama, *m.*, drama

dramaturgo, *m.*, dramatist

duda, *f.*, doubt; no cabe duda, doubtless, there's no doubt; sin duda, doubtless, without doubt

dudar, to doubt

dudoso,-a, doubtful

dueño, *m.*, owner, master

dulce, sweet; *m. pl.*, candy

dulzura, *f.*, sweetness, tenderness

durante, during

durar, to endure, to last

duro,-a, hard

e, and (used only before a word beginning with i or hi, but not hie)

económico,-a, economic

echar, to throw, to cast; echar al correo, to mail; echar de menos, to miss; echar la culpa a, to blame; echarse a + *inf.*, to begin to

edad, *f.*, age; la Edad Media, the Middle Ages

edificio, *m.*, building

educación, *f.*, education, upbringing

educativo,-a, educational

efecto, *m.*, effect; en efecto, in fact, actually, as a matter of fact

ejecutar, to perform, to execute

ejemplar, exemplary, model; *m.*, copy (of a book)

ejemplo, *m.*, example

ejercer (z), to exert, to exercise, to practice (a profession)

ejercicio, *m.*, exercise; hacer ejercicios, to exercise

ejército, *m.*, army

elección, *f.*, election

eléctrico,-a, electric

elefante, *m.*, elephant

elegir (i, j), to elect

elemento, *m.*, element

elevar, to raise, to elevate

embarcarse (qu), to embark, to set sail

embargo: sin embargo, nevertheless, however

emoción, *f.*, emotion

empeñarse en, to insist on

emperador, *m.*, emperor; emperatriz, *f.*, empress

empezar (ie, c), to begin

empleado,-a, employee

emplear, to use, to employ

empleo, *m.*, job

emprender, to undertake

empresa, *f.*, enterprise, undertaking

empujar, to push

en, in, on, at

enamorado,-a (de), in love (with)

encantador,-a, charming

encantar, to enchant, to charm

encanto, *m.*, charm, enchantment

encargar (gu), to put in charge; encargarse de, to take charge of

encender (ie), to light, to ignite

encerrar (ie), to enclose, to lock up

encima, above; encima de, on top of, above

encogerse (j) de hombros, to shrug one's shoulders

encontrar (ue), to find, to meet; encontrarse, to be, to be found; encontrarse con, to meet

enemigo,-a, enemy

enero, *m.*, January

enfadar, to anger; enfadarse, to become angry

enfermedad, *f.*, illness

enfermera, *f.*, nurse

enfermo,-a, sick, ill, sick person

enfrente (de), opposite

engañar, to deceive, to fool

engaño, *m.*, deceit, fraud

enojado,-a, angry

enojar, to anger; enojarse, to become angry

enojo, *m.*, anger

enorme, enormous

ensalada, *f.*, salad

ensayista, *m.*, essayist

ensayo, *m.*, essay

enseñanza, *f.*, teaching

enseñar, to teach, to show

entender (ie), to understand

enterarse (de), to find out (about), to become aware (of)

entonces, then; en aquel entonces, at that time

entrada, *f.*, entrance, (admission) ticket

entrar (en), to enter

entre, between, among

entregar (gu), to deliver, to hand over; entregarse, to devote oneself

entrevista, *f.*, interview, conference

entusiasmo, *m.*, enthusiasm

enviar (í), to send

envolver (ue), to wrap up

época, *f.*, epoch, time, period

equipo, *m.*, team

equivocarse (qu), to be mistaken

error, *m.*, error, mistake

erudito, *m.*, scholar

escalera, *f.*, staircase, stairs

escaparse, to escape

escena, *f.*, scene

esclavo,-a, slave

escoger (j), to choose, to select

esconder, to hide

escribir, to write; máquina de escribir, typewriter; por escrito, in writing, written; escribir al dictado, to write at dictation

escritor,-a, writer

escritorio, *m.*, desk

escuchar, to listen (to)

escudero, *m.*, squire, attendant

escuela, *f.*, school

escultor,-a, sculptor

ese: de esa manera (de ese modo), in that way; a eso de, at about (hour); por eso, therefore

esfuerzo, *m.*, effort

espacio, *m.*, space

espada, *f.*, sword

espalda, *f.*, back, shoulders

espantar, to frighten; espantarse, to become frightened

España, *f.*, Spain

español,-a, Spanish, Spaniard; *m.*, Spanish (language); a la española, in the Spanish style

especial, special

especie, *f.*, species, kind, sort

espectáculo, *m.*, spectacle, show

espejo, *m.*, mirror

esperanza, *f.*, hope

esperar, to wait (for), to await, to hope, to expect

espeso,-a, thick

espiar (í), to spy (on)

espíritu, *m.*, spirit

esposo, *m.*, husband; esposa, *f.*, wife

esquina, *f.*, corner; doblar la esquina, to turn the corner

establecer (zc), to establish; establecerse, to settle down

estación, *f.*, season, station

estado, *m.*, state

los Estados Unidos, *m. pl.*, the United States

estallar, to break out

estante, *m.*, shelf, bookcase; estante para libros, bookcase

estaño, *m.*, tin

estar (estoy), to be; estar conforme (con), to be in agreement (with); estar de acuerdo (con), to be in agreement (with); estar de vuelta, to be back; estar a punto de + *inf.*, to be about to; estar listo,-a, to be ready; estar para + *inf.*, to be about to; estar por + *inf.*, to be in favor of; ¿a cuántos estamos?, what is today's date?

estatua, *f.*, statue

este, *m.*, east

este: esta noche, tonight; de esta manera (de este modo), in this way

estilo, *m.*, style

estimar, to estimate, to esteem

estómago, *m.*, stomach

estrecho,-a, narrow; *m.*, strait

estrella, *f.*, star

estremecerse (zc), to shudder

estuco, *m.*, stucco

estudiante, *m. or f.*, pupil, student

estudiar, to study

estudio, *m.*, study

Europa, *f.*, Europe

europeo,-a, European

evidente, evident

evitar, to avoid

exacto,-a, exact

examen, *m.*, examination, test

examinar, to examine

excelente, excellent

exigir (j), to demand, to require

existir, to exist

éxito, *m.*, success; tener éxito (en), to be successful (in)

expedición, *f.*, expedition

experiencia, *f.*, experience

experimentar, to experience

explicación, *f.*, explanation

explicar (qu), to explain

explorador, *m.*, explorer

explosión, *f.*, explosion

exponer (expongo), to expose, to expound

exportar, to export

expresar, to express

expresión, f., expression

expulsar, to expel

extender (ie), to extend; extenderse, to extend, to spread

extensión, f., area

extinguir (g), to extinguish, to put out

extranjero,-a, foreign, foreigner

extraño,-a, strange

extremo,-a, extreme; m., end, tip, extreme; el Extremo Oriente, the Far East

fábrica, f., factory

fabricar (qu), to make, to manufacture

fácil, easy

facturar, to check (luggage)

falda, f., skirt

falso,-a, false, untrue

falta, f., mistake, lack: hacer falta, to be lacking; nos hace(n) falta, we need, we lack

faltar, to be lacking (to need)

fama, f., fame, reputation

familia, f., family

famoso,-a, famous

favorito,-a, favorite

fe, f., faith

febrero, m., February

fecha, f., date

feliz, happy

femenino,-a, feminine

fenicio,-a, Phoenician

feo,-a, ugly

feria, f., fair

feroz, ferocious

ferrocarril, m., railroad

fiarse (í) de, to trust

fiebre, f., fever

fiel, faithful

fiesta, f., holiday, party; día de fiesta, holiday

figura, f., figure

figurar, to figure; figurarse, to imagine; se me figura, I imagine

fijar, to fix, to set; fijarse en, to notice, to stare at

fijo,-a, fixed, set, firm

fila, f., row

filosófico,-a, philosophical

filósofo, m., philosopher

fin, m., end; fin de semana, weekend; a fin de, in order to; a fin de que, in order that; a fines de, at the end of; al fin, por fin, at last, finally

fingir (j), to pretend

fino,-a, delicate, fine

firmar, to sign

firme, firm

físico,-a, physical

flor, f., flower

florecer (zc), to flourish

fluir (y), to flow

fonda, f., inn

fondo, m., bottom; pl., funds; a fondo, thoroughly

forma, f., form

formal, formal, polite

formar, to form

fortaleza, f., fort, fortress

fortuna, f., fortune

fósforo, m., match

foto, f., photo, picture; sacar fotos, to take pictures

fotografía, f., photograph, photography

fracaso, m., failure

francés, francesa, French; m., French (language)

Francia, f., France

frase, f., sentence

frazada, f., blanket

frecuencia, f., frequency; con frecuencia, frequently

frecuente, frequent

fresa, f., strawberry

fresco,-a, cool, fresh; hacer fresco, to be cool (weather); m., fresco painting

frío,-a, cold; m., cold; hacer (mucho) frío, to be (very) cold (weather); tener (mucho) frío, to be (very) cold (person)

frontera, f., frontier

fruta(s), f., fruit

fuego, m., fire

fuera (de), outside (of); fuera de sí, beside oneself

fuerte, strong, heavy

fuerza, f., force, strength

fumar, to smoke

función, f., performance, show

funcionar, to function, to work

fundador, m., founder

fundar, to found, to establish

furia, f., fury

fútbol, m., soccer, football

futuro, m., future

gaita, f., bagpipes

galán, m., lover, suitor

gallego,-a, Galician

gallina, f., hen

gallo, m., rooster

gana, f., appetite, desire; tener ganas de, to feel like; de buena (mala) gana, willingly (unwillingly)

ganadería, f., cattle-raising

ganar, to earn, to win

gastar, to spend (money)

gasto, m., expense

gato, m., cat

gemir (i), to groan, to moan

general, general; m., general; por lo general, usually, generally

género, m., class, gender, kind, material (cloth)

generoso,-a, generous

gente, f., people

genuino,-a, genuine

geografía, f., geography

geográfico,-a, geographic

gerundio, m., gerund, present participle

gesto, m., gesture

gitano,-a, gypsy

glorioso,-a, glorious

gobernador, m., governor

gobernar (ie), to govern

gobierno, m., government

golpe, m., stroke, blow

gordo,-a, fat; premio gordo, first prize

gorra, f., cap

gota, f., drop

gótico,-a, Gothic

gozar (c) de, to enjoy

gracia, f., charm, grace; pl., thanks; dar las gracias, to thank

grado, m., grade, degree, rank

graduarse (ú), to be graduated, to graduate

gramática, f., grammar

grande (gran), large, big, great

grave, serious

griego,-a, Greek; m., Greek (language)

gris, gray

gritar, to shout

grito, m., shout, war cry; dar un grito, dar gritos, to shout

grupo, m., group

guante, m., glove

guapo,-a, handsome, pretty

guardar, to guard, to keep; guardar cama, to stay in bed; guardar silencio, to remain silent

guardia, m., guard, policeman

guerra, f., war

guía, m., guide; f., guidebook

guiar (í), to guide, to drive

guisante, m., pea

guitarra, f., guitar

gustar, to be pleasing; nos gusta(n), we like

gusto, m., pleasure, taste; con mucho gusto, gladly, with great pleasure

haba (el), f., bean

haber (he), to have (auxiliary); hay, there is, there are (impersonal); hay que + inf., one must; haber de + inf., to be (supposed) to, to have to; hay lodo (polvo), it is muddy (dusty); hay sol, it is sunny; hay luna, there is moonlight

hábil, skillful

habilidad, f., skill, ability

habitación, f., room

habitante, m., inhabitant

hablador,-a, talkative

hablar, to speak

hacer (hago), to do, to cause, to make; hacer buen (mal) tiempo, to be good (bad) weather; hacer calor (frío), to be hot (cold) (weather); hacer fresco, to be cool; hacer sol, to be sunny; hacer viento, to be windy; hacer caso de, to heed, to pay attention to; hacer de, to work as, to act as; hacer ejercicios, to exercise; hacer el papel de, to play the role of; hacer falta, to be lacking (to need); hacer pedazos, to smash, to tear to shreds; hace + time expression, ago; hace poco, a little while ago; hacer una pregunta, to ask a question; hacer una visita, to pay a visit; hacer un viaje, to take (make) a trip; hacerse, to become; hacer(se) daño, to harm, to hurt (oneself), to cause damage

hacia, toward

hacha (el), f., ax

hallar, to find; hallarse, to find oneself, to be

hambre (el), f., hunger; tener (mucha) hambre, to be (very) hungry

hasta, until, even; hasta que, until

hazaña, f., exploit, deed

hecho,-a, done, made; m., deed, fact; de hecho, in fact

helado, m., ice cream

helar (ie), to freeze; helarse, to freeze over

hemisferio, m., hemisphere

herida, f., wound

herir (ie, i), to wound

hermano, m., brother; hermana, f., sister; los hermanos, brother(s) and sister(s)

hermoso,-a, beautiful
hermosura, f., beauty
héroe, m., hero
heroico,-a, heroic
hervir (ie, i), to boil
hielo, m., ice
hierba, f., grass; mala hierba, weeds
hierro, m., iron
hijo, m., son; hija, f., daughter; hijos, children
hilo, m., thread
hispanoamericano,-a, Spanish American
historia, f., history, story
histórico,-a, historic
hoja, f., leaf, sheet (of paper)
¡hola!, hello
hombre, m., man
hombro, m., shoulder; encogerse de hombros, to shrug one's shoulders
honrado,-a, honorable, honest
honrar, to honor
hora, f., hour, time; ¿a qué hora?, at what time?; ¿qué hora es?, what time is it?; dar la hora, to strike the hour
hoy, today; hoy día, nowadays; hoy mismo, this very day; de hoy en adelante, from now on, henceforth
huérfano,-a, orphan
huésped, m., guest, host
huevo, m., egg
huir (y), to flee
humanidad, f., humanity, mankind
humano,-a, human
húmedo,-a, humid
humo, m., smoke
hundirse, to sink

ida : billete de ida y vuelta, round-trip ticket
idealista, idealistic
idioma, m., language
iglesia, f., church
igual, equal
iluminar, to light up, to illuminate
ilusión, f., illusion
ilustre, famous, illustrious
imagen, f., image
imaginarse, to imagine
imitar, to imitate
impaciente, impatient
impedir (i), to prevent, to hinder
imperativo,-a, imperative; m., imperative mood
imperfecto,-a, imperfect; m., imperfect tense
imperio, m., empire

impermeable, m., raincoat
importancia, f., importance
importante, important
importar, to import, to be important; no importa, it doesn't matter
imposible, impossible
impresión, f., impression
impuesto, m., tax
incaico,-a, adj., Inca
incluir (y), to include
independencia, f., independence
Indias, f., Indies
indicar (qu), to indicate
indicativo,-a, indicative; m., indicative mood
indígena, m. or f., native
indio,-a, Indian
industria, f., industry
infancia, f., infancy, babyhood
infinitivo, m., infinitive
infinito,-a, infinite
influencia, f., influence
influir (y) en, to influence, to have influence on
informar, to inform
informe, m., report
ingeniero, m., engineer
Inglaterra, f., England
inglés, inglesa, English; m., English (language)
iniciar, to initiate, to begin
injusticia, f., injustice
inmediatamente, immediately
inmenso,-a, immense
inocente, innocent
inquietud, f., restlessness, uneasiness
insecto, m., insect
insistir (en), to insist (on)
inspirar, to inspire
instrucción, f., instruction
instrumento, m., instrument
inteligencia, f., intelligence
inteligente, intelligent
intención, f., intention
intentar, to intend, to attempt
interés, m., interest
interesante, interesting
interesar, to interest, to be interesting; interesarse (por), to be interested (in)
interrogativo,-a, interrogative
interrumpir, to interrupt
íntimo,-a, intimate
inútil, useless
invierno, m., winter
invitado,-a, (invited) guest
invitar, to invite
ir (voy), to go; ir de compras, to go shopping; ¡Vaya un(a) . . . !, What a . . . !; irse, to go away
ira, f., anger, ire

isla, f., island
istmo, m., isthmus
italiano,-a, Italian; m., Italian (language)
izquierdo,-a, left; a la izquierda, at (to) the left

jabón, m., soap
jamás, never, ever
jamón, m., ham
jardín, m., garden
jefe, m., boss, leader
jinete, m., horseman
joven, young; m. or f., young person
joya, f., jewel
juego, m., game
jueves, m., Thursday
juez, m., judge
jugar (ue, gu) a, to play
juguete, m., toy
juicio, m., judgment
julio, m., July
junio, m., June
juntarse, to assemble; juntarse con, to get together with, to join
junto a, next to, beside
juntos,-as, together
jurar, to swear
justicia, f., justice
justo,-a, just, exact
juventud, f., youth

kilogramo, m., kilogram
kilómetro, m., kilometer

labio, m., lip
labrador, m., farmer
lado, m., side; al lado de, beside
ladrillo, m., brick
ladrón, m., thief
lago, m., lake
lágrima, f., tear
lámpara, f., lamp
lana, f., wool
lanzar (c), to throw
lápiz, m., pencil
largo,-a, long
lástima, f., pity
lavar, to wash; lavarse, to get washed, to wash oneself
lección, f., lesson
lectura, f., reading
leche, f., milk
lechero, m., milkman
leer (y), to read
legumbre, f., vegetable
lejano,-a, distant
lejos, far; lejos de, far from; a lo lejos, in the distance
lengua, f., language, tongue
lento,-a, slow
león, m., lion
letra, f., letter (of the alpha-

bet)
levantar, to lift, to raise; levantarse, to stand up, to get up
leve, slight, light
ley, f., law
leyenda, f., legend
libertad, f., liberty
libertador,-a, liberating; m., liberator
libra, f., pound
libre, free; al aire libre, in the open air
librería, f., bookstore
libro, m., book
ligero,-a, light
limitar, to limit
límite, m., limit, boundary
limosna, f., alms, charity
limpiar, to clean; limpiarse, to get clean, to clean oneself
limpio,-a, clean
lindo,-a, pretty
línea, f., line
líquido, m., liquid
lírico,-a, lyric, lyrica
lista, f., list
listo,-a, ready, clever; estar listo, to be ready; ser listo, to be clever
lobo, m., wolf
loco,-a, crazy, insane
lodo, m., mud; hay lodo, it is muddy
lograr, to attain; lograr + inf., to succeed in
lucir (zc), to shine; lucirse, to show off
lucha, f., fight, struggle
luchar, to fight, to struggle
luego, soon, then; luego que, as soon as; desde luego, of course, at once
lugar, m., place; en lugar de, instead of; tener lugar, to take place
luna, f., moon; hay luna, there is moonlight
lunes, m., Monday
luz, f., light

llamar, to call; llamarse, to be called, to be named
llanero, m., plainsman
llano,-a, flat, smooth; m., plain
llanta, f., (automobile) tire
llanto, m., sobbing, crying
llave, f., key
llegar (gu), to arrive; llegar a, to reach; llegar a ser, to become
llenar, to fill; llenarse (de), to become filled (with)
lleno,-a, full
llevar, to carry, to wear; llevar a cabo, to carry

out; **llevarse**, to carry away; **llevarse bien (mal) con**, to get along well (badly) with

llorar, to cry, to weep

llover (ue), to rain

lluvia, *f.*, rain

madera, *f.*, wood

madre, *f.*, mother

madrileño,-a, Madrilenian (inhabitant of Madrid)

madrugada, *f.*, dawn, early morning

madrugar (gu), to rise early

maduro,-a, ripe, mature

maestro,-a, teacher, master; **obra maestra**, masterpiece

magnífico,-a, magnificent

maíz, *m.*, corn

majestad, *f.*, majesty

mal, badly, poorly, ill; *m.*, evil, harm, illness; **salir mal**, to fail (an examination)

maldición, *f.*, curse

maleta, *f.*, suitcase

malo,-a (mal), bad, ill; *m. or f.*, evil person; **mala hierba**, weeds; **de mala gana**, unwillingly; **hacer mal tiempo**, to be bad weather

mamá, *f.*, mamma, mother

mandar, to order, to send

manejar, to manage, to drive

manera, *f.*, manner; **de manera que**, so that; **de esta (esa) manera**, in this (that) way; **de ninguna manera**, by no means

manga, *f.*, sleeve

mano, *f.*, hand

manta, *f.*, blanket

mantener (ie, mantengo), to maintain, to support

mantequilla, *f.*, butter

manzana, *f.*, apple

manzano, *m.*, apple tree

mañana, tomorrow; *f.*, morning; **de la mañana, por la mañana**, in the morning; **pasado mañana**, day after tomorrow

mapa, *m.*, map

máquina, *f.*, machine; **máquina de escribir**, typewriter

mar, *m. or f.*, sea

maravilla, *f.*, marvel, wonder

maravilloso,-a, marvelous

marcar (qu), to designate, to mark

marcha, *f.*, march, progress;

ponerse en marcha, to set out

marchar, to walk, to march; **marcharse**, to go away

marido, *m.*, husband

marinero, *m.*, sailor

mármol, *m.*, marble

martes, *m.*, Tuesday

marzo, *m.*, March

más, more; **lo más pronto posible**, as soon as possible; **más tarde**, later; **más vale**, it is better; **cada vez más**, more and more

mascar (qu), to chew

matar, to kill

maullar (ú), to mew (meow)

mayo, *m.*, May

mayor, older, greater; *m. or f.*, grown-up, adult

media, *f.*, stocking

medianoche, *f.*, midnight

medicina, *f.*, medicine

médico, *m.*, doctor

medio,-a, half; *m.*, means; **por medio de**, by means of; **la Edad Media**, the Middle Ages; **y media**, half past

mediodía, *m.*, noon

medir (i), to measure

mejilla, *f.*, cheek

mejor, better, best

mejorar, to improve

memoria, *f.*, memory; **de memoria**, by heart

mencionar, to mention

menester, *m.*, need; **es menester**, it is necessary

menor, younger, youngest; least

menos, less, fewer, minus; **a menos que**, unless; **echar de menos**, to miss

mentir (ie, i), to lie

mentira, *f.*, lie

menudo,-a, small, minute; **a menudo**, often

mercado, *m.*, market

mercancías, *f. pl.*, merchandise

merecer (zc), to deserve

mérito, *m.*, merit

mes, *m.*, month; **el mes próximo**, next month

mesa, *f.*, table; **poner la mesa**, to set the table

meseta, *f.*, plateau

meter, to put (in), to insert

mexicano,-a, Mexican

México, *m.*, Mexico

mezclar, to mix

miedo, *m.*, fear; **tener miedo**, to be afraid

miembro, *m.*, member, limb

mientras (que), while; **mientras tanto**, meanwhile

miércoles, *m.*, Wednesday

milagro, *m.*, miracle

militar, military; *m.*, soldier, military man

milla, *f.*, mile

millón, *m.*, million

mina, *f.*, mine

minero,-a, mining

ministro, *m.*, (cabinet) minister

minuto, *m.*, minute

mirada, *f.*, glance

mirar, to look (at)

miserable, wretched, miserable

miseria, *f.*, misery, poverty

misión, *f.*, mission

misionero, *m.*, missionary

mismo,-a, same, himself, herself, itself; **ahora mismo**, right now; **hoy mismo**, this very day

misterio, *m.*, mystery

misterioso,-a, mysterious

mitad, *f.*, half

moda, *f.*, fashion, style; **de última moda**, in the latest style

modelo, *m.*, model, pattern

modesto,-a, modest

modismo, *m.*, idiom

modo, *m.*, manner; **de este (ese) modo**, in this (that) way; **de ningún modo**, by no means; **de otro modo**, otherwise; **de modo que**, so that

mojar, to wet; **mojarse**, to get wet

molestar, to disturb, to annoy, to bother; **molestarse (en)**, to take the trouble (to)

molino, *m.*, mill

momento, *m.*, moment

monasterio, *m.*, monastery

moneda, *f.*, coin

montaña, *f.*, mountain

montañoso,-a, mountainous

montar, to ride (horseback)

monte, *m.*, mountain

monumento, *m.*, monument

moral, moral; *f.*, morality, ethics

morder (ue), to bite, to gnaw

moreno,-a, dark-haired, brunette

morir (ue, u), to die; **morirse**, to pass away

moro,-a, Moor, Moorish

mostrar (ue), to show; **mostrarse**, to appear

mover (ue), to move

movimiento, *m.*, movement

mozo, *m.*, waiter, porter, servant

muchacho, *m.*, boy; **muchacha**, *f.*, girl

muchedumbre, *f.*, crowd

mucho,-a, much; *pl.*, many; *adv.*, much, hard, a great deal; **muchísimo,-a**, very much; **mucho tiempo**, a long time

mudar, to change; **mudar de casa**, to move

mueble, *m.*, article of furniture; *pl.*, furniture

muerte, *f.*, death

mujer, *f.*, wife, woman

muleta, *f.*, cape

mundial, *adj.*, world-wide, world

mundo, *m.*, world; **todo el mundo**, everybody

muñeca, *f.*, doll, wrist

murmurar, to murmur, to gossip, to grumble

muro, *m.*, wall, mural

musa, *f.*, muse

museo, *m.*, museum

música, *f.*, music

músico,-a, musical; *m.*, musician

muy, very

nacer (zc), to be born

nacimiento, *m.*, birth, representation of the Nativity scene; **de nacimiento**, by birth

nación, *f.*, nation

nacional, national

nada, nothing, not anything

nadar, to swim

nadie, no one, not anyone

naranja, *f.*, orange

nariz, *f.*, nose

naturaleza, *f.*, nature

navaja, *f.*, razor

nave, *f.*, ship

navegante, *m.*, navigator

navegar (gu), to navigate

Navidad, *f.*, Christmas

neblina, *f.*, fog; **hay neblina**, it is foggy

necesario,-a, necessary

necesidad, *f.*, necessity

necesitar, to need

negar (ie, gu), to deny; **negarse a**, to refuse to

negativo,-a, negative

negocio, *m.*, business

negro,-a, black

nevar (ie), to snow

ni, neither; **ni . . . ni**, neither . . . nor

nieto, *m.*, grandson; **nieta**, *f.*, granddaughter

nieve, *f.*, snow

ninguno,-a (ningún), no, (not) any; **de ninguna manera (de ningún modo)**, by no means; **en ninguna parte**, nowhere

niño,-a, child; *pl.*, children

no, no, not; **no obstante**,

notwithstanding, nevertheless

noche, *f.,* night, evening; **de noche,** at night; **esta noche,** tonight; **de la noche, por la noche,** in the evening

nombrar, to name

nombre, *m.,* name; **nombre de pila,** baptismal (given) name

norte, *m.,* north

norteamericano,-a, North American, American

nota, *f.,* grade, mark

notar, to notice

noticia, *f.,* news item; *pl.,* news

novedad, *f.,* new thing, novelty **sin novedad,** same as usual, nothing new

novela, *f.,* novel

noviembre, *m.,* November

novio, *m.,* sweetheart, fiancé, bridegroom; **novia,** *f.,* sweetheart, fiancée, bride

nube, *f.,* cloud

nuevo,-a, new; **de nuevo,** again

nuez, *f.,* nut

número, *m.,* number

numeroso,-a, numerous

nunca, never

o, or; **o . . . o,** either . . . or

obedecer (zc), to obey

obligación, *f.,* obligation

obligar (gu), to obligate, to compel

obra, *f.,* work; **obra maestra,** masterpiece

observar, to observe

obstante: no obstante, notwithstanding, nevertheless

obtener (ie, obtengo), to obtain, to get

ocasión, *f.,* opportunity, occasion; **tener ocasión de,** to have the opportunity to

occidental, western

océano, *m.,* ocean

octubre, *m.,* October

ocupado,-a, busy, occupied

ocupar, to occupy; **ocuparse de,** to look after, to take care of, to give attention to

ocurrir, to occur, to happen

ocho días, a (one) week

odiar, to hate

odio, *m.,* hatred

oeste, *m.,* west

ofender, to offend

oficial, *m.,* official, officer

oficina, *f.,* office

ofrecer (zc), to offer

oído, *m.,* ear, hearing

oír (oigo, y), to hear; **oír hablar de,** to hear about; **oírse,** to be heard

¡ojalá!, God grant . . . !, Would to God . . . ! If only . . . !

ojo, *m.,* eye

ola, *f.,* wave

oler (hue), to smell

olvidar, to forget; **olvidarse de,** to forget

omitir, to omit

operación, *f.,* operation

opinión, *f.,* opinion

oponerse (opongo) a, to oppose

opuesto,-a, opposite, opposed

orden, *f.,* order, command; *m.,* order (in a series)

oreja, *f.,* ear

organizar (c), to organize

orgullo, *m.,* pride

orgulloso,-a, proud, haughty

oriental, eastern, oriental; **la Banda Oriental,** Eastern Edge (former name of Uruguay)

Oriente, *m.,* Orient, the East; **el Extremo Oriente,** the Far East

origen, *m.,* origin

orilla, *f.,* shore, bank (of a river)

oro, *m.,* gold

orquesta, *f.,* orchestra

oscuridad, *f.,* darkness

oscuro,-a, dark

oso, bear

otoño, *m.,* autumn

otro,-a, other, another; **otra vez,** again; **de otro modo,** otherwise

oveja, *f.,* sheep

paciencia, *f.,* patience

padre, *m.,* father; *pl.,* parents

pagar (gu), to pay (for)

página, *f.,* page

país, *m.,* country, nation

paisaje, *m.,* countryside

paja, *f.,* straw

pájaro, *m.,* bird

palabra, *f.,* word

palacio, *m.,* palace

pálido,-a, pale

palo, *m.,* stick, pole

pan, *m.,* bread

panadería, *f.,* bakery

panamericano,-a, Pan-American

panecillo, *m.,* roll

pantalones, *m. pl.,* trousers, pants

paño, *m.,* cloth

pañuelo, *m.,* handkerchief

papá, *m.,* papa, dad

papel, *m.,* paper, role; **hacer el papel de,** to play the role of

paquete, *m.,* package

par, *m.,* pair, couple; **(abierto) de par en par,** wide open

para, for, in order to, by; **para que,** in order that; **para sí,** to himself (herself, etc.); **estar para,** to be about to; **servir para,** to be useful (good) for

paraguas, *m.,* umbrella

parar, to stop; **pararse,** to stop (oneself)

pardo,-a, brown

parecer (zc), to seem, to appear; **al parecer,** apparently; **a mi (su, etc.) parecer,** in my (his, etc.) opinion; **parecerse a,** to resemble

pared, *f.,* wall

pareja, *f.,* couple

paréntesis: entre paréntesis, between parentheses

pariente, *m.,* relative

parque, *m.,* park

párrafo, *m.,* paragraph

parte, *f.,* part; **en (por) todas partes,** everywhere; **en ninguna parte,** nowhere; **tomar parte,** to take part

partido, *m.,* game

partir, to leave, to depart

pasado,-a, past, last; *m.,* past; **pasado mañana,** the day after tomorrow; **el lunes (mes, año) pasado,** last Monday (month, year)

pasajero,-a, passenger

pasaporte, *m.,* passport

pasar, to pass, to spend (time), to happen, to go

pasearse, to stroll, to take a walk

paseo, *m.,* stroll, drive, boulevard; **dar un paseo,** to take a walk, ride

pasión, *f.,* passion, enthusiasm

pasivo,-a, passive

paso, *m.,* step, pace

pastel, *m.,* pie, pastry

patio, *m.,* courtyard

patria, *f.,* (native) country, fatherland

patriota, *m.,* patriot

patrón, *m.,* owner, boss; **(santo) patrón,** patron saint

pavo, *m.,* turkey

paz, *f.,* peace

pecho, *m.,* chest

pedazo, *m.,* piece; **hacer pedazos,** to smash, to tear to shreds

pedir (i), to ask for, to request

pegar (gu), to stick, to spank

peinar, to comb; **peinarse,** to comb one's hair

peine, *m.,* comb

pelear, to fight

película, *f.,* film, movie

peligro, *m.,* danger, peril

peligroso,-a, dangerous

pelo, *m.,* hair

pelota, *f.,* ball, jai-alai

peluquería, *f.,* beauty parlor, barber shop

peluquero, *m.,* hairdresser, barber

pena, *f.,* trouble, sorrow; **valer la pena,** to be worthwhile

penetrar (en), to penetrate, to enter

pensamiento, *m.,* thought

pensar (ie), to think, to intend; **pensar en,** to think about; **pensar de,** to think of (have an opinion of)

peor, worse, worst

pequeño,-a, small, little

pera, *f.,* pear

perder (ie), to lose; **perder de vista,** to lose sight of; **pierda (Vd.) cuidado,** don't worry

perdón, *m.,* pardon

perdonar, to pardon, to forgive

perezoso,-a, lazy

perfecto,-a, perfect

periódico, *m.,* newspaper

periodista, *m.,* journalist

perla, *f.,* pearl

permanecer (zc), to remain

permiso, *m.,* permission

permitir, to permit

pero, but

perro, *m.,* dog

perseguir (i, g), to pursue, to persecute

persona, *f.,* person

personaje, *m.,* character (in a play, novel, etc.)

pertenecer (zc), to belong

pesado,-a, heavy

pesar, to weigh; **a pesar de,** in spite of

pescado, *m.,* fish

pescador, *m.,* fisherman

pescar (qu), to fish

peseta, *f.,* peseta (monetary unit of Spain)

peso, *m.,* weight, peso (monetary unit of several Spanish-American countries)

picaresco,-a, picaresque

pícaro,-a, roguish, naughty, rogue, rascal

pico, *m.*, peak, beak (of a bird)

pie, *m.*, foot; a pie, on foot; de pie, standing; de pies a cabeza, from head to foot

piedra, *f.*, stone

pierna, *f.*, leg

pila: nombre de pila, baptismal (given) name

pimiento picante, *m.*, hot pepper

pintar, to paint

pintor, *m.*, painter; pintor de cámara, court painter

pintoresco,-a, picturesque

pintura, *f.*, painting

pirámide, *f.*, pyramid

pirata, *m.*, pirate

pisar, to tread, to step on

piscina, *f.*, pool

piso, *m.*, floor, story, apartment

pizarra, *f.*, blackboard

placer (zc), to be pleasing; *m.*, pleasure

planta, *f.*, plant

plata, *f.*, silver

plátano, *m.*, banana

platino, *m.*, platinum

plato, *m.*, plate, dish

playa, *f.*, beach, seashore

plaza, *f.*, square, plaza

plomero, *m.*, plumber

pluma, *f.*, pen, feather

pluscuamperfecto, *m.*, pluperfect (tense)

población, *f.*, population, town

pobre, poor

poco,-a, little; *pl.*, few; *m.*, a little bit; dentro de poco, in a little while; hace poco, a little while ago; poco a poco, little by little

poder (ue), to be able, can, could; *m.*, power

poderoso,-a, powerful

poesía, *f.*, poem, poetry

poeta, *m.*, poet; poetisa, *f.*, poetess

policía, *m.*, policeman; *f.*, police

política, *f.*, politics, policy

político,-a, political; *m.*, politician

polvo, *m.*, dust; hay polvo, it is dusty

pollo, *m.*, chicken

poner (pongo), to put, to set, to lay (eggs); poner la mesa, to set the table; poner un telegrama, to send a telegram; ponerse, to put on, to become;

ponerse a + *inf.*, to begin to; ponerse en marcha, to set out; ponerse de acuerdo, to come to an agreement; se pone el sol, the sun is setting

por, by, through, along, for; por + *adj.* or *adv.* + que, no matter how . . .; por eso, therefore; por desgracia, unfortunately; por consiguiente, therefore; por escrito, in writing; por fin, finally, at last; por la tarde, in the afternoon; por lo común (por lo general), generally; por lo visto, apparently; por medio de, by means of; por supuesto, of course

pordiosero, *m.*, beggar

porque, because; ¿por qué?, why?

portarse, to behave

portugués, portuguesa, Portuguese; *m.*, Portuguese (language)

porvenir, *m.*, future

poseer (y), to possess

posesión, *f.*, possession

posesivo,-a, possessive

posible, possible; lo más pronto posible, as soon as possible; todo lo posible, everything possible

postre, *m.*, dessert

practicar (qu), to practice

precio, *m.*, price

precioso,-a, precious

preciso,-a, necessary

precursor, *m.*, forerunner

preferir (ie, i), to prefer

pregunta, *f.*, question; hacer una pregunta, to ask a question

preguntar, to ask

premio, *m.*, prize; premio gordo, first prize

preocuparse (de, por), to worry (about)

preparar, to prepare

preposición, preposition

presenciar, to witness, to be present

presentar, to present, to introduce; presentarse, to appear, to present oneself

presente, present

presidente, *m.*, president

prestar, to lend; prestar atención, to pay attention

pretérito, *m.*, preterite (tense)

primavera, *f.*, spring (season)

primero,-a (primer), first

primo,-a, cousin

principal, main, principal

príncipe, *m.*, prince; princesa, *f.*, princess

principiar, to begin

principio, *m.*, beginning; a principios de, at the beginning of

prisa, *f.*, hurry; darse prisa, to hurry; tener prisa, to be in a hurry

prisionero, *m.*, prisoner

probar (ue), to prove, to taste, to test

problema, *m.*, problem

proceder, to proceed

producir (zc), to produce

producto, *m.*, product

profesión, *f.*, profession

profesional, professional

profesor,-a, teacher

profundo,-a, deep, profound

programa, *m.*, program

progresivo,-a, progressive

prohibir, to prohibit, to forbid

promesa, *f.*, promise

prometer, to promise

pronombre, *m.*, pronoun

pronto, soon, quickly; de pronto, suddenly; lo más pronto posible, as soon as possible; tan pronto como, as soon as

pronunciar, to pronounce

propiedad, *f.*, property

propietario, *m.*, proprietor

propina, *f.*, tip

propio,-a, proper, own

proponer (propongo), to propose, to suggest

propósito, *m.*, purpose

prosa, *f.*, prose

proseguir (i, g) el camino, to continue on one's way

proteger (j), to protect

protestar, to protest

proverbio, *m.*, proverb

provincia, *f.*, province

próximo,-a, next; el mes próximo, next month

proyecto, *m.*, project, plan

prueba, *f.*, proof, test, trial

publicar (qu), to publish

público,-a, public; *m.*, audience, public

pueblo, *m.*, town, people

puente, *m.*, bridge

puerta, *f.*, door

puerto, *m.*, port

pues, then, well

puesta, *f.*, setting; la puesta del sol, sunset

puesto,-a, placed, put; *m.*, position, post, job; puesto que, since

pulsera: reloj de pulsera, wrist watch

punto, *m.*, point, dot; en

punto, sharp; el punto de vista, viewpoint; estar a punto de, to be about to

que, that, which, who, whom, than; ¿qué?, what?; ¡qué . . . !, what a . . . !, how . . . !

quebrar (ie), to break

quedar(se), to remain; quedarle (a uno), to remain (to someone), to have left; quedarse con, to keep

queja, *f.*, complaint

quejarse (de), to complain (of)

quemar, to burn

querer (ie), to want, to wish, to love; querer decir, to mean

querido,-a, dear, beloved

queso, *m.*, cheese

quien, who, whom, he (she) who; ¿quién?, who?

quienquiera, quienesquiera, whoever

quince días, two weeks

quinto,-a, fifth

quitar, to take away; quitarse, to take off

quizá(s), perhaps

radio, *m.* or *f.*, radio

rápido,-a, rapid

raro,-a, rare, strange; raras veces, rarely, seldom

rato, *m.*, (little) while

raya, *f.*, dash (—)

rayo, *m.*, ray, thunderbolt, flash of lightning

raza, *f.*, race (of people)

razón, *f.*, reason; tener razón, to be right; no tener razón, to be wrong

real, royal, real; *m.*, real (¼ of a peseta)

realidad, *f.*, reality

realista, realist, realistic

realizar (c), to fulfill, to realize (a profit)

recibir, to receive

recibo, *m.*, receipt

reciente, recent

reclamar, to claim, to demand

recoger (j), to gather, to pick up

recomendar (ie), to recommend

reconocer (zc), to recognize

reconquista, *f.*, reconquest

recordar (ue), to remember

recorrer, to travel over, to go over

recuerdo, *m.*, souvenir, remembrance; *pl.*, regards;

dar recuerdos (a), to give regards (to)

recurso, *m.*, recourse, resource, means

redondo,-a, round

reducir (zc), to reduce

referir (ie, i), to narrate, to refer; **referirse a**, to refer to

refresco, *m.*, refreshment

regalar, to present (as a gift)

regalo, *m.*, gift, present

región, *f.*, region

registrar, to inspect, to search

regla, *f.*, rule, ruler

regresar, to return

reina, *f.*, queen

reinado, *m.*, reign

reinar, to reign, to rule

reino, *m.*, kingdom

reírse (í) de, to laugh at

reja, *f.*, grating

relativo,-a, relative

reloj, *m.*, clock, watch

remedio, *m.*, remedy, cure

rendir (i), to subdue, to render, to yield; **rendirse**, to surrender

renglón, *m.*, line (of a page)

renovar (ue), to remodel, to renew

reñir (i), to quarrel, to scold

reparar: reparar en, to look at, to observe

repartir, to divide, to distribute

repente: de repente, suddenly

repetir (i), to repeat

replicar (qu), to reply

representar, to represent

república, *f.*, republic

resfriado, *m.*, cold (illness)

resfriarse (i), to catch cold

resignarse (a), to resign oneself (to)

resistir, to resist

resolver (ue), to solve, to resolve

respetar, to respect

respirar, to breathe

responder, to answer, to respond

respuesta, *f.*, answer, response

restaurante, *m.*, restaurant

resultado, *m.*, result

retrato, *m.*, portrait

reunión, *f.*, meeting

reunir (ú), to gather, to bring together; **reunirse**, to meet, to assemble

revista, *f.*, magazine

rey, *m.*, king; **Reyes Magos**, the Magi (Three Wise Men)

rezar (c), to pray

rico,-a, rich

ridículo,-a, ridiculous

riego, *m.*, irrigation

riesgo, *m.*, risk

rincón, *m.*, corner

río, *m.*, river

riqueza, *f.*, wealth

risa, *f.*, laughter, laugh

risueño,-a, smiling, laughing

robar, to steal, to rob

rodear, to surround

rodilla, *f.*, knee; **de rodillas**, kneeling

rogar (ue, gu), to ask, to beg

rojo,-a, red

románico,-a, Romanesque

romano,-a, Roman

romper, to break, to tear

ropa, *f.*, clothes

rosa, *f.*, rose

rostro, *m.*, face

roto,-a, broken, torn

rubio,-a, blond

rueda, *f.*, wheel

ruido, *m.*, noise

ruina, *f.*, ruin

rumor, *m.*, murmur, sound

ruso,-a, Russian; *m.*, Russian (language)

ruta, *f.*, route

sábado, *m.*, Saturday

sábana, *f.*, bedsheet

saber (sé), to know (how)

sabio,-a, wise; *m.*, wise man, learned man

sacar (qu), to take out; **sacar fotos**, to take pictures

sacerdote, *m.*, priest

saco, *m.*, sack, bag, jacket

sacrificar (qu), to sacrifice

sacrificio, *m.*, sacrifice

sal, *f.*, salt

sala, *f.*, hall, living room

salida, *f.*, departure, exit

salir (salgo) (de), to leave, to go out; **salir bien (mal)**, to pass (fail)

salón, *m.*, hall

saltar, to jump, to leap

salud, *f.*, health

saludar, to greet

saludo, *m.*, greeting, salute

salvar, to save, to rescue

salvo,-a, safe; **sano y salvo**, safe and sound

sandalia, *f.*, sandal

sangre, *f.*, blood

sangriento,-a, bloody

sano,-a, healthy, sound; **sano y salvo**, safe and sound

santo,-a (San), saint, holy; **santo patrón**, patron saint

sastre, *m.*, tailor

sastrería, *f.*, tailor shop

satisfacción, *f.*, satisfaction

satisfacer (satisfago), to satisfy

satisfecho,-a, satisfied

seco,-a, dry

secretario,-a, secretary

secreto,-a, secret; *m.*, secret

sed, *f.*, thirst; **tener sed**, to be thirsty

seda, *f.*, silk

seguida: en seguida, at once, immediately

seguir (i, g), to follow, to continue

según, according to

seguridad, *f.*, security, certainty

seguro,-a, sure, certain, safe

selva, *f.*, jungle, forest

sello, *m.*, seal, stamp

semana, *f.*, week; **fin de semana**, weekend; **la semana pasada**, last week; **la semana que viene**, next week

semejante, similar, alike

semestre, *m.*, semester, term

sencillo,-a, simple

sensación, *f.*, sensation, feeling

sentado,-a, seated

sentarse (ie), to sit down

sentido, *m.*, sense, meaning; **sentido común**, common sense

sentimiento, *m.*, sentiment, feeling

sentir (ie, i), to regret, to be sorry, to feel; **sentirse**, to feel (well or ill)

señor, *m.*, gentleman, master, Mr.; **señora**, *f.*, lady, madam, Mrs.; **señorita**, *f.*, young lady, Miss

separar, to separate; **separarse (de)**, to withdraw (from)

septiembre, *m.*, September

ser, to be; *m.*, being; **llegar a ser**, to become; **ser aficionado(-a) a**, to be devoted to; **ser listo,-a**, to be clever

sereno,-a, calm, serene; *m.*, night watchman

serie, *f.*, series

serio,-a, serious; **en serio**, seriously

servicio, *m.*, service

servilleta, *f.*, napkin

servir (i), to serve; **servir de**, to serve as; **servir para**, to be useful for, to be good for

seudónimo, *m.*, pen name

severo,-a, severe

si, if, whether

sí, yes; **creo (digo) que sí**, I think so

sí, himself (herself, etc.); **fuera de sí**, beside oneself; **para sí**, to himself (herself, etc.); **volver en sí**, to regain consciousness, to come to

siempre, always

siesta, *f.*, (afternoon) nap

siglo, *m.*, century; **el Siglo de Oro**, the Golden Age

significado, *m.*, meaning

significar (qu), to mean

siguiente, following; **al día siguiente**, on the following day

silencio, *m.*, silence; **guardar silencio**, to remain silent

silla, *f.*, chair

sillón, *m.*, armchair

simpático,-a, nice, pleasant, likeable

sin, without; **sin que**, without; **sin duda**, doubtless, without doubt; **sin embargo**, nevertheless; **sin novedad**, same as usual, nothing new

singular, singular, strange

sino, but (on the contrary); **no . . . sino**, only

sinónimo, *m.*, synonym

sistema, *m.*, system

sitio, *m.*, place, site, siege

situado,-a, situated

soberbio,-a, proud, haughty, superb

sobrar, to be left over, to have too much (many)

sobre, on, over, about; *m.*, envelope; **sobre todo**, especially

sobretodo, *m.*, overcoat

sobrino, *m.*, nephew; **sobrina**, *f.*, niece

socio,-a, member, partner

sol, *m.*, sun; **hace (hay) sol**, it is sunny; **la puesta del sol**, sunset; **se pone el sol**, the sun is setting

solamente, only

soldado, *m.*, soldier

soler (ue), to be accustomed to, to be in the habit of

solicitar, to solicit, to apply for

sólo, only; **solo,-a**, alone; **a solas**, alone

soltar (ue), to loosen

sombra, *f.*, shade, shadow

sombrero, *m.*, hat

sonar (ue), to sound, to ring

sonido, *m.*, sound

sonreír (i), to smile

sonrisa, *f.*, smile

soñar (ue), to dream; **soñar con**, to dream of

sopa, *f.*, soup

sordo,-a, deaf

sorprender, to surprise; sorprenderse (de), to be surprised (at)

sorpresa, *f.*, surprise

sospechar, to suspect

subir, to go up, to climb; subir a, to get into (a vehicle)

subjuntivo, *m.*, subjunctive

subrayar, to underline

suceder, to occur, to happen

suceso, *m.*, event, occurrence

sucio,-a, dirty

sudor, *m.*, perspiration, sweat

sueldo, *m.*, salary

suelo, *m.*, floor, ground

sueño, *m.*, dream, sleep; tener sueño, to be sleepy

suerte, *f.*, luck; tener (mucha) suerte, to be (very) lucky

suficiente, sufficient

sufrir, to suffer

Suiza, Switzerland

sujeto,-a, subject; *m.*, subject

sumamente, extremely

superior, upper, superior

superlativo,-a, superlative

suplicar (qu), to beg, to implore

supuesto: por supuesto, of course

sur, *m.*, south

suspirar, to sigh

sustantivo, *m.*, noun

sustituir (y), to substitute

tabaco, *m.*, tobacco

tal, such, such a; con tal que, provided that; tal vez, perhaps

talento, *m.*, talent

también, also, too

tampoco, neither

tan, so; tan . . . como, as . . . as

tanto,-a, as much, so much; mientras tanto, meanwhile

taquígrafo,-a, stenographer

tardanza, *f.*, delay, tardiness

tardar (en) + *inf.*, to be late (in), to delay (in)

tarde, late; *f.*, afternoon; más tarde, later; de la tarde, por la tarde, in the afternoon

tarea, *f.*, task, homework

tarjeta, *f.*, card

taxímetro, taxi, *m.*, taxi

taza, *f.*, cup

té, *m.*, tea

teatral, theatrical

teatro, *m.*, theater

técnico,-a, technical; *m.* or *f.*, technician; *f.*, technique

techo, *m.*, roof

teléfono, *m.*, telephone

telegrama, *m.*, telegram; poner un telegrama, to send a telegram

televisión, *f.*, television

televisor, *m.*, television set

tema, *m.*, theme, topic, plot

temblar (ie), to tremble

temer, to fear

templado,-a, temperate

templo, *m.*, temple

temprano, *adv.*, early; temprano,-a, early

tener (ie, tengo), to have; tener . . . años, to be . . . years old; tener calor (frío), to be warm (cold); tener cuidado, to be careful; tener dolor (de cabeza), to have a (head)ache; tener éxito, to be successful; tener ganas de + *inf.*, to feel like; tener la culpa (de), to be to blame (for); tener lugar, to take place; tener miedo, to be afraid; tener por + *adj.*, to consider; tener prisa, to be in a hurry; tener que + *inf.*, to have to, must; tener razón, to be right; tener sed (hambre), to be thirsty (hungry); tener sueño, to be sleepy; tener suerte, to be lucky; tener ocasión de, to have the opportunity to

tenis, *m.*, tennis

tercero,-a (tercer), third

terminar, to finish, to end

terreno, *m.*, land, ground

territorio, *m.*, territory

tertulia, *f.*, party, gathering

tesoro, *m.*, treasure

testigo, *m.* or *f.*, witness

testimonio, *m.*, testimony

tiempo, *m.*, time, weather; a tiempo, on time; hace buen (mal) tiempo, the weather is good (bad); ¿cuánto tiempo?, how long?; mucho tiempo, a long time

tienda, *f.*, store

tierra, *f.*, ground, earth, land

tinta, *f.*, ink

tintero, *m.*, inkwell

tío, *m.*, uncle; tía, *f.*, aunt

típico,-a, typical

tipo, *m.*, type

tirano, *m.*, tyrant

tirar, to throw; tirar de, to pull

título, *m.*, title

tocadiscos, *m.*, record player

tocar (qu), to touch, to play (music); tocarle (a uno), to be one's turn

todavía, still, yet

todo,-a, all; *pl.*, everybody; todo el día, all day; todos los días, every day; todo el mundo, everybody; en (por) todas partes, everywhere; sobre todo, especially; todo lo posible, everything possible

tomar, to take, to eat, to drink; tomar parte, to take part

tono, *m.*, tone, voice

tontería, *f.*, nonsense, foolishness

tonto,-a, foolish, stupid

torcer (ue, z), to twist, to turn

torero, *m.*, bullfighter

toro, *m.*, bull; la corrida de toros, bullfight

toronja, *f.*, grapefruit

torre, *f.*, tower

tortilla, *f.*, omelet

trabajador,-a, hard-working; *m.* or *f.*, worker

trabajar, to work

trabajo, *m.*, work

traducción, *f.*, translation

traducir (zc), to translate

traer (traigo), to bring

traidor,-a, treacherous, traitor

traje, *m.*, suit

tranquilo,-a, tranquil, calm, quiet

tranvía, *m.*, streetcar

tratar, to treat; tratar de + *inf.*, to try to; tratarse de, to be a question of, to be concerned with

través: a través de, through, across

tren, *m.*, train

tribu, *f.*, tribe

trigo, *m.*, wheat

triste, sad

tristeza, *f.*, sadness

triunfar, to triumph

tronar (ue), to thunder

trono, *m.*, throne

tropa, *f.*, troop

tropezar (ie, c), to stumble; tropezar con, to come upon

trueno, *m.*, thunder

tumba, *f.*, tomb

turbar, to disturb; turbarse, to feel upset, disturbed

turco,-a, Turk, Turkish

turista, *m.* or *f.*, tourist

u, or (used only before words beginning with o or ho)

último,-a, last, latest; de última moda, in the latest style

único,-a, only

unidad, *f.*, unity

unión, *f.*, union

unir(se) a, to unite, to join

universidad, *f.*, university

unos,-as, several; unos cuantos (unas cuantas), several, a few

usar, to use

uso, *m.*, use

útil, useful

uva, *f.*, grape

vaca, *f.*, cow

vacaciones, *f. pl.*, vacation

vacío,-a, empty

valer (valgo), to be worth; valer la pena, to be worthwhile; más vale, it is better

valiente, brave

valor, *m.*, value, courage

valle, *m.*, valley

vapor, *m.*, steam, steamship

variar (í), to vary

varios,-as, several

varón, *m.*, male

vasco,-a, vascongado, -a, Basque

vaso, *m.*, glass

vasto,-a, vast

¡Vaya un(a) . . . !, What a . . . !

vecino,-a, neighbor, neighboring

vencer (z), to conquer, to defeat, to overcome

vendedor, *m.*, seller

vender, to sell

veneno, *m.*, poison

venganza, *f.*, revenge, vengeance

venir (ie, vengo), to come; la semana que viene, next week

ventana, *f.*, window

ver, to see

verano, *m.*, summer

veras: de veras, really, truly

verbo, *m.*, verb

verdad, *f.*, truth; ¿no es verdad?, ¿verdad?, isn't it so?

verdadero,-a, true, real

verde, green

vergüenza, *f.*, shame

verificarse (qu), to take place

verso, *m.*, verse

vestíbulo, *m.*, vestibule

vestido, *m.*, dress

vestir (i), to dress (someone), to wear; vestirse, to get dressed

vez, f., time; a veces, at times; a la vez, at the same time; alguna vez, sometime, ever; algunas (varias) veces, sometimes, several times; a su vez, in your (his, her, its, their) turn; cada vez más, more and more; de vez en cuando, from time to time; en vez de, instead of; muchas veces, often; otra vez, again; raras veces, rarely, seldom; tal vez, perhaps

viajar, to travel

viaje, m., trip; hacer un viaje, to take (make) a trip

viajero,-a, traveler

viceversa, vice versa

vicio, m., vice

víctima, f., victim

victoria, f., victory

vid, f., grapevine

vida, f., life

vidrio, m., glass

viejo,-a, old, old person

viento, m., wind; hacer viento, to be windy

viernes, m., Friday; Viernes Santo, Good Friday

villancico, m., Christmas carol

vinagre, m., vinegar

vino, m., wine

violencia, f., violence

violento,-a, violent

violeta, f., violet

virreinato, m., viceroyalty

virrey, m., viceroy

virtud, f., virtue

visigodo, Visigoth

visita, f., visit; de visita, on a visit; hacer una visita, to pay a visit

visitar, to visit

víspera, f., eve

vista, f., sight, view; el punto de vista, viewpoint; perder de vista, to lose sight of

visto: por lo visto, apparently

viudo, m., widower; viuda, f., widow

vivir, to live

vivo,-a, alive, bright (color)

volar (ue), to fly

volcán, m., volcano

voluntad, f., will

volver (ue), to return; volver a + inf., to . . . again; volver en sí, to regain consciousness, to come to

voto, m., vote, vow

voz, f., voice; en voz alta, aloud; dar voces, to shout

vuelo, m., flight

vuelta, f., return; billete de ida y vuelta, round-trip ticket; dar una vuelta, to take a stroll; estar de vuelta, to be back

y, and

ya, already, indeed; ¡ya lo creo!, of course!, I should say so!; ya no, no longer; ya que, since

zapatería, f., shoe store

zapatero, m., shoemaker

zapato, m., shoe

a, an, un, una; (with units of measure), el, la

able: to be able, poder (ue); **not to be able to help . . . ,** no poder menos de + *inf.*

about, acerca de, unos,-as; **at about,** a eso de + *time;* **to be about to,** estar para + *inf.,* estar a punto de + *inf.*

absent, ausente

abundant, abundante

accent, el acento

accept, aceptar

accident, el accidente

accompany, acompañar

accordance: in accordance with, de acuerdo con, conforme a

account, la cuenta

accustom, acostumbrar; **to be accustomed to,** acostumbrarse a, tener la costumbre de; **to get accustomed to,** acostumbrarse a

acquire, adquirir (ie, i)

act, el acto; **to act as,** hacer (hago) de

action, la acción

actor, el actor; **actress,** la actriz

add, añadir, agregar (gu)

address, la dirección; **to address** (a letter), dirigir (j)

admiration, la admiración

admire, admirar

advance, adelantar, avanzar (c)

advantage, el provecho; **to take advantage (of),** aprovecharse (de)

adventure, la aventura

advice, el consejo, los consejos

advise, aconsejar

afraid: to be afraid, tener (ie, tengo) miedo

after, después de, después (de) que, tras

afternoon, la tarde, **in the afternoon,** por la tarde

again, de nuevo, otra vez, volver (ue) a + *inf.*

against, contra

age, la edad; **Golden Age,** el Siglo de Oro

ago: a little while ago, hace poco

agree to, convenir (ie, convengo) en; **to be in agreement (with),** estar conforme (con), estar de acuerdo (con); **to come to (reach) an agreement,** ponerse (pongo) de acuerdo

air, el aire; **in the open air,** al aire libre

Alice, Alicia

all, todo,-a

almost, casi

alone, solo,-a, a solas

along, por

also, también

although, aunque

always, siempre

A.M., de la madrugada, de la mañana

Amazon (river), el Amazonas

America, (la) América; **Spanish America,** la América Hispana; **American,** americano,-a

among, entre

and, y; (before a word beginning with **i** or **hi,** but not **hie**), e

Andes, los Andes

anger, el enojo, la ira; **to anger,** enojar; **to become (get) angry,** enojarse, enfadarse

animal, el animal

Anna, Ana

anniversary, el aniversario

annoy, molestar

another, otro,-a

answer, la respuesta; **to answer,** contestar, responder

any, cualquier(a); *neg.,* ninguno,-a

anyone, *neg.,* nadie

anything, cualquier cosa; *neg.,* nada

anywhere, *neg.,* en ninguna parte

apart: to draw apart (from), apartarse (de), alejarse (de)

apparatus, el aparato

apparently, al parecer, por lo visto

appear, aparecer (zc); **to appear at (the window),** asomarse a (la ventana)

apple, la manzana

appoint, nombrar; **appointment,** la cita

approach, acercarse (qu) a

approximately, aproximadamente

April, abril

Arab, árabe; **Arabic** (language), el árabe

architect, el arquitecto

Argentina, la Argentina

arm, el brazo

armchair, el sillón

army, el ejército

aroma, el aroma

around, alrededor de

arrive, llegar (gu)

article, el artículo

artist, el (la) artista

as, como, que; **as** + *adj.* or *adv.* + **as,** tan . . . como; **as much (as many)** + *noun* + **as,** tanto,-a (tantos,-as) . . . como; **as a matter of fact,** en efecto; **as for,** en cuanto a; **as if, as though,** como si; **as soon as,** así que, en cuanto, luego que, tan pronto como; **as usual,** sin novedad

ashamed: to be ashamed of, tener (ie, tengo) vergüenza (de)

ask (for information), preguntar; (request), pedir (i)

asleep: to fall asleep, dormirse (ue, u)

assemble, reunirse (ú)

assure, asegurar

astonished: to be astonished, asombrarse

at, a, en; **at about,** a eso de; **at daybreak,** al amanecer; **at 11 o'clock,** a las once; **at night,** de noche; **at nightfall,** al anochecer; **at the beginning of,** a principios de; **at the end of,** a fines de, al cabo de; **at what time?,** ¿a qué hora?; **at least,** al (a lo) menos; **at once,** en seguida; **at the right (left),** a la derecha (izquierda); **at the same time,** a la vez; **at this time,** a esta hora

attack, atacar (qu)

attend, asistir (a)

attention: to pay attention (to), poner (prestar) atención (a)

attitude, la actitud

attract, atraer (atraigo)

August, agosto

aunt, la tía

author, el autor

authority, la autoridad

automobile, el automóvil, el coche

autumn, el otoño

avenue, la avenida

avoid, evitar

away: to go away, irse (voy), marcharse

Aztec, azteca

back: to be back, estar de vuelta

bad, malo, -a (mal); **badly,** mal

baker, el panadero

bank, el banco; **banker,** el banquero

banquet, el banquete

Barbara, Bárbara

barbarous, barbarian, bárbaro,-a

barber, el peluquero, el barbero; **barber shop,** la peluquería

baseball, el béisbol

basket, la cesta

bath, el baño; **to take a bath,** bañarse

battle, la batalla

be, ser, estar; **to be able,** poder (ue); **to be about to,** estar para, estar a punto de; **to be afraid,** tener (ie, tengo) miedo; **to be a question of,** tratarse de; **to be ashamed (of),** tener vergüenza (de); **to be astonished,** asombrarse; **to be back,** estar de vuelta; **to be careful,** tener cuidado; **to be cold** (person), tener frío; (weather), hacer frío; (thing), estar frío,-a; **to be cool,** hacer fresco; **to be enough,** bastar; **to be foggy,** haber (hay) neblina; **to be fond of,** ser aficionado,-a (a); **to be frightened,** asustarse, espantarse; **to be glad (to, of),** alegrarse (de); **to be good for,** servir (i) para; **to be hungry (thirsty),** tener hambre (sed); **to be in agreement (with),** estar conforme (con), estar de acuerdo (con); **to be in love (with),** estar enamorado,-a (de); **to be lucky,** tener suerte; **to be mistaken,** equivocarse (qu); **to be muddy,** haber lodo; **to be one's turn,** tocarle (qu) (a uno); **to be right,** tener razón; **to be room for,** caber (quepo); **to be sleepy,** tener sueño; **to be sorry,** sentir (ie, i); **to be sunny,** haber sol, hacer sol; **to be (supposed) to,** haber de + *inf.;* **to be tight,** apretar (ie); **to be too much (many),** sobrar; **to be warm (hot)** (weather), hacer calor; **to be windy,** hacer viento; **to be worth,** valer (valgo); **to be worthwhile,** valer la pena; **to be wrong,** no tener razón; **to be . . .**

years old, tener . . . años;
to be beside oneself, estar fuera de sí; **to be deceived,** engañarse; **to be graduated,** graduarse; **to be in favor of,** estar por; **to be pleasing to (to be pleased with),** agradar a uno; **to be tired,** estar cansado,-a; **to be lacking,** faltar, hacer falta

beach, la playa

bear, el oso

bearings: to get one's bearings, orientarse

beast, la bestia

beautiful, bello,-a, hermoso, -a; **beauty,** la belleza, la hermosura

because, porque; **because of,** a causa de

become, hacerse (hago), llegar (gu) a ser; (involuntary), ponerse (pongo) + *adj.;* **to become angry,** enfadarse, enojarse; **to become quiet,** callarse; **to become tired,** cansarse

bed, la cama; **to go to bed,** acostarse (ue); **to stay in bed,** guardar cama

bedroom, la alcoba, el dormitorio

bee, la abeja

beef, la carne; **roast beef,** carne asada, rosbif

before, antes de, antes (de) que; **(in the presence of),** ante

beg, rogar (ue, gu), suplicar (qu); **beggar,** el mendigo, el pordiosero

begin, comenzar (ie, c), empezar (ie, c), ponerse (pongo) a + *inf.,* echarse a + *inf.;* **beginning,** el principio, el comienzo; **at the beginning of,** a principios de

behave (oneself), portarse

being, el ser

believe, creer (y)

bell, la campana

belong, pertenecer (zc)

beloved, querido,-a

beside, junto a, al lado de; **beside oneself,** fuera de sí

best, el (la) mejor

better, mejor; **it is better,** es mejor, más vale

between, entre

Bible, la Biblia

bicycle, la bicicleta

big, grande

bird, el pájaro, el ave (*f.*)

birthday, el cumpleaños

bitter, amargo,-a

black, negro,-a; **blackboard,**

la pizarra

blame, echar la culpa (a)

blanket, la frazada

blond, rubio,-a

blouse, la blusa

blue, azul

boat, el buque, el barco, la nave

boil, hervir (ie, i)

book, el libro; **book case,** el estante (para libros); **bookkeeper,** el contador; **bookstore,** la librería

bored: to get bored, aburrirse

born: to be born, nacer (zc)

boss, el patrón, el jefe

bottle, la botella

bouquet, el ramo

boy, el muchacho

bracelet, el brazalete

Brazil, el Brasil

bread, el pan

break, romper; **to break in pieces,** hacer (hago) pedazos

breakfast, el desayuno; **to eat (have) breakfast,** desayunarse

brick, el ladrillo

brilliant, brillante

bring, traer (traigo)

broken, roto,-a

brother, el hermano

brush, el cepillo; **to brush,** cepillar, limpiar; **to brush one's teeth,** limpiarse los dientes

build, construir (y); **building,** el edificio; **built,** construido,-a

bull, el toro; **bullfight,** la corrida de toros; **bullfighter,** el torero

bus, el autobús

business, el negocio

busy, ocupado,-a

but, pero, sino

butter, la mantequilla

buy, comprar; **buying,** el comprar

by, por, en, de, para; **by day,** de día; **by dint of,** a fuerza de; **by no means,** de ningún modo, de ninguna manera; **by heart,** de memoria; **by working,** trabajando

cage, la jaula

call, llamar; **to be called,** llamarse

campaign, la campaña

can (to be able), poder (ue); (probability), use future tense; **it can't be helped,** no hay remedio

Canada, el Canadá

candy, los dulces

capable, capaz

cape, la capa

capital (city), la capital

captain, el capitán

care: to take care (of), cuidar (a, de); **to take care of oneself,** cuidarse; **to be careful,** tener (ie, tengo) cuidado

carpenter, el carpintero

carry, llevar; **to carry away,** llevarse; **to carry out,** llevar a cabo

case, el caso; **in case,** en caso de que

cast, echar

Castilian, castellano,-a

cat, el gato

catastrophe, la catástrofe

cathedral, la catedral

cause, causar

celebrate, celebrar

cent, el centavo

century, el siglo

ceremony, la ceremonia

certain, cierto,-a; **it is certain,** es cierto

chain, la cadena

chair, la silla

chapter, el capítulo

charge, cobrar; **to take charge of,** encargarse (gu) de

Charles, Carlos

charming, simpático,-a, amable, encantador,-a

chase, perseguir (i, g)

cheap, barato,-a

check, el cheque; **to check,** facturar

cheese, el queso

cherry, la cereza

chicken, el pollo

child, niño,-a

choose, escoger (j)

Christmas, la Navidad

church, la iglesia

circus, el circo

citizen, el ciudadano

city, la ciudad

civil, civil

civilization, la civilización

class, la clase; **classroom,** sala de clase, el aula (*f.*)

clear, claro,-a

clerk, el dependiente

climate, el clima

clock, el reloj

close, cerrar (ie)

closet, el armario

cloud, la nube

club, el club

coat, el abrigo

coffee, el café; **coffee cup,** taza para café; **cup of coffee,** taza de café

coin, la moneda

cold, frío,-a; (*m.*), el frío;

(illness), el resfriado, el catarro; **to be cold (weather),** hacer frío; (person), tener (ie, tengo) frío; (thing), estar frío,-a

collection, la colección

color, el color

Columbus, Colón

comb, el peine; **to comb one's hair,** peinarse

combat, combatir

come, venir (ie, vengo); **to come to** (= to regain consciousness), volver (ue) en sí; **to come to an agreement,** ponerse (pongo) de acuerdo; **to come upon,** dar (doy) con, tropezar (ie, c) con

comfortable, cómodo,-a

commerce, el comercio

companion, el compañero, la compañera

company, la compañía

compile, compilar

complain (of), quejarse (de)

compose, componer (compongo)

condemn, condenar

confess, confesar (ie)

conquer, conquistar, vencer (z)

conquest, la conquista

consciousness: to regain consciousness, volver (ue) en sí

consent (to), consentir (ie, i) (en)

consider, dar (doy) por, tener (ie, tengo) por, considerar

consist (of), consistir (en)

construct, construir (y); **construction,** la construcción

consult, consultar

contain, contener (ie, contengo)

continent, el continente

continue, continuar (ú)

contract, el contrato

contribute, contribuir (y)

conversation, la conversación, la charla

convert (to), convertir (ie, i) (en)

convince, convencer (z)

cook, el cocinero, la cocinera; **to cook,** cocer (ue, z), cocinar

cool, fresco,-a; **to be cool,** hacer fresco

copper, el cobre

copy, copiar

correct, correcto,-a; **to correct,** corregir (i, j); **correctly,** correctamente

cost, costar (ue)

cotton, el algodón

could, poder (ue); (polite request), pudiera; (probability), use conditional
count, contar (ue)
countess, la condesa
country, el campo; (nation), el país
course: of course, desde luego, por supuesto
cousin, el primo, la prima
cover, cubrir; **covered,** cubierto,-a
cow, la vaca
create, crear
criminal, el criminal
critic, el crítico
cross, la cruz; **to cross,** atravesar (ie), cruzar (c)
cruel, cruel; **cruelly,** cruelmente; **cruelty,** la crueldad
cry, llorar
cup, la taza
cure, curar
curious, curioso,-a; **curiously,** curiosamente, con curiosidad
current, la corriente
custom, la costumbre
cut, cortar

dance, el baile; **to dance,** bailar; **dancer,** el bailarín, la bailarina
danger, el peligro; **dangerous,** peligroso,-a
dare (to), atreverse (a)
dark, oscuro,-a; **darkness,** la oscuridad
date, la fecha
daughter, la hija
day, el día; **the day after tomorrow,** pasado mañana; **by day,** de día; **every day,** todos los días; **some day,** algún día; **the next day,** el (al) día siguiente; **this very day,** hoy mismo; **at daybreak,** al amanecer
dear, querido,-a
debt, la deuda
deceive, engañar; **to be deceived,** engañarse
December, diciembre
decide (to), decidirse (a)
declare, declarar
decorate, decorar
dedicate (oneself), dedicar(se) (qu)
deed, la hazaña
deep, hondo,-a
defeat, vencer (z)
defend, defender (ie)
delay (in), tardar (en); **without delay,** cuanto antes
deny, negar (ie, gu)

depart, partir, salir (salgo)
descend, descender (ie), bajar
describe, describir
desert, el desierto; **deserted,** desierto,-a
deserve, merecer (zc)
dessert, el postre
destroy, destruir (y)
detail, el detalle
devote, dedicar (qu), consagrar
dictator, el dictador
dictionary, el diccionario
die, morir (ue, u)
difficult, difícil; **difficulty,** la dificultad
dignity, la dignidad
diligent, diligente, aplicado,-a; **diligently,** diligentemente
dint: by dint of, a fuerza de
dirty, sucio,-a
disappear, desaparecer (zc)
disaster, el desastre
disciple, el discípulo
discover, descubrir
discuss, discutir
dish, el plato
distance: in the distance, a lo lejos
distribute, distribuir (y)
divide, dividir; **divided by,** dividido por
do, hacer (hago); **to have nothing to do with,** no tener (ie, tengo) nada que ver con; **no sooner said than done,** dicho y hecho
doctor (title), el doctor; (profession), el médico
document, el documento
doll, la muñeca
dollar, el dólar
Dominic, Domingo
donkey, el burro, el asno
door, la puerta
doubt, la duda; **to doubt,** dudar; **doubtful,** dudoso,-a; **doubtless, there's no doubt,** sin duda, no cabe duda
downstream, río abajo
drama, el drama; **dramatist,** el dramaturgo
draw apart (from), apartarse (de)
dream, el sueño; **to dream,** soñar (ue); **to dream of,** soñar con
dress, el vestido; **to dress (oneself),** vestir(se) (i)
drink, la bebida; **to drink,** beber
drive, conducir (zc), manejar
drop, dejar caer

drown, ahogar (gu); **to be drowned,** ahogarse
drugstore, la botica, la farmacia
dry, seco,-a
during, durante

each, cada; **each other,** uno a otro, una a otra
early, temprano
earn, ganar
earth, la tierra
easy, fácil; **easily,** fácilmente
eat, comer; **to eat breakfast,** desayunarse
Ecuador, el Ecuador
effort, el esfuerzo
egg, el huevo; **to lay an egg,** poner (pongo) un huevo
eight, ocho; **eight o'clock,** las ocho; **eighteen(th),** diez y ocho (dieciocho); **eighth,** octavo,-a; **eight hundred,** ochocientos,-as; **eighty,** ochenta
either (in negative sentence), tampoco; **either . . . or** (in negative sentence), ni . . . ni
electrical, eléctrico,-a
elevator, el ascensor
eleven, once; **eleven o'clock,** las once
Elizabeth, Isabel
embrace, dar un abrazo, abrazar (c)
Emil, Emilio
employ, emplear; **employee,** el empleado, la empleada
empty, vacío,-a
end, terminar; **to end by,** acabar por; **at the end of,** a fines de, al cabo de
enemy, el enemigo, la enemiga
England, Inglaterra; **English,** inglés, inglesa; (language), el inglés
enjoy, gozar (c) de; **to enjoy oneself,** divertirse (ie, i)
enough, bastante; **to be enough,** bastar
enter, entrar (en), pase Vd.
enterprise, la empresa
enthusiasm, el entusiasmo; **enthusiastically,** con entusiasmo
envelope, el sobre
equals (=), son
era, la época
erase, borrar
error, el error
essay, el ensayo
eternal, eterno,-a
Europe, Europa
even: even though, aunque; **not even,** ni siquiera

evening, la noche; **every evening,** todas las noches
ever, jamás, nunca
every, todos los . . . , todas las . . . ; **everybody, everyone,** todos, todo el mundo; **every day,** todos los días; **every morning,** todas las mañanas; **everything,** todo; **everywhere,** en (por) todas partes
evident, evidente
examination, el examen, la prueba; **examine,** examinar
exercise, el ejercicio
exert, ejercer (z)
expedition, la expedición
expensive, caro,-a
experience, la experiencia
explain, explicar (qu)
explore, explorar; **explorer,** el explorador
explosion, la explosión
expose, exponer (expongo)
extinguish, extinguir (extingo)
extraordinary, extraordinario,-a
eye, el ojo; **eyeglasses,** los anteojos

face, la cara, el rostro; **to face,** dar (doy) a
fact: in fact, as a matter of fact, en efecto
factory, la fábrica
fail: to fail to, dejar de + *inf.;* **failure,** el fracaso
faint, desmayarse
faithfully, fielmente
fall, la caída; **to fall (down),** caer(se) (caigo); **to fall asleep,** dormirse (ue, u); **to fall in love (with),** enamorarse (de)
false, falso,-a
fame, la fama
family, la familia
famous, famoso,-a, célebre
"fan," el aficionado
farmer, el labrador, el campesino
father, el padre
favor, el favor; **to be in favor of,** estar por; **favorite,** favorito,-a
February, febrero
feel, sentir(se) (ie, i); **to feel like,** tener (ie, tengo) ganas de
fellow pupil, condiscípulo
female, la hembra
Ferdinand, Fernando
ferocious, feroz
fever, la fiebre
few: a few, varios,-as,

algunos,-as, unos cuantos (unas cuantas); **fewer,** menos

fiancé, el novio; **fiancée,** la novia

fierce, bravo,-a

fifteen, quince; **fifth,** quinto, -a; **fifty,** cincuenta

fight, luchar (con), pelear (con)

finally, al fin, por fin, finalmente

find, encontrar (ue), hallar; **to find out,** saber (supe) (*pret.*); averiguar (gü), enterarse (de)

finish, terminar, acabar

fire, el fuego

firm, firme

first, primero,-a (primer)

fish, pescar (qu); **fishing,** el pescar, la pesca

five, cinco; **five hundred,** quinientos,-as

flat, llano,-a

flee, huir (y)

flower, la flor

foggy: it is foggy, hay neblina

follow, seguir (i, sigo)

fond (of), aficionado,-a (a)

food, el alimento

foot, el pie; **on foot,** a pie

for, para, por; **as for,** en cuanto a

forbid, prohibir

force, la fuerza

foreign, extranjero,-a

forest, el bosque

forget, olvidar, olvidarse de

former (the), aquél, aquélla, aquéllos, aquéllas

fortune, la fortuna

found (= establish), fundar

four, cuatro; **forty,** cuarenta; **four hundred,** cuatrocientos,-as; **fourteen,** catorce; **fourth,** cuarto,-a

France, Francia; **French,** francés, francesa; (language), el francés; **in the French style,** a la francesa

Fred, Federico

freeze, helar (ie); **to freeze over,** helarse

frequently, frecuentemente, con frecuencia

fresh, fresco,-a

Friday, el viernes

friend, el amigo, la amiga; **friendship,** la amistad

frighten, asustar, espantar; **to be frightened,** asustarse, espantarse

from, de, desde; **from time to time,** de vez en cuando; **from now on,** de hoy en adelante

frontier, la frontera

fruit, las frutas

full, lleno,-a

fun: to make fun of, burlarse de

function, la función

furniture, el mueble, los muebles

future, el futuro, el porvenir

garden, el jardín

gather (up), recoger (j)

general, general; (title), el general

generous, generoso,-a

genius, el ingenio

gentleman, el señor, el caballero

George, Jorge

German, alemán, alemana; (language), el alemán; **Germany,** Alemania

get, obtener (ie, obtengo), conseguir (i, consigo); **to get angry,** enojarse, enfadarse; **to get bored,** aburrirse; **to get dressed,** vestirse (i); **to be getting late,** hacerse tarde; **to get lost,** perderse (ie); **to get married (to),** casarse (con); **to get one's bearings,** orientarse; **to get ready to,** disponerse (dispongo) a; **to get up,** levantarse; **to get washed,** lavarse; **to get wet,** mojarse

gift, el regalo

girl, la muchacha

give, dar (doy); **giving,** el dar; **give regards,** dar recuerdos

glad: to be glad (of, to), alegrarse (de)

glance, la mirada

glorious, glorioso,-a; **glory,** la gloria

glove, el guante

go, ir (voy), andar; **to go away,** irse, marcharse; **to go out,** salir (salgo); **to go to bed,** acostarse (ue); **to go up,** subir

God, Dios; **god,** el dios; **God grant that . . . !,** ¡Ojalá que . . . !

gold, el oro; **Golden Age,** el Siglo de Oro

good, bueno,-a (buen); **to be good for,** servir (i) para; **goodness,** la bondad

govern, gobernar (ie); **government,** el gobierno; **governor,** el gobernador

grade, la nota

graduate, to be graduated, graduarse (ú)

granddaughter, la nieta; **grandmother,** la abuela; **grandson,** el nieto

grapefruit, la toronja

grass, la hierba

grateful: to be grateful (for), agradecer (zc)

gray, gris

great, grande (gran); **greatness,** la grandeza

Greek, griego,-a

green, verde

greet, saludar

grieve, afligir (j)

ground, el suelo

group, el grupo

grow, crecer (zc)

guard, el guardia, la guardia

guest, el invitado, la invitada, el huésped

guidebook, la guía

guitar, la guitarra

hair, el pelo, el cabello; **to comb one's hair,** peinarse

half, medio,-a, la mitad

hall, la sala, el salón

hand, la mano; **to hand (over),** entregar (gu); **to shake hands,** darse la mano; **on the other hand,** en cambio

hang (up), colgar (ue, gu)

happen, ocurrir, suceder, pasar; **to happen to,** acertar (ie) a + *inf.*

happiness, la felicidad, la alegría; **happy,** alegre, feliz

hard, *adv.*, mucho

harvest, la cosecha

hat, el sombrero

hate, odiar

have, tener (ie, tengo); (auxiliary), haber (he); **to have breakfast,** desayunarse; **to have just . . . ,** acabar de + *inf.*; **to have left** (= remaining), quedarle (a uno); **to have lunch,** almorzar (ue, c); **to have nothing to do with,** no tener nada que ver con; **to have too much,** sobrarle (a uno); **to have to,** tener que + *inf.*

he, él; **he who,** el que, quien

head, la cabeza

health, la salud

hear, oír (oigo, y); **to hear of (about),** oír hablar de

heart: by heart, de memoria

heat, el calor

heed: to pay heed to, hacer (hago) caso de

height, la altura; **in height,** de alto

Helen, Elena

help, la ayuda; **to help,** ayudar; **it can't be helped,** no hay remedio; **not to be able to help . . . ,** no poder (ue) menos de + *inf.*

hen, la gallina

henceforth, de hoy en adelante

Henry, Enrique

her (possessive), su, sus; (direct object), la; (after prep.), ella; **herself,** se; **to herself,** para sí; **with her(self),** consigo

here, aquí, acá

hero, el héroe; **heroic,** heroico,-a; **heroically,** heroicamente

hers, el (la, los, las) suyo(-a, -os, -as)

hide, esconder, ocultar

high, alto,-a

him (direct object), le, lo; (after prep.), él; **himself,** mismo; (reflexive), se; (after prep.), sí; **to himself,** para sí; **with him(self),** consigo

hinder, impedir (i)

his, su, sus; el (la, los, las) suyo(-a, -os, -as)

historic, historical, histórico,-a; **history,** la historia

hit, dar (doy) en

holiday, el día de fiesta

home, (la) casa; **at home,** en casa; **(to) home,** a casa; **homework,** la tarea

honor, el honor; **to honor,** honrar

hope, la esperanza; **to hope,** esperar

horse, el caballo; **on horseback,** a caballo

hospital, el hospital

hot, caliente; **to be hot (weather),** hacer calor

hour, la hora

house, la casa

how?, ¿cómo?; **how (well she sings)!,** ¡qué (bien canta)!; **how (dark) it is,** lo (oscuro) que es; **how long?,** ¿cuánto tiempo?; **how much?,** ¿cuánto, -a?

however, sin embargo; **however + adj. or adv.,** por + *adj.* or *adv.* + que

human, humano,-a

hundred, ciento (cien)

hungry: to be hungry, tener (ie, tengo) hambre

hurry: to hurry (to), apresurarse (a + *inf.*), darse (doy) prisa (a + *inf.*)

hurt, doler (ue), hacer (hago) daño (a); **to hurt**

(oneself), hacer(se) (hago) daño

I, yo; **I should say so!**, ¡ya lo creo!
idealist, idealista
if, si; **as if**, como si
ill, enfermo,-a; **illness**, la enfermedad
image, la imagen
imagination, la imaginación; **to imagine**, imaginarse
imitate, imitar
immediately, en seguida, inmediatamente
important, importante
impossible, imposible
impression, la impresión
in, en; (after superlative), de; **in order to**, para; **in regard to**, en cuanto a; **in the (French) style**, a la (francesa); **in the open air**, al aire libre; **in this (that) way**, de este (ese) modo, de esta (esa) manera; **in accordance with**, de acuerdo con, conforme a; **in a little while**, dentro de poco; **in fact**, en efecto; **in spite of**, a pesar de
include, incluir (y)
independence, la independencia
Indian, el indio
indicate, indicar (qu)
indulgent, indulgente
influence, la influencia; **to have influence on**, influir (y) en
inhabitant, el habitante
injustice, la injusticia
inn, la fonda
inside (of), dentro (de)
insist (on), insistir (en), empeñarse (en)
inspector, el inspector
inspire, inspirar
instantly, al instante
instead of, en vez de, en lugar de
instrument, el instrumento
intelligence, la inteligencia; **intelligent**, inteligente
intend, pensar (ie) + inf.
interest, el interés; **to interest**, interesar; **interesting**, interesante
interrupt, interrumpir
into, en
inventor, el inventor
invite, invitar, convidar
island, la isla
it (direct object), lo, la; (after prep.), él, ella; **its**, su, sus
Italian, italiano,-a; (language), el italiano

jacket, la chaqueta, la americana
James, Diego, Jaime
Jane, Juana
January, enero
jewel, la joya, la alhaja
job, el empleo, el puesto
John, Juan; **Johnny**, Juanito
join, unir(se) a
Joseph, José
journalist, el periodista
judge, el juez
July, julio
June, junio
jungle, la selva
just: to have just . . . , acabar de + inf.

keep, guardar, quedarse con; **to keep one's word**, cumplir (con) la palabra; **to keep on**, seguir (i, sigo); **to keep silent**, callarse
kind, bondadoso,-a, la especie; **kindness**, la bondad
king, el rey
kitchen, la cocina
kneeling, de rodillas
knife, el cuchillo
know (a fact), saber (sé); (a person), conocer (zc); **to know how**, saber

lack, carecer (zc) de; **to be lacking**, faltar, hacer falta
lady, la dama, la señora, la señorita; **young lady**, la señorita
lake, el lago
land, la tierra
language, la lengua, el idioma
large, grande
last, durar; **last night**, anoche; **last (year, month, Wednesday)**, el (año, mes, miércoles) pasado
late, tarde; **to be getting late**, hacerse tarde; **later**, más tarde
latter (the), éste, ésta, éstos, éstas
laugh (at), reírse (í) (de)
law, la ley; **lawyer**, el abogado
lay (an egg), poner (un huevo)
lazy, perezoso,-a
leaf, la hoja
lean (on, against), apoyarse (en)
learn, aprender
least (the), el (la) menor, los (las) menores; **at least**, a lo (al) menos
leave, salir (salgo) (de),

dejar; **to take leave (of)**, despedirse (i) (de)
left: at (to) the left, a la izquierda; **to have left (= remaining)**, quedarle (a uno)
leg, la pierna
lend, prestar
less, menos
lesson, la lección
letter, la carta; (alphabet), la letra
liberty, la libertad
library, la biblioteca
lie, la mentira; **to lie**, mentir (ie, i)
life, la vida
lift, levantar, alzar (c)
light, la luz
like, como; **I like**, me gusta(n); **I would like**, me gustaría(n), quisiera; **to feel like**, tener (tengo) ganas de
limit, el límite; **to limit**, limitar
lion, el león
listen (to), escuchar
literature, la literatura
little (quantity), poco,-a; (size), pequeño,-a; **a little while ago**, hace poco; **in a little while**, dentro de poco
live, vivir; **living room**, la sala
lively, animado,-a
long, largo,-a; **a long time**, mucho tiempo; **how long?**, ¿cuánto tiempo?; **no longer**, ya no
look (at), mirar; **to look for**, buscar (qu); **to look out of (the window)**, asomarse a (la ventana)
lose, perder (ie); **to lose sight of**, perder de vista; **loss**, la pérdida; **to get lost**, perderse
Louis, Luis
Louise, Luisa
love, el amor; **to love**, querer (ie), amar; **to be in love (with)**, estar enamorado, -a (de); **to fall in love (with)**, enamorarse (de)
lower, bajar
luck, la suerte; **to be lucky**, tener (ie, tengo) suerte
Lucy, Lucía
luggage, el equipaje
lunch, el almuerzo; **to have lunch**, almorzar (ue, c)

machine, la máquina
Madame, señora
magazine, la revista
mail, echar al correo

make, hacer (hago); **to make a mistake**, hacer un error; **to make a trip**, hacer un viaje; **to make fun (of)**, burlarse (de); **to make one's way to**, dirigirse (j) a
male, el varón
mama, mamá
man, el hombre; (husband), el marido; **old man**, el viejo
manager, el administrador, el director
manufacture, fabricar (qu)
many, muchos,-as; **how many?**, ¿cuántos,-as?
map, el mapa
marble, el mármol
March, marzo
mark, la nota; **to mark**, marcar (qu)
market, el mercado
marry, casar; **to get married (to)**, casarse (con)
Martha, Marta
Mary, María
masterpiece, la obra maestra
material, el material
mathematics, las matemáticas
matter, el asunto; **as a matter of fact**, en efecto; **it doesn't matter**, no importa; **no matter how . . .** , por + adj. or adv. + que
May, mayo
mayor, el alcalde
me, me; (after prep.), mí; **with me**, conmigo
meal, la comida
mean, significar (qu), querer (ie) decir
means: by no means, de ningún modo, de ninguna manera
meanwhile, mientras tanto
measure, medir (i)
meat, la carne
medicine, la medicina
meet, encontrar (ue), encontrarse con, reunirse (ú); (make one's acquaintance), conocer (zc); **meeting**, la reunión
melancholy, la melancolía
member, socio,-a
memory, el recuerdo, la memoria
merchandise, las mercancías; **merchant**, el comerciante
mere, simple
merit, el mérito
Mexican, mexicano,-a; **Mexico**, México
Michael, Miguel
midnight, la medianoche

mile, la milla
military, militar
milk, la leche
million, el millón
mine, el (la, los, las) mío(-a, -os, -as)
miute, el minuto
miser, el avaro; miserly, avaro,-a
misfortune, la desgracia
Miss, (la) señorita; to miss, echar de menos
mistake, el error, la falta; to be mistaken, equivocarse (qu)
Mister (Mr.), (el) señor; Mr. & Mrs., los señores
mix, mezclar
moan, gemir (i)
model, el modelo
modern, moderno,-a
modest, modesto,-a
moment, el momento
monarch, el monarca
Monday, el lunes
money, el dinero
month, el mes; last month, el mes pasado
monument, el monumento
moon, la luna
Moor, el moro
more, más; the more . . . , the more, cuanto más . . . , (tanto) más; more and more, cada vez más
morning, la mañana; good morning, buenos días; every morning, todas las mañanas; in the morning, por la mañana
most (the), el (la, los, las) más
mother, la madre
mountain, la montaña, el monte; mountainous, montañoso,-a
mounted, montado,-a
move, mover(se) (ue)
Mrs., (la) señora
much, mucho,-a; adv., mucho; how much?, ¿cuánto,-a?; so much, tanto,-a; too much, demasiado,-a; to be too much, sobrar
mud, el lodo; to be muddy, haber (hay) lodo
multiplied by, por
murmur, murmurar
museum, el museo
music, la música; musical, músico,-a; musician, el músico
must (probability), uso fu ture tense or deber de + inf.; (obligation), tener (ie, tengo) que, deber; one must, hay que + inf.
my, mi, mis

narrow, estrecho,-a
nation, la nación
nature, la naturaleza, el genio
navigate, navegar (gu)
near, cerca de; nearby, cercano,-a
necessary, necesario,-a
necklace, el collar
necktie, la corbata
need, necesitar, hacerle falta (a uno), faltarle (a uno)
needle, la aguja
neighbor, neighboring, vecino,-a
neither, tampoco; neither . . . nor, ni . . . ni
never, nunca, jamás
nevertheless, sin embargo, no obstante
new, nuevo,-a; nothing new, sin novedad
news, la(s) noticia(s); newspaper, el periódico, el diario
next, próximo,-a, siguiente; the next day, el (al) día siguiente
night, la noche; at night, de noche; at nightfall, al anochecer; last night, anoche
nine, nueve; nine hundred, novecientos,-as; nineteen-(th), diez y nueve (diecinueve); ninety, noventa; ninth, noveno,-a
no, ninguno,-a (ningún); no longer, ya no; no one, nadie; no sooner said than done, dicho y hecho
noise, el ruido
none, ninguno,-a
noon, el mediodía
nor, ni; neither . . . nor, ni . . . ni
not, no; not even, ni siquiera; not now, ahora no; not yet, todavía no; not to be able to help . . . , no poder menos de + inf.
nothing, nada; nothing new, sin novedad; to have nothing to do with, no tener (ie, tengo) nada que ver con
notice, notar, hacer (hago) caso de
notify, avisar
notwithstanding, no obstante
novel, novela; novelist, el novelista
November, noviembre
now, ahora; from now on, de hoy en adelante; not now, ahora no; right now, ahora mismo; nowadays, hoy día, actualmente

number, el número
numerous, numeroso,-a
nurse, la enfermera

obey, obedecer (zc)
object, el objeto
observe, observar, reparar en
occur, ocurrir, acontecer (zc)
o'clock: at eight o'clock, a las ocho
October, octubre
of, de; of course, desde luego, por supuesto
off: to take off, quitarse
office, la oficina
often, a menudo, muchas veces
oil, el aceite
old, viejo,-a; (former), antiguo,-a
omit, omitir
on, en; on (entering), al (entrar); on Mondays, los lunes; on the other hand, en cambio; on time, a tiempo; on foot, a pie; on purpose, de propósito
once: at once, en seguida
one, uno,-a (un); the one who, el (la) que; one hundred, cien(to); no one, nadie
only, no . . . más que
open, abierto,-a; to open, abrir; to open wide, abrir de par en par; in the open air, al aire libre
operation, la operación
opponent, el adversario
oppose, oponerse (opongo) (a); opposite, opuesto,-a
or, o; (before word beginning with o or ho), u
orange, la naranja
orchard, la huerta
orchestra, la orquesta
order, la orden; to order, mandar, ordenar; in order to, para; in order that, para que
orphan, el huérfano, la huérfana
other, otro,-a; each other, uno a otro, una a otra; on the other hand, en cambio; otherwise, de otro modo
ought, deber
our, nuestro,-a; ours, el (la, los, las) nuestro(-a, -os, -as)
out: to carry out, llevar a cabo; to go out, salir (salgo); to look out of (the window), asomarse a (la ventana); to take out, sacar (qu)

own: (my, your, our, his, her, its, their) own, propio, -a
owner, el dueño

package, el paquete
page, la página
pain, el dolor
paint, pintar; painter, el pintor; painting, la pintura, el cuadro
pair, el par
palace, el palacio
paragraph, el párrafo
parents, los padres
park, el parque
parlor, la sala
part: to take part (in), tomar parte (en)
party, la fiesta, la tertulia
pass, pasar
passenger, el pasajero, la pasajera
passion, la pasión
passport, el pasaporte
patience, la paciencia
patriot, el patriota
patron (saint), el (santo) patrón
Paul, Pablo
pay (for), pagar (gu); to pay heed (to), hacer (hago) caso (a, de); to pay attention (to), prestar (poner) atención (a); to pay a visit, hacer una visita
peace, la paz
peak, el pico
pear, la pera
pearl, la perla
peasant, el campesino, el labrador
pen, la pluma
pencil, el lápiz
people, la gente, las personas
per, por
perfume, el perfume
perhaps, tal vez, quizás
period, la época
permit, permitir
persist (in), empeñarse (en)
person, la persona
Peru, el Perú
Peter, Pedro
Philip, Felipe
philosopher, el filósofo
phonograph, el tocadiscos
piano, el piano
picture, el cuadro; (movie), la película; to take a picture, sacar (qu) una fotografía; picturesque, pintoresco,-a
pie, el pastel
piece, el pedazo; piece of furniture, el mueble; to break in pieces, hacer

(hago) pedazos

pity, la piedad, la lástima; it is a pity, es lástima; pitying glance, la mirada de piedad

place, lugar, sitio; to place, poner (pongo), colocar (qu); to take place, verificarse (qu), tener lugar

plan, el plan

plane, el avión; by plane, en (por) avión

plant, la planta

plate, el plato

platform, el andén

platinum, el platino

play (theatrical), la comedia; to play (music), tocar (qu); (a game), jugar (ue); to play the role of, hacer (hago) el papel de

please, por favor; to please (to be pleasing), gustar, agradar

plumber, el plomero

plus, y, más

P.M., de la tarde, de la noche

poem, la poesía, el poema

poet, el poeta; poetess, la poetisa; poetry, la poesía

police, la policía; policeman, el policía

political, político,-a; politician, el político

poor, pobre

popular, popular

portrait, el retrato

Portuguese, portugués, portuguesa; (language), el portugués

possession: to take possession of, apoderarse de

possible, posible

post card, la tarjeta postal

postman, el cartero

pound, la libra

powerful, poderoso,-a

practice, la práctica; to practice, practicar (qu)

prefer, preferir (ie, i)

prepare, preparar

present, regalar, presentar

preserve, conservar

president, el presidente

pretty, bonito,-a

price, el precio

pride, el orgullo

prince, el príncipe; princess, la princesa

print, imprimir

prison, la cárcel

prize, el premio

probable, probable; probably (use future or conditional), probablemente

problem, el problema

proceed, andar; proceed on

one's way, proseguir el (su) camino

procession, la procesión

produce, producir (zc)

program, el programa

progress, el progreso; to progress, adelantar

prohibit, prohibir

project, el proyecto

promise, prometer

property, la propiedad

propose, proponer (propongo)

protect, proteger (j)

protest, protestar

proud, orgulloso,-a; proudly, orgullosamente, con orgullo

provided that, con tal que

public, público,-a; (m. sing.), el público

publish, publicar (qu)

punish, castigar (gu); punishment, el castigo

pupil, el alumno, la alumna; fellow pupil, el condiscípulo

purchase, la compra

purpose: on purpose, de propósito

purse, la bolsa

put, poner (pongo); to put in, meter; to put on, ponerse

pyramid, la pirámide

quarrel, reñir (i)

question: to be a question of, tratarse de

quickly, rápidamente, aprisa, pronto, de prisa

quiet: to become quiet, callarse

quite, bastante

race, la raza

radio, el (la) radio

rain, la lluvia; to rain, llover (ue)

raise, levantar, alzar (c); (bring up), criar (í)

rapidly, rápidamente

ray, el rayo

reach, llegar (gu) a; to reach an agreement, llegar a un acuerdo, ponerse (pongo) de acuerdo

read, leer (y); reader, el lector; reading, el leer, la lectura

ready, listo,-a, dispuesto,-a; to get ready to, disponerse (dispongo) a

realize, darse (doy) cuenta

de; really, de veras

receipt, el recibo; to receive, recibir

recognize, reconocer (zc)

recommend, recomendar (ie)

refer to, referirse (ie, i) a

refreshment, el refresco

refuse (to), negarse (ie, gu) (a)

regain consciousness, volver (ue) en sí

regard: in regard to, en cuanto a; to give regards, dar (doy) recuerdos

region, la región

reign, reinar

relate, contar (ue)

relative, el pariente

reliable, seguro,-a, cierto,-a; to rely on, contar (ue) con

religious, religioso,-a

remain, quedar(se)

remember, acordarse (ue) (de), recordar (ue)

repent, arrepentirse (ie, i) (de)

rescue, salvar

resemble, parecerse (zc) a

respect, respetar

rest, el descanso, el reposo; to rest, descansar

restaurant, el restaurante

result, el resultado; to result (in), resultar

return (go back), volver (ue), regresar; (give back), devolver (ue)

rice, el arroz

rich, rico,-a

Richard, Ricardo

ride: to take a ride, dar un paseo (en coche)

right, derecho,-a; at (to) the right, a la derecha; right now, ahora mismo; to be right, tener (ie, tengo) razón

rise, ascender (ie), subir

rival, el adversario

river, el río

road, el camino

roast, asar; roast beef, carne asada, rosbif

role: to play the role of, hacer (hago) el papel de

Roman, romano,-a

room, la habitación, el cuarto; to be room for, caber (quepo)

rose, la rosa

round-trip ticket, el billete de ida y vuelta

rug, la alfombra

run, correr; to run along (down, through), correr por

Russian, ruso,-a; (language), el ruso

sacrifice, sacrificar (qu)

sad, triste; sadness, la tristeza

safe and sound, sano y salvo

sailor, el marinero

Saint, Santo,-a (San)

salad, la ensalada

salt, la sal

same, mismo,-a; same as usual, sin novedad; at the same time, a la vez

sand, la arena

satisfy, satisfacer (satisfago)

Saturday, el sábado

save, conservar, salvar

say, decir (i, digo); I should say so!, ¡ya lo creo!; no sooner said than done, dicho y hecho

scarcely, apenas

school, la escuela

science, la ciencia; scientist, el científico

sculptor, el escultor, la escultora

season, la estación

seat, el asiento; (theater), la localidad; seated, sentado,-a

second, segundo,-a

secret, secreto,-a

secretary, el secretario, la secretaria

see, ver (veo)

seem, parecer (zc)

seize, coger (j)

sell, vender; selling, el vender

semester, el semestre

send, enviar (í), mandar

sentence, la frase

September, septiembre

serape, el sarape

serious, grave, serio,-a

servant, el criado, la criada

serve, servir (i); to serve as, servir de

set, poner (pongo); to set the table, poner la mesa

settle, arreglar

seven, siete; seven hundred, setecientos,-as; seventeen(th), diez y siete (diecisiete); seventh, séptimo,-a; seventy, setenta

several, varios,-as

severe, severo,-a; severely, severamente

sew, coser

shake hands, darse la mano

shall (use present or future tense)

sharp, agudo,-a; eight o'clock sharp, las ocho en punto

shave, afeitar; to shave

oneself, afeitarse

she, ella

shed, derramar

shine, brillar

ship, el buque, la nave

shirt, la camisa

shoe, el zapato; **shoemaker**, el zapatero

shop, la tienda

short, corto,-a, bajo,-a

should, deber (debiera); **I should say so!,** ¡ya lo creo!

shoulder, el hombro; **to shrug one's shoulders,** encogerse (j) de hombros

shout, el grito; **to shout,** gritar, dar (doy) gritos (voces)

show, enseñar, mostrar (ue), demostrar (ue)

shrug: **shrug one's shoulders,** encogerse (j) de hombros

side, el lado; **sidewalk,** la acera

sigh, el suspiro

sight: **to lose sight of,** perder (ie) de vista

sign, firmar

signal, la señal

silent: **to keep silent,** callarse

silk, la seda

silver, la plata

similar, semejante

simple, sencillo,-a; **simpleminded,** simple

since, ya que, puesto que

sing, cantar; **singer,** el cantor, la cantora, el (la) cantante

sir, señor

sister, la hermana

sit (down), sentarse (ie)

six, seis; **six hundred,** seiscientos,-as; **sixteen(th),** diez y seis (dieciséis); **sixth,** sexto,-a; **sixty,** sesenta

skill, la habilidad; **skillful,** hábil

skirt, la falda

sky, el cielo

slave, el esclavo, la esclava

sleep, dormir (ue, u); **to be sleepy,** tener (ie, tengo) sueño

sleeve, la manga

slowly, lentamente, despacio

small, pequeño,-a

smash, hacer (hago) pedazos

smell, oler (huelo); **to smell (of, like),** oler a

smile, la sonrisa; **to smile,** sonreír (í)

smoke, el humo; **to smoke,** fumar; **smoking,** el fumar

smoothly, suavemente

snow, la nieve; **to snow,** nevar (ie)

so, tan; **so much,** tanto,-a; **so that,** de modo (manera) que

soap, el jabón

soldier, el soldado

solve, resolver (ue)

some, alguno,-a (algún); **some day,** algún día; **someone,** alguien

son, el hijo

song, la canción

soon, pronto; **as soon as,** así que, en cuanto, luego que, tan pronto como; **no sooner said than done,** dicho y hecho

sorry: **to be sorry,** sentir (ie, i)

soul, el alma (f.)

sound, el sonido; **safe and sound,** sano y salvo

soup, la sopa

south, el sur; **South America,** la América del Sur, Sudamérica

souvenir, el recuerdo

Spain, España; **Spaniard,** el español, la española; **Spanish,** español,-a; (language), el español; **Spanish America,** la América Hispana; **in the Spanish style,** a la española

spank, pegar (gu)

speak, hablar

species, la especie

spectacle, el espectáculo

spend (time), pasar; (money), gastar

spill, derramar

spite: **in spite of,** a pesar de

sport, el deporte

spread, esparcir (z)

spring, la primavera

spy, el espía; **to spy,** espiar (í)

square, cuadrado,-a

stamp, el sello

stand up, levantarse; **standing,** de pie

star, la estrella

stare (at), fijarse en, reparar en

start, iniciar, principiar, empezar (ie, c), comenzar (ie, c)

state, el estado

statue, la estatua

stay, quedar(se); **to stay in bed,** guardar cama

steal, robar

steel, el acero

stenographer, la taquígrafa

step, el paso; **to step (on),** pisar

still, todavía; **to keep still,**

callarse

stocking, la media

stone, la piedra

stop, cesar de + inf., parar(se), dejar de + inf.

store, la tienda

strange, extraño,-a

street, la calle

strike, dar (la hora); (against), dar (doy) en

stroll, pasearse, dar (doy) una vuelta, dar un paseo

struggle, luchar

stucco, el estuco

student, el (la) estudiante, alumno,-a; **studious,** aplicado,-a; **to study,** estudiar

style, el estilo; **in the French (Spanish) style,** a la francesa (española)

succeed (in), lograr + inf.

such (a), tal

suddenly, de pronto, de repente

suffer, sufrir

suffice, bastar; **sufficient,** suficiente, bastante

suit, el traje; **suitcase,** la maleta

summer, el verano; **summer vacation,** las vacaciones de verano

sun, el sol; **sunset,** la puesta del sol; **it is sunny,** hay sol, hace sol

Sunday, el domingo; **every Sunday,** todos los domingos; **on Sundays,** los domingos

support, mantener (ie, mantengo)

supreme, supremo,-a

sure, seguro,-a; **I am sure,** estoy seguro,-a

surprise, sorprender; **to be surprised (at),** sorprenderse (de)

surround, rodear

sweetheart, el novio, la novia

swift, rápido,-a

swim, nadar; **swimming,** el nadar

sword, la espada

table, la mesa; **tablecloth,** el mantel; **to set the table,** poner (pongo) la mesa

tailor, el sastre

take, tomar, llevar; **taking,** el tomar; **to take a bath,** bañarse; **to take advantage (of),** aprovecharse (de); **to take a picture,** sacar (qu) una fotografía; **to take a ride,** dar un paseo (en coche); **to**

take a trip, hacer (hago) un viaje; **to take a walk,** dar un paseo, pasearse; **to take care of,** cuidar (a, de); **to take charge (of),** encargarse (gu) (de); **to take leave of,** despedirse (i) de; **to take off,** quitarse; **to take out,** sacar (qu); **to take part (in),** tomar parte (en); **to take place,** tener (ie, tengo) lugar, verificarse (qu); **to take possession of,** apoderarse de

talent, el talento

talk, hablar

tall, alto,-a

tax, el impuesto

tea, el té

teach, enseñar; **teacher,** maestro,-a, profesor,-a

telegram, el telegrama

telephone, el teléfono

tell, decir (i, digo)

ten, diez; **tenth,** décimo,-a

tennis, el tenis

terror, el terror

test, el examen, la prueba

than, que, del que, de la (los, las) que; (before number), de

thank (for), agradecer (zc)

that (adj.), ese, esa, aquel, aquella; (pron.) ése, ésa, aquél, aquélla; (neuter pron.) eso, aquello; (conj.) que; **that of,** el (la) de; **in that way,** de esa manera (de ese modo)

the, el, la, los, las

theater, el teatro

their, su, sus; **theirs,** el (la, los, las) suyo(-a, -os, -as)

them, los, las; **to them,** les; (after prep.), ellos,-as

then, luego

there, allí, allá; **there is (are),** hay; **there was (were),** había, hubo; **there's no doubt,** no cabe duda

therefore, por consiguiente, por eso

Theresa, Teresa

they, ellos,-as

thief, el ladrón

thing, la cosa

think, pensar (ie); **to think of,** pensar en; (opinion), pensar de

third, tercero,-a (tercer)

thirsty: **to be thirsty,** tener (ie, tengo) sed

thirteen(th), trece

thirty, treinta

this, este,-a; (neuter pron.), esto; **this (one),** éste,-a; **this very day,** hoy mismo;

in this way, de esta manera (de este modo)

thoroughly, a fondo

though: as though, como si; **even though,** aunque

thousand, mil

threaten, amenazar (c)

three, tres; **three hundred,** trescientos,-as

throne, el trono

through, por, a través de

throw, tirar, echar

Thursday, el jueves

ticket, el billete; **ticket office,** la taquilla; **round-trip ticket,** el billete de ida y vuelta

tight: to be tight, apretar (ie)

till, hasta

time, el tiempo; (hour), la hora; (in a series), la vez; **this time,** esta vez; **a long time,** mucho tiempo; **at the same time,** a la vez; **at this time,** a esta hora; **at what time?,** ¿a qué hora?; **from time to time,** de vez en cuando; **on time,** a tiempo; **what time is it?,** ¿qué hora es?; **"times"** (×), por

tip, la propina

tired, cansado, -a (with estar); **to become tired,** cansarse; **tiresome,** cansado,-a (with ser)

to, a, para; **to himself,** para sí; **to the left,** a la izquierda; **to the right,** a la derecha

today, hoy; **tomorrow,** mañana; **the day after tomorrow,** pasado mañana; **tonight,** esta noche

too, demasiado; **too much,** demasiado,-a; **to be too much (many),** sobrar

tooth, el diente; **to brush one's teeth,** limpiarse los dientes

top, la cumbre

touch, tocar (qu)

tourist, el (la) turista

toward, hacia

town, el pueblo

train, el tren

translate, traducir (zc)

travel, viajar; **traveler,** viajero,-a

treasure, el tesoro

treat, tratar; **treatment,** el tratamiento

tree, el árbol

tremble, temblar (ie)

trip, el viaje; **to make (take) a trip,** hacer (hago) un viaje; **round-trip ticket,** billete de ida y vuelta

true: it is true, es verdad; **truth,** la verdad

trust, fiarse (í) de

try to, tratar de + inf.

Tuesday, el martes

turn, torcer (ue, z); **to be one's turn,** tocarle (qu) (a uno); **turn on (light),** encender (ie)

twelve (twelfth), doce

twenty, veinte

twice, dos veces

two, dos; **two hundred,** doscientos,-as; **two weeks,** quince días

tyrant, tirano,-a

umbrella, el paraguas

uncle, el tío

understand, comprender, entender (ie)

undertake, emprender

undo, deshacer (deshago)

unfold, desarrollar(se)

unfortunate, infeliz, desgraciado,-a; **unfortunately,** por desgracia

United States (the), los Estados Unidos

university, la universidad

unless, a menos que

until, hasta, hasta que

unwillingly, de mala gana

up: get up, levantarse; **go up,** subir

upon (entering), al (entrar); **to come upon,** tropezar (ie, c) con, dar con

us, nos; **to us,** nos; (after prep.), nosotros

use, usar, emplear; **used to,** soler (ue) (or use imperfect tense); **useless,** inútil

usual: same as usual, sin novedad; **usually,** por lo común, por lo general

vacation, las vacaciones; **summer vacation,** las vacaciones de verano

vague, vago,-a

valley, el valle

vary, variar (í)

vendor, el vendedor

verb, el verbo

verse, el verso

very, muy; **this very day,** hoy mismo

vice, el vicio

victim, la víctima

victory, la victoria

view, la vista

village, la aldea

Vincent, Vicente

violet, la violeta

virtue, la virtud

visit, visitar; **to pay a visit,** hacer (hago) una visita

voice, la voz

volume, el tomo

voyage, el viaje

wait (for), esperar, aguardar

waiter, el camarero, el mozo

wake up, despertarse (ie)

walk, andar, caminar; **to take a walk,** dar un paseo, pasearse

wall, el muro, la pared

want, desear, querer (ie)

war, la guerra; **World War,** la Guerra Mundial

warm, caliente; **to warm oneself,** calentarse (ie); **to be warm (weather),** hacer calor; **to be warm (person),** tener calor

warn, advertir (ie, i)

wash, lavar; **to wash oneself,** lavarse; **to get washed,** lavarse

watch, el reloj; **to watch,** mirar, velar, reparar en

water, el agua (f.)

way: to make one's way to, dirigirse (j) a; **to proceed on one's way,** proseguir (i, prosigo) el camino; **in this way,** de este modo, de esta manera; **in that way,** de ese modo, de esa manera

we, nosotros,-as

wealth, la riqueza

wear, llevar

wedding, la boda

Wednesday, el miércoles

week, la semana, ocho días; **two weeks,** quince días; **last week,** la semana pasada; **weekend,** el fin de semana

well, bien

west, el oeste

wet, mojado,-a; **to get wet,** mojarse

what (conj.), lo que; **what?,** ¿qué?, ¿cuál,-es?; **what a . . . !,** ¡qué . . . !, ¡vaya un,-a . . . !; **at what time?,** ¿a qué hora?; **what time is it?,** ¿qué hora es?; **whatever,** cualquier(a)

when, cuando; **when?,** ¿cuándo?; **whenever,** cuandoquiera

where, donde; **where?,** ¿dónde?; **wherever,** (a)dondequiera; **from where?,** ¿de dónde?

whether, si

which, que, el (la) cual, los (las) cuales, el (la, los, las) que, lo cual, lo que;

which?, ¿cuál,-es?

while, mientras (que); m., el rato; **a little while ago,** hace poco; **in a little while,** dentro de poco

white, blanco,-a

who, quien, que, el (la, los, las) que, el (la) cual, los (las) cuales; **who?,** ¿quién,-es?; **whoever,** quien(es)quiera; ¿prep. + quién,-es?; **whose,** cuyo,-a; **whose?,** ¿de quién,-es?

whole (the), todo el, toda la

why?, ¿por qué?, ¿para qué?

wide, ancho,-a; **wide open,** abiertos(-as) de par en par; **width,** la anchura; **in width,** de ancho

wife, la esposa, la señora, la mujer

will (use future tense); **will you . . . ?,** ¿Quiere Vd. . . . ?

willingly, de buena gana

win, ganar

wind, el viento; **it is windy,** hace viento

wind (a watch), dar cuerda (a un reloj)

window, la ventana

winter, el invierno

wise, sabio,-a

wish, desear, querer (ie)

with, con; **with me,** conmigo; **with you,** contigo, con Vd. (vosotros, Vds.)

without, sin, sin que; **without delay,** cuanto antes

witness, el (la) testigo

wolf, el lobo

woman, la mujer

wonder: I wonder . . . (use future or conditional)

wood, la madera; **wooden,** de madera

wool, la lana; **woolen,** de lana

word, la palabra; **to keep one's word,** cumplir (con) la palabra

work, el trabajo, la obra; **to work,** trabajar, funcionar

world, el mundo; adj., mundial; **world-wide,** mundial

worry: not to worry, perder (ie) cuidado

worse, peor; **worst,** el (la) peor

worth: to be worth, valer (valgo); **to be worthwhile,** valer la pena

would (use conditional)

wounded, herido,-a

wrap, envolver (ue)

write, escribir; **written,** escrito,-a; **writer,** el escritor, la escritora; **in writing,** por escrito

wrong: to be wrong, no tener (ie, tengo) razón

year, el año

yesterday, ayer

yet, todavía; **not yet,** todavía no

you, Vd., Vds., tú, vosotros, -as; (*ind. obj.*), le, les, te, os; (after prep.), Vd., Vds., ti, vosotros,-as;

with you (*fam. sing.*), contigo

young, joven; **younger,** menor; **youngest,** el (la) menor; **young lady,** la señorita

your, su, sus, tu, tus, vuestro(-a, -os, -as); **yours,** el (la, los, las) suyo(-a, -os, -as); el (la, los, las) tuyo(-a, -os, -as); el (la, los, las) vuestro(-a, -os, -as); **yourself** (*fam.*), te, os; (*formal*), se